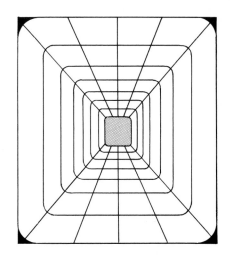

Patterns
and Perspectives
in Environmental
Science

Report Prepared for the

National Science Board

National Science Foundation

1972

Library of Congress Catalog Card Number 73-600219

For sale by the Superintendent of Documents, U.S. Government Printing Office, Washington, D.C. 20402
Price: $7.30   Stock Number 3800–00147

ii

62o8
PAT

FOREWORD

This report has been prepared as a companion volume, a supplement to the third annual report of the National Science Board, *Environmental Science—Challenge for the Seventies* (NSB 71-1), which was transmitted to the Congress by the President in June 1971. It contains much of the information and interpretation that formed the basis for the conclusions and recommendations of the annual report.

The present document makes no attempt to present a complete view of environmental science or a coherent description of the natural environment. These undertakings would be both impracticable and overambitious within the confines of a single volume. Rather, this volume is a compendium of the views and judgments of a large number of scientific leaders, addressed to a broadly representative array of topics that serve to illustrate, but not define, the scope and nature of environmental science today.

The National Science Board is deeply grateful to these many individuals for their thoughtful, candid, and sometimes controversial opinions. In some cases the views expressed are in conflict with others contained in the report itself or held by other members of the scientific community. Hopefully these conflicting views will challenge scientists to resolve these differences and will point out that there are, in fact, many areas in environmental science that demand substantial investigation before any degree of adequate understanding is achieved. It is these differences that contribute significantly to the "patterns and perspectives" and help to identify directions of needed scientific advance.

In accepting this report and recommending its publication, the Board does not endorse all views contained herein, but hopes that the report will prove informative to the general reader, that it will provide useful insights to assist policymakers, whether in government or in private institutions, and that it will contribute to the discussions of scientists—students, teachers, and other professionals —who are most intimately concerned with the status and future progress of environmental science.

H. E. Carter
Chairman,
National Science Board

ACKNOWLEDGEMENTS

The National Science Board owes a debt of gratitude to a large number of people for their assistance in the preparation of this report. The Board expresses its appreciation to all of them for a job well done.

Valuable aid was provided by the consultants who gave freely of their opinions and served as a general sounding board regarding the handling of the final format of this report, as well as its companion volume, *Environmental Science: Challenge for the Seventies.* This group included: Dr. Julian R. Goldsmith (former member of the National Science Board), University of Chicago; Dr. Louis J. Battan, University of Arizona; Dr. John E. Cantlon, Michigan State University; Dr. Wilbert M. Chapman (deceased), Ralston Purina Company; Dr. Roger Revelle, Harvard University; and Dr. Gilbert F. White, University of Colorado.

The major responsibility for preparation of this report was undertaken by the Staff of the National Science Foundation, working in consultation with the Board and the consultants. Dr. Lawton M. Hartman, III and Dr. Eugene W. Bierly directed the effort. The result is unique: a profile of a section of science that is rich in information, broad in scope, and explicit as to the present status of understanding. The National Science Board expresses its sincere appreciation for the dedicated work of these men.

The report has been edited by Mrs. Patricia W. Blair, special editorial consultant to the Board. The Board recognizes that her conscientious effort to present each contribution in its best light has made the report much more valuable.

The following staff members of the Foundation and others have contributed in various ways, and the Board acknowledges the time and effort that these people gave from their already busy offices:

Dr. James R. Barcus, Program Director, Solar Terrestrial Program

Dr. William E. Benson, Head, Earth Sciences Section

Dr. John L. Brooks, Program Director, General Ecology Program

Mrs. Josephine K. Doherty, Program Manager, Regional Environmental Systems Program

Dr. H. Frank Eden, Program Director, Meteorology Program

Dr. John E. Geisler, Associate Program Director, Meteorology Program

Dr. Walter H. Hodge, Head, Ecology and Systematic Biology Section

Dr. Phillip L. Johnson, Division Director, Environmental Systems and Resources

Mrs. Joan M. Jordan, Assistant Program Director, General Ecology Program

Dr. Edward J. Kuenzler, Program Director, Biological Oceanography Program

Dr. Lawrence H. Larson, Program Director, Physical Oceanography Program

Miss Roberta J. Mears, Assistant Program Director, Biological Oceanography Program

Dr. John M. Neuhold, Program Director, Ecosystem Analysis Program

Dr. Richard I. Schoen, Program Director, Aeronomy Program

Mr. Peter H. Wyckoff, Program Manager, Weather Modification Program

and, from outside the Foundation,

Mrs. Eileen Cavanaugh, Smithsonian Center for Violent Phenomena

Dr. Charles Cooper, San Diego State University

Miss Margaret Deane, Bureau of Occupational Health and Environmental Epidemiology, State of California

Mrs. Barbara L. Kendall, National Center for Atmospheric Research

Dr. Allen Kneese, Resources for the Future

Dr. William H. Matthews, Associate Director, Study of Critical Environmental Problems, M.I.T.

The endless task of typing and filing of correspondence was handled efficiently and effectively by Mrs. Judith M. Curtis, NSF. Her accurate typing of material for this volume as well as the first, particularly in situations where time was at a premium, is much appreciated.

Special credit must be given to Mr. John C. Holmes, Head of the Printing and Reproduction Section, NSF. Mr. Holmes has made a difficult job much easier through his understanding of the problems and the positive approach he took in solving them.

There are others who have helped this report to come into being who are not listed by name. To these people, the Board offers its thanks.

Finally, the Board acknowledges its great debt to the approximately 150 scientists who responded to the Board's request for information and analysis. Their frank and sometimes controversial papers are the basis for this report. It could not have been written without them. To these busy scientists, who took precious time to furnish information, the National Science Board is extremely grateful. It is these contributors who have made *Patterns and Perspectives in Environmental Science* a reality.

INTRODUCTION

A report on environmental science is at best a risky undertaking. As was noted in the third report of the National Science Board, *Environmental Science—Challenge for the Seventies* (NSB 71-1):

> Environmental Science is conceived . . . as the study of all of the systems of air, land, water, energy, and life that surround man. It includes all science directed to the system-level of understanding of the environment, drawing especially on such disciplines as meteorology, geophysics, oceanography, and ecology, and utilizing to the fullest the knowledge and techniques developed in such fields as physics, chemistry, biology, mathematics, and engineering.

Indeed, the natural environment is so all-encompassing, so complex, that any attempt at exposition would appear doomed from the outset.

This report has a more limited, but perhaps more crucial, purpose: to assemble, in one place, enough material to permit the identification of fundamental patterns that might help in appraising the status of environmental science today. It seeks a basis for tentative assessments of:

1. The availability of essential data and successful theoretical formulations;

2. The present capability of environmental science to predict future events; and, hence,

3. The capacity of science to serve society in its growing concern with the condition of the natural environment and what man is doing to it.

To achieve this end, many leading environmental scientists were asked by the National Science Board to prepare informal statements on specific, assigned topics covering a representative sample of environmental phenomena. They were asked to include their personal opinions and judgments on the current status of scientific knowledge and understanding. This volume comprises a selection among the responses to those requests.

In order that the document not be misunderstood, or be judged with reference to inappropriate criteria, several important caveats need to be stated.

First, no attempt has been made to provide a complete description of the natural environment. Rather, the topics have been selected to illustrate a fundamental feature of environmental science—namely, that interactions prevail among all environmental regimes.

Second, the report does not attempt a definitive scientific review of environmental science. Such a review, representing the consensus of informed opinion, is probably not possible today and, at the very least, could not be undertaken without a massive team effort. Nor does the report attempt to duplicate the many excellent surveys that continue to be prepared on the status of individual disciplines within the "environmental sciences."

Third, this volume is not primarily concerned with pollution, a subject of enormous environmental concern but one that is receiving extensive attention in many other places.

Fourth, in preparing this report for publication, it has not been feasible to update the original papers. Thus, the material is now nearly two years old. In most instances this does not affect the conclusions presented, even though advances in environmental science are being recorded at an increasing rate.

Finally, it has been assumed, as a matter of policy, that all the material included in this report has a reasonable scientific basis, even though some of the opinions expressed may cause controversy among specialists, both contributors and others. In certain instances, differences of opinion will be observed in statements devoted to the same topic. It is hoped that any resulting controversy or disagreement will help to illustrate the present status of environmental science and, indeed, to generate constructive and extensive discussion among scientists.

Specific attribution of papers and associated illustrative material has been deliberately avoided. The exigencies of the publishing schedule have not permitted authors an opportunity to review the edited product, and, where consistency could be assured, material from two or more papers have been combined; thus, while every effort has been made to retain scientific accuracy and individual style, authors should not be expected to bear individual responsibility for the final version. Furthermore, in order to encourage candid opinions, contributors were told from the first that informality was sought and that individual acknowledgments would not be made.

"Patterns and perspectives" in environmental science begin to emerge from a reading of the various papers in this report. Several questions recur. How adequate are the experimental data that comprise an essential underpinning for scientific progress? To what extent does a satis-

factory theoretical structure exist, as distinct from a largely qualitative understanding? How mature are attempts at mathematical modeling? How adequate is the scientific basis for environmental control? Has environmental science reached the point where regulatory standards can be formulated in terms of demonstrated benefits and costs to society? What further scientific activity is needed? What needs to be done?

The National Science Board, in its third report, sought the broad outlines of the answers to such questions at this point in time. Its findings and recommendations comprise the first volume of the third report, a summary of which is appended. It is hoped that the publication of these papers—the raw material, so to speak— will help to generate further discussion of the topics covered and their implications for environmental science as a whole, its organization and staffing, its choice of priorities, its methods of investigation, and the extent of established information and theory that can serve as the foundation of future progress. In this case, as in so many others, discussion and controversy are an important prelude to action.

CONTENTS

Page

FOREWORD iii

ACKNOWLEDGEMENTS v

INTRODUCTION vii

I THE SOLAR-TERRESTRIAL ENVIRONMENT

Elements of the Solar-Terrestrial
System 3

Terrestrial Effects of Solar Activity .. 13

II DYNAMICS OF THE SOLID EARTH

1. Deep Earth Processes 21

   An Overview of Deep-Earth
   Chemistry and Physics 21

   A Note on the Earth's Magnetic Field 23

2. Continental Structures and Processes
   and Sea-floor Spreading 26

   Continental Drift and Sea-floor
   Spreading 26

   Practical Implications of Major
   Continental Processes 32

3. Earthquakes 35

   Earthquake Prediction and Prevention 35

4. Volcanoes 40

   Volcanoes and Man's Environment .. 40

   Aspects of Volcanic Science 44

III CLIMATIC CHANGE

1. Cyclical Behavior of Climate 51

   Long-term Temperature Cycles
   and Their Significance 51

   Fluctuations in Climate over Periods
   of less than 200 Years 55

   Environmental Cyclic Behavior: The
   Evidence of Tree Rings and Pollen
   Profiles 59

2. Causes of Climatic Change 62

   Basic Factors in Climatic Change 62

   The Radiation Balance 65

Page

Climatic Change and the Effects of
Civilization 69

Environmental Change in Arid
America 73

IV DYNAMICS OF THE ATMOSPHERE-OCEAN SYSTEM

1. Oceanic Circulation and Ocean-
   Atmosphere Interactions 77

   Oceanic Circulation and the Role
   of the Atmosphere 77

   On Predicting Ocean Circulation 79

   Hydrodynamic Modeling of
   Ocean Systems 81

   Effects of Antarctic Water on
   Oceanic Circulation 83

   Tropical Air-Sea Rhythms 84

2. Atmospheric Circulation 89

   Modeling the Global Atmospheric
   Circulation 89

3. Weather Forecasting 93

   Short-, Medium-, and Long-Term
   Forecasting 93

   Long-Range Weather Forecasting ... 97

   Short-Term Forecasting, including
   Forecasting for Low-Altitude
   Aviation 101

4. Clear Air Turbulence 105

   Clear Air Turbulence and
   Atmospheric Processes 105

   Prediction and Detection of
   Wave-Induced Turbulence 107

   A Note on Acoustic Monitoring 112

5. Urban Effects on Weather and Climate ... 113

   Urbanization and Weather 113

   The Influence of Urban Growth on
   Local and Mesoscale Weather 116

   Urban Effects on Weather—the
   Larger Scales 118

ix

V SEVERE STORMS

  1. Hurricanes 123

       The Origin of Atlantic Hurricanes ... 123

       A report on Project STORMFURY: Problems in the Modification of Hurricanes 127

       The Scientific Basis of Project STORMFURY 130

       A Note on the Importance of Hurricanes 132

       Geomorphological Effects of Hurricanes 133

  2. Tornadoes 137

       Status of Tornado Research 137

       Tornadoes—Their Forecasting and Potential Modification 144

       Tornado Forecasting and Warning .. 146

  3. Hail 149

       Hailstorm Research and Hail Suppression 149

       Current Status of Hail Prevention ... 154

  4. Lightning 157

       Basic Processes of Lightning 157

       Reduction of Lightning Damage by Cloud Seeding 160

VI PRECIPITATION AND REGIONAL WEATHER PHENOMENA

  1. Drought 165

       The Causes and Nature of Drought and its Prediction 165

  2. Precipitation Modification 169

       Artificial Alteration of Natural Precipitation 169

       The Status of Precipitation Management 172

  3. Fog 180

       Modification of Warm and Cold Fog . 180

       Fog Dispersal Techniques 182

  4. Tropical Weather 184

       Monsoon Variations and Climate and Weather Forecasting 184

       Tropical Meteorology, with Special Reference to Equatorial Dry Zones. 187

  5. Dust 191

       African Dust and its Transport into the Western Hemisphere 191

VII WATER RESOURCES, FORESTRY, AND AGRICULTURE

  1. Water Resources 197

       Estimating Future Water Supply and Usage 197

       Water Movement and Storage in Plants and Soils 200

       A Note on Subsidence and the Exhaustion of Water-Bearing and Oil-Bearing Formations 203

  2. Forestry 205

       Water Quality in Forests 205

       Factors Relating Forest Management to Water Quality 212

  3. Agriculture 215

       Global Food Production Potentials ... 215

       The Hazard of Drought 218

VIII AQUATIC ECOSYSTEMS

  1. Component Relationships 225

       Trophic Dynamics, with Special Reference to the Great Lakes 225

       Effects of Artificial Disturbances on the Marine Environment 230

       Marine Flora and Fauna in the Antarctic 231

       Systems Approaches to Understanding the Oceans and Marine Productivity 233

  2. Oceanic Production 236

       Primary Plant and Animal Life in the World Ocean 236

       The Southern Oceans in the Production of Protein 240

       Scientific Aspects of North Pacific Fisheries 242

       Some Scientific Problems Associated with Aquatic Mammals 245

  3. Estuaries and Coastal Zones 248

Page

The Relationship of Fisheries to Estuaries, with Special Reference to Puget Sound 248

Prospects for Aquaculture 250

4. Dynamics of Lakes 254

Lake Circulation Patterns 254

The Effects of Thermal Input on Lake Michigan 257

5. Lake Eutrophication and Productivity 261

Fishery Deterioration in the Great Lakes 261

Problems or Eutrophication in the Great Lakes 267

Pollution and Recovery in Lake Washington 270

IX TERRESTRIAL ECOSYSTEMS

1. Component Relationships 277

Environmental Design 277

Maintenance of the Biosphere, with Special Reference to Arid Lands ... 280

Energy Relationships in Ecological Systems 285

A Note on Soil Studies 291

2. Forest Ecosystems 292

The Forest as an Ecosystem 292

A Note on Hubbard Brook 293

Tropical Forests 295

Comparison of Temperate and Tropical Forests 298

3. Forest Animals 302

Problems of Animal Ecology in Forested Areas 302

Wilderness as a Dynamic Ecosystem, with Reference to Isle Royale National Park 303

4. Forest Fire 306

Research into Fire Ecology 306

The Role of Fire in Forest Management and Ecology 308

5. Polar Ecosystems 313

Polar Flora and Vegetation 313

Page

X ENVIRONMENTAL CONTAMINANTS

Effects of Environmental Pollutants and Exposures on Human Health and Well Being 319

1. Airborne Chemicals 329

Chemical Contaminants in the Atmosphere 329

Atmospheric Contaminants and Development of Standards 332

Modeling the Atmosphere 335

Problems in the Ecology of Smog 337

2. Airborne Biological Materials 339

Atmospheric Dispersal of Biologically Significant Materials 339

Biological Monitoring Techniques for Measuring Aeroallergens 345

3. Pests and Pesticides 350

Environmental Pollution and Pesticides 350

Pesticides and the Pollution Problem . 354

4. Marine Contaminants 357

Effects on the Ocean of Atmospheric Circulation of Gases and Particulate Matter 357

Oil on the Sea Floor 361

5. Environmental Disease 364

Malaria 364

Other Parasitic Diseases 367

XI HUMAN ADAPTATION TO ENVIRONMENTAL STRESS

Genetic Adaptation to the Environment 373

Aspects of Man's Adaptation in the Tropics 378

Adaptation to High Altitude 379

Adaptation to Smog and Carbon Monoxide 385

APPENDIX: Summary and Recommendations 391

SELECTED REFERENCES 395

INDEX 401

CONTRIBUTORS 423

NATIONAL SCIENCE BOARD 426

LIST OF ILLUSTRATIONS

Figure   *Page*

THE SOLAR-TERRESTRIAL ENVIRONMENT

I–1: Solar Flare 4
I–2: The Interplanetary Medium 6
I–3: The Magnetosphere 7
I–4: The Ionosphere 9
I–5: Atmospheric Temperature Distribution 12

DYNAMICS OF THE SOLID EARTH

II–1: Regions of the Earth's Interior 21
II–2: Chronology of Earth's Magnetic Field Reversals 24
II–3: Six Shifting Plates of the Earth 27
II–4: Continental Drift 33
II–5: Seismicity of the Earth 36
II–6: The Upper Mantle in the Region of
       Fiji-Tonga-Raratonga 37
II–7: Seismic Risk in the United States 38
II–8: U.S. Volcanoes 45

CLIMATIC CHANGE

III–1: Average Water Level in Lake Victoria 51
III–2: Changes in the Temperature of the
        Ocean Surface 53
III–3: Temperature Curves Derived from Oxygen
        Isotope Ratios of Deep-Sea Cores 54
III–4: Variations of the Mean Annual Temperature
        of the Northern Hemisphere 56
III–5: Precipitation Patterns from Tree Rings 60
III–6: Computer Simulation of Sea-Level
        Pressure Field 65
III–7: Factors in the Radiation Balance of the Earth .. 67
III–8: Observed Lagged Temperature Variation of
        the Northern Hemisphere 70
III–9: Lagged Temperature Curve for the Northern
        Hemisphere Corrected for CO_2 71
III–10: Lagged Temperature Curve for the Northern
        Hemisphere Corrected for CO_2 and Dust 71

DYNAMICS OF THE ATMOSPHERE-OCEAN SYSTEM

IV–1: Sea-Surface Temperatures 77
IV–2: Classification of Waves and Currents 81
IV–3: Antarctic Waters and Their Circulation 83
IV–4: Canton Island Data 85
IV–5: Walker's "Southern Oscillation" 86
IV–6: SIRS Sounding 90
IV–7: Availability of Upper Air Data 92
IV–8: Data Required for Forecasts 94
IV–9: Forecasting Skill 99
IV–10: Waves and Turbulence in the Clear
       Atmosphere 110
IV–11: Weather Changes Resulting from Urbanization 114
IV–12: Heat Island Effect 117

SEVERE STORMS

V–1: A History of Hurricane Seedlings 124
V–2: Hurricane Beulah, 1967 124

Figure   *Page*

V–3: Probability Forecasts for Hurricanes 125
V–4: Hurricane Losses by Years 127
V–5: Hurricane Camille, 1969 134
V–6: Comparative Losses due to Severe Storms
      and Hurricanes 137
V–7: Radar View of a Hooked Echo 139
V–8: Contour-mapped PPI Display 142
V–9: Contour-mapped Digital Display 143
V–10: Severe Weather Warning 147
V–11: Structure of Hailstone Embryos 150
V–12: Hail Suppression at Kericho, Kenya 153
V–13: A Midwest Thunderstorm 155
V–14: Lightning 157
V–15: The Initiation of a Lightning Stroke 159

PRECIPITATION AND REGIONAL WEATHER PHENOMENA

VI–1: Annual Worldwide Precipitation 166
VI–2: Precipitation Processes 169
VI–3: Lattice Structures of AgI and Ice 173
VI–4: Temperature Dependence of Nucleating Agents 174
VI–5: Optimum Seeding Conditions 176
VI–6: Simulated Effect of Cloud Seeding 177
VI–7: Concentration of Ice Nuclei in a City 179
VI–8: A Driving Hazard 180
VI–9: Results of Fog-Seeding Programs 182
VI–10: Monsoonal Areas 184
VI–11: Array for Barbados Oceanographic and
       Meteorological Experiment (BOMEX) 186
VI–12: Frequency of Tropical Cyclones 189
VI–13: Dust over the Tropical Atlantic 191

WATER RESOURCES, FORESTRY, AND AGRICULTURE

VII–1: Disposition of Water Diverted for Irrigation
        Purpose 199
VII–2: The Hydrologic Cycle 201
VII–3: Subsidence in Long Beach, California 203
VII–4: Ownership of U.S. Forest Lands 205
VII–5: Effects of Forest Fires 208
VII–6: Relation of Sediment Particle-Size to Flow Rate 210
VII–7: Effect of Land Use on Sediment Yield and
        Channel Stability 211
VII–8: Potentially Arable Land in Relation to
        World Population 215
VII–9: Transplanted Species 216
VII–10: Comparative Perceptions of Feasible
        Adjustments to Drought 219

AQUATIC ECOSYSTEMS

VIII–1: Trophic Levels 225
VIII–2: Effect of Alewives on Zooplankton 229
VIII–3: Sensitivity of Phytoplankton to Insecticides .. 234
VIII–4: Some Phytoplankton 237
VIII–5: Some Zooplankton 238
VIII–6: An Antarctic Food Chain 239
VIII–7: Distribution of the World's Fisheries 243
VIII–8: The Fate and Distribution of Marine Pollutants 245
VIII–9: A Purse Seine 246

Figure		*Page*
VIII–10:	Cost of Economic Activities in Corpus Christi Bay	249
VIII–11:	Scheme for Using Sewage in Aquaculture	252
VIII–12:	Upwelling of Coastal Lake Waters	256
VIII–13:	Thermal Influence of Electric Power Generation on Lake Michigan	258
VIII–14:	Commercial Fish Catch — Lake Michigan	261
VIII–15:	The Effect of Fertilizer on Nitrate Concentrations in Rivers	265
VIII–16:	Transparency Measurements in Lake Washington	271
VIII–17:	Measurements of Algae, Phosphorus, and Nitrogen in Lake Washington	273

TERRESTRIAL ECOSYSTEMS

IX–1:	Seral Stages of a Deciduous Forest	277
IX–2:	A Systems Model for a Grassland Ecosystem	279
IX–3:	Mosquito Submodel	282
IX–4:	A Model Validation Study	284
IX–5:	Major World Biomes	286
IX–6:	Plant-Mouse-Weasel Chain	287
IX–7:	Energy Budget of a Horse	288
IX–8:	Relation Between Food Intake and Calorific Equivalence of Invertebrates	290
IX–9:	Ecological Effects of Deforestation	294
IX–10:	The Effect of Tree Cover Removal in the Tropics	297
IX–11:	Comparison of Temperate and Tropical Forest Types	299
IX–12:	Life Expectancy and Survivorship of Isle Royale Moose	305
IX–13:	Effect of Fire on Mesquite Shrubs	306
IX–14:	Quantities of Nutrients Released by Burning Tropical Vegetation	309
IX–15:	A Section of the Tundra Biome	313
IX–16:	Flow Diagram of a Wet Coastal Tundra Ecosystem	315

ENVIRONMENTAL CONTAMINANTS

X–1:	Composition of Clean, Dry Air	329
X–2:	Pollution — An Environmental Problem	331
X–3:	Atmospheric Scales	332
X–4:	A System for Discussing Air Pollution	333
X–5:	Projection of Physical, Economic, and Social Relationships	338

Figure		*Page*
X–6:	Atmospheric Particulate Matter Important in Aerobiology	339
X–7:	Components of a Model for Pollen Aerobiology	341
X–8:	Average Annual Losses from Crop Diseases in the United States	342
X–9:	Distribution of Ragweed Pollen in the United States	346
X–10:	Efficiency of Cylindrical Collectors for Ragweed Pollen	348
X–11:	Resistance of Insects and Mites to Pesticides	350
X–12:	Pesticide Usage and Agricultural Yields	351
X–13:	Resurgence of California Red Scale	355
X–14:	Concentration of DDT in a Lake Michigan Food Chain	356
X–15:	Comparison of Caucasian Dust Fall and the Soviet Economy	359
X–16:	PCB Residue in Fish, Birds, and Mammals	360
X–17:	Petroleum Hydrocarbon Contamination in the Marine Environment	361
X–18:	Changes in Malaria Morbidity Before and After Mosquito Control	364
X–19:	Areas of Major Malaria Potential	366
X–20:	World Distribution of Schistosomiasis	368
X–21:	Ejection of Small Droplets into the Atmosphere by Bursting Bubbles	370

HUMAN ADAPTATION TO ENVIRONMENTAL STRESS

XI–1:	Distribution of the Yanomama Indians in South America	375
XI–2:	Cytogenetic Findings in 49 Yanomama Indians from Two Villages in Venezuela	375
XI–3:	Frequency of Sickle-cell Gene in Liberia	377
XI–4:	Changes in Oxygen Consumption Capacity of Lowlanders upon Upward Migration	380
XI–5:	Oxygen Consumption Capacity Among High-Altitude Natives	381
XI–6:	Growth Rate Differences Between Nuñoa and U.S. Children	384
XI–7:	Possible Epidemiological and Pathophysiological Mechanisms Relating Carbon Monoxide and Myocardial Infarction	386
XI–8:	Rates of Chronic Bronchitis and Emphysema for Smokers and Non-Smokers	387
XI–9:	Hemodynamic and Respiratory Responses of Five Normal Subjects to Carboxyhemoglobin (COH_b)	389

PART I

THE
SOLAR-TERRESTRIAL
ENVIRONMENT

ELEMENTS OF THE SOLAR-TERRESTRIAL SYSTEM

The natural environment of man consists of a single, gigantic system, all of whose parts continuously interact. It has been customary over the centuries to view certain of these parts in isolation: the atmosphere of winds and moisture; the hydrosphere of oceans, lakes, rivers, and groundwater; the biosphere of living things; and the lithosphere, or the crustal portion of the "solid" earth. Only during recent decades has a general awareness been developing that the behavior of each of these parts is fundamentally influenced, and indeed frequently controlled, by the behavior of the others. Even less apparent to many has been the role of the more remote parts of our environment: (a) the deeper reaches of the earth that lie beneath the crust, and (b) the vast region that extends from the upper levels of the atmosphere to the sun — and even beyond to the sources of much of the cosmic radiation that continues to bombard the earth. The latter is designated here as the "solar-terrestrial system" and forms the starting point of this review of the status of environmental science. The system can be divided conveniently into five parts:

The Sun — an undistinguished star, but the principal source of the energy that drives our environmental system.

The Interplanetary Medium — previously considered a vacuum, this enormous region between the sun and the near-earth environment is now known to be filled with matter, largely electrons and protons (hydrogen nuclei), originating in the outer reaches of the solar atmosphere (the "corona") and rushing outward at great speeds as the "solar wind."

The Magnetosphere — that region of space in which the earth's magnetic field dominates charged-particle motion. An enormous storehouse of solar energy, the magnetosphere is

bounded, on the sunward side, by the "magnetopause," which is the inner boundary of a transition region (the "magnetosheath") beyond which lies the solar wind. In the direction away from the sun, the magnetosphere stretches beyond the orbit of the moon in a long tail, like the tail of a comet.

The Ionosphere — a region containing free electrically charged particles by means of which radio waves are transmitted great distances around the earth. Within the ionosphere are several regions, each of which contains one or more layers that vary in height and ionization depending on time of day, season, and the solar cycle.

The Upper Atmosphere — an electrically neutral region, whose chief characteristics derive from the absorption of solar ultraviolet radiation. The upper atmosphere (the "thermosphere" and "mesosphere") overlaps the lowest level of the ionosphere but also extends below it. Near 50 kilometers from the earth, at the "stratopause," the upper atmosphere gives way to the atmosphere layers that immediately surround the earth (the "stratosphere" and "troposphere").

This enormous volume of space is matched by the great range of physical mechanisms that occur. In the closer regions of the upper atmosphere, solar-terrestrial science is concerned with many of the concepts that meteorologists have evolved in dealing with the weather systems of the lower atmosphere; at the outer extremes, the methods of astrophysics and high-temperature plasma physics must be utilized. The status of solar-terrestrial science is thus strongly dependent on the specific phenomena being considered, for scientific progress has not been uniform across this complex system.

At the same time, the solar-terrestrial system, considered as a whole, is both the source of beneficial radiation, without which life itself could never have developed on the earth, and the mechanism for controlling harmful radiation. Without this control mechanism, life could not long survive. The whole range of solar-terrestrial relationships is therefore of the greatest environmental concern.

The past twenty years have produced a wealth of detail and at least partial understanding of the activity going on in this region. The knowledge has *not* produced quantitative models of the dynamical effects on the earth environment. The effects are too complicated — in the same way that weather is still too complicated for satisfactory quantitative modeling. But the knowledge informs us about what is happening, allowing us to understand the effects and to avoid them in some cases, thus permitting intelligent planning for the future.

The Sun

A powerful source of energy, generated by thermonuclear processes, the sun can nevertheless be expected to remain in its present condition, emitting radiation at a more or less constant rate, for an extremely long time. This surmise is based on astronomical observations of stars similar to the sun. Scientific attention is therefore directed principally to aspects of solar activity, and its attendant radiation, that are more variable in time.

Most of the variability in solar radiation is associated with (a) the 11-year solar-activity (or sunspot) cycle, (b) the "active regions" that are often displayed at the peak of the cycle and are the source of intense fluxes of extreme ultraviolet (EUV) radiation, X-rays, and energetic particles (chiefly protons and electrons), and (c) the "solar flares" that burst forth from within these active regions. (See Figure I-1)

None of these three phenomena is well understood and the outstanding

questions about the sun at present are:

1. What is the basic reason for the 11-year solar-activity cycle?

2. What are the mechanisms underlying the emission of the more "exotic" portions of the spectrum — i.e., X-rays and

EUV radiation at the short wavelength end and radio waves at the long end? Is there anything that we should know about such relatively unexplored regions of the spectrum as the infrared and millimeter-wave radiations?

3. What is the basic mechanism responsible for solar flares?

The Eleven-Year Solar-Activity Cycle — The basic mechanism that produces this cycle is not known. It is almost surely bound up with the internal structure of the sun, which will not be accessible to direct observation for the foreseeable future. Thus, the answer to the first question is not likely to be reached with any degree of certainty for a considerable time, although theoretical mechanisms to explain solar activity should be generated and tested as far as possible against observation. It remains the most basic of all outstanding questions of solar physics.

Active Regions — There is more hope that a solution will ultimately be found to the problem of growth of individual active regions, as well as the occurrence of flares within these regions. It is known, for example, that magnetic fields play an important role in the associated enhanced ultraviolet and X-ray emissions, in the growth of sunspots (around which magnetic fields attain strengths as great as 1,000 gauss), and in the sudden birth of flares. Observations suggest that regions of strong magnetic field are carried outward by convection from the interior of the sun. When these magnetic fields break through the visible surface, we see their effect in the form of active regions and sunspots. As the magnetic fields extend outward into the solar atmosphere, they encounter less and less material. Flares originate at some location within this outer solar atmosphere.

It is, thus, likely that answers to the second question posed above will

Figure I–1 — SOLAR FLARE

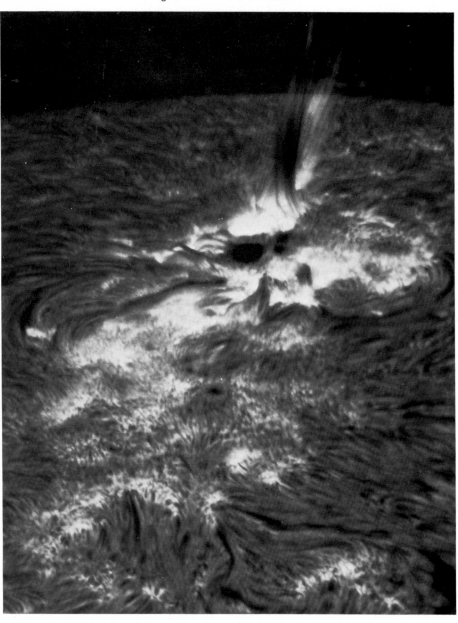

Solar flares usually lasting only a few minutes form very rapidly in disturbed regions around sunspots. Flares occur quite frequently near the maximum of the solar activity cycle and are related to catastrophic changes in the powerful magnetic fields that are associated with sunspots.

come eventually from a gradual extension of present work, in the form of refinement of satellite and space-probe observations and the continuation of the ground-based observations that have provided the core of our knowledge about the sun.

Solar Flares — Solar flares are cataclysmic outbursts of radiation, similar to those generally observed from active regions, but in immensely greater quantities and with much higher energies. Fortunately, individual flares are short-lived (of the order of an hour at most), and the most intense ones are quite rare, even at the peak of the solar cycle.

The effects of flares on the near-earth environment make them by far the most important solar phenomenon. The sudden surges of radiation they produce constitute a major hazard to manned space flights and a hazard of uncertain magnitude to the passengers and crew of supersonic-transport aircraft on transpolar flights, where natural solar-radiation shields are less effective than elsewhere. Flares also increase the electrical conductivity of the lower part of the earth's ionosphere, giving rise to severe interruptions of radio and telegraph communications, particularly at high latitudes.

Considerable progress in predicting major solar flares has been made through observations of time variations of the magnetic field configuration within known active regions in the lower solar atmosphere. While improvements in empirical forecasting techniques of this kind can be expected, truly accurate predictions must await an understanding of the basic physical mechanisms responsible for the development of a flare. Many promising suggestions have been put forward, but none has proved entirely satisfactory. Some think a flare is caused by the annihilation of magnetic fields. Another interesting possibility has emerged from satellite probes of the "auroral substorms" that occur in the earth's outer mag-

netosphere (see page 8). There is an apparent analogy between many of the observed radiation characteristics of these substorms and those of solar flares, opening up the possibility that their mechanisms are basically similar, though with modifications appropriate to the different solar environment.

Other Research Needs — Solar EUV radiation is largely responsible for the existence of the earth's ionosphere, and the broad nature of that responsibility is now fairly clear. Many of the details, however, remain beyond our grasp. The detailed structure of the sun's radiation spectrum in the EUV and X-ray regions, the points of origin of these radiations at the sun, and the mechanisms responsible for producing them are still areas of considerable uncertainty. Much progress is likely to come from the satellite and space-probe programs aimed at long-term monitoring of solar radiation in these wavelength regions with high angular resolution.

The Interplanetary Medium

The broad features of the interplanetary medium are known and understood. (See Figure 1-2) Interplanetary space is in fact filled with material, or plasma, from the outer reaches of the solar atmosphere (the "corona"). It is made up for the most part of electrons and protons (hydrogen nuclei), with small quantities of helium and traces of heavier nuclei. As a result of the instability of the outer solar corona against expansion, this material is rushing outward from the sun at speeds of the order of 400 kilometers per second, forming the "solar wind."

Many important details are still missing from this picture, however. For example, solar-wind matter is believed to constitute a sample of the material that exists in the upper solar corona. After a solar flare has erupted, however, the nuclear com-

position of the solar wind has been seen to change quite suddenly to one that contains up to 20 percent helium, with appreciable amounts of heavier elements. This material is probably that of the *lower* solar atmosphere, near the base of the corona or in the chromosphere, where flares originate. Spacecraft are providing an opportunity to study fairly directly these interesting differences in the chemical composition of different regions of the sun itself. Comparison of solar-wind compositions with the terrestrial composition may produce insights into how the earth and solar system were formed.

"Collisionless" Shock Waves — Another important area for study is the reason for the fluid-like behavior of the solar wind. In conventional fluids, particles interact by collisions, but collisions between individual solar-wind particles are extremely rare. Nevertheless, the solar wind displays many of the properties of a continuous fluid. In particular, the wind's outward expansion is supersonic, in the sense that its speed relative to the sun and planets is greater than the speed with which waves can propagate through the medium. As it sweeps past any solid body in the solar system, the wind forms a standing shock wave upstream of the body, analogous to the shock wave ahead of an aircraft in supersonic flight. The width of the wave that forms around the earth is determined by the outward extent of the earth's magnetic field, rather than by that of the solid earth itself, because the material in the solar wind, being a good electrical conductor, is strongly affected by magnetic fields. The earth's shock wave is much larger than that formed around other, more weakly magnetized bodies like the moon, Venus, and Mars.

Collisionless shock waves are phenomena that may have an important bearing on our understanding of the basic plasma physics that holds the key to controlled thermonuclear fusion. They have been difficult to

Figure I–2 — THE INTERPLANETARY MEDIUM

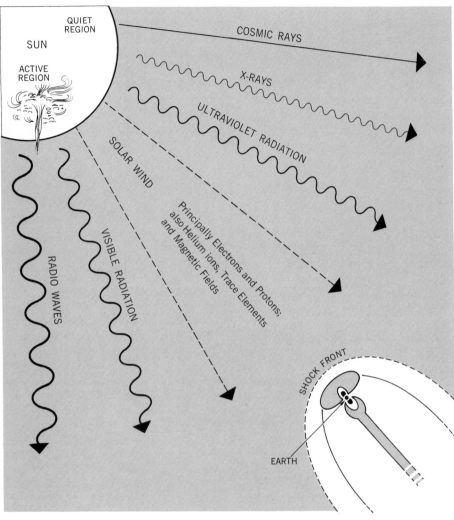

In addition to visible radiation, both steady and sporadic electromagnetic emissions from the sun extend over a large range of wavelengths (radio to X-ray). Low energy charged particles in the expanding outer corona form the solar wind which, together with the extended solar magnetic field, dominates the environment of the interplanetary medium. Occasionally, great flares in active regions emit charged particles of cosmic ray energy.

diffuse outward from the sun much as chimney smoke diffuses in the turbulent atmosphere. This turbulence is highly variable and depends on the general background of solar activity at any particular time.

Since the effects of energetic particles reaching the vicinity of the earth are generally undesirable, an ability to predict their arrival would be useful. One fact that helps in their prediction is that, because the sun rotates, interplanetary magnetic field lines stretch out in a spiral, much like water drops from a rotating garden sprinkler. Hence, the earth is connected magnetically to a point well to the western side of the sun's visible disc rather than to the center, and intense flares originating in the western portion of the disc are more likely to produce serious effects than those erupting in the eastern portion. Nevertheless, a great deal more work, both observational and experimental, is needed to lay the foundation for accurately predicting the arrival of potentially harmful particles.

Blast Waves — Major solar flares are accompanied by blast waves which move out from the sun at speeds of the order of 1,000 kilometers a second, sweeping the ambient solar-wind plasma ahead of them and bringing in their train a greatly enhanced solar-wind flow. The more intense blast waves are not appreciably affected by interplanetary conditions. As the blast waves encounter the earth, they produce major effects on the magnetosphere, giving rise to worldwide magnetic storms and visible auroras (often at much lower latitudes than the conventional auroral zones). They also provide the most important sources of fresh material for the radiation belts that surround the earth.

Ability to predict these effects is a matter of some practical importance, since serious interruptions in radio communications and even in domestic power supplies may result.

produce under laboratory conditions, and their properties even harder to measure, because the probes used have generally been larger than the thickness of the shock wave itself. Now, however, the shock wave on the sunward side of the earth's magnetosphere provides a natural laboratory for studying collisionless shocks; space-probe techniques, in which the probe dimensions are much smaller than the shock thickness, are likely to produce a great deal of valuable information.

The Interplanetary Magnetic Field — The solar-wind material is permeated by a weak magnetic field, also of solar origin. This interplanetary magnetic field plays an important role in guiding the highly energetic flare particles toward or away from the earth. The detailed behavior of the field is exceedingly complex, however, and not well understood. Furthermore, the picture is complicated by the often irregular, or "turbulent," structure of the magnetic field, which causes particles to

Short-term prediction of blast waves is not too difficult, since the appearance of an intense flare on the sun gives one or two days advance warning. Longer-term prediction is involved with the problem, discussed earlier, of long-term prediction of flares themselves; this problem remains unresolved due to our relative lack of understanding of the basic mechanisms underlying solar activity.

In general, the major practical result of increasing our knowledge of the interplanetary medium would be an improved ability to predict solar-flare particle effects in the vicinity of the earth. Basic advances in our understanding of the processes governing collisionless plasmas, and of the origin of the solar system itself, are also likely consequences, and should be pursued.

The Magnetosphere

The magnetosphere (see Figure I-3) is the outer region of the earth's ionized atmosphere, in which the medium is sufficiently rarified that collisions between charged and neutral particles can be neglected and the behavior of the charged particles is dominated by the earth's magnetic field. It can be regarded as the region in which control of the environment by the solar wind gives way to control by the earth. As such, it is an enormous storehouse of solar energy, extending out to a distance of some 10 earth-radii in the direction of the sun and to a much greater distance, perhaps as much as 1,000 earth-radii, in the opposite direction.

The magnetosphere extends from the "magnetopause," where the geomagnetic field terminates, down to a height of about 250 kilometers above the surface of the earth, and thus includes a large part of the conventional ionosphere. This section will be devoted to the outer regions of the magnetosphere proper; the inner portion will be treated as part of the ionosphere in the next section.

The Sunward Side — The magnetopause marks the true boundary between the plasma originating at the sun and that belonging to the earth. On the sunward side of this boundary lies the immense shock wave described in the previous section, which stands some 15 earth-radii out from the center of the earth, as well as a region about 5 earth-radii thick known as the "magnetosheath"; the latter is made up of solar-wind plasma that has been disoriented by passage through the shock wave, together with tangled irregular magnetic field.

The existence of something like the magnetopause had been predicted theoretically long before the Space Age; its existence has now been verified by satellites and space-probes carrying magnetometers. But many of its observed properties remain puzzling. Furthermore, most of the observations have been confined to near-equatorial regions, while many of the important problems of energy transfer from the solar wind to the magnetosphere hinge on the existence and properties of the magnetopause over the polar caps. Here practically no information exists.

The Geomagnetic Tail — The configuration of the outer magnetosphere in the direction pointing away from the sun is quite different from that in the solar direction. Instead of being compressed by the solar wind into a volume sharply bounded by the magnetopause, the magneto-

Figure I–3 — THE MAGNETOSPHERE

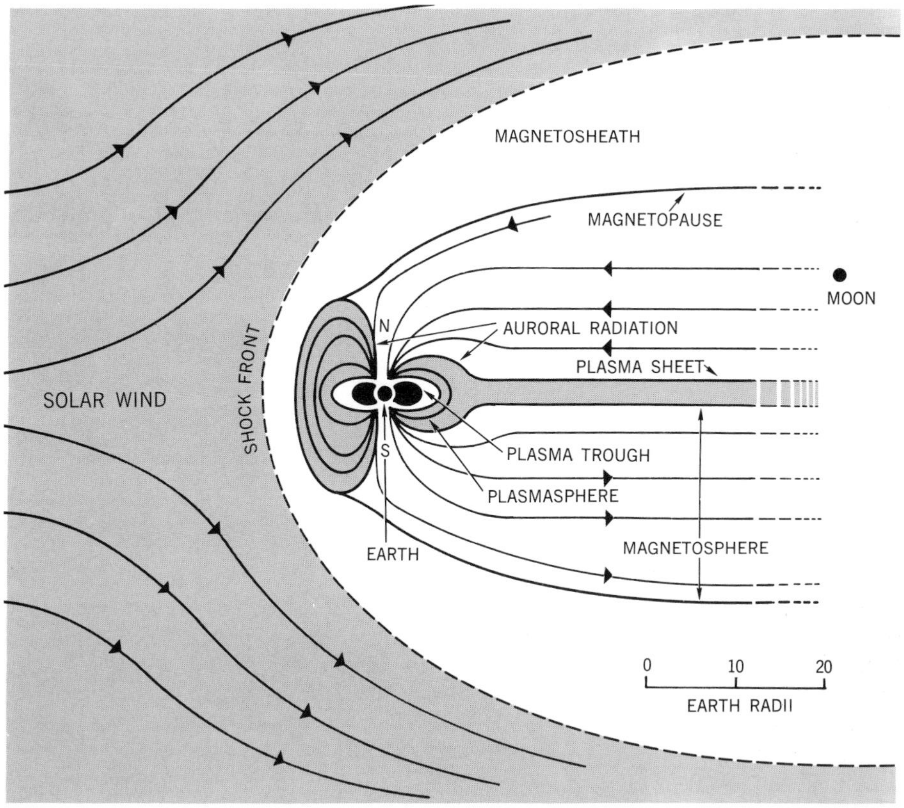

This conceptual model of the earth's magnetic field is based on years of spacecraft observations. The dot marked "moon" indicates the relative distance at which the moon's orbit intersects the plane containing the sun-earth line and geomagnetic axis.

sphere in the anti-solar direction is stretched out by the action of the solar wind into a long "tail," much like the tail of a comet. The geomagnetic field lines are straight, with the field itself directed away from the earth (and the sun) in the southern half and toward the earth in the northern half.

The geomagnetic tail is now recognized to play a vitally important intermediate role as a reservoir of stored solar-wind energy. Its formation requires some form of energy transport across the boundary between the magnetosphere and the solar wind, but whether this transport is accomplished by a process analogous to viscosity in a fluid, or by the coupling together of geomagnetic and interplanetary magnetic fields, or by some more exotic process is not yet known.

Equally mysterious are the processes by which the tail releases energy. While some of the enormous energy stored in the tail is continually being drained into the earth's atmosphere, the most dramatic releases are associated with relatively short bursts, known as auroral substorms, which can recur at intervals of a few hours. They are accompanied by disruptions of radio communications and surges on long power lines that can result in power outages. Associated increases in radiation-belt particle fluxes shorten the lives of communication satellites by degrading the performance of the solar cells on which their power supply depends.

As noted earlier, the substorms are thought to have many analogies to solar flares. An understanding of their mechanisms may thus lead to an understanding of the flare mechanism. This understanding is vital to our future ability to predict the whole gamut of solar-terrestrial phenomena that affect communications and power supplies and may also provide some insight into the plasma-confinement mechanisms that are needed to achieve controlled thermo-nuclear fusion. Fortunately, the substorm mechanism can be studied directly through satellite probes of the tail region in which the release of energy takes place.

Radiation Belts — The great energy released in the form of an auroral substorm also serves to replenish the radiation belts that surround the earth with magnetically trapped particles. The discovery of these belts was the first dramatic result of the Space Age in terms of exploration of our near-space environment. A broad mapping of their structure and behavior has now been obtained, although no complete explanation yet exists of the sources of the belts or of their dynamic behavior. At first the belts were thought to be fairly static and well-behaved. Nature seemed to have presented us with an example of stably confined high-temperature plasma. It is now clear, however, that the individual particles in the outer portions of the belts are continuously experiencing a variety of processes, including convection in space, acceleration, and precipitation into the atmosphere. Plasma instabilities of some kind associated with the growth of hydromagnetic and electromagnetic waves in the magnetosphere seem to be of major importance. Similar instabilities have prevented the confinement of high-temperature plasmas in the laboratory.

The Plasmapause — In addition to confining the magnetosphere to a sharply bounded cavity on the sunward side, and stretching it out into a long tail in the anti-solar direction, the solar wind apparently generates a vast system of convection that affects the plasma throughout the outer magnetosphere. This convection system pulls plasma from the sunward side of the magnetosphere over the top of the polar caps into the tail, where a return flow carries it back toward the earth, around the sides, and back out to the front of the magnetosphere.

Another of the great boundary surfaces of the magnetosphere, known as the "plasmapause," marks the dividing line between plasma that is influenced by this convection and plasma that is tightly bound to the earth and corotates with it. The plasmapause generally lies some 4 earth-radii out from the center of the earth above the equator, and follows the shape of the geomagnetic field lines from there to meet the ionosphere at about 60° magnetic latitude. In common with other magnetospheric boundaries, such as the magnetopause, it is extremely well marked, and the properties of the magnetospheric plasma change abruptly in crossing it.

Although the close relationship between the plasmapause and the boundary of the convection region has been fairly well established, several features of the plasmapause remain unexplained. These include the sharpness of the plasma changes on either side, the shape of the plasmapause at any given instant, and its radial motions in time. There is some evidence that inward movements of the plasmapause during magnetic storms have a bearing on the so-called ionospheric storms, when the density of the mid-latitude ionosphere drops sharply, leading to a deterioration in radio communication. Experiments aimed at probing the plasmapause are presently being planned with the aim of improving our understanding of the mechanisms influencing its formation and its dynamic behavior.

The Ionosphere

The ionosphere (see Figure I-4) is defined here as the electrically charged component of the earth's upper atmosphere, consisting of free electrons, heavy positively charged ions, and a relatively small number of heavy negatively charged ions. The non-charged component — i.e., the atmosphere itself — will be considered in the next section.

Figure I-4 — THE IONOSPHERE

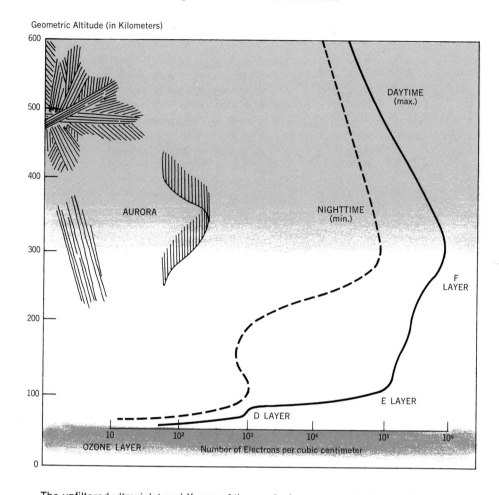

Geometric Altitude (in Kilometers)

The unfiltered ultraviolet and X-rays of the sun ionize many molecules, producing the ionosphere. The ionosphere has several layers, each characterized by a more or less regular maximum in electron density. The difference between the day and night profile is due to the availability of solar radiation.

propagating long waves, but it has an undesirable effect on radio propagation at the higher frequencies through absorption of the radio-wave energy.

The F Region — In the case of the F region, where the concentrations of free electrons reach their peak, ionization is now known to be created by EUV radiation from the sun. The contributions of the various portions of the solar spectrum within this band are quite well understood. The principal unknowns arise basically from the fact that the atmosphere at these altitudes is so rarified that collisions between electrons, ions, and neutral particles are extremely rare, so that an individual electron has a very long lifetime and can move considerable distances from the region in which it is formed. As a result, the electron concentration at any given time and place is strongly influenced by motions, including winds, atmospheric waves, and diffusion. Many of the anomalies in the behavior of the F region, which have been recognized since the early days of radio propagation, are almost certainly based on motions of this kind.

Much of the current interest in the F region is focused on the explanation of these anomalies and the information they can provide on the winds of the outer atmosphere. One outstanding anomaly is that the daytime F region is usually denser in winter than in summer, despite the decreased sunlight available. Another is that the F region tends to be maintained throughout the long polar night when the sun disappears completely for long periods of time. This latter phenomenon seems at least partly due to bombardment of low-energy particles from the outer magnetosphere, but movement of electrons from lower latitudes probably also plays a role.

The most powerful tool to emerge in recent years for studying the F region is the so-called incoherent

Our understanding of the formation and behavior of the ionosphere is considerably more advanced than in the areas discussed previously. Major breakthroughs have been made, particularly in the past two decades, when direct probing through rockets and satellites has been possible. Nevertheless, as is usually the case, increasing knowledge has raised new and previously unsuspected questions, some of which have considerable practical importance.

The ionosphere is conventionally divided into three fairly distinct regions:

1. The D region, lying between about 60 and 95 kilometers altitude;

2. The E region, extending from 95 to about 140 kilometers; and

3. The F region, containing the bulk of the ionization and extending upward from 140 kilometers.

The E and F regions are capable of reflecting medium- and short-wave radio waves and thus permit long-distance communication. The D region plays an important role in

(Thomson) scatter radar technique, which allows direct ground-based investigation of high-lying ionization. This has added immensely to our knowledge of the mechanisms influencing the F region. It has been possible to measure not only electron concentration, but also temperatures of the different plasma components and effects of electric fields in causing motion of the plasma. Results from existing and planned scatter radar installations will undoubtedly add a great deal to our knowledge of this outermost region of our atmosphere, and will, hopefully, lead to improvements in our ability to predict changes in radio propagation conditions.

Two F-region phenomena are of special interest at this time. These are the "polar wind" and the "ionospheric storm," both of which are more than mere curiosities. The polar wind, which has been predicted on theoretical grounds but not yet adequately verified observationally, arises because of the existence of the long geomagnetic tail described in the previous section. The F-region plasma can diffuse quite freely along the direction of the earth's magnetic field, and as long as the field lines loop back into the opposite hemisphere of the earth no plasma is lost thereby. In the polar regions, however, the field lines are greatly stretched by the solar wind and eventually become lost in interplanetary space. When F-region plasma travels out along these field lines, it ultimately disappears. This outward flow is expected to be at least partly supersonic; it plays a large part in the loss of the lighter constituents (hydrogen and helium) from the atmosphere.

Ionospheric storms, by contrast, have been recognized observationally for many years but still have no adequate theoretical explanation. Over most of the earth they appear as a rather rapid decrease in the electron concentration of the F region, accompanied by a corresponding in-

ability to propagate radio signals that normally propagate freely. Recovery from this effect is much less rapid than its onset. The ultimate explanation for ionospheric storms may lie in a combination of inward motion of the plasmapause, discussed in the last section, movement of the F region caused by electric fields, and changes in the photochemistry of the region.

The E Region — As one moves downward from the peak of the F region, photochemistry becomes steadily more important relative to motions in determining the characteristics of the ionosphere. The E region, which is largely formed by solar X-radiation together with some EUV radiation, shows quite different characteristics from the F region, and many of these differences arise from photochemical causes. Movements of the ionization are still important, however, in that they give rise to very substantial electric fields and currents because of the difference between the collision characteristics of electrons and ions. In fact, the whole situation is analogous to a dynamo, in which an electrical conductor moves in a fixed magnetic field and thereby generates an electric field. For this reason, the region is often referred to as the "dynamo region" of the ionosphere.

The E region is the seat of the major current systems responsible for surface magnetic-field variations. The latter are particularly pronounced near the magnetic equator, where the magnetic field lines are horizontal, and in auroral zones, where irregular changes in ionospheric conductivity are associated with particle bombardment. The great concentrations of ionospheric current in these regions are known respectively as the "equatorial electrojet" and the "auroral electrojet" by analogy with the jet streams of the lower atmosphere. While the broad reasons for the existence of these electrojets are fairly well understood, they still present many puzzling features. The growth of small but intense irregularities within and near the electro-

jets, in particular, presents a challenge in geophysical plasma physics that has not yet been fully met.

The development of the thin, dense layers of electrons known collectively as "sporadic E," once an outstanding problem, now appears to be largely explicable in terms of the interaction of vertical wind shears with metallic ions of meteoric origin. This problem is not completely solved, however, and is still an active field for theory and experiment. The continuous influx of meteoric material to the atmosphere has turned out to be quite important to both the E and D regions of the ionosphere. There are many unanswered questions connected with this meteoric material, including its chemical composition, its distribution within the atmosphere, and its ultimate fate.

The D Region — After years of relative neglect, a great deal of interest is presently focused on the D region, which is the real meeting ground between the lower and upper atmosphere. It now appears certain that many of the strange facets of this region's behavior are basically due to meteorological effects connected in as yet unknown ways with the lower atmosphere. Thus, on certain winter days the D-region electron concentration rises abnormally; this "winter anomaly" is associated with sudden warmings of the stratosphere and mesosphere which are probably connected with the breakdown of the polar winter vortex of the general atmospheric circulation. D-region electron concentrations usually display a high degree of variability during winter, while they are relatively stable from day to day in summer. These effects, and others of a similar kind, are currently arousing a great deal of interest both among meteorologists, who are extending their concepts upward into this unexplored region of the atmosphere, and among ionospheric workers, who are bringing their interests downward.

The practical importance of the D region arises from the fact that it efficiently absorbs radio waves at the higher frequencies (MF and HF), and reflects them at the lower frequencies (LF and VLF). Both of these properties are greatly modified by solar disturbances, since the energetic radiation and particles emitted from the sun at these times penetrate through the thin upper regions of the ionosphere and deposit most of their energy in the D region. When intense solar flares give rise to fluxes of energetic solar protons, for example, the protons are funnelled by the earth's magnetic field to the polar regions, where they enter the atmosphere and create very intense ionization in the 50- to 100-kilometer altitude range. The consequent strong absorption of HF radio waves (known as "polar cap absorption") completely disrupts short-wave radio communication over the polar regions, sometimes for days on end. The X-rays emitted from the same flares cause mild, brief fadeouts that extend over the sunlit hemisphere of the earth.

While the problem of predicting these effects is ultimately the problem of predicting intense solar flares, it is also important to learn as much as possible about the relationship between the detailed characteristics of individual flares and the nature and magnitude of the ionospheric response. A great deal has already been achieved in this area through a combination of ground-based radio observations and direct rocket and satellite measurements of the radiations and particles responsible.

Ionospheric Modification — One interesting recent development is the possibility of artificial modification of the ionosphere. Research on this problem is still in its infancy, but success could lead to a major increase in our ability to use the ionosphere for radio-propagation purposes. Uncontrolled modification has been produced artificially by high-altitude nuclear detonations; attempts are now being made to modify the ionosphere in more sophisticated ways by releasing ion clouds from rockets and by use of high-power radars on the ground. This approach is likely to lead eventually to greater insight into the mechanisms that control the natural ionosphere as well as provide us with a new range of possible practical uses.

The Upper Atmosphere

This section deals with the neutral gas of the upper atmosphere, as distinct from the electrically charged component that forms the ionosphere. In terms of altitude, the two overlap; indeed, they are closely coupled together in many ways, so that several of the problems mentioned in the preceding section are inseparable from the problems of the neutral upper atmosphere. The neutral upper atmosphere also shows a range of properties not directly related to the ionosphere, however, and those are the questions of concern here.

Like the ionosphere, the neutral atmosphere has long been divided into altitude regions, based mainly on thermal structure. (See Figure I-5) The very lowest region of the atmosphere, in which the earth's weather systems are located, is known as the troposphere; here the temperature generally decreases with increasing altitude. Above the tropopause the temperature first remains constant and then increases with increasing altitude through the stratosphere, terminating at a temperature maximum near 50 kilometers altitude known as the stratopause. Above this lies the mesosphere, a region of decreasing temperature with height, which extends to about 85 kilometers. The temperature at the mesopause is lower than anywhere else in the atmosphere, and can be below $-150°$ centigrade. Above the mesopause lies the thermosphere, in which the temperature steadily increases with altitude, eventually reaching a fairly steady value in excess of $1,000°$ centigrade. The warm regions of the upper atmosphere owe their high temperatures to the absorption of solar ultraviolet radiation, by ozone near the stratopause and by EUV radiation in the thermosphere.

The Thermosphere — The intense heating experienced by the thermosphere must set up some kind of circulation pattern, analogous to the circulation of the lower atmosphere but differing in many important respects because of the extreme rarity of the medium and the influence of the ionosphere. Little is known about this circulation, but the effects of the variable heat input on the density of the thermosphere can be directly detected through changes in the orbital period of satellites that travel through the upper thermosphere. As solar activity increases, the thermosphere heats up, expands outward, and increases the frictional drag on satellites, thereby appreciably shortening their lifetimes.

Thermospheric heating depends on the structure of the sun's EUV spectrum and its variability with solar activity, neither of which is known adequately, and on the constitution of the upper atmosphere and the manner in which the various atoms and molecules absorb the radiation. The non-uniformity of the heating from equator to poles causes strong temperature gradients which in turn give rise to very strong winds. Some of the properties of these thermospheric winds have been inferred from their influence on the F region of the ionosphere, which is amenable to exploration by ground-based radio sounding, but this information is still very sparse.

The principal chemical components of the thermosphere are atomic oxygen, helium, and hydrogen; the two latter, being the lightest constituents of the atmosphere, tend to diffuse toward the higher regions; atomic hydrogen, in particular, is so light that appreciable numbers of atoms

Figure I–5 — ATMOSPHERIC TEMPERATURE DISTRIBUTION

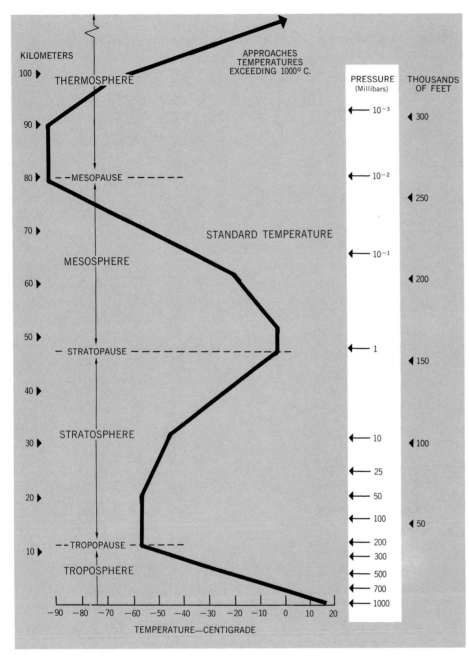

This chart shows the average distribution of temperature with height (lapse rate) of the mid-latitude atmosphere. Lines ending with the word "pause" indicates the boundary between two spheres. These boundaries are not always well established.

drogen scatters sunlight at night, but its properties have been little explored.

The Mesosphere — This region, which overlaps the D region of the ionosphere, is the object of much current interest. It is a region of extreme complexity, in which meteorological phenomena, mixing, and photochemistry all play a part. It is made up mostly of molecular nitrogen and oxygen, just like the lower atmosphere, but it contains many minor constituents which, because of their chemical reactivity or ready ionizability, dominate the energies of the region. Among these are ozone, atomic oxygen, nitric oxide, water vapor, and many others. The region has proved extremely difficult to explore directly, since the atmosphere is too dense to allow satellites to remain long in orbit and too high for the balloon techniques that are used at lower altitudes. Most existing information has come from rocket soundings, but even here the problems are severe because of the comparatively high density and the fact that rockets generally travel through the region at supersonic speeds, creating shock waves that disturb conditions locally.

The photochemistry of the region has recently been under intensive study, both through rocket experiments and by way of laboratory measurements of the rates of the various key chemical reactions. A broad picture of the important mechanisms is beginning to emerge, but the roles played by transport and movements in carrying constituents from one point to another are still largely unexplored. Of special importance is the question of turbulence in the mesosphere and its influence on mixing of the various constituents. Many of the problems of dispersing pollutants in the lower atmosphere arise from mechanisms similar to those of distributing minor constituents in the mesosphere; many of the photochemical reactions responsible for smog formation are also the same. Thus, the work presently being car-

can attain escape velocity and leave the earth entirely. The region in which an atom can proceed outward without colliding with other atoms is known as the exosphere, the true outer limit of the neutral atmosphere. The exosphere's presence can be detected from the ground because hy-

ried out in the relatively less complicated mesosphere may produce significant insights into these practical problems of the lower atmosphere.

Research Needs in the Upper Atmosphere — The greatest single need in this area of geophysics is for a systematic exploration of the properties of the upper atmosphere using rocket and satellite techniques. At present we have only tantalizing

glimpses of many of the important features, and little or no information on how they change with time of day, season, solar activity, and altitude. The techniques exist, and all that is required is a sustained synoptic program aimed at studying a variety of upper-atmosphere parameters simultaneously under a wide range of conditions. Such a program would add immensely to our knowledge of the upper reaches of the

atmosphere, and of the mechanisms occurring there that may be important to our existence. Because of the complexity of the region, single problems cannot be handled in isolation, and there is a real need for a thorough exploration of the entire region. Some scientists believe, however, that we now have enough general knowledge of what goes on in space that future studies should be limited and carefully aimed at specific goals.

TERRESTRIAL EFFECTS OF SOLAR ACTIVITY

The sun and the motions of the of the earth about it essentially determine the earth's climate. The time of day and the season are associated with well-known, normal variations in the weather. Superimposed on these regular patterns, however, are extremely large deviations from climatology. Some of these can be explained (and, hence, forecast with some success) on the basis of physical equations; some are so irregular or little understood as to require a statistical and probabilistic approach to prediction.

Advances in Forecasting Technique

For many decades, atmospheric scientists attempted to relate solar perturbations to terrestrial weather features, with no significant success. Until recently, the only data available to them were those collected from ground-based observatories and weather stations. When radio arrived on the scene, scientists began to relate variations in radio propagation to observed changes in the character of the sun.

The Space Age produced a revolution in understanding and procedure. It became clear that, in general, the farther one moves away from the troposphere, the more one's environment is influenced by solar perturbations. In the region above the meso-

pause, at about 80 kilometers from the earth, variations in temperature and density result almost entirely from irregular solar emissions and hardly at all from the moving pattern of low-level cyclones and anticyclones.

These new insights — together with the realization that men, equipment, and their activities above the lower, protective atmosphere are vulnerable to (and may benefit from) environmental changes — gave impetus to a rush of new, very-high-altitude scientific missions and related activities. These include observations from rockets, satellites, and improved ground-based platforms; computerized data-processing techniques; and prediction.

Solar Forecasting Services — Atmospheric scientists, ionospheric and solar physicists, and even astronomers have shared in these new activities. But the atmospheric scientist, in becoming involved with the expanded environment, brings with him a special point of view: he is vitally concerned with data standardization, real-time use and rapid transmission of data, and the tailoring of his products to operational needs. He brings added emphasis with regard to synoptic coverage. He uses meteorological techniques in studying high-altitude variations such as anomalous variations in neutral density. He even applies Rossby's concepts to circulation features on the "surface" of the sun.

A combination of the viewpoints and methods of various kinds of scientists has now brought a new and important scientific service into being — the solar forecast center. The first such center was established by the U.S. Air Force with a nucleus of highly trained and cross-disciplined scientists from the Air Weather Service and the Air Force Cambridge Research Laboratories; their mission was to provide tailored, real-time support to military operations affected by the environment above the "classical atmosphere." The ionospheric-prediction activity of the National Oceanic and Atmospheric Administration (NOAA) has been enlarged to provide a complementary service for the civilian community.

Major Problem Areas

Solar forecasting centers and other such forecasting services undertake to meet the needs of a variety of customers, including radio communicators, astronauts, and scientific researchers. The most important areas of interest for such customers are as follows:

The Ionosphere — High frequency (HF) (3-30 mHz) radio communications are widely used as an inexpensive, fairly reliable means of transmitting signals over long distances.

13

The HF radio communicator therefore requires long-range and short-term forecasts of the specific frequencies that will effectively propagate throughout the day. This is known as frequency management and means, in short, the determination of the frequency that can be used from a particular transmitter to a particular receiver at a particular time. Propagation of the HF signal to a distant receiver employs single or multiple "reflections" from the ionosphere and the earth. Since the state of the ionosphere is dynamic and highly responsive to solar activity, the number of usable frequencies depends on (a) the intensity of ionizing solar ultraviolet and X-ray emissions and (b) the degree of disturbance of the magnetospheric-ionospheric environment. These are in addition to such factors as time of day, latitude, and equipment characteristics.

The HF communicator also requires forecasts and real-time advisories of short-wave fadeouts caused by X-ray emissions related to solar flares. If he gets these, he can insure that alternate means of communication (satellite or microwave methods) are available for use in sending the highest-priority messages. He can also differentiate between communication outages caused by propagation and those caused by equipment malfunction. If he knows that an outage is due to a short-wave fadeout, the communicator can simply wait for his circuit to return to normal to continue low-priority traffic rather than take time-consuming action to switch frequencies.

Other solar-terrestrial disturbances which disrupt communications, such as "polar cap absorption" events, geomagnetic-ionospheric storms, and auroral and geomagnetic substorm events, must also be forecast to allow the communicator to prepare to use alternate means of communication.

Finally, the communicator needs an accurate and complete history of ionospheric disturbances to post-analyze his system's performance. Outages that have been attributed to poor propagation when no disturbances were observed can then be identified as being due to mechanical or procedural problems.

High-Altitude Density — Space vehicles which spend all or part of their orbits in the region from 100 to 1,000 kilometers above ground are subject to significant drag from the neutral atmosphere. The density of this region and the resulting satellite drag are dynamic parameters. Their variations reflect heating of the high atmosphere produced by solar ultraviolet variations and corpuscular precipitations, mostly at polar latitudes.

Satellite drag perturbs the orbital parameters of the vehicles and, in turn, complicates cataloguing, tracking, and control. Density variations can sometimes alter the orbit enough to carry the vehicle out of an area of scientific interest or otherwise degrade its mission. If mission controllers are to be able to compensate adequately for orbital changes, they need the following:

1. A dynamic, accurate model of the global distribution of atmospheric density throughout the region of interest;

2. Accurate observations of such parameters of the model as ultraviolet flux, solar-wind energy, and density; and

3. Accurate forecasts of these parameters.

Space Radiation — Man in space faces radiation hazards from galactic cosmic rays, trapped radiation, and storms of particles (mostly protons) from solar flares.

Cosmic radiation is so penetrating that there is no practical means of shielding against it. Astronauts simply must live with it. Its intensity is low enough that it does not pose a serious hazard.

The trapped-radiation environment of near-earth space, however, is so intense that prolonged exposure would be fatal. Consequently, mission planners avoid that region by orbiting below it or arranging to pass through it quickly.

Solar-flare radiation poses a threat for a lightly shielded astronaut. The threat is not especially significant, however, because (a) major events occur rarely, (b) the astronaut can be shielded effectively from most of the radiation (in effect, the Apollo command module is a "storm cellar"), and (c) the astronaut can return to the safety of a shielded vehicle before significant doses have time to build up.

Despite the rather low critical nature of this hazard, certain space-environment support is essential to protect man effectively from the hazards of solar-flare radiation. Mission planners need forecasts of the likelihood of a particle event to insure that they have enough options available in case an event occurs. Observations of the flare radiation are needed to alert the astronauts. Techniques are required to project the course and intensity of an observed event so that the radiation threat can be accurately assessed.

Today there is some concern over the radiation hazard to passengers and crew of supersonic transports, especially for polar flights. Though not completely resolved, it appears that the threat is minimal, since solar cosmic-ray events sufficiently intense to cause undesirably high radiation doses are exceedingly rare and probably occur less than once every ten years. But forecasts, observations, and alerts will be needed to insure full protection. Warning systems are being developed, but warnings are unlikely to reach aircraft already in polar regions unless communication satellites can be used that are not subject to the "polar blackout" that accompanies any biologically dangerous particle flux.

Electromagnetic radiation from solar flares can be observed by sensitive radio receivers in the form of radio "noises," or interference, if the sun happens to be in the direction that the antenna is "looking." Observations of the sun's radio emission are required to advise system operators of the nature of the signal they are observing.

General Observational Data — The researcher needs forecasts and real-time advisories of the occurrence of selected solar and geophysical events in order to schedule and conduct experiments. He needs a consistent base of comparable observational data that can be vigorously examined for significant relationships.

The State of the Art

To meet the needs of these various operational and research communities, varied capabilities, skills, and understanding are required. Individually or institutionally, the atmospheric scientist and his colleagues must provide the following:

1. Observations of the sun and the space environment;

2. Rapid communications and data processing;

3. Forecasts of significant solar activity and geophysical responses.

In addition, they must have an understanding of the needs of specific systems and operations, in order to present advice to an operator in the form that will benefit him most.

Observations of the Sun and the Space Environment — The observations must be continuous, consistent, comparable, and, where appropriate, synoptic. They should include, but not be limited to, solar flares, active-region parameters, solar radio emission, space radiation, solar wind, the ionosphere, and the geomagnetic field.

U.S. civilian and military agencies maintain a network of operational solar observatories around the globe. This network is supplemented by numerous scientific observatories. Nearly continuous patrol of solar chromospheric activity has been achieved thereby. But the data obtained are not as useful in operational situations as, ideally, they might be.

First, they are subject to considerable inconsistency due to the subjective evaluations of the individual observers. To obtain the final description of a solar event, many often highly divergent observations are statistically combined. But in the quasi-real-time frame of operational support, evaluation of a solar event must be made on the basis of only one or two observations.

Second, patrol of the sun's radio emission is not complete. Gaps in synoptic coverage exist, frequencies useful for diagnosing solar activity are not always available, and some observatories report uncalibrated data. Operational radio patrol is about 90 percent effective, nonetheless.

Unmanned satellites are patrolling energetic-particle emission and some other space parameters for operational use. Real-time energetic-particle patrol presently exceeds 20 hours a day; X-rays, 16 to 18 hours; and solar wind, 8 to 9 hours. The observations are limited, however, in that: (a) they are not continuous; (b) data acquisition and processing are expensive; (c) all needed parameters are not sampled; (d) different sensors are not intercomparable; (e) sensor response changes; and (f) the vehicles have limited lifetimes. Other scientific satellites are sampling the space environment, but limited readout and data-processing capabilities and experimenters' proprietary rights prevent these data from being used operationally.

Observations of the ionosphere are being made using vertical- and oblique-incidence ionosondes, riometers, and sudden-ionospheric-disturbance sensors. For operational use, however, timely receipt of data is available from only about 20 locations around the world.

Several other observations of solar and geophysical parameters are being made for operational use. These include radio maps of the sun, ground-based neutron monitors, and geomagnetic-field observations. In general, they suffer from the same limitations as the observational networks described earlier.

The recent establishment of World Data Centers for storing and exchanging space data represents a significant advance. These centers are supported by the Inter-Union Commission on Solar-Terrestrial Physics of the International Council of Scientific Unions. However, the primary benefit comes to the research community rather than directly to the operational community. Furthermore, the program still suffers from inconsistencies, incomparabilities, and incompleteness of much of the data.

Rapid Communications and Data Processing — Rapid communication and processing of data are essential for timely forecasts. Even in the absence of forecast capability, they are required to make maximum operational use of observations.

The Air Force has designated a special teletype circuit for the rapid movement and exchange of solar-physical data within the United States. Both civil and military agencies have access to it. This circuit makes possible near-real-time relay. Data from the overseas observatories must be relayed by more complex and time-consuming means.

Up to a year or two ago, processing of the data was done by hand. Systems to process the data by machine have now begun to come into use, and the future will see more and more use of computers in operational space-environment support.

Forecasts of Significant Solar Activity and Geophysical Responses — Geophysically significant solar events must be forecast several hours, days, weeks, or even years in advance. Significant factors of the earth's environment, such as density at satellite altitudes and the state of the ionosphere, must also be forecast. In general, the shorter the forecast period, the more stringent the accuracy requirement.

Research on forecasting techniques has been under way for many years. The approaches have been many and varied, and no single technique has yet stood up under the test of continued operational use. Since knowledge of the physics of solar processes is lacking, present techniques are based on statistical correlations and relationships, observed solar features, even the influence of planetary configurations. By a combination of many techniques and subjective skills, operational forecasters have now developed a limited ability to forecast solar activity.

How well can solar activity be forecast? It is fairly safe to say that forecasting cannot be done well enough for the operator to place full reliance on it. Predictions can be used to advantage, but the operator knows he must have alternatives available to compensate for an incorrect forecast. As a rough approximation (doubtless open to challenge), no better than one out of every two major, geophysically significant solar events can be forecast 24 hours in advance. Additionally, at least three forecasts of events that do *not* occur are issued for every forecast that proves accurate. The most valuable forecasting tool has proved to be persistence. If a region of solar activity hasn't produced a major event, it probably won't. If a major event has occurred, another is likely to follow. Such factors as region size and radio-brightness temperature, magnetic structures, and flare history have also proved of some value.

One factor that complicates the forecast problem is that most research schemes attempt to predict large "solar flares." In reality, what the system operator or mission controller is interested in is the geophysically *significant* solar event, whether large or small. Experience has shown that most large solar flares are geophysically significant, but some are not. Most small flares are of no consequence, but a disturbing percentage are.

Forecasting of terrestrial proton events *after* a flare has occurred has been more successful, although it is not without limitations due to uncertainties and unavailability of relevant data. The storm of particles emitted by a flare takes a day or two to propagate from the sun to the earth, and this time interval permits a forecaster to analyze the diagnostic information contained in the electromagnetic emissions that accompanied the solar event. Analysis of radio-burst signatures and X-ray enhancements indicates whether the particles have been accelerated. Quantitative forecasts of the course and magnitude of the event are often possible.

Other aspects of the space environment are being forecast with varying degrees of success. The mean 10.7-centimeter radio flux from the sun is an input into high-altitude-density models; efforts to forecast it have been reasonably successful, in part because the parameter varies rather slowly. In contrast, practically no capability exists for forecasting variability in the geomagnetic field, another important input; short-term prediction of geomagnetic storms is particularly difficult.

Forecasts of ionospheric parameters for radio communicators have been made for many years. The field is quite extensive and complex. The Space Environment Laboratory, of NOAA, issues monthly, and sometimes more frequent, outlooks on radio propagation conditions. Monthly median predictions are generally adequate for most frequency-management applications, though significant improvements could be made by more frequent modification of the median predictions. Ability to forecast ionospheric disturbances is closely tied to the ability, discussed earlier, to forecast geophysically significant solar activity.

Understanding of Operational Needs

Effective application of space environment observations and forecasts requires, first, physical knowledge of the interaction between the environment and the specific activity being supported. Equally important, the forecaster and the operator must develop an effective rapport, based on a thorough knowledge by the former of the latter's system or mission. All parties must recognize that many things can happen to man's space-related activities which are significant but which cannot be explained.

The Direction of Future Scientific Effort

There is a clear, continuing need to advance the state of the art of operational solar and space-environmental support. Capabilities are already far from adequate, and the increasing sophistication of the activities that are affected requires a matching growth in capabilities.

Future scientific efforts need to focus on the following:

1. Techniques to provide accurate long-range and short-term forecasts of geophysically signifi-

cant solar events. Basic research on the *physics* of events is required to get away from the admitted limitations of statistical techniques.

2. Ionospheric forecasting and specification techniques, especially in the area of short-term frequency management. The problem is especially acute during magneto-ionospheric storms and within polar latitudes.

3. Modeling of high-altitude atmospheric density that is dynamic — i.e., which reflects hour-to-hour and day-to-day variations.

4. Better and more complete observations of solar and geophysical phenomena and techniques and hardware to process, format, and transmit data with minimal delay.

5. Operationally useful work on the propagation conditions of energetic particles between the sun and the earth.

6. Techniques to forecast geomagnetic disturbances accurately. The level of disturbance of the geomagnetic field must be related to operationally significant applications such as the ionosphere and high-altitude neutral density.

7. Finally, the researcher should not be satisfied with research alone. He must push his advances into the realm of "development" and their application to the many activities of mankind.

PART II

DYNAMICS OF
THE SOLID EARTH

1. DEEP EARTH PROCESSES

An Overview of Deep-Earth Chemistry and Physics

We recall that the earth consists of three parts: a thin crust, five to forty miles thick; a "mantle," below the crust, extending a little less than half-way down to the center; and a core. (See Figure II-1) The crust is the heterogeneous body on which we live and grow our food, and from which we derive all mineral resources, metals, and fuels. It is the only part of the earth that is accessible and directly observable; the composition of the mantle and core must be inferred from observations on the surface.

The crust, the oceans, and the atmosphere above them form the environment in which we live. This environment has been shaped through geologic time and continues to be shaped by forces which originate in the mantle beneath it. Its nature and the processes that occur in it mold the environment and determine what part of the surface will be land and what part sea, which oceans will expand and which contract, which continents will move apart and which come together. Forces mainly within the mantle determine where mountains will rise, where stresses will cause rocks to fracture and flow, where earthquakes will occur, how intense and how frequent they will be. (Earthquakes, it may be recalled, have killed more than one million people in this century.) Most volcanoes have their source in the mantle. They destroy towns and crops; the gases and solid particles they discharge into the atmosphere contribute significantly to atmospheric "pollution," in the form, for instance, of huge amounts of sulfur oxides; at the same time, volcanoes provide the very ingredients (water, carbon dioxide) without which life would be impossible.

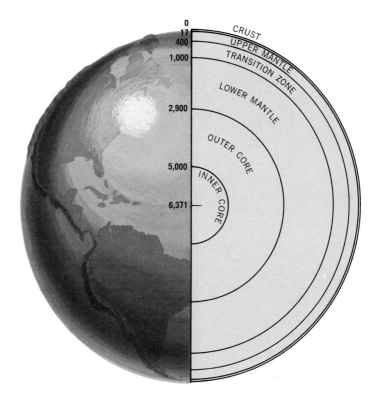

Figure II-1—REGIONS OF THE EARTH'S INTERIOR

This idealized view of the interior of the earth shows the distance in kilometers from the surface to the several regions. This view is admittedly simplified; as time goes on, our knowledge of the structure of the earth's interior will undoubtedly become more detailed and complex.

This interaction of crust and mantle cannot be overemphasized. The whole of the environment, the total ecology, is essentially a product of mantle activity.

Participation of the core in crustal affairs is much less clear. At the moment the core is of interest mainly as the source of the earth's magnetic field; but there are reasons to believe that it may yet play a more fundamental role in the earth's economy, perhaps as a source of gravitational energy or perhaps in converting some of the earth's kinetic energy of rotation into heat.

Problems and Methodologies

Problems of the deep interior are essentially (a) to determine the chemical composition and physical nature of the materials composing the mantle and core, which are nowhere accessible to direct observation, and (b) to determine the distribution and nature of the energy sources and forces that

21

cause deformation, flow, and volcanism.

What observations, and what methods of study, do we have?

Seismic Waves — Seismic (elastic) waves are propagated between the focus of an earthquake and receivers (seismographs) appropriately located on the earth's surface. The speed of propagation depends on the physical properties of the propagating material; this knowledge of speed versus depth within the earth provides a clue as to variations of physical properties — hence, of composition — with depth. A serious problem arises in that physical properties are sensitive to pressure, and pressures inside the earth greatly exceed those that can conveniently be created in the laboratory for the purpose of studying their effects on physical properties. High pressures, of the order of those existing in the core, can be created by means of explosive shock waves, but precise measurement of physical properties under shock conditions remains exceedingly difficult and costly.

Measurable Properties of the Earth as a Whole — Properties such as earth's total mass, its moment of inertia (best determined from observing the motion of artificial satellites), and the frequency of its free oscillations (i.e., the "tone" at which the earth vibrates, like a struck bell, when disturbed by a sufficiently violent earthquake) provide constraints on density distribution and physical properties in the form of global averages. For instance, the variation in physical properties with depth deduced from seismic studies must average out to the values deduced from these global constraints.

Lava — The nature of molten material (lava) that rises from the mantle and spills out on the surface (from volcanoes) provides information on the chemical nature of the source. The problem is not straightforward, however, for the chemical composition of the liquid that forms by partial melting of a system as complicated as ordinary rock is not generally the same as that of the parent rock; it varies, moreover, as a function of pressure and temperature. A great deal of painstaking experimental work at high pressure is required before the chemistry of the earth's mantle will be understood.

The "Heat Flow" — The heat that escapes across the surface of the earth from the interior provides information on the distribution of heat sources and temperature within the earth. (This heat flow, incidentally, amounts to some 30 million megawatts and is equivalent to the output of about 30,000 large modern power plants.) The manner in which this heat is transferred within the earth is not precisely known; it is generally believed that transfer in the deep interior is mostly by "convection": mass motion of hot stuff rising while an equivalent amount of cold stuff is sinking elsewhere. Convection is generally believed to provide a mechanism to move the crust. Earthquakes may well be the expression of strains set up by this motion, and the geographic distribution of earthquakes may reflect the present pattern of convective flow in the mantle.

The chief problems are: (a) How does the solid mantle flow? How do we best describe its response to mechanical forces? (b) What flow pattern do we expect in a body as complicated and heterogeneous as the earth? We are faced here with some difficult mathematical problems in fluid dynamics. It must also be remembered that, contrary to the common state of affairs in engineering studies of fluid dynamics, where the initial conditions are precisely stated and controllable, conditions in the earth regarding flow properties and distribution of heat sources and temperature are *not* known and must be deduced from a comparison of theory with geological or geophysical observations.

Sea-Floor Spreading — Geological studies regarding past history of the earth provide information as to what has happened. Most importantly, they provide information as to the rate at which the crust deforms or moves, the sense of its motion, and its duration. This is essential input to the solution of the dynamical problems mentioned in the previous paragraph.

In this respect, the last decade has seen what may well be the most important and far-reaching development since the days of Hutton (1795). What has now become known as "sea-floor spreading" (or "plate tectonics" or "global tectonics") is the general proposition that new oceanic crust is constantly generated from the mantle along submarine ridges while an equivalent amount of crust is resorbed into the mantle at other places; in between, the whole crust moves at rates of a few inches per year. This general pattern of motion provides an important and much-needed clue to the behavior of the mantle.

Phase Changes — It is well known in materials science that, at high pressure or temperature, substances may occur under forms with properties quite different from those of the same substance under normal conditions ("phase changes"). A typical example is that of common carbon that occurs either as graphite (a soft material used for lubrication) or diamond (the hardest known mineral). It is now clear that phase changes do occur in the mantle, the lower half of which has properties quite different from those of its upper half even though its gross chemical composition may be roughly the same. Again, a very large amount of difficult experimentation on high pressure is needed to ascertain the form under which common minerals could occur in the earth's deep interior. It is not unlikely that such studies could lead to the discovery and synthesis of new materials of engineering importance; for example, very hard substances might be produced.

Evaluation of Present Knowledge

In spite of recent advances, our ideas and knowledge of the deep interior remain largely qualitative. We know roughly, but not exactly, what the mantle consists of. We suspect that phase changes occur at certain depths, but we cannot pinpoint the exact nature of these changes. We can estimate roughly how much heat is generated in the mantle and its source (mostly radioactive disintegration), but cannot tell yet how the sources of heat and temperature are distributed. We do not have precise information as to the mechanical and flow properties of the mantle, and haven't yet solved the mathematical equations relevant to convection, even though approximate solutions have been found. We don't even know whether the whole mantle, or only its upper part, participates in the motion.

The situation regarding the core is similarly vague. We know that it consists dominantly of iron, but cannot determine what other elements are present. We know that the outer two-thirds of the core is liquid, and that motion in this metallic liquid generates the earth's magnetic field, but the details of the process are still obscure, and the full set of equations that govern the process has not yet been solved. Important physical properties of the core, such as its electrical conductivity, are still uncertain by one or more powers of ten. The source of the energy that drives the terrestrial dynamo is still obscure. Even though we suspect that motions in the core are the cause of observable effects at the surface (e.g., irregular changes in the length of the day, small periodic displacements of the earth with respect to its rotation axis), we still cannot assess these effects qualitatively. We suspect interactions between the core and mantle which ultimately affect the crust, but cannot focus precisely on any of them.

Goals and Requirements for Scientific Activity

To understand our total environment, to see how it came to be the way it is, and how it is changing from natural — as opposed to human — causes, and to control it to our best advantage (e.g., by curtailing earthquake damage or by muzzling dangerous volcanoes with due regard to their positive contributions to human ecology), we need a better understanding of the constitution and behavior of the deeper parts of the earth. To reach this understanding requires a concerted and sustained effort in many directions, encompassing a wide range of scientific disciplines, from fluid mechanics to materials science, from electromagnetic theory to solid-state physics.

Observational Networks — If we can foretell the future from the recent past, it is clear that a key to further progress is the establishment and maintenance of a first-rate global network of observatories such as the worldwide network of standard seismographic stations established under the VELA program of the Department of Defense. This network has enabled seismologists to determine more precisely than ever before just where earthquakes occur, and has brought into sharp focus a remarkable correlation between earthquakes and other geological features that had only been dimly perceived. This correlation is fundamental to the notion of global tectonics. Among other examples of progress resulting from improvement in instrumentation, one can mention the determination of the depth in the mantle at which some of the phase changes occur and refinements in the fine structure of the inner core.

Deep Drilling — Much speculation could be avoided, and much information gained, from analysis (of the type to which lunar samples are subjected) of samples from the mantle obtained by deep drilling. Drilling through the sedimentary cover of the ocean floor has already been most rewarding in its confirmation of the relative youth and rate of motion of the oceanic crust. But more is needed, and deeper penetration through the crust into the mantle at several points will eventually become necessary.

High-Pressure Experiments — Finally, it would seem that a major effort should be made to gain more knowledge of the properties and behavior of materials subjected to pressures of the order of those prevailing in the deep interior (tens of millions of pounds per square inch). Too much is now left to guessing; solid-state theory is presently inadequate and would anyhow need experimental confirmation.

A Note on the Earth's Magnetic Field

The earth's magnetic field was one of the earliest subjects of scientific inquiry. The field's obvious utility in navigation, as well as the intrinsic interest of the complex phenomena displayed, have led people to study it ever since the sixteenth century.

The study of the earth's field divides into two parts: that of the main part of the field, which changes only slowly (over hundreds of years), and that of the rapid variations (periods of seconds to a year). The latter are caused by things that happen in the upper atmosphere and in the sun; they are largely the concern of space research. The former, the slowly varying field, is the subject considered here.

Interest in the slowly varying field has been greatly increased by the realization that it has frequently reversed in the past. (See Figure II-2) The reversals have been helpful in establishing the history of the oceans and the movements of the continents. The study of the magnetic field can be expected to contribute — indeed, is beginning to contribute — to the search for oil and minerals. Measurement of the magnetic field has become one of the principal tools for studying the earth.

The Origin of the Earth's Magnetic Field

These applications lend a new interest to the origin of the field itself. A theory as to its origin has proved hard to find. Only in our own day has anything plausible been suggested. Although a theory of the origin has no discernible immediate practical importance, it is a part of the story of the earth without which we cannot be said to understand what is going on. Maybe we can get on very well without understanding, but one feels happier if important practical techniques have a proper theoretical underpinning.

The difficulty of discovering the origin of the slowly varying field is due largely to its lack of relation to anything else. It is not related to geology or geography and goes its own way regardless of other phenomena. In some places, some of the changes are due to the magnetization of rocks near the surface of the earth, but this is not the case over most of the field.

Fashionable theory holds that the magnetic field is produced by a dynamo inside the earth. The earth has a liquid core; the motions in this core

Figure II–2—CHRONOLOGY OF EARTH'S MAGNETIC FIELD REVERSALS

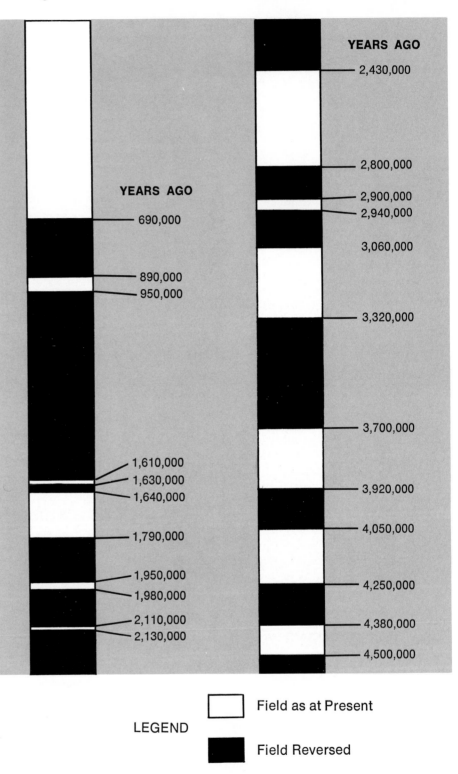

LEGEND

☐ Field as at Present

■ Field Reversed

This figure shows reversals in the polarity of the earth's magnetic field, a phenomenon of global extent that is known to occur but has never been witnessed. These data are derived from measurements of the direction (N-S) of magnetism frozen into lava as it hardens. The effects of the reversals are unknown.

are believed to cause it to act as a dynamo and to produce electric currents and magnetic fields. The theory of the process is one of the most difficult branches of theoretical physics. Its study is closely related to a wide range of problems concerning the motions of liquids and gases in the presence of magnetic fields, especially to the problems of generating thermonuclear energy.

But no realistic treatment of the earth's dynamo has yet been given. The subject does not require a large-scale organized attack. It needs thought and ideas that will come from a few knowledgeable and clever people. It is a subject for the academic, theoretical physicists with time to think deeply about difficult problems and with access to large computing facilities.

Perhaps the field's oddest feature is that, as already noted, it occasionally reverses direction (most recently, perhaps, about 10,000 B.C.). Some scientists have suggested that these reversals have profound biological effects, that whole species could become extinct, perhaps as a result of a large dose of cosmic rays being let in as the reversal takes place. There is some observational evidence to support this thesis. Other scientists do not believe that this would happen, however, and do not regard as conclusive the observational evidence for extinction of species at the time of reversal. The matter is clearly of some importance. At various times in the past, the majority of all forms of life are known to have been rather suddenly extinguished, and this is a phenomenon we would do well to understand. If reversals of the magnetic field might play a part in this drama, then we have added reason for understanding their cause and their effects.

2. CONTINENTAL STRUCTURES AND PROCESSES AND SEA-FLOOR SPREADING

Continental Drift and Sea-Floor Spreading

The idea that continents move about on the surface of the earth was advanced about a century ago and has always had adherents outside of the United States. In this country, where no direct evidence existed, the concept was first greeted with skepticism and then, for fifty years, was viewed as nonsense. All American thinking in geology — economic or academic — was built on the alternative concept of a relatively stable earth.

This is now changed. The past few years have seen a basic revolution in the earth sciences. Continents move, and the rates and directions can be predicted in a manner that few would have dreamed possible but a short while ago. As a consequence, all aspects of American geology are being reinterpreted, and in most cases they are being understood for the first time.

The continents are an agglomeration of superposed, deformed, melted, and remelted rocks with differing ages covering a span of three billion years. These rocks are eroded in some places and covered with sediment in others. The end result is a very complex configuration of rocks with a history that has not been deciphered in more than a century of effort by land geologists.

The ocean basins are very different. The rocks are all relatively young; they are simply arranged and hardly deformed at all; erosion and deposition are minimal. Consequently, it was logical that their history would be unraveled before that of the continents if only someone would study it.

Oceanographers have been engaged in just such a study for about two decades. It has been enormously expensive compared to continental geology — and trivially cheap compared to lunar exploration. Thus, the haunting possibility exists that the same effort on the continents might have yielded the same results despite the complexities. In the event, the breakthrough was made at sea by the invention of a whole new array of instruments and the development of a system of marine geophysical exploration. The results have now been synthesized with those from the land to provide the data for the ongoing revolution in the earth sciences.

Present understanding was achieved in what in retrospect seems a curious sequence. We depart from it to present the new ideas in more orderly fashion.

Continental Drift

First, a little geometry. The movement of a rigid, curved plate over the surface of a sphere can occur only as a rotation around a point on the sphere. This simple theorem, stated by Euler, has been the guide for much that follows. Earthquakes on the surface of the earth are distributed in long lines that form ellipses and circles around almost earthquake-free central regions. If there are plates, it is reasonable to assume that they correspond to the central regions and that the earthquakes are at the edges where plates are interacting.

The motion of earthquakes confirms the existence of plates with marvelous persuasiveness. Euler's theorem specifies the orientation of earthquake motion, and it has been confirmed for many plates. Moreover, for any given plate the earthquakes in front are compressional as two plates come together; they are tensional in the rear, where plates are moving apart. Along the sides they are as expected when one plate moves past another. (See Figure II-3)

The knowledge that plates exist and are moving has immediate importance with regard to such matters as earthquake prediction. For example, one boundary between two plates runs through much of California along the San Andreas Fault. We can measure the rate of offset in some places and we now know that related offsets must occur everywhere else along the plate boundaries.

Earthquakes indicate that moving plates exist now. But the evidence that they existed in the past is of a different sort. This comes from a vast array of geological and geophysical observations — topographic, magnetic, gravity, heat flow, sediment thickness, crustal structure, rock types and ages, and so on. Integration of these observations indicates that, where plates move apart, new igneous rock rises from the interior of the earth and solidifies in long strips. These in turn split apart and are consolidated into the trailing edges of the two plates. Because the rising rock is hot, it expands the trailing edges of the plates. The expansion elevates the sea floor into long central ridges, of which the Mid-Atlantic Ridge is but a part. As the new strip of plate moves away, it cools and gradually contracts. The cooling and contraction cause the sea floor to sink. This is why the ridges have gently sloping sides that gradually descend

Figure II–3—SIX SHIFTING PLATES OF THE EARTH

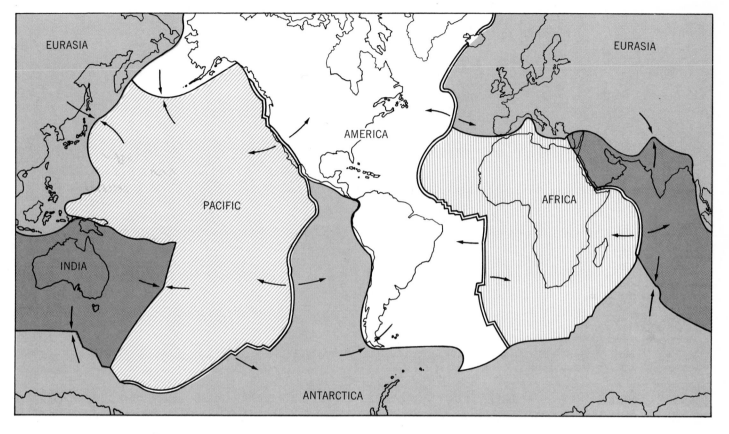

This diagram shows the six major "plates" of the earth. The double lines indicate zones where spreading or extension is taking place. The single lines indicate zones where the plates are converging or compression is taking place. Earthquake activity is found wherever the plates come in contact.

into the deep basins. The basins are merely former ridges.

Sea-Floor Spreading

The magnetic field of the earth reverses periodically, and a record of its polarity is forever preserved in the orientation of magnetic minerals in volcanic rocks which cooled at any particular time. This apparently unrelated fact gives us clues to the motion of the plates. The new rocks at the trailing edges of the plates record the magnetic polarity like a tape recorder and then, like a magnetic tape, they move on and the next polarity change is recorded. This occurs in each of the plates moving away from their common boundary. As a result, the sea

floor in the Atlantic, for example, is a bilaterally symmetrical tape recording of the whole history of the earth's magnetic field since the basin first formed as a result of Africa and South America splitting apart. We usually read a tape recording by moving the tape, but the stereo records of the oceans are read by moving a ship or airplane with the proper instruments over the sea floor. From work on land and at sea, the changes in magnetic polarity have been dated. We can thus convert the magnetic records into age-of-rock records and prepare a geological map of the sea floor. In the Atlantic, to continue with the previous example, the youngest rocks are in the middle; they grow progressively older toward the continents.

The remains of sea-surface microorganisms rain constantly onto the sea floor to form layers of ooze and clay. Where the crust is young, the layers are thin; they thicken where they have had more time to accumulate. The very youngest crust, which has just cooled, is exposed as black, glossy, fresh rock of the type seen in lava flows in Iceland and Hawaii. The outpouring of lava occurs at a relatively constant rate but the plates spread apart at different rates depending on the geometry. Consequently, lava piles up into very long volcanic ridges with a relief that varies with the spreading rate. A slow spreading rate produces mountainous ridges; fast spreading produces low, gently sloping, but very long hills.

Most of the remaining topography of the sea floor is in the form of roughly circular volcanoes which can grow as large as the island of Hawaii. These volcanoes remain active for tens of millions of years and during that time they drift as much as a thousand miles. If they develop on young crust, they necessarily sink with the crust as it cools. This seems to be the explanation for the drowned ancient islands commonly found in the western Pacific. Once they were islands, but now they are as much as a mile deep.

The phenomena that occur where two plates come together are naturally different from those that occur where they spread apart. If the plates come together at rates of less than a few inches per year they seem to crumble and deform into young mountain ranges. Where they come together faster, the deformation cannot be accommodated by crumbling. Instead, the plates overlap and one of them plunges deep into the interior where it is reheated and absorbed. This produces the most intense deformations on the surface of the earth. A line of fire of active volcanoes, deep depressions of oceanic trenches, and swarms of earthquakes mark the line of junction. Ancient rocks of the continents are now being reinterpreted as having once been deep-sea and marginal-sea sediments that were deposited where plates came together. They occur in central California, the Alps, and many other mountain ranges. Typically, they are highly deformed, which seems quite reasonable considering what must happen when plates smash together.

Implications of the New Knowledge

Since the sea floors are young, continental rocks contain what records may exist of ancient plate motions. The present revolution in understanding was needed to serve as a guide to geological exploration, however. Land

geologists had long noted similarities between the rocks on opposite sides of the South Atlantic. In the past few years, many more confirming correlations have been discovered. Knowing that the continents were once joined, we can reconstruct, in the mind's eye, a history in which they were once but a small distance apart and the nascent Atlantic was a narrow trough.

We should pause for a moment to consider how important to economic resource development the new ideas may be. The continental shelves of Atlantic coastal Africa and South America, for example, contain salt deposits and sediments in thick wedges that seem to lack any dam to trap them. These deposits contain oil. We can imagine the difficulties American oil geologists had in interpreting their records and predicting where to drill when they had no idea of how the oil-bearing rocks accumulated. How easy it may now become, when their origin can be readily explained as occurring in the long narrow trough of the newborn Atlantic!

Until now exploration has been adequate to demonstrate the existence of continental drifting and global deformation, but much remains to be done to flesh out the reconstruction of the history. If the exploration at sea continues and is matched by comparable effort at continental margins and on land, we may hope to see the beginning of a deep new understanding of the earth.

Continental Structures and Processes

Our knowledge of continental crustal processes, except in the vicinity of the continental margins, has lagged behind our knowledge of oceanic crustal processes. One reason for the great progress in the study of oceanic crustal processes is the beautifully simple pattern of magnetic anomalies, magnetic-field reversals, and earthquake and volcanic activity in the

vicinity of the continental margins that led to the discovery of sea-floor spreading. But another reason must be that the earth scientists who made these advances were not inhibited by the traditions and prejudices of scores of years of separation into highly compartmentalized sub-disciplines. Of course, the continental crust is complex, and simple patterns, if they exist, are obscured by the geological and geophysical scars of billions of years of continental damage and rebuilding. But the attitudes and study methods that led to the discovery of sea-floor spreading and downward-plunging plates will be needed if we are to improve our knowledge and understanding of continental processes during the 1970's.

Structure of the Continental Crust

The average thickness of the continental crust of the United States, as determined by seismic measurements, is 41 kilometers; its volume is about $40,000 \times 10^4$ km^3. The average crustal thickness in the west of the Rocky Mountains is 34 kilometers, while the average thickness to the east of the mountains is 44 kilometers.

The volume of the western crust is only about $10,000 \times 10^4$ km^3. Thus, the western crust accounts for only one-fourth of the continental total by volume, as compared to $30,000 \times 10^4$ km^3 for the eastern crust, although its surface area is almost a third of the total. Average seismic velocities also suggest that the western crust is less dense than the eastern crust. Thus, the western crust — the portion of the crust in which continental dynamic processes (earthquakes, volcanic eruptions, magmatism, ore deposition, and mountain-building) have been active during the past 100 million years or so — is the lesser fraction of the continent in terms of volume and mass.

Further Western-Crust Data — A recent reinterpretation of a network of 64 seismic-refraction profiles recorded by the U.S. Geological Survey in California, Nevada, Idaho, Wyoming, Utah, and Arizona from 1961 to 1963 indicates that crustal thickness reaches maxima under the Sierra Nevada Range (42 km.), the Transverse Ranges of southern California (37 km.), and in southwestern Nevada (36 km.). The crust is relatively thin under the Coast Ranges of California (24 to 26 km.), the Mojave Desert (28 km.), and parts of the central Basin and Range Province in Nevada and Utah (29 to 30 km.). The base of the crust dips generally from the Basin and Range Province toward greater depths in the Colorado Plateau (43 km.), the middle Rocky Mountains (45 km.), and the Snake River Plain (44 km.). A velocity boundary zone between the upper and lower crust can be well determined only beneath the middle Rocky Mountains, the Snake River Plain, and the northern part of the Basin and Range Province. The average velocity of the western crust is low, typically about 6.1 to 6.2 kilometers per second, but significantly higher in the Colorado Plateau (6.2 to 6.5 km/sec), and the Snake River Plain (6.4 km/sec). Upper-mantle velocity is less than 8.0 kilometers per second under the Basin and Range Province, the Sierra Nevada, and the Colorado Plateau and equal to or greater than 8.0 kilometers per second under the Coast Ranges of California, the Mojave Desert, and the middle Rocky Mountains.

Recent refraction work indicates that the average crustal velocity in the Columbia Plateau is high, as expected, but that the crust is about 10 to 15 kilometers thinner than it is in adjacent areas. Thus, the Columbia Plateau has seismic properties similar to those of a somewhat overthickened oceanic crust. So does the Diablo Range of California. The Franciscan formation (a metamorphosed structure) exposed in the Diablo Range, believed by many geologists to have been deposited in a Mesozoic oceanic trench, apparently extends to a depth of 10 to 15 kilometers; it was de-posited directly on a basaltic crust that now extends to a total depth of about 25 kilometers.

Composition of the Continental Crust

In a rock of a given composition, both metamorphic degree and water content affect seismic velocities at various pressures and temperatures. Recent laboratory research in the United States suggests that pressures and temperatures at most crustal depths would place the rocks within the stability field of eclogite rather than basalt. Seismic velocities in the lower crust formerly interpreted as appropriate for basalt are therefore regarded by many petrologists as more appropriate for more silicic rock. However, the presence of significant amounts of water in the lower crust would produce abundant hydrous minerals in a rock of basaltic composition; this would result in seismic velocities similar to those in the lower crust.

Given such uncertainties, it seems that the only positive assertion that can be made about the average composition of the continental crust is that it is intermediate and probably not too different from monzonite. The lower crust may be basaltic, intermediate, or even silicic, and the most reliable guide to its composition is probably geologic association. For example, in the Snake River Plain, where basalt is exposed at the surface, it seems reasonable to interpret the high velocities of the lower crust as indicative of basalt. In other areas, the higher velocities should probably be regarded as indicative of intermediate rock.

Structure and Composition of the Upper Mantle

Seismic probing of the upper mantle has established the existence of two important velocity transition zones: one at a depth of about 400 kilometers, in which magnesium-rich olivine is transformed with increasing pressure to spinel; and another at a depth of about 650 kilometers, in which spinel is presumed to be transformed to compact oxide structures with increasing pressure. Recent estimates of the density of the uppermost mantle, based on statistical models using all available evidence, yield densities of 3.5 to 3.6 grams per cm^3, significantly higher than the densities deduced from the usual velocity-density relations. Rocks of this density and the seismic velocities observed just below the Mohorovicic discontinuity could be either eclogite or iron-rich peridotite. Given the lateral heterogeneity of the upper mantle indicated by the variable seismic velocities, it seems most reasonable to regard the upper mantle as grossly heterogeneous, consisting primarily of peridotite but with large lenses, or blocks, of basaltic, eclogitic, intermediate, and perhaps even silicic material distributed throughout.

There is much seismic evidence that a low-velocity zone for both P- and S-waves exists in the upper mantle in the western third of the United States, with a velocity minimum at a depth of 100 to 150 kilometers. This zone seems to be particularly pronounced in the Basin and Range Province. The low-velocity zone for P-waves is apparently absent or greatly subdued in the eastern two-thirds of the United States. The most likely explanation for the low-velocity zone is that the mantle rocks there are partially molten.

Continental Margin Processes

The interaction of the laterally spreading sea floors with the continental margins — resulting in the downward plunging of rigid lithospheric plates beneath the continents, accompanied by shallow- to deep-focus earthquakes and volcanic activity — has been elucidated by a beautiful synthesis of geological and geophysical evidence. The new "global tectonics" appears to provide an adequate explanation of the structure and continental-margin processes of most of the circum-Pacific belt.

Along the California coast the pattern is different, however. No oceanic trench lies seaward of California, and the earthquakes are confined to narrow, vertical zones beneath the San Andreas fault system to depths that do not exceed about 15 kilometers. Thus, the brittle behavior of the crust in coastal California is confined roughly to the upper half of the crust. Fault-plane solutions of the earthquakes occurring along the San Andreas fault system are predominantly right-lateral strike-slip, but some solutions indicating vertical fault movements are also obtained. As already noted, both geological and geophysical studies suggest that the Mesozoic Franciscan formation of the Coast Ranges was deposited in an oceanic trench. These observations and inferences are compatible with the concept of a westward-drifting continent colliding with an eastward-spreading Pacific Ocean floor, resulting in continental overriding of the Franciscan Trench and the East Pacific Rise and development of the San Andreas system as a complex transform fault. The pattern of these relations is not tidy, however, and many problems remain to be solved in unraveling the structure and continental-margin processes of California.

Isotopes and the Evolution and Growth of Continents

Lead and strontium isotopic studies of continental and oceanic rocks completed during the past decade have contributed greatly to a better understanding of processes involved in the growth and development of continents through geologic time. The studies of continental igneous rocks indicate addition of primitive (mantle-derived) material and hence support the concept of continental growth.

Lead isotope studies of feldspars representing significant volumes of crustal material place constraints on the rate of transfer of uranium, thorium, and lead from the mantle to the crust and suggest early development (3,500 to 2,500 million years ago) of a significant portion of the crust. Geochronologic studies of Precambrian rocks show that at least half of the North American crust was present 2,500 million years ago, lending support to this thesis.

Lead and strontium data obtained on young volcanic rocks in the oceanic environment have provided direct information on the existence of significant isotopic and chemical heterogeneities in the upper mantle. Systematics provided by these decay schemes allow estimates on the times of development and preservation of these chemical heterogeneities, many of which must have been generated in Precambrian time. If a dynamic crust-mantle system is assumed, the data for the oceanic environment can be interpreted as reflecting events related to the development and growth of continental regions.

Studies of volcanic rocks being erupted at the continental margins allow an isotopic evaluation of the concept of ocean-plate consumption in this environment. Lead isotopes in volcanic rocks of the Japanese arc are compatible with partial melting of the underthrust volcano-sedimentary plate. Strontium isotopes in calc-alkaline rock series have placed significant constraints on the basalt-hybridization theory and the concept of partial melting of older crust, however.

Local studies of lead and strontium in continental igneous rocks have allowed evaluation of the involvement of crustal material in the genesis and differentiation of these rocks. The studies are circumscribed, however, by the lack of chemical and isotopic knowledge of the lower crust. If the isotopic anomalies of some conti-

nental rocks are related to generation in, or assimilation of, the lower crust, this region must be characterized by low uranium/lead and rubidium/strontium ratios relating to earlier depletion of uranium and rubidium, perhaps at the time of initial crustal formation.

Although these isotopic studies have provided many answers, they have also generated new questions and problems. Continued work on oceanic volcanic rocks and ultramafic rocks of mantle mineralogy are needed. High-pressure experimental work to determine trace-element partitioning in the mantle is needed to make full use of the isotopic variations that have been observed. Chemically and isotopically, less is known about the lower crust than the upper mantle and upper continental crust. Direct sampling of this environment is a distinct possibility with modern drilling technology; it would provide sorely needed information not only from the isotopic standpoint but also for many other earth-science disciplines.

Tectonics and the Discovery of Mineral Deposits

Adequate supplies of mineral raw materials are essential to our economy, but they are becoming increasingly difficult to find as we are forced to seek ore deposits that offer only subtle clues to their existence and location. The science of ore exploration is advancing rapidly, however. And as it does, more is being learned of the basic principles controlling the occurrence and distribution of ore deposits and their relation to continental structures. Economic geologists are increasingly adept at predicting where deposits are apt to occur — where in terms of geologic and tectonic environment and where in terms of geographic areas.

The essential first step toward increasing our knowledge in this field is to plot known mineral deposits and districts on a geologic-tectonic map. This effort is well under way. American geologists are participating in an international committee for the Geologic Map of the World, sponsored by a commission of the International Union of Geological Sciences which is compiling a world metallogenic map. A first version of the North America map has been completed.

Although the scale of the map (1 : 5,000,000) necessitates severe condensation of data, the general distribution of many ore types can be represented and compared. For example, the relation of the strata-bound massive sulfide deposits to volcanic (eugeosynclinal) belts of Precambrian rocks in the Shield, Paleozoic rocks in the Appalachians, and Mesozoic rocks in the Cordillera shows rather clearly. Nickel sulfide ores are distributed around the periphery of the Superior Province. A rather distinct class of magnetite-chalcopyrite replacement deposits in carbonate rock seems to follow the Cordilleran margin of the continent. Tungsten deposits lie east of the quartz-diorite line. Many epigenetic deposits in the interior of the continent seem related to transverse structures (lineaments), and a suggestion of zonation on a continental scale seems to be emerging.

Further refinement of the metallogenic map is under way. In combination with general studies of continental processes and structures, this will enable exploration geologists to locate promising areas in which to search for additional mineral deposits.

Needed Research on Continental Processes

The Continental Margins — The concepts of global plate tectonics for the first time give earth scientists a general working hypothesis to explain the varied continental processes that characterize the mountain-building associated with active continental margins: transcurrent faulting, volcanism, thrust faulting, and the like. Clearly,

an intensification and broadening of geological and geophysical research along continental margins such as the coastlines of California, Oregon, and Washington is critically needed.

Geologic Processes in the Continental Interior — All earth scientists recognize that the continental plates have been actively deformed, and that concepts of rigid continental plates must be modified in practice. In particular, many students of the geology of the western United States recognize that the continental crust in and west of the Rocky Mountains has been actively deformed over the past 100 million years or so, and is still being actively deformed in many places. Plate tectonics is not irrelevant, however. Application of the attitudes and study methods that led to the concepts of global plate tectonics can be expected to lead to significant and dramatic advances in our knowledge of continental processes.

If the westward-drifting continent overrode the eastward-spreading Pacific Ocean plate and continental margin features such as oceanic ridges and trenches, where are these features now? Is the Basin and Range Province behaving similarly to a spreading ocean floor? If so, where are the spreading centers? Are they along the Wasatch Mountain front, or the Rio Grande rift zone? What dynamic continental processes are occurring east of the Rocky Mountains, and how do they relate to the active processes of the western crust?

Seismic Monitoring — Seismology is now being focused in unprecedented detail on the active continental processes along the California continental margin. A similar focusing of seismological effort on the earthquake zones of Washington and the continental interior is needed. In particular, intensification of seismological effort is recommended for the Ventura-Winnemucca earthquake zone of California and Nevada; the Rocky Mountain zone of Arizona, Utah,

Idaho, Wyoming, and Montana; the Rio Grande rift zone of Colorado and New Mexico; the Mississippi Valley earthquake zone of Illinois and Missouri; and the earthquake zones of the New England region. Seismic monitoring should be accompanied by measurements of crustal strain and appropriate geological and geophysical exploration of major crustal features.

Structural and sedimentary basins, in which large reserves of petroleum and other economic fuels and minerals are concentrated, are among the most prominent and significant geologic features of the continents, but the processes of their formation are poorly understood. An intensive three-dimensional study of all aspects of the development of one or more structural and sedimentary basins through geologic time, relating that development to economic deposits and environmental assets and liabilities pertinent to wise long-term use of the land, would make a great contribution to our knowledge of continental processes. The beginning of such a study has been made in the Wind River Basin of central Wyoming, but this study has been concentrated mainly on the upper part of the earth's crust. Basin development is necessarily controlled by upper-mantle as well as crustal processes, and therefore detailed geophysical study of the deep crustal and upper-mantle foundations of one or more large basins is needed.

Deep Continental Drilling — Our knowledge of the composition of the lower continental crust is clearly inadequate. In addition to more detailed geophysical exploration of the deep crust, a program of deep continental drilling is critically needed. Locations for penetrating the lower crust that will be within the reach of present drilling technology can be selected from geophysical studies.

Geochemical Research — Although we have good qualitative understanding of the major features of the geochemical cycles, we are still deficient in detailed quantitative knowledge of the geochemical cycles of practically all elements. Research on geochemical cycles of the elements, such as essential carbon, for example, should be intensified. Research on the behavior of fugitive constituents (e.g., water and sulfur dioxide) in igneous and metamorphic processes is also critically needed to improve our understanding of continental geochemical processes and their relations to tectonics.

If research on continental structure and processes is intensified and strengthened, we can expect the 1970's to be as exciting a decade of discovery for the continents as the 1960's were for the oceans and the continental margins.

Practical Implications of Major Continental Processes

Recent verification that the crust of the earth moves readily over the earth's interior in the form of large sliding plates has reoriented geological thinking in a number of ways that affect our understanding of where many natural resources occur. We also have new insights into such natural hazards as biological extinctions, the development of ice ages, major earthquake belts, and regions of volcanism, to cite just a few natural hazards that are of continuing interest. In fact, the new ideas of continental drift and sea-floor spreading have demanded a re-evaluation of many of the premises underlying the subjects of geology, geochemistry, oceanography, and long-term changes in atmospheric circulations.

Resource Distribution

Much of our information on geological and geochemical distributions comes from a study of ancient systems that have existed over great lengths of geological time. In many instances, it is clear that these ancient systems operated differently from those of today. It now appears that the earth's sliding-plate mechanism has caused relative motions between continental and oceanic regions, formed and destroyed ocean floors, developed mountain belts, and changed the positions of land masses with respect to the equator or to the poles in times that are short compared to the time it took to form many of our major natural resources.

Evidence is building up that we are currently in a stage in earth history that is considerably more active than that pertaining over much of the geological past. It is beginning to appear that mountain belts are longer and higher, earthquake activity greater, and a large array of other features more pronounced in present times than in an average geological period in the past. Furthermore, by relative motions between the continental land masses and the pole of rotation of the earth, it seems that climates may have changed rather radically in the recent geological past.

This means that we must take a new look at theories of the origin of many mineral deposits, natural fuels, and surface deposits, so that we may better predict their locations and extensions. For example, it is clear that the petroleum deposits in the Prudhoe Bay area of Alaska were formed at much lower latitudes, the potash salt deposits of Saskatchewan were formed closer to the equator, and the onset of the devastating ice ages was brought about by shifts in oceanic circulation resulting from shifting land masses. It is necessary to know these correlations if we are to understand the processes that cause the development of petroleum and salt deposits, polar ice-caps, and many other resources or hazards that are of concern to man.

Minerals — The new understanding of the down-thrusting of ocean floor beneath continental edges has led to correlations between these zones of downward motion and a superjacent distribution of certain types of mineral deposits. For example, it has been discovered that copper deposits of the type found in the southwestern United States, which supply most of our copper today, occur in belts that lie above these zones and that the age of emplacement of the deposits generally coincides with the time of the downthrusting movement. Thus, it appears that the disappearance of crust, the development of volcanoes, and associated mineral deposits are tied together by a process that involves the melting and fractionating of downdragged materials. This has led to much prospecting activity in regions where the downward disappearance of crust is known from large-scale effects. The result has been the development and discovery of a number of new, hitherto unsuspected deposits.

Another way of seeking new areas for prospecting has been the prediction of extensions of known mineral belts where they occurred before continental land masses were separated. For example, South America fitted into Africa in a single supercontinent not too long ago, geologically speaking. (See Figure II-4) The locations of gold, manganese, iron, tin, uranium, diamonds, and other mineral deposits in Africa are much better known than those in South America, although it is expected that South America's mineral potential east of the Andean chain will eventually be

Figure II—4—CONTINENTAL DRIFT

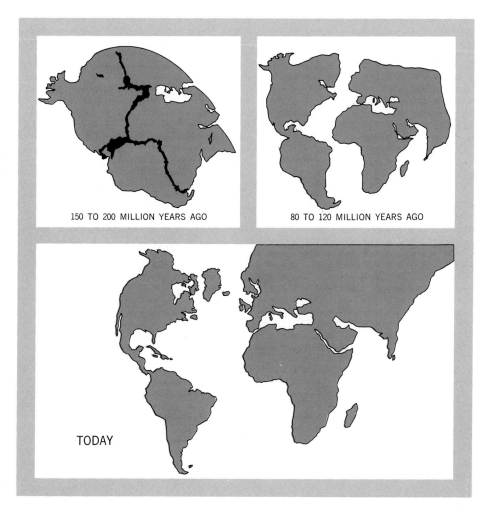

150 TO 200 MILLION YEARS AGO

80 TO 120 MILLION YEARS AGO

TODAY

In 1912 Wegener noted the striking similarity in the shape of the coastline of the Americas and of Europe and Africa. He suggested that at one time there had been a single supercontinent as shown in the upper left of the figure. Wegener postulated that the landmass broke up and allowed the continents to drift apart as shown in the upper right until they assumed the position of today.

The same applies to sediment accumulations and potential depths of gas accumulation in such regions as the North Sea, where reserves of natural gas are now a substantial factor in the economies of neighboring countries.

Thermal Water — An example of the possibility of unexpected return from the study of major crustal processes is seen in the power potential of the thermal waters of the Salton Sea area in California. Lower California is splitting off from the mainland by the same process of sea-floor generation as in the mid-Atlantic — namely, by the upwelling of hot rock materials from depth. This zone of upwelling and splitting apart continues up the Gulf of California and into the continental region underlying the Imperial Valley, undoubtedly causing the great fault systems that have produced the California earthquakes.

The heated waters resulting from thermal upwelling represent a great power potential. It is estimated, for example, that the power potential in the Salton Sea, Hungary, and other regions where there are large, deep reservoirs of heated water is of the same order of magnitude as the known oil reserves of the earth. Steamwells and natural geothermal heat have been exploited commercially in volcanic regions of Italy, Iceland, and New Zealand, and on an experimental basis in the Salton Sea area.

Environmental Pollution

Nature is the greatest polluter of the environment. Geochemical processes have concentrated radioactive elements at the surface, so that man is constantly bombarded by a gamma-ray flux much larger than the average for the earth as a whole. Streams and rivers carry rock flour from the action of glaciers in high latitudes and hydrated ferric oxides, clays, and other debris in lower latitudes to such an extent that deltaic and coastal deposits cause problems for shipping

as great as in comparable regions of Africa. Prospecting for mineral belts in northeastern Brazil, the Guianas, and southern Venezuela in areas assumed to be extensions of African belts has begun to disclose similar deposits.

Petroleum and Natural Gas — Similarly, where continents have been broken apart by rifting motions with the development of a seaway, the new edges are subject to the deposition of shelf-type sediments. Prior to the

understanding of continental drift, many of these continental shelves were believed to be ancient. Now it is known that all such new edges are bounded by thick sections of younger sediments which may have oil-bearing potential. This knowledge, coupled with the geological information provided in anticipating depths of drilling as well as structures, has led major oil companies to undertake a worldwide prospecting program. The result has been the discovery of new areas of economic importance.

and water transport, harbors, and re-sort beaches. When a drainage system cuts through a large mineral deposit, it dumps its load of partially oxidized and soluble metal salts into down-stream waters.

In order to measure environmental pollution and change, it is necessary to know the base levels of *natural* pollution and their distributions and dynamics in space and time. The response to thermal pollution in rivers can be predicted on the basis of ob-serving the ecology of warm waters in tropical regions. The same applies to oceanic waters. Natural variations in radioactivity provide us with sta-tistics on the effect of a widely dispersed distribution of radioactive wastes. Variations in the trace-ele-ment abundances in natural waters and soils give us an insight into the effect of these on biological systems. Thus, it can be said that a study of

the geochemical and geological dis-tributions and processes forms a nec-essary base for the observation of perturbations to the natural levels and rates.

Atmospheric Changes

The history of climatic change, as different land masses approached or receded from the equator, has left its record on the ecology and on surface deposits. In addition, evolutionary change of living organisms has super-imposed progressive changes in the chemistry of the earth's surface. Thus, early in earth's history, great thicknesses of banded iron formations resulted from a combination of evolv-ing bioorganisms and the atmosphere of the time.

Atmospheric change has been closely coupled with the evolution of

photosynthesis processes and, more recently, with the nature and extent of land areas in the more tropical regions of the earth. There is good evidence to indicate that the partial pressures of oxygen and carbon diox-ide in the atmosphere are significantly different from those in the past, with some estimates indicating a drastic variation in the content of oxygen in particular. An understanding of the balance between major tropical forest areas, such as in the Amazon region, and the partial pressure of oxygen in the atmosphere would be of some sig-nificance. But precise measurements of the rate of change of oxygen partial pressure with the oxygen-generating living systems on land and in the oceans have not been made on a time-scale of interest to human existence. We therefore know little of the short-term effects that might result from a substantial change in human land use.

3. EARTHQUAKES

Earthquake Prediction and Prevention

The earthquakes that we are really interested in predicting are the largest ones, those capable of taking human life and causing property damage. Earthquakes of this size have occurred countless times in the past few million years, mostly in relatively narrow belts on the earth's surface.

The destructive powers of earthquakes and resulting tsunami waves are well known. For example, the extremely destructive Alaskan earthquake of 1964 killed about 100 people and caused measurable damage to 75 percent of Anchorage's total developed worth. The earthquake also generated tsunamis that caused severe damage throughout the Gulf of Alaska, along the west coast of North America, and in the Hawaiian Islands.

A very severe earthquake in 1960 killed approximately 2,000 people in Chile and rendered about a half million people homeless. Property damage was estimated to be about $500 million. Tsunami damage from this earthquake occurred along the shores of South America, certain parts of North America (principally southern California), the Hawaiian Islands, New Zealand, the Philippines, Japan, and other areas in and around the perimeter of the Pacific Ocean. About $500,000 damage was suffered by the southern California area, while about 25 deaths and $75 million damage were suffered by the Hawaiian Islands. The Philippines incurred about 32 deaths. Japan sustained approximately $50 million damage.

Earthquake Zones — There are two catastrophe-prone zones (see Figure II-5): first, a region roughly encompassing the margin of the Pacific Ocean from New Zealand clockwise to Chile, including Taiwan, Japan, and the western coasts of Central and South America; and second, a roughly east-west line from the Azores to Indonesia and the Philippines, including Turkey and Iran and the earthquake zones of the Mediterranean, especially Sicily and Greece.

The parts of the United States with a history of severe earthquake incidence are the Aleutians, south and southeastern Alaska, and the Pacific coast of continental United States. The two worst earthquakes of the twentieth century in this country were the "Good Friday" quake near Anchorage, noted above, and the San Francisco quake of 1906. In terms of energy release, the 1964 shock may have been two or three times as potent as that of 1906.

Statistical Generalities — The problem of earthquake prediction is closely related to statistical studies of earthquake occurrence. Such studies enable us to make the following generalizations:

1. Somewhere on the earth there will be a catastrophic earthquake, one capable of causing death in inhabited areas, on the average of between 2 and 100 times a year. Greater precision is not possible, since a strong earthquake in a sparsely populated area will create no major hazard, while the same earthquake in a densely populated region may or may not cause loss of life, depending on how well the buildings are constructed.

2. In any given region in the earthquake-prone zones, a catastrophic shock will occur on the average of once per so many years, depending on the size of the region and how active it is.

But statistical prediction of this sort is unsatisfactory for an inhabitant of a specific region. This person is most concerned with his own region and with a time-scale of much less than 100 years. This person probably needs several months' advance notice of an impending earthquake, although we are nowhere near that goal.

Even if it were possible to predict an earthquake to the nearest minute or hour, major sociological problems, of the sort associated in the United States with civil defense, would need to be solved. What kind of warning system should there be? How does one handle the dispersal of the crowds involved in possible mass exodus? And what would be the reaction of the public if predictions failed to prove out in, say, 25 percent of the cases?

Why Earthquakes Occur

The occurrence of earthquakes involves the physics of friction. According to the modern theory of rigid-plate tectonics, the earth's surface is covered with a small number of relatively rigid, large plates all in motion relative to one another. At some lines of contact between two plates, the plates are receding from one another and surface area is being created by the efflux of matter from the earth's interior. Along other lines, plates are approaching one another, area is being destroyed, and surface matter is being returned to the interior. Along a third class of contacts, area is neither created nor destroyed, and the relative motions are horizontal.

Figure II–5—SEISMICITY OF THE EARTH

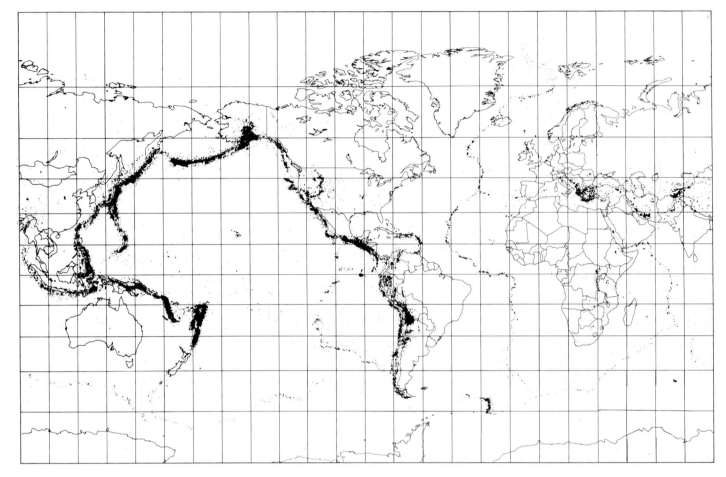

Earthquakes occur in well-defined zones where the plates adjoin. The character of the earthquakes varies with the nature of the plates' contact.

However steady the slow motion of the plates at their centers, the motions are not steady at their edges. As the giant plates move relative to one another, they rub against their neighbors at their common edges. The friction at the edges seizes the plates and allows the accumulation of stress at the contact. When the stress at these contacts exceeds the friction, the contact breaks, a rupture takes place, and an earthquake occurs. (See Figure II-6)

A map of earthquake locations, therefore, is actually a map of the plates, and the character of earthquakes varies with the nature of the plates' contact. The character of the earthquakes in the Aleutians and along the San Andreas Fault of California are significantly different, for example: the first is a zone of compression with surface area being consumed, while the second is a zone of relative horizontal motions with conservation of area.

Approaches to Earthquake Prediction

The prediction problem is, therefore, the problem of finding a way to determine the first breakage of the frictional contact between two plates at a particular point along the plate boundary. This problem can be approached by three methods: a search for premonitors, stress measurement, and historical studies.

Search for Premonitors — When solids approach the breaking point, they enter a nonlinear regime of plastic deformation in which the physical properties of the materials change markedly. Although the stresses continue to accumulate at a constant rate, the strains increase greatly prior to fracture. Indeed, in some cases, much of the deformation observed in earthquakes is not associated with abrupt displacements in rupture but is due to "creep" — i.e., plastic deformation — certainly occurring after, and probably occurring *before,* the shock. Pre-shock creep has been observed in laboratory experiments on fracture and has been reported by Japanese seismologists prior to some Japanese earthquakes.

Figure II-6—THE UPPER MANTLE IN THE REGION OF FIJI-TONGA-RARATONGA

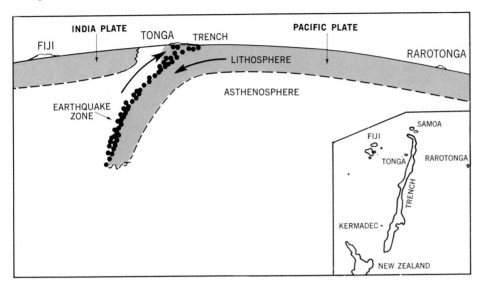

This figure depicts an area where the Pacific plate (east of the Tonga trench) meets with the India plate, pushing the lithospheric mass of the Pacific plate downward forming the Tonga trench. Earthquakes take place all along this zone, closer to the surface near the trench and at progressively greater depth beneath the continental (India plate) mass.

Changes in the rate of strain are another potential premonitor. These changes would be accompanied by an increase in the rate of occurrence of microearthquakes — i.e., very small earthquakes that are indicators of "creaking." The U.S. program for earthquake prediction has a strong component devoted to the problem of detecting changes in rates of strain along parts of the San Andreas fault system, including triangulation and leveling, tilt, distance measurements, and microearthquake observations. Some intermediate-sized earthquakes have been preceded by observed increases in rates of microearthquake activity and by increases in the strain rate, as measured by changes in the lengths of reference lines drawn across known faults and by changes in the tilt rate.

Other physical properties in the vicinity of earthquake faults may change prior to rupture. These include magnetic susceptibility, electrical resistivity, and elastic-wave velocities. There is one, as yet un-duplicated, example of a Japanese earthquake preceded by major changes in the local magnetic field. A minute change in the magnetic field has also been noted in the neighborhood of one part of the San Andreas Fault about one day before each of several microearthquakes occurred. Changes in the other properties have been observed in laboratory experiments on rock fracture but have not been verified in earthquake examples.

Stress Measurement — There is considerable debate about the values of the critical stress required to cause rupture. Seismological estimates place the stress drop at about 10 to 100 atmospheres (bars). Laboratory experiments show the stress drop to be perhaps one-fourth the shear stress across the frictional surface, although there appears to be some seismological evidence that the fractional stress drop rises with increasing earthquake magnitude. In any event, the overburden pressure should be enough to seal faults shut, and no earthquakes should occur below about 2 kilome-ters. But earthquakes do occur below this depth. Thus, one must find some reason why friction at depth is reduced. One way of doing so is to invoke the role of water as an important lubricant: that is, rocks lose some or all of their shear strength when interstitial water is raised in temperature.

No major progress has yet been made on *in situ* measurement of shear stress and determination of pore water pressure and temperature (to determine critical shear rupture stress). In principle, direct stress measurement may be the simplest way to predict earthquakes, but it may also be the most difficult to effect in practice.

Historical Method — In this case, we ignore the physics of the earthquake mechanism in large part, and concentrate instead on the history of earthquake occurrence (seismicity) as a mathematical sequence. We can then investigate this historical sequence for regularities — if any are present. The search may take two forms: (a) a search for triggering effects — i.e., a tendency for earthquakes to occur at certain preferred times; and (b) a search for organization within a local catalog.

Triggering is a cross-correlation problem in which two time-series are compared, one of which is the catalog or compilation of the earthquake history for a particular region. No significant triggering effects have yet been found, although the earth tides should be the most likely candidate. In a number of cases, earthquake activity at a distance from a given region seems to be reduced following a large shock. However, this effect may be "psychoseismological": that is, seismologists are more likely to report aftershocks in an active area and to neglect reporting for other areas. Furthermore, the occurrence of a large shock in one region will reduce the tendency for another to occur in the same region, and will increase the likelihood of a shock occurring in a neighboring region over a time-scale of several years.

Organization is an auto-correlation problem — i.e., one must search for predictive elements in the time-series of shocks for a given region within the series itself, without benefit of comparison with other time-series. Although a given earthquake catalog does not appear to be wholly random, the "signal-to-noise" ratio is small. The differences from randomness are small, and the problems of extracting the organized part from the random part has not yet been solved.

The Limits of Prediction

In Active Areas — All three methods of prediction in active areas share one major difficulty: even in California, where most U.S. activity in prediction research is concentrated, the rate of occurrence of truly large shocks is small.

We have not had a great earthquake in California since careful seismological records began to be kept. The three great historical shocks — San Francisco (1906), Lone Pine, or Owens Valley (1872), and Fort Tejon, near Los Angeles (1857) — all occurred in earlier times. The historical method postulates that the order of small- and intermediate-sized shocks can be used to predict when large shocks will occur. However, seismologists do not really know what they are looking for, since a large shock has not taken place in the modern era of California seismology.

The same criticism applies to the other two methods. In the search for premonitory effects and the measurement of *in situ* stress, the presumption is that the anomalous, or critical, states will be obtained for the large shock by studying these states for the small or intermediate shocks. Whether this is correct or not will be seen after the next large shock. Indeed, our pre-

dictive capabilities for the second and succeeding large shocks, after the next one has occurred, will be much better on all accounts, for we will then know what we are looking for.

In Stable Regions — Problems of prediction are difficult enough in regions of high activity such as the circum-Pacific belt. They are almost impossible in regions with little or no history of seismicity. For example, the region from the Rocky Mountains to the Atlantic Coast is supposed to be stable; yet two of the greatest earthquakes in U.S. history occurred east of the Rockies. Destructive earthquakes of record occurred in southeastern Missouri in 1811 (the shock was felt over an area of two

million square miles; it relocated the Mississippi River) and near Charleston, South Carolina, in 1886.

Seismic-risk studies show the New York area to have a hazard roughly 100 times smaller than southern California. Does this mean that the largest shocks on the southern California scale would recur in the New York area at an interval of 10,000 years? Or are the largest possible shocks for the New York area less than the largest for southern California? The 1811 and 1886 experiences show that stable regions are not immune. But we still have no way of determining where in stable United States a great earthquake is likely to occur — or when. (See Figure II-7)

Figure II–7—SEISMIC RISK IN THE UNITED STATES

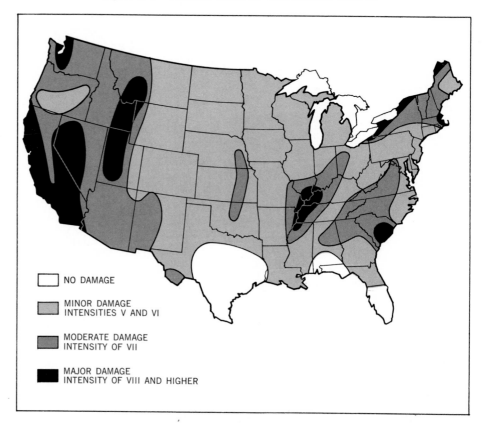

NO DAMAGE

MINOR DAMAGE
INTENSITIES V AND VI

MODERATE DAMAGE
INTENSITY OF VII

MAJOR DAMAGE
INTENSITY OF VIII AND HIGHER

This figure delineates the areas where earthquakes have occurred and have caused damage within the United States. The range is from areas of no damage in southern Texas and Florida to areas of major damage such as the western coast of California. Intensities are measured from 0 to 8 in terms of the Richter scale.

Minimizing Earthquake Damage

About 10,000 people a year die as a consequence of earthquakes. Most of them live in underdeveloped parts of the world, where housing is not well constructed; indeed, the United States and Canada may be among the few places in the earthquake zones of the world where building construction is even slightly seismo-resistant, because reinforcing steel is used in public buildings and wood framing in private residences in the seismic zones.

Much more needs to be done, however. Structural engineers can now determine the response of a building to a given excitation with reasonable accuracy. The basic problem remains that of knowing what the ground motion will be in a large earthquake, so that appropriate building standards can be established. Some measurements of ground motion in earthquakes of intermediate size are available, but there are no good records for large shocks. In California, the next great shock may cause property damage amounting to billions of dollars. Loss of life may well be in the thousands. Some of this hazard can be reduced if appropriate changes in the building codes for new construction are made with the aim of minimizing casualty from great earthquakes.

Until now, there has been severe disregard of the earthquake hazard.

Tracts of homes are built within a few feet of the trace of the 1906 San Francisco earthquake, for example. This section of the fault has remained locked since 1906, but some creep has recently been observed. Acceleration of the creep could imply a significant hazard in an important urban area.

"Man-Made" Earthquakes

Some natural earthquakes have been triggered by man. The triggering agents have included underground nuclear explosions, the filling of dam reservoirs, and the injection of water into porous strata. In all cases, the earthquakes occurred near the triggering agent. In all cases, the energy released in the earthquake was already stored in the ground from natural sources.

The water-injection case that occurred near Denver, Colorado, is of considerable interest. In that case, it can be surmised that the water injected into a shallow well at the Rocky Mountain Arsenal between 1962 and 1965 lowered the friction on a pre-existing fault and allowed a series of earthquakes to be initiated. The occurrence of shocks was correlated to the pumping history in the well. They showed an increasing migration with time and an increasing distance from the well — all this in a region with no previous history of earthquakes. In

this case, the water seems to have acted as a lubricant to reduce the friction. The migration of the shocks was due to stress propagation by concentrations at ends of ruptured segments.

Can Great Earthquakes be Prevented?

Although these earthquakes were triggered by man in his usual way of modifying the environment without thought for the consequences, the experience in Colorado prompts an interesting speculation. Suppose, for example, one were to envision the following situation some years from now: Pumping stations are located astride all the major earthquake zones of the world. They serve to raise the water pressure on the fault surfaces several kilometers below the surface, thereby reducing the friction. The large plates are thus lubricated and, without the friction at their edges, they move at faster rates than at present, releasing the accumulated stress in a series of small, harmless earthquakes and avoiding the human toll of destructive, catastrophic earthquakes.

There are many years of research between the first bit of serendipity at Denver and this fantasy, however. In the meantime, work on the prediction problem must go ahead until the solution to the prevention problem makes prediction gladly meaningless.

4. VOLCANOES

Volcanoes and Man's Environment

In many parts of the world volcanoes are an important part of man's environment. They are usually considered destroyers. But although volcanoes do a great deal of damage, and have taken many thousands of lives over the past few centuries, they are benefactors in the long run.

Volcanic regions, especially those in which the surface has been covered with volcanic ash, tend to be very fertile. The effect is most marked in tropical regions where leaching rapidly removes plant nutrients from the upper part of the soil; there, new ash falls restore the lost materials. A close correlation between population density and soil type has been shown in Indonesia, for example, with by far the densest populations in areas where very young or still active volcanoes have added ash to the soil. World over, the agricultural population clusters in the most fertile regions; it is likely to do so increasingly as population grows and food supplies become less adequate. Yet some of the most fertile areas, close to active volcanoes, are the most subject to volcanic destruction. Furthermore, volcanoes that have been quiet for centuries may still be active and may erupt again. In order to continue to make use of these badly needed rich agricultural areas close to volcanoes, we must learn to forecast volcanic activity, and to deal with it when it comes.

A Brief Overview

Volcanoes are places where molten rock or gas, or usually both, issue at the surface of the earth. As the molten rock, known as magma, rises from depth, it contains dissolved gases; but as the magma enters zones of lesser pressure near the earth's surface, some of the gas comes out of solution and forms bubbles in the liquid. The bubbles tend to escape from the magma, but in order to do so they must move to the upper surface of the liquid and rupture the surface. When the viscosity of the magma is relatively low — as it is, for example, at Kilauea Volcano, in Hawaii — the bubbles escape easily; but when the viscosity is high, they escape less readily and accumulate in the magma instead, their size and pressure increasing until they are able to burst their way free. This produces an explosion. Thus, volcanic eruptions may consist of a relatively gentle outwelling or spurting of molten rock, which flows away from the vents as lava flows, or of violent explosions that throw shreds of the molten rock or solid fragments of older rock high into the air, or of any mixture of the two.

The fragments thrown out by explosions are known as pyroclastic material. The large fragments are bombs, blocks, scoria, or cinder; the sand- to dust-size material is called volcanic ash. Some eruptions discharge mostly gas; and gas is given off, sometimes copiously, by many volcanoes between eruptions.

The fact that a volcano has not erupted for centuries does not make it less dangerous. We have many examples of volcanoes that have been dormant for hundreds of years, only to return to life with catastrophic eruptions. At the beginning of the Christian era, Vesuvius had been quiet for hundreds of years; but in A.D. 79 it erupted, destroying all the agricultural land on its flanks and close to its base, and the cities of Pompeii, Herculaneum, and Stabia. The greatest eruption of recent years, at Kamchatka in 1956, took place at a long-inactive volcano that had been given so little attention that it had not even received a name. The name we use for it today, Bezymianny, means "no name." Many other examples could be given, including that of Arenal, in Costa Rica, in 1968.

Within the U.S., the active volcanoes of Hawaii and Alaska are well known. Familiar, too, is the line of great volcanic mountains along the Cascade Range, from northern Washington into northern California. Although the latter are not usually considered to present any volcanic risk, they really do. Several eruptions have taken place in the Cascade Range in the past 170 years, the latest at Lassen Peak, California, during the years 1914 to 1919. Six thousand years ago a tremendous eruption at the site of the present Crater Lake, in Oregon, covered hundreds of thousands of square miles with ash and devastated the area immediately around the mountain. Other Cascade volcanoes may behave similarly in the future. Several appear to be in essentially the same state as Mt. Mazama, at Crater Lake, before its great eruption.

Lava Flows

Streams of liquid rock are lava flows. Where the magma has low viscosity and the supply is large, a lava flow may spread for tens of miles. Some flows in the Columbia River lavas of Washington and Oregon have been traced for distances of more than 100 miles and over areas of more than 10,000 square miles. Since 1800, lava flows on the island of Hawaii have covered more than 300 square miles of land surface. Much of this was unused land on the upper slopes of the mountains, but in 1955 a large part of the six square miles buried by lava was prime agricultural land. Again in 1960, several hundred acres of rich sugar land were covered. On the other hand, the lava built out the shoreline of the island, creating half a square mile of new land.

The land buried by lava flows is not lost forever. The rapidity with which vegetation reoccupies the lava surface varies greatly with climate. In warm areas of high rainfall, plants move in quickly. The lava flows of 1840, on the eastern end of the island of Hawaii, are already heavily vegetated. In dry or cold areas the recovery is much less rapid.

It has been found that simply crushing the surface of the lava, as by running bulldozers over it, greatly speeds reoccupation by plants, apparently because the crushed fine material retains moisture. Certain types of plants can be successfully planted on a surface treated in this way within a few years of the end of the eruption. In 1840, Hawaiians were found growing sweet potatoes on the surface of a lava flow only about seven months old. Experimentation with ways of treating the flow surface and with various types of plants will probably make it possible to use many flow surfaces for food crops within two years of the end of the eruption.

Methods for the Diversion of Lava Flows — Several methods have been suggested. In 1935 and 1942, lava flows of Mauna Loa, Hawaii, were bombed in an effort to slow the advance of the flow front toward the city of Hilo. The results indicated that, under favorable circumstances, the method could be successful. They also indicated, however, that not all lava flows could be bombed with useful results.

It has been suggested that lava flows can be diverted by means of high, strong walls, not in order to stop the flow but only to alter its course. Walls of this sort, although poorly planned and hastily built, were successful to a limited degree during the 1955 eruption. Walls built during the 1960 eruption were of a different sort, designed to confine the lava like dams rather than to divert it. Although the lava eventually overtopped them, they appear to have considerably reduced the area destroyed and were probably responsible for the survival of a large part of a beach community and a vitally important lighthouse.

Whether such walls would be effective against the thicker, more viscous lava flows of continental volcanoes is not known. Thick, slow-moving lava flows at Paricutin Volcano, in Mexico, did not crush the masonry walls of a church that was buried by the lava to roof level. Walls generally would be useless against lava of any viscosity where the flow is following a well-defined valley. Fortunately, the flows of continental volcanoes usually are shorter and cover less area than Hawaiian flows, thus reducing the area of risk. Much more research is needed on ways to control lava flows.

Ash Falls

It was formerly believed that ash from the great explosion of Krakatoa Volcano, between Java and Sumatra, drifted around the earth three times high in the stratosphere. Although it now appears that the brilliant sunsets once regarded as evidence of this were probably caused instead by an aerosol of sulfates resulting from interaction of volcanic sulfur dioxide gas and ozone, it has been repeatedly demonstrated that violent eruptions may throw volcanic ash high into the upper atmosphere, where it may drift for hundreds of miles. For instance, ash from the 1947 eruption of Hekla, in Iceland, fell as far away as Moscow; ash from the eruption of Quizapu, in Chile, fell at least as far away as Rio de Janeiro, 1,850 miles from the volcano; and ash from the Crater Lake eruption has been traced as far as central Alberta.

Although it has not been absolutely proved, it appears probable that large amounts of ash in the atmosphere affect the earth's climate. Ash from the 1912 eruption of Mt. Katmai, Alaska, is believed to have reduced by about 20 percent the amount of solar radiation reaching the earth's surface at Mt. Wilson, in southern California, during subsequent months; ash from the Laki eruption in Iceland drifted over Europe and appears to have caused the abnormally cold winter of 1783-84. Other examples have been cited, although some investigators find no evidence for it.

Heavy ash falls may destroy vegetation, including crops, within a radius of several miles around the volcano. Ash from the Katmai eruption destroyed small vegetation at Kodiak, 100 miles away, although bigger trees survived. During the 1943 eruption of Paricutin, even the big trees were killed where the ash was more than three feet deep. Even a few inches of ash will smother grass.

Serious indirect consequences may arise. A great famine that resulted from destruction of vegetation and reduction of visibility to the point where the fishing fleet could not work followed the Laki eruption and is said to have killed a large proportion of the population of Iceland. Around Paricutin, thousands of cattle and horses died, partly of starvation and partly from clogging of their digestive systems from eating ash-laden vegetation. Even if it causes nothing worse, ash-covered vegetation may cause serious abrasion of the teeth of grazing animals. Cane borers did serious damage to sugar cane in the area west of Paricutin, because the ash had destroyed another insect that normally preyed on the borers. Any disturbance of the natural regime may have surprising results!

Direct damage to fruit and nut trees can be reduced by shaking the ash from the branches; and collapse of roofs of dwellings under the weight of ash can be reduced by shoveling or sweeping off the ash. Much additional research is needed on ways to reduce other damage from ash.

Light ash falls are beneficial. The ash acts as a mulch, and helps to retain water in the soil for plant use and to supply needed plant foods. Within a few months after the eruption, areas covered with a thin layer of ash commonly look as though they had been artificially fertilized. The fertility probably could be further increased by proper treatment of the ash-covered ground.

Fragmental Flows

Glowing avalanches ("nuées ardentes") are masses of red-hot fragments suspended in a turbulent cloud of expanding gas. The main portion of the mass travels close to the ground and is closely guided by topography, but above it is a cloud of incandescent dust that is much less restricted in its spread. The avalanches are exceedingly mobile; they may travel as fast as 100 miles an hour. Some glowing avalanches are caused when large volumes of hot debris are thrown upward nearly vertically by explosions and then fall back and rush down the slopes of the volcano. This happened, for instance, on the island of St. Vincent, in the Lesser Antilles, in 1902. The results were disastrous; thousands of people died. The glowing avalanches of Mt. Pelée, Martinique, in the same year, appear to have originated from low-angle blasts at the edge of a steep-sided pile of viscous lava (a volcanic dome) that grew in the crater of the volcano. They devastated the mountain slopes, destroyed the city of St. Pierre, and took over 30,000

human lives. Still other glowing avalanches result from collapse of the side of the dome after it has grown beyond the crater, or from collapse of thick lava flows on the slope of the volcano. Those formed by collapse of a summit dome are common on Merapi Volcano, in Java.

The association of glowing avalanches with domes is so common that any volcano on which a dome is growing or has grown should be suspect. Particularly where a growing dome has expanded onto the outer slope of the volcano, the area downslope is subject to glowing avalanches and probably should be evacuated until some months after the dome has stopped growing and achieved apparent stability.

Glowing avalanches are guided by existing valleys, and their courses can be predicted to some extent. The upper parts of big ones may override topographic barriers, however. St. Pierre was destroyed by the upper part of a big avalanche that continued over a ridge while the main mass of the avalanche turned and followed a valley.

Ash flows resemble glowing avalanches in being emulsions of hot fragments in gas. They are also exceedingly mobile and travel distances as great as 100 miles or more so rapidly that, when they finally come to rest, the fragments are still so hot they weld themselves together. An historical example occurred in the Valley of Ten Thousand Smokes, Alaska, in 1912. Older ones cover many thousands of square miles in western continental United States. A fairly recent example is the Bishop tuff in California.

The great speed of glowing avalanches and ash flows probably makes effective warning impossible once they have started; and their great mobility and depth appears to make control by means of walls unfeasible. The only hope of averting future dis-

asters seems to be in recognizing the existence of conditions favorable to their generation, and issuing a long-range warning in advance of their actual initiation.

Mudflows are slurries of solid fragments in water. Not all of them are volcanic, but volcanic ones (lahars) are common. They may be either hot or cold, and they may originate in various ways: by the ejection of the water of a crater lake, by rapid melting of ice or snow, or, most commonly, by heavy rains. The water mixes with loose pyroclastic or other debris on the sides of the volcano and the mud rushes downslope, with speeds of up to 60 miles an hour, sweeping up everything loose in its path. In the last several centuries, mudflows have probably done more damage, and taken more lives, than any other volcanic phenomenon. They were, for instance, the principal cause of damage during the 1963 eruption of Irazu, in Costa Rica.

At Kelut Volcano, in Java, explosive eruptions repeatedly ejected the water of the crater lake, causing mudflows on the flanks that took thousands of lives and destroyed plantations and rice paddies in the rich agricultural area near the base of the volcano. In 1919 alone, an area of 50 square miles of arable land was buried and about 5,100 persons were killed. In an effort to improve the situation, Dutch engineers drove a series of tunnels through the flank of the volcano and lowered the level of the crater lake to the point that the volume of water remaining would be insufficient to cause big mudflows. This was effective. During the big eruption of 1951 only seven persons were killed, all on the upper slopes of the volcano, and no damage was done to the agricultural land at the base. The eruption destroyed the tunnel entrances, however, and they were not reconstructed in time to prevent a new disaster in 1966. A new tunnel, completed in 1967, has again drained the lake to a low level. As

Indonesian authorities are well aware, the present menace on Kelut is increasing as a result of the steady increase of population on the fertile flanks of the volcano.

In Java, attempts were made to warn of hot mudflows by installing thermal sensors in the upper parts of the valleys on the slopes of volcanoes, with an electrical alarm system in villages on the lower slopes. It was hoped that the villagers would have time to reach high ground before the mudflow arrived. In places, artificial hills were built to serve as refuges. The alarms were unreliable, however, and did not work at all for cool mudflows.

Mudflows, being essentially streams of water, are closely controlled by topography, and it is possible to anticipate which areas are most threatened. Dams built to try to contain the mudflows from Kelut failed when the small reservoirs behind them became overfull. It might be possible, however, in some favorable localities, to use diversion barriers like those suggested for Hawaiian lava flows. In general, the best possibility seems to be to learn to recognize the situations most likely to lead to mudflows, and issue warnings when these develop.

Gases

The most abundant gas liberated at volcanoes is water. Less abundant are carbon gases, sulfur gases, ammonia, hydrogen, hydrochloric acid, and hydrofluoric acid. Sulfur dioxide and sulfur trioxide unite with water to form sulfurous and sulfuric acids.

The acid gases may be injurious to plants downwind from the volcano. Mild gas damage resembles smog damage in cities. More severe damage causes fruit to drop and leaves to turn black and fall; it may kill the plant. Serious damage of this sort has been experienced on coffee plantations to the lee of the volcanoes Masaya, in Nicaragua, and Irazu, in Costa Rica, and less severe damage has occurred in Hawaii.

Suggested countermeasures have included trapping the gases at the vents in the volcanic crater and discharging them at higher levels in the atmosphere by means of a high flue, or precipitating them by means of chemical reactions. Valuable chemicals might be recovered in the process. Local application of chemicals directly on the plants in order to neutralize the acids has been tried, but this is expensive and not wholly effective. Further research on this subject is indicated.

Predicting Eruptions

Accurate prediction of time, place, and nature of volcanic eruptions would go far toward eliminating the disasters that arise from them. However, although some progress has been made in this direction, we are still a long way from being able to make accurate predictions. The indications that have been used to predict time and place of eruptions are: earthquakes, swelling of the volcano, change of temperature or volume of gas vents (fumaroles) or hot springs, changes of elevation in areas near the volcano, and opening or closing of cracks in the ground.

Tumescence — Scientists of the Hawaiian Volcano Observatory have found that Kilauea Volcano swells up before eruptions and shrinks once the eruption has started. However, the tumescence may continue for months, or even years, before eruption finally takes place; furthermore, it sometimes stops and detumescence occurs without any eruption. (The magma may be drained away by intrusion into the subsurface structure of the volcano.) Tumescence, therefore, does not indicate when an eruption will occur, but only that the potential for eruption is present.

Earthquakes — Some eruptions are preceded by swarms of shallow earthquakes over periods of a few hours or days. These, combined with the swelling of the volcano, are the most useful short-range tool for prediction. The eruption of Vesuvius in A.D. 79 was preceded by ten years of very frequent earthquakes, and with our present knowledge we could probably have made a general long-range prediction that the volcano was likely to erupt, though we still probably could not have said just when. Other eruptions appear to have had no definite seismic prelude.

Upheavals and Cracks — Marked swellings or upheavals have taken place before eruptions at some volcanoes, though more commonly none has been detected. This may be partly because of lack of appropriate instruments in proper positions. Upheaval of the land causes the shoreline in the vicinity of Naples to shift seaward a few hours or days before some eruptions of Vesuvius. A similar upheaval preceded the eruption of Monte Nuovo, in the Phlegrean Fields northwest of Naples, in 1538. In 1970 the region was again being upheaved, with the opening of cracks and increase of fumarolic action in the nearby crater of Solfatara Volcano; these things suggested strongly that an eruption would take place in the area soon.

Tilt Patterns — In 1943, at Showa Shin-Zan, in Japan, the ground surface was pushed up to form a bulge 150 feet high and 2½ miles across before the eruption finally started. The 1960 eruption of Manam Volcano, near New Guinea, was preceded by a large number of earthquakes and tumescence that resulted in tilting of the ground surface through an angle ranging from 8 to 18 seconds of arc. Tilting of the ground surface has been observed before eruptions at some other volcanoes, but it has not been found commonly. In retrospect, workers at Nyamuragira Volcano, in central Africa, believed that swarms of earthquakes would have made it possible to predict the 1958 eruption about 30 hours before the outbreak, but no such prediction was made. At most volcanoes, including most of those in western United States, the instrumental installations necessary to

recognize either earthquake preludes or diagnostic tilt patterns are still lacking.

History — The prediction of the type of eruption rests almost wholly on a knowledge of the past history of the volcano. What has happened before is most likely to happen again. In most instances, however, the his-

tory must be deduced from careful geological studies, and we still do not know the history of most of the earth's volcanoes.

Clearly, it will be some time before we can consistently predict eruptions at most volcanoes, including those in some of the most heavily populated areas.

Aspects of Volcanic Science

Giant strides have been made in our understanding of the dynamics of the earth's surface and of the behavior of rock systems at pressures and temperatures equivalent to subcrustal conditions within the earth. Yet our knowledge of the basic physics and mechanisms involved in volcanic processes are at best sketchy, our explanations speculative and largely qualitative, and our predictions based on observed history rather than fundamental understanding of the real mechanics involved.

The number of scientists conducting serious investigations of volcanoes is fairly small; they are concentrated in the countries where most of the earth's 450 active volcanoes are found — the circum-Pacific belt (New Zealand, the Philippines, Japan, eastern Soviet Union, Alaska, and western North and South America) and an east-west region extending from Java through the Mediterranean. Most of today's students are Japanese, American, Russian, Italian, Australian, Indonesian, or Dutch.

Interaction with Man and Environment

Volcanoes are spectacular in state of eruption, and their effects on life and property have often been devastating. Damage is inflicted by several means: fall of fine-grained ash from

the atmosphere; ash flows; lava flows; and tidal waves associated with violent eruptions. The most devastating and dangerous eruptions are those that produce ash flows or violent blasts. These are also among the least understood, because the eruptions are short-lived and have not been well studied.

The United States has over 30 active volcanoes, mostly in Alaska. (See Figure II-8) Within continental United States, large dormant volcanoes include Mt. Rainier, Mt. Baker, Mt. St. Helens, Mt. Shasta, and Mt. Lassen. Phreatic (steam-blast) eruptions occurred in Hawaii in 1924; the hazard grows with population density.

Alteration of the environment near an erupting volcano can be dramatic. Some believe the decline of Minoan civilization on Crete (about 1500 B.C.) resulted from the eruption of the volcano Thera. More recently, an ash fall associated with the 1968 eruption of Cerra Negro, Costa Rica, threatened to choke off San Juan, the capital city. In the United States, historic lava flows from Kilauea and Mauna Loa, on Hawaii, have reached the sea, burying productive sugar cane fields. The 1959 flow accompanying an eruption along the east rift zone of Kilauea buried the town of Kapoho. The 1950 flow from Mauna Loa reached the sea, endangering for a time the town of

Kailua-Kona on the west side of Hawaii.

Among the greatest direct threats to life are eruptions producing ash flows. A spectacular and devastating historic eruption of this type occurred on Martinique in 1902. An ash eruption from Mt. Pelée flowed down the flank of the mountain at an estimated 50 to 100 miles per hour and buried the town of St. Pierre, with a loss of 38,000 lives. A passing ship observed a similar eruption at Mt. Katmai, Alaska, in 1912; it produced the Valley of Ten Thousand Smokes, but there was no known loss of life. Such eruptions could recur nearly anywhere along the Aleutian chain. An eruption of this type in a populated region would be a catastrophe.

One of the most dramatic examples of the effect of volcanic action on the environment was the eruption of Krakatoa, in 1883, in eastern Sumatra. Krakatoa is a large, cauldron-type volcano. It erupted with an energy estimated as equivalent to 100 to 150 megatons of TNT. Some 36,000 people lost their lives in this eruption and the tidal wave that accompanied it. The blast was believed to have been the result of sea water entering the magma chamber after a two-week period of relative quiet. The resulting acoustic wave produced in the atmosphere propagated to the antipodes

Figure II–8—U.S. VOLCANOES

HAWAII

Haleakala
Mauna Loa
Kilauea

ALASKA

Bogoslof Island
Mt. Shishaldin
Mt. Pavlof
Mt. Redoubt
Mt. Katmai

CANADA

Mt. Baker
Mt. St. Helens
Mt. Rainier
Mt. Hood
Mt. Adams
Mt. Jefferson
Crater Lake
Columbia River Plateau
Mt. Shasta
Lassen Peak
Snake River Plains
Mono Craters
Yellowstone
Great Basin
UNITED STATES
San Juan Mountains
San Francisco Mountains
Jemez Mountains
Datil Mountains
Big Bend Region

MEXICO

EXPLANATION
▲ Active Volcanoes
● Quaternary Volcanoes
▬ Other Volcanic Areas

This figure indicates the active volcanoes of the U.S. as well as Quaternary volcanoes and other areas of volcanic activity.

and back eight times as recorded by microbarographs around the world. Fine-grained ash was dispersed throughout the atmosphere and produced distinctly red sunsets as far away as Europe.

Long-Term Effects — Volcanoes may also have an important effect on man's environment on geologically long time-scales. Fine-grained airborne volcanic material may have a serious effect on the long-term heat balance of the earth, for example, by changing the reflection properties of the upper atmosphere. The ash from Krakatoa reduced the incident solar flux to the surface by about 20 percent of its normal value. Such effects have been postulated as a possible contributing cause for continental glaciation. In this view, glaciations result from a reduced heat flux to the earth's suface as a consequence of fine ash in the atmosphere dispersed by a higher general level of volcanic activity.

In addition, most of the gases that produce the atmospheres and oceans, the products of outgassing of the earth's interior, probably reach the surface through volcanoes. Hence, the nature of volcanism is intimately tied to such general questions as the nature and evolution of planetary atmospheres.

Ability to Forecast Eruptions

Perhaps the most serious matter is that of predicting catastrophic and unexpected eruptions. Volcanic soils are among the most fertile in the world; consequently, the slopes of even active volcanoes are populated and used for agricultural purposes. Furthermore, the time between violent volcanic events varies from several decades to several thousand years—a short time geologically but a long time on the scale of man's life and memory. There is thus a significant amount of economic pressure to occupy hazardous places. It is virtually certain that violent eruptions like those at Krakatoa, Vesuvius, or Mt. Pelée will occur in the future.

Our ability to explain or predict volcano behavior is poor and restricted to a few isolated, well-studied ex-

amples. The behavior of Kilauea, on the island of Hawaii, is one of the most systematically monitored and historically well-studied volcanoes in the world, along with Asama and Sukurajima in Japan. (In 1914, Sukurajima erupted and seven villages were destroyed; property damage was some $19 million, as 25 square kilometers were buried under new lava; no lives were lost.) Kilauea has been monitored almost continuously since 1912, the year that Jagger established the Hawaiian Volcano Observatory (HVO), operated since 1917 by the U.S. Geological Survey (USGS). Integrated geological, geophysical, and petrological chemical observations have been made of Kilauea's eruptions and the lavas produced. Small-scale earthquakes accompanying upward movement of molten rock at depth have also been studied. Swelling of the volcano prior to eruption has been monitored by precise leveling and strain measurements. All this has resulted in a basis for eruption prediction based on previous experience.

The ability to predict eruptions at Kilauea has little use elsewhere, however, since each volcano has it own personality which must be studied to be understood. Furthermore, Hawaiian-type volcanism, while it has been destructive of property, is the most passive of all types of eruption. And, in spite of a long history of observation and systematic data collection at Hawaii, we are still basically ignorant of some important and interesting facts: details of the melting processes operative in the earth's mantle that are responsible for the generation of the lava; the mechanics of the propagation of fractures in the mantle crust and the hydrodynamics of transport of the lava to the surface; the relationship of the lava to the fragments of subcrustal (mantle) rocks contained in some lavas; the nature of the mantle underlying Hawaii; and, finally, why the Hawaiian chain (and the active volcanism) is marching southeastward across the Pacific.

Diversion and Modification Through Technology

Hilo, the second largest city in the Hawaiian Islands, lies in the bottom of a shallow, trough-like valley on the east flank of Mauna Loa and Kilauea. By chance, the most voluminous historic flows have occurred on Mauna Loa's west side and have, therefore, flowed away from Hilo. In 1938 and 1942, however, lava flows erupted from the east side of the peak and proceeded downslope toward Hilo. The U.S. Army Air Force, acting on recommendations of geologists from the HVO, bombed lava tubes in the upper part of the 1942 flow, successfully diverting the flow of hot lava from the interior of the tubes onto the surface of the flow and possibly slowing the forward advance of the flow's leading edge some fifteen miles down the hill. The flow did not reach Hilo. The effectiveness of the bombing is a matter of conjecture, however, since termination of the extrusion of lava from Mauna Loa occurred at about the same time.

While there have been no direct attempts to alter the cycle of activity of any volcano, a 1.2-megaton atomic experiment conducted by the Atomic Energy Commission on October 2, 1969, in Amchitka Island in the Aleutians, may represent — though not by design — the first such project. Kiska Volcano, on Kiska Island, erupted on September 12, about three weeks before the experiment was to be held some 500 kilometers away. Had this eruption occurred three or four weeks later, a controversy about the possible cause-and-effect relationships between the blast and the eruption would undoubtedly have ensued. The experiment on Amchitka was preceded by considerable debate among seismologists about the possible effects on the seismicity of that part of this tectonically active island chain. Since seismicity and volcanism are intimately related on a worldwide basis, the relevant areas in the Aleutians should be carefully monitored for pos-

sible alteration of the local volcanic regimen.

Potential Sources of Basic Information

It is clear that many disciplines will contribute to progress in volcanology — field geology, experimental and observational petrology, geophysics, geochemistry, fluid mechanics, and others. Advances in our knowledge of volcanic mechanisms can be expected from detailed observations, experiments, and, eventually, theoretical (mathematical) models.

Field Observations — Any significant advance in our knowledge and understanding of volcanoes must be observationally based. Like all geological processes, the number of parameters involved and the complexity of the physical processes are very great. Eruptions amount to large-scale and uncontrolled natural experiments. Meaningful quantitative data can only be provided by systematic observations by prepared observers with adequate instruments in the right place at the right time.

Any really basic, thorough understanding of volcano mechanisms, volcano physics, and, eventually, eruption prediction will follow detailed observational work — both long-term investigations of individual volcanoes and ad hoc, short-term investigations of volcanoes in a state of eruption. The fruits of such observation can be seen at Kilauea. Extended study by the USGS has produced a detailed geological, physical, and chemical description of this volcano. Detailed knowledge of the behavior of Kilauea, particularly prior to eruption, is known, and reliable eruption prediction by HVO has become routine. The Hawaii experience underscores two important points: (a) The ability to predict the behavior of specific volcanoes is based on experience and careful observation over a substantial period of time. (b) Systematic collec-

tion of several types of data (geophysical, geological, petrological, chemical) is required.

Laboratory Experiments — There are a number of laboratory experiments that may yield useful information: the chemical evolution of magmas and mineralogical and chemical evolution with time in relation to eruption history are important parameters to establish. Petrologic and chemical observation of volcanic products can be closely correlated to the eruption history of observed (recent) events or to carefully reconstructed ones, yielding data about the evolution of magmas that culminate in violent terminal activity.

Laboratory investigation of physical properties of lava and magmatic systems, especially volatile-bearing ones, is needed. Little is known about the physical characteristics of lavas under dynamic conditions — for example, expansion during rise in a volcano from depth. The formation of volcanic ash and catastrophic eruptions are associated with inhibited vesiculation (bubbling) of lava during rapid rise to the surface. These eruptions are the most destructive, and they are not well understood.

Experimental petrology (investigations of rock systems in controlled situations in high-pressure vessels in the laboratory) will yield data useful in the quantitative reconstruction of specific events as captured in rock textures and in mineralogical associations in volcanic rocks. By comparison of laboratory results with observed relationships in volcanic rocks, much can be inferred about the history of formation of specific volcanic rocks that can never be directly observed because the rocks occur too deep within the volcano.

Simulation Experiments — Some progress could come from large-scale simulation of certain volcanic processes, in much the same way as our understanding of meteorite-impact physics was greatly aided by high-yield atomic-explosion experiments. It might be feasible to simulate certain aspects of volcanic eruptions on a rather large scale. Such experiments would yield useful information on the interior ballistics problem (flow within the interior of volcanoes) and also on the exterior ballistics of volcanic ejecta, especially ballistics of large fragments.

Small-scale model simulation of volcanic processes is an exceedingly difficult endeavor because of the necessity to satisfy similitude requirements for both heat and mass transfer. However, much has been learned in a qualitative way about other geological processes — e.g., convection of the earth's mantle and motion of ocean currents — by such experiments. The results, while semiquantitative, nonetheless can be quite informative, especially when closely tied to field observation. Model methods could profitably be applied (and have been to a limited degree) to a number of volcanic mechanisms, such as the emplacement of lava and ash flows.

Mathematical Description — Volcanic processes are complex. The eruption of volcanoes involves the flow of a fluid system from a high-pressure reservoir at depth to the surface through a long rough pipe, or conduit. In this process of fluid flow, heat and momentum are exchanged both within the system and with the vent walls. As the erupting medium rises, the confining pressure decreases and a number of things result — exsolution and expansion of the volatile phases (gas), and cooling due to expansion. Near the surface, these processes are rate-controlled rather than simple equilibrium ones.

Mathematical description of the hydrodynamic and heat-transfer problems are rudimentary. There exists abundant literature in engineering and physics, however, which could be applied readily to a number of volcanic processes. For example, in the last decade our knowledge of the behavior of complex multi-phase systems involving gas, solid, and liquid phases has advanced because of their importance in engineering practice (e.g., to determine the flow in rocket nozzles). General hydrodynamic codes for the description of the deformation of material under shock loading have been developed to describe target effects around explosions and impacts, and these codes can be modified to describe volcanic situations. Further, the flow in gas and oil wells and reservoirs is probably similar to the flow in some volcanoes and their reservoirs. Also, the interaction of the high-velocity stream of gas and fragments ejected by an erupting volcano into the atmosphere is a special case of the interaction of a jet with fluid at rest. These problems appear to be ripe and could develop very swiftly.

The science of petrology has progressed very rapidly in the last decade, to the extent that many quantitative estimates can be made regarding the temperatures and pressures of the formation of certain minerals and mineral assemblages found in volcanic rocks. These are very important constraints on mathematical formulation of the eruption problem. But the greatest single impediment to the formation of mathematical descriptions of volcanoes in state of eruption is the lack of systematic, quantitative field data regarding eruption parameters (mass flow rate, temperature, velocities and direction of fragments ejected, the abundance and chemical composition of the gas phase, and petrography and chemistry of the rocks produced).

State of Observational Data and Tools

Present data on active volcanoes are quite incomplete, although the means of acquisition of important information are available. One reason data are incomplete is that, prior to modern jet transportation, it was simply impossible for qualified scientists to arrive at the scene in time to gather the most interesting information, which occurs in the first few hours or days of activity of many volcanic events.

For the past ten years, the Department of Defense and National Aeronautics and Space Administration have applied a powerful array of remote-sensing and photographic techniques to the investigation of some volcanoes. The 1963 eruption of Surtsey, in Iceland, was studied, for example. These methods hold great promise and if applied to the study of eruptions would produce a substantial increase in the quantity of available data as well as provide new kinds of information. Even though means exist for highly sophisticated and complete investigations, however, the number of eruptions that have been thoroughly exploited is negligibly small.

The investigation of active volcanoes requires cooperation between fairly small numbers (3 to 10) of well-qualified professional observers, with technical support (including communications, logistics, and transportation) to be provided at very short notice. The Smithsonian Institution has set up a facility to fill part of this need: The Center for Short-Lived Phenomena, in Cambridge, Massachusetts. The center serves effectively as an information source for scientists covering a number of specialties, including volcanology and geophysics. The center notifies potentially interested scientists by telephone or wire of events such as volcanic eruptions; it then, on very short notice, organizes teams to visit the sites, ideally within 24 hours. The function of the center is to dispense information and to organize logistics for adequately prepared individuals with their own funding. The number of such scientists is well below the number required to monitor the world's interesting volcanic events, however, and the results fall far short of what is possible within the capabilities of modern transportation and modern data-gathering methods.

Requirements of Science

We expect advances in our understanding of fundamental volcanic mechanisms to evolve from two broad types of investigations:

1. *Long-term investigations* of individual volcanoes, volcanic features, and volcanic fields. These studies will focus on the origin of the magmas and land forms and their evolution through time. The goal of the research is to develop the details of the physical processes producing these features and the reasons for their evolution. Some of this kind of work is in progress in the United States.

2. Well-coordinated and *short-term field investigations* of volcanoes in eruption by teams of prepared and qualified scientists capable of responding on very short notice. This is a new kind of activity, not currently well organized.

PART III

CLIMATIC CHANGE

1. CYCLICAL BEHAVIOR OF CLIMATE

Long-Term Temperature Cycles and Their Significance

The earth's climate results from three fundamental factors:

1. *The earth's mass*, which provides a gravitational field of sufficient strength to hold all gases released from the interior except hydrogen and helium;

2. The amount of *energy* emitted by the sun, the *distance* of the earth from the sun, and the earth's *reflectivity*, which combine to provide surface temperatures on earth suitable for the existence of a substantial hydrosphere, including oceans, rivers, lakes, and, at certain times, conspicuous ice masses;

3. *The astronomical motions* of the earth which, together with the inclination of the earth's axis on the plane of the ecliptic, provide diurnal and seasonal cycles.

If these three fundamental factors (and their components) were to remain constant through time, the earth's climate would not change except for short-range phenomena related to the hydro-atmosphere. Geological history and direct human observation show, however, that climate *has* changed and is changing conspicuously, with variations ranging from a few to many millions of years. The causes for these changes are numerous and varied, and often multiple.

Affecting mankind most, either favorably or unfavorably, are the changes that occur across time intervals ranging from tens of years to 50,000 years. The former may encourage men to undertake great agricultural and industrial activity in regions affected by climatic amelioration, only to have their efforts destroyed when climate deteriorates; the latter have brought about the great glacial/interglacial cycles of the past million years, which strongly affected the entire biosphere and directed the course of human evolution.

Short-Range Climatic Change

Short-range climatic variations (years to centuries) have been monitored by direct observation since the dawn of recorded history, but accurate climatic measurements date only from the middle of the seventeenth century when the Accademia del Cimento of Florence and the Royal Society of London began their works. For more than a hundred years these observations were restricted to Europe.

Global climatic cycles for which an explanation is immediately clear are the diurnal cycle, due to the rotation of the earth, and the yearly cycle, due to the revolution of the earth around the sun. A 2.2-year cycle due to alternating easterlies and westerlies in the equatorial stratosphere also appears rather well established. If the effect of the daily, seasonal, and yearly cycles is eliminated, climatic records — including temperatures, pressure, precipitation, wind strength, and storm occurrences — may also exhibit apparent periodicities. Thus, in 1964 Schove listed a dozen possible cycles, which ranged in wavelength from 2 to 200 years. An apparent 20-year periodicity, for instance, is shown by the 10-year moving average temperature record for July in Lancashire, England. A similar periodicity is not visible, however, in the temperature record for January. The problem is that an infinite record would be necessary in order to prove that a cyclical phenomenon is really stationary — i.e., that conditions at the end of a cycle are identical to those at the beginning.

Figure III–1 — AVERAGE WATER LEVEL IN LAKE VICTORIA

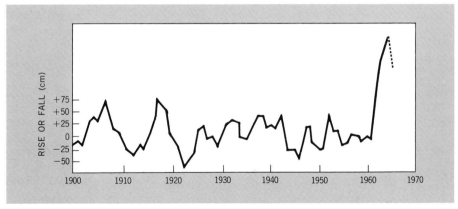

This graph indicates that the rise and fall of water level in Lake Victoria from 1900 to the middle of the 1920's was correlated with the 11-year sunspot cycle. After that period, however, the correlation broke down.

The Role of Solar Activity — An example of the erroneous conclusions to which inadequate analysis of cyclical phenomena may lead is shown in Figure III-1. A relationship between sunspots and water level in Lake Victoria may be inferred from the record between 1900 and 1925, but this relationship breaks down completely after 1925. As a matter of fact, the search for causal relationship between climate and the solar sunspot cycle, which averages 11.2 years but ranges from 8 to 18 years, has proved rather unsuccessful. A climatic effect probably does exist, but it is small and masked by other phenomena.

Changes in solar activity may induce changes up to a factor of a thousand in the short wavelength region of the solar spectrum, but this region represents only a hundred-thousandth of the total energy emitted by the sun. Thus, the change in solar energy output produced by variations in solar activity is at most one percent. Work by the Smithsonian Institution has shown, however, that the amount of solar energy received at the outer boundary of the earth's atmosphere at the mean distance from the sun (the so-called "solar constant," equal to 1.3 million ergs per square centimeter per second) has remained constant within the limits of error of the observations during the past 50 years.

Examples From the Past — Secular climatic changes are often impressive. For example, Lake Constance froze completely in the winter of 1962-63 for the first time since 1829-30; Lake Chad poured water into the Sahara in 1959 for the first time in 80 years; precipitation in northeast Brazil has decreased 50 percent during the past 50 years; arctic temperatures rose some 2° centigrade between 1885 and 1940; and the average temperature of the atmosphere and ocean surfaces increased 0.7° centigrade during the same time. Some of these changes are regional (i.e., temperature rises in one region while decreasing in an adja-

cent one), but others, including the latter one just mentioned, are not.

Global climatic changes ranging across time intervals of decades to many centuries are known from historical records and geological or paleontological observations. Exceptionally good weather prevailed in Europe between A.D. 800 and 1200, when glacier boundaries were about 200 meters higher, when the Vikings sailed across the northern seas, and when Greenland received its name. A few centuries of colder climate followed: the Baltic froze solid in the winter of 1322-23, an event that has not been repeated since; Iceland was blocked by ice for six months of the year during the first half of the seventeenth century (compared to 1-3 weeks today); and all Alpine glaciers readvanced substantially in the same period. Since the beginning of the nineteenth century, climate has improved again. Whether these climatic changes are cyclical or not is not known, although "cycles" of 80 and 200 years, presumably induced by solar changes, have been mentioned in the literature.

Long-Range Climatic Change

Climatic changes across longer time intervals (a few thousand years to millions of years) can only be inferred from the geological and paleontological records. The occurrence of modern-looking blue-green algae in chert deposits dating from two billion years ago indicates that the radiation balance of the earth has not changed much over this extremely long time interval. However, three times since the beginning of the Cambrian era, about 600 million years ago, the radiation balance of the earth has been sufficiently disturbed to produce conspicuous glaciations. This happened during the Early Paleozoic (about 450 million years ago), Late Paleozoic (about 250 million years ago), and Late Cenozoic (the past few million years). At these times, ice-sheets some 2 kilometers thick repeatedly

covered as much as 30 percent of the continental surface.

Why Glaciation Occurs — For these major glaciations to develop, the radiation balance of the earth must have become negative with respect to its normal state during nonglacial times. That is, the amount of solar radiation reflected back into outer space must have become greater. Cooling of the earth by a decrease of incoming solar radiation does not seem likely because, according to the 1953 calculations of Opik, formation of the ice-sheets to the extent known would have entailed cooling the equatorial belt down to 8° centigrade, whereas the paleontological record indicates that warm-water faunas have existed ever since the beginning of the Cambrian. Therefore, the radiative balance of the earth must have become negative through the effect of terrestrial phenomena alone.

Many such phenomena could have done the trick. For instance, an increase in continentality would have increased the earth's reflectivity and produced cooling, since land absorbs less solar energy than the sea. Displacement of continental masses toward high latitudes should favor glaciation. Finally, an increase in atmospheric haze produced by volcanic activity and dust storms could have reduced the amount of solar energy reaching the earth's surface and, at the same time, reflected into space a portion of the incoming solar radiation. Once the earth's surface temperature is reduced below a certain critical value by one or another or a combination of these factors, ice may begin to develop. Ice is highly reflective, of course, so that more ice means more solar energy reflected, lower temperatures, and even more ice. Indeed, ice appears to be self-expanding and to come to a stop only when the ocean has cooled so much as to provide insufficient evaporation for feeding the ice-sheets.

The pattern of glaciation is best known for the past few hundred thousand years, a time during which ice-sheets repeatedly formed and advanced to cover North America as far south as a front running from Seattle to New York, and Europe as far south as a front running from London to east of Moscow. A substantial ice-sheet also repeatedly covered Patagonia, and mountain glaciers formed wherever high mountains and mountain ranges were available. The repeated advances of the ice-sheets were separated by interglacial times during which all continental ice-sheets disappeared except those of Greenland and Antarctica. We are presently in the middle of one of these interglacial times.

The advances and retreats of continental ice have left the glaciated lands littered with glacial debris, ranging in size from fine sand and clays to boulders as large as a house. From the study of these sediments, geologists have concluded that the ice-sheets formed and swept across the northern continents at least five times during the recent past. The sediments are so mangled, however, that it is difficult to reconstruct a complete history of the glacial events.

"Globigerina Ooze" — For a more complete record one must turn to the deep sea. About 40 percent of the deep ocean floor is covered with a sediment known as "Globigerina ooze." This sediment is rich with the empty shells of planktonic Foraminifera, microscopic protozoans freely floating near the surface when alive. Of the fifteen common species of planktonic Foraminifera, several are restricted to equatorial and tropical waters, several to temperate waters, and one to polar waters. When climate changes, the foraminiferal species move north or south, and these movements are recorded in the sediment on the ocean floor by alternating layers of empty shells belonging to warm, temperate, and cold species. Sediment core samples up to 20 meters long have been recovered. Paleontological analysis of the chang-

ing foraminiferal faunas through these cores reveals the climatic changes that occurred while the sediment was being deposited. In addition, it is known that foraminiferal shells formed during cold intervals contain a greater amount of the rare oxygen isotope ^{18}O than shells formed during warm intervals. Thus, oxygen isotopic analysis of the foraminiferal shells yields accurate information on the actual temperature of the ocean surface and its variations through time. The results given by micropaleontological and isotopic analysis are essentially identical.

Because Globigerina ooze accumulates at the rate of a few centimeters per thousand years, a deep-sea core 20 meters long reaches sediments half a million years old. Deep-sea cores can be dated by various radioactive methods, including radiocarbon and the ratio of thorium-230 to protactinium-231. Thus, climatic changes can not only be followed in continuity by studying deep-sea sediments but can also be dated.

The study of many deep-sea cores from the Atlantic and the Caribbean has made it possible to reconstruct a continuous curve showing the temperature changes of the surface ocean water at low latitudes over the past 425,000 years. This curve, shown in Figure III-2, exhibits a number of

alternating high- and low-temperature intervals, with a gross periodicity of about 40,000 years. A comparison of this curve with the chronology of continental glaciation, based largely on radiocarbon dating, shows that the most recent low-temperature interval (70,000 to 15,000 years ago) represents the last major glaciation. One may safely infer that earlier low-temperature intervals of the oceanic curve represent earlier continental glaciations.

Sediments older than the oldest ones represented in Figure III-2 have been recovered recently from the ocean floor by the drilling vessel *Glomar Challenger;* analysis of these sediments, yet to be performed, should show how far back in the past temperature variations as large as those of Figure III-2 continue. For the time being, sections of older marine sediments now occurring on land have been used. One of these sections, representing sediment deposited about 1.8 million years ago in southern Italy, shows that climatic variations as large as the most recent ones were already occurring at that time.

The General Temperature Curve — The apparent periodicity of 40,000 years is intriguing. No terrestrial phenomenon of the type described before is believed to take place with

Figure III–2 — CHANGES IN THE TEMPERATURE OF THE OCEAN SURFACE

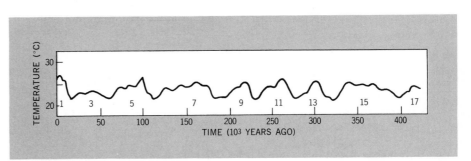

Changes in the ocean surface temperature over the past 425,000 years have been reconstructed from deep-sea cores. Present time is at the left of the graph. The numbers above the time axis are for reference, indicating the peak of the long-term cycles.

such periodicity. These terrestrial phenomena last either much shorter times, like volcanic eruptions or dust storms, or much longer times, like changes in the relative position or extent of continents and oceans. There are, however, certain astronomical motions of the earth that occur in cycles of tens of thousands of years. Because of the attraction of the moon, the sun, and the planets on the bulge of the earth, the earth's axis precesses with a periodicity of 26,000 years; the obliquity of the ecliptic with respect to the terrestrial equatorial plane changes with a periodicity of 40,000 years; and the eccentricity of the earth's orbit changes with a periodicity of 92,000 years. The result of these motions is that, in the high latitudes, periods of warm summers and cold winters alternate every 40,000 years with periods during which summers are colder and winters warmer.

Long before research on deep-sea sediments indicated the probable occurrence of climatic cycles 40,000 years long, the Serbian physicist Milankovitch and the German meteorologist Köppen had suggested that long periods of cool summers could trigger a glaciation even if accompanied by warmer winters. They reasoned that winter is cold enough anyway at high latitudes for snow to accumulate on the ground, while cool summers would allow permanent snow to expand year after year. The earth's reflectivity would thus increase, temperature would decrease, more snow would accumulate, and a major glaciation would rapidly develop.

This theory was enlarged by Geiss and Emiliani to include plastic ice-flow, heat absorption by ice-melting, and downbuckling of the earth's crust under the weight of the ice-sheets in order to explain the disappearance of the major ice-sheets (Greenland and Antarctica excluded) at the end of each glaciation. As it now stands, the theory seems to account for glacial and interglacial events and their time-scale during the recent past. It also accounts for the timing of high interglacial sea levels related to ice melting. That is, the times when summers were warmest, as calculated from astronomical constants, were also the times when sea level stood high as determined by radioactive dating of fossil shells and corals.

The generalized temperature curve of Figure III-2 shows, superimposed on the major oscillations, a number of smaller oscillations. Mathematical analysis of the original isotopic curves of the deep-sea cores has shown that these smaller oscillations are related to the precession of the equinoxes. Precession of the equinoxes is apparently also responsible for the occurrence of more than one high sea level during interglacial intervals, occurring whenever northern summers coincide with perihelion and resulting from partial or even total melting of Greenland ice.

Figure III-3 shows the original oxygen isotopic curves for two deep-sea cores from the Caribbean. The horizontal scale shows the depth below the top of the core, the tops of the cores being on the left side (0 cm).

The tops represent modern sediments, and the time-scale for the various cores can be evaluated by comparing each curve with the generalized temperature curve of Figure III-2. The vertical axis represents the $^{18}O/^{16}O$ concentrations, which are inversely proportional to temperature. The more negative values, therefore, represent higher temperatures.

As shown in Figure III-3, isotopic values as negative as the ones occurring at the tops of the cores, representing the present interglacial conditions, occur only occasionally below. Temperature was considerably lower than today during much of the previous interglacial intervals, with periods of temperatures as high as today occurring only for a short time (a few thousand years at most) at the peaks of the previous interglacial ages. The present period of high temperature began about 8,000 years ago and reached a peak 2,000 years later. It was followed by a 2°-centigrade temperature decrease about 4,000 years ago, in turn followed by a 1°-centigrade increase.

The Present Situation

All these changes, short-term as well as long-term, regional as well as

Figure III–3 — TEMPERATURE CURVES DERIVED FROM OXYGEN ISOTOPE RATIOS OF DEEP-SEA CORES

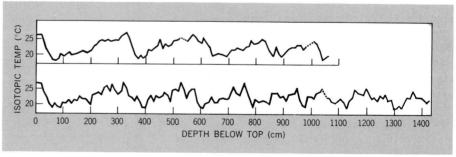

Sediments formed from shells of microscopic protozoans are known to have a high concentration of ^{18}O when formed during cold periods. Therefore, high values of the ratio $^{18}O/^{16}O$ indicate cool temperatures; low values indicate warm temperatures. The point at which the core is sampled can be dated by other means. Several centimeters of core represent a thousand years.

global, must be carefully monitored and studied. Because the environmental balance is delicate, and because it can be affected not only by natural changes but also by man-made ones, a thorough understanding of climatic history and dynamics is important indeed. Furthermore, many climatic events appear to result from triggering actions involving only a small amount of energy. An understanding of these actions is important not only to prevent catastrophic climatic changes (as, for instance, the development of new glaciation or the melting in part or in whole of the ice-caps of Greenland and Antarctica) but also to develop methods for climatic control.

Judging from the record of the past interglacial ages, the present time of high temperatures should be drawing to an end, to be followed by a long period of considerably colder temperatures leading into the next glacial age some 20,000 years from now. However, it is possible, or even likely, that human interference has already altered the environment so much that the climatic pattern of the near future will follow a different path. For instance, widespread deforestation in recent centuries, especially in Europe and North America, together with increased atmospheric opacity due to man-made dust storms and industrial wastes, should have increased the earth's reflectivity. At the same time, increasing concentration of industrial carbon dioxide in the atmosphere should lead to a temperature increase by absorption of infrared radiation from the earth's surface. When these human factors are added to such other natural factors as volcanic eruptions, changes in solar activity, and resonances within the hydro-atmosphere, their effect can only be estimated in terms of direction, not of amount.

Long-Term Temperature Change — Because climatic changes across intervals of years to centuries are so much affected by the time-characteristics of our turbulent hydro-atmosphere, no immediate breakthroughs are to be expected toward a global view of climatic dynamics across these intervals. Much progress has been made, however, in the study of climatic changes across longer time intervals, in which the intractable turbulent effects cancel out. Studies already under way concern: the amplitude of the glacial/interglacial temperature change at different latitudes and in oceans other than the Atlantic, using oxygen-isotopic analysis of suitable deep-sea cores; short-range (years to centuries) climatic changes through oxygen-isotopic analysis of deep-sea cores for anaerobic basins; and climatic change in the absence of ice on earth using deep-sea cores of Middle and Early Cenozoic and of Late Mesozoic age obtained by the D. V. *Glomar Challenger.*

Prospects for Controlling Change — Judging from past results, the current and planned research should contribute importantly to our understanding of many climatic problems related to the evolution of man's environment and to the possibilities for altering or controlling it. Research conducted so far, for instance, has made much clearer the significance of the earth's reflectivity as a major climatic factor. If reflectivity is indeed so important, then control of today's earth reflectivity by plastic films or other means may be a way to control the climatic deterioration already under way. Again, because glaciation is essentially a runaway phenomenon, early control should be much easier than later attempts at modifying an already established adverse situation.

Fluctuations in Climate Over Periods of Less Than 200 Years

Factors thought to be responsible for climatic fluctuations of less than 200 years' duration (and the sciences involved) are:

1. *Short-term fluctuations in solar radiation* (solar and atmospheric physics) — There is no evidence of changes in the solar constant greater than 0.2 percent, although variations do occur in the particle (X-ray) flux and also, it is thought, in the ultraviolet bands shorter than 0.2 microns.

Correlations have been established between ultraviolet flux and stratospheric ozone concentrations, but the exact nature of the links between ozone and the intensity of the stratospheric circulation, and the consequences for the troposphere regime, are uncertain.

2. *Changes in atmospheric constituents* (meteorology, atmospheric chemistry) — Carbon dioxide (CO_2) is a major absorber of infrared radiation from the earth, whereas aerosols (especially dust) affect solar radiation by scattering and absorption. The ratio of absorption to scattering is about 5/3 for urban sites and 1/5 for prairie and desert areas.

The nearly global rise of temperature in the first forty years of this century (see Figure III-4) has been attributed to increasing CO_2 content, although this is by no means an accepted theory. The magnitude of the

Figure III–4 — VARIATION OF THE MEAN ANNUAL TEMPERATURE
OF THE NORTHERN HEMISPHERE

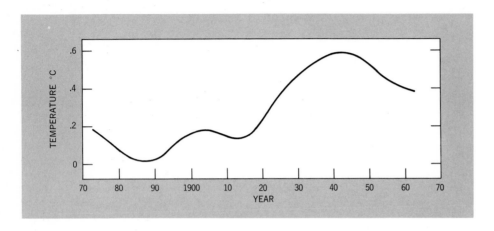

The graph shows the variation of mean annual temperature near the surface of the northern hemisphere during the past century. Variations in the world mean annual temperature are similar. The curve is based on data from several hundred stations, weighted for the area represented by each station. The data are expressed in terms of ten-year overlapping means of the departures from the 1885–90 mean.

effect for a given increase in CO_2 concentration is still in dispute. (A 1°-centigrade increase might require an increase in concentration of from as little as 25 percent to as much as 80 percent; at present rates of CO_2 increase, such a temperature increase would take between 50 and 300 years.)

Little is known about the effects of volcanic and man-made dust. The *net* effect of major eruptions, such as that of Mt. Agung in 1963, on total solar radiation received amounted to a decrease of only 6 percent. Turbidity measurements indicate a widespread increase in atmospheric dust content in this century, but the role of man in this, and its meteorological consequences, are largely unknown.

3. *Air-sea interaction* (meteorology, oceanography) — Changes of ocean surface temperatures appear to lag two to three years behind long-term atmospheric trends, but feedback effects — by which oceanic processes reinforce an initial atmospheric trend — are of great importance. Short-lived anomalies such as the dry summers in northeastern United States during the early 1960's can be attributed to persistent sea-temperature anomalies. Little is known about the factors determining the duration of a trend or its eventual reversal.

4. *Inherent variability in the atmospheric circulation* (meteorology, fluid dynamics) — The year-to-year patterns of development of the seasonal weather regimes seem to be essentially random. Thus, individual extreme seasons may occur in spite of a general trend in the opposite direction. Instances are the severe English winters of 1739-40 and 1878-79, both of which followed a series of mild winter seasons. An extensive snow cover or sea-temperature anomaly may help to

trigger circulation changes if other conditions are suitable.

On the 50- to 200-year time-scale, changes in the disposition of the wind-flow patterns between 10,000 and 30,000 feet are important. There is evidence of an approximately 200-year fluctuation in the northern hemisphere westerlies, with peaks in the early 1300's, 1500's, 1700's, and 1900's and with shorter, less regular fluctuations superimposed. Weakening of the westerlies in recent decades has been accompanied by an equatorward shift of the wind belts.

Finally, and most fundamentally, the extent to which global climate is *precisely* determined by the governing physical laws is unknown. Theoretical formulations indicate the possibility that all changes in the atmospheric circulation need not be attributable to specific causes. That is, the atmosphere may not be a completely deterministic system.

Although much recent attention has been given to changes in atmospheric constituents, it is not yet possible to be at all positive as to which, if any, of these four groups of factors are the major determinants of relatively short-term climatic fluctuations — i.e., those of less than 200 years' duration. Even the secular changes in the strength of the wind belts and their latitudinal location, noted in (4) above, may be determined by forcing of extraterrestrial or terrestrial origin.

Characteristics of the Fluctuations

The amplitude of 100- to 200-year fluctuations of temperature is estimated to be of the order of 1° centigrade; decadal averages of winter temperature have a range of 2° centigrade. It is generally accepted that the longer the duration of a climatic fluctuation, the larger is the area affected in any given sense and the greater is the response of vegetation, glaciers, and other "indicators." Thus, over the time period from the mid-nineteenth century to the present, the amplitude and incidence of temperature fluctuations in Europe and eastern North America are broadly similar. But certain of the minor fluctuations lasting perhaps 25 to 30 years are missing, or of opposite direction, in some localities in these areas. Minor fluctuations within North America itself also show spatial and temporal irregularities.

There is no clear evidence that any of the fluctuations are strictly periodic — i.e., that they are rhythms. Around the North Atlantic, the amplitude of the fluctuations over the past 300 years or so appears to have increased while their duration has decreased by comparison to the previous centuries. Periods of about 23, 45-60, 100, and 170 years have been suggested, but not statistically established, from observational data and indirect historical records in Europe. Recent analyses of cores from the Greenland ice-cap also indicate fluctuations in ^{18}O (oxygen-isotope) contents with a period of about 120 years.

The spatial pattern of climatic change during this century is complex. Annual and winter temperatures increased over much of the globe from approximately 1890 to 1940, especially in high latitudes of the northern hemisphere; net cooling has occurred over about 80 percent of the globe since the latter date. There is virtually no correlation between the over-all global changes and trends in particular areas, which strongly suggests that the controls of regional fluctuations are distinct from those for global changes.

In low latitudes, the most important fluctuations involve precipitation, with a decrease of the order of 30 percent in many parts of the tropics around 1900. During most of the first half of this century, the equatorial rain belt tended to be narrower, and the tropical arid zone wider, than either during the preceding half-century or since the 1940/50's. This change did not affect monsoon Asia, but the same pattern of change occurred on the east coasts of Australia and North America up to about 40° latitude. The other major area affected by precipitation change is central Asia, where the 1950/60's have been much drier.

Interactions with Society

Fluctuations in climate—either natural or man-induced — can have important economic and social implications for man. For example, studies in England and the eastern United States since about 1940 indicate a return to conditions of the early nineteenth century. What would be the implications of such a sustained deterioration of climate in the middle and high latitudes of the northern hemisphere? What would be the effects of man's intentional or accidental modification of large-scale and local climate?

Effects of Continuing Deterioration — Even beyond such frost-susceptible, high-value crops as the Florida citrus fruits, farming activities can be markedly affected by changes in temperature and moisture balance, especially those occurring in spring and fall. The growing season in England, for example, has shortened by an average of two weeks since 1950, as compared with the years 1920 to 1940. Cereal cultivation was revived in Iceland only in the 1920's, after a gap of four centuries or more. Many more summers like that of 1969 — when sea-ice persisted along the northern coast for most of the summer and grain harvests were ruined — could seriously threaten that country's marginal economy. The effect on the fishing industry of Iceland (and other European countries) could also be serious.

The increased frequency of severe winters in northwest Europe since 1939-40, as compared with the preceding twenty years, has been reflected in greater disruption of transport and increased requirements for domestic heating, winter fodder for cattle, and the like. Through a series of chain reactions, for example, the winter of 1969-70 had a serious effect on the whole East German economy.

The relationships between climatic changes and farming are generally nonlinear. In view of the second- or third-order interactions among weather, pests and diseases, soil, and crops, the implications of recent changes may be more significant agriculturally than the basic climatic fluctuations might suggest. This is as true in temperate middle latitudes as it is in semi-arid or other marginal climates. For example, lower air and sea temperatures in spring in northeastern North America are believed to have affected fish (especially salmon) by accentuating the sublethal effects of DDT.

Effect of Man's Activities — Non-meteorologists tend to base estimates on assumptions of a constant mean and variance of the climatic elements. But there is a serious need to scrutinize long-term weather/climate modification schemes with respect to their possible interaction with climatic trends. Cloud-seeding programs designed to augment snowfall in mountain areas, for example, may increase avalanche hazard and spring-summer runoff. If the planned increase coincides with an unrecognized trend to greater precipitation (or falling temperatures), the effects may exceed expectations.

Unintentional effects of man, through increased atmospheric pollution (dust, carbon dioxide and other gases, supersonic aircraft trails in the stratosphere), are of international concern, particularly with respect to their health implications. The possible broader effects on global climate and, directly or indirectly, on man's economic activities may be even more critical. Although the role of CO_2 is reasonably well understood, the effect of dust on solar and terrestrial radiation is virtually unknown.

In an historical context, it has been suggested that the Rajasthan Desert of northwest India may have originated largely through overgrazing, with the resultant increase in atmospheric dust content leading to conditions that further decreased rainfall. Correct identification of natural and man-made tendencies is vital in such instances if attempts are to be made to reverse the processes.

Evaluation of Current Status

Data — The data base available for the study of climatic fluctuations lasting less than 200 years is limited in a number of respects:

Spatial coverage of climatic data covering approximately the last century and a half is restricted. Direct observations are particularly limited for the southern hemisphere generally, the oceans, the high arctic, mountain areas in general, and parts of the tropics. Fortunately, more extensive records are available for the European-North Atlantic sector, the area where climatic fluctuations have been pronounced.

Climatic data available for a substantial length of time is restricted to only a few categories, however — mainly temperature, precipitation, and pressure. Indices of volcanic activity and dust since the late seventeenth century are available. But records of solar radiation, atmospheric CO_2, and other dust content, for example, exist only for shorter periods and provide a more restricted spatial coverage.

Reconstruction of changes over the past two centuries is now possible, using (a) snow/ice cores from Greenland and Antarctica, which provide records of O^{18} changes with good time-resolution over thousands of years, and (b) tree-ring indices in selected areas — the arid margins for moisture changes and the arctic

(or alpine) margins for temperature changes. Other techniques for reconstructing past climates do not allow the necessary degree of time-resolution, mainly because of inherent limitations in available dating methods.

Data on the extraterrestrial and terrestrial variables that may cause fluctuations are even more limited. Carbon dioxide, for example, has been measured in a few places over the past 100 years but regular monitoring is very recent. The monitoring of turbidity has only just begun in a limited way, and extensive and reliable measurements are similarly available for only about a decade. Fluctuations in solar radiation will only be determined from satellite data, although there are several centuries of sunspot records.

Changes in other terrestrial variables such as sea-surface temperatures, extent of snow cover, pack-ice and frozen ground, cloudiness, and total atmospheric vapor content cannot be assessed with sufficient accuracy from available (or foreseeable) ground networks. Satellite monitoring will again be indispensable.

The fact that "artificial" climatic changes due to man's activities may obscure, or accentuate, natural trends further complicates efforts to study climatic changes over the past 200 years.

Theoretical Formulations — The development of operative numerical models of the atmosphere and oceans which account for the major observed features of global climate represents a significant recent advance. Theoretical formulations are generally available as far as atmospheric-circulation models are concerned, although theories of "almost intransitive" systems need further development. Tidal phenomena in the atmosphere have been a subject of much recent study, but their possible implications for climatic fluctuations have not yet been established. Some phenomena — e.g., the

scattering/absorption properties of aerosols; interactions between stratospheric ozone and the general circulation — still present important theoretical problems.

Interactions — The possible impact of climatic fluctuations on man's activities — agriculture, fisheries, domestic heating, transportation, construction industries, and so on — appears to have been generally neglected, particularly in terms of modeling and long-range planning. Ecosystem studies of the International Biological Program will provide some information pertinent to these problems, but the difficulty with all short-term programs of this type is that climate tends to be regarded as an environmental constant.

Some Controversial Topics — Concerning the stability of the arctic pack-ice, would it re-form under present climatic conditions if attempts were made to remove it? Data shortcomings for this area and the problem of ocean and atmospheric advection of heat have prevented resolution of this question.

It has been argued that the apparent recent increase of atmospheric turbidity may account for the downturn of temperature since about 1940. If this were to be confirmed, a continued deterioration could be expected, other things remaining constant.

The problem of changes induced by turbidity is related to the more general, and equally important, problem of distinguishing between "natural" and man-induced climatic change. This is especially significant in assessing the actual and potential effects of large-scale, long-term weather/climate modification programs.

Instrumentation — The technical aspects of required instruments are, in general, adequately covered. With respect to determinations of atmospheric turbidity, however, the application of LIDAR (light detection and ranging) needs further evaluation and refinement. Similarly, routine availability for grid-points of all data collected by satellites is essential for maximum climatological use of the information.

Adequate deployment (including long-term satellite coverage) presents the major problem. The number of long-term "benchmark" stations for measuring the variables referred to earlier, in addition to the climatic parameters, is inadequate for many regions of the globe.

Requirements for Scientific Activity

The present climatic fluctuation may be of immediate economic significance for areas with marginal climate, especially in high latitudes. Over the longer term, possible changes elsewhere could be of major importance for the planning of agricultural production, architectural design, heating requirements, and transportation systems. It may not be possible to forecast climatic fluctuations with any confidence for a decade or more, if at all, but any planning should incorporate the best advice of climatologists.

Data Collection — Continued and intensified monitoring of atmospheric dust content, especially in mid-ocean and high-elevation sites, is needed. Satellite monitoring of global cloudiness, snow and ice cover, atmospheric vapor content, and sea-surface temperature, with routine data reduction, is also required.

Data collection needs to be planned to continue on a long-term basis, through such programs as the Global

Atmospheric Research Program and the World Weather Watch. The perspective must certainly be global. (In this connection, it is worth noting that in much of tropical Africa basic data networks are now seriously reduced below what they were in the colonial era, and this will greatly restrict future analyses.) Planning for data collection is urgent within the next year or two. It cannot be stressed too strongly that studies of climatic change require a long series of records.

Data Analysis — Exhaustive analysis of all available historical weather information, especially outside Europe, is needed to provide perspective on the recent period. Historians could contribute significantly here. The reliability of the data must be assessed and it must be stored in a form suitable for application of modern retrieval systems.

Collection and synthesis of all available "historical" information may take twenty years. It will, however, provide essential information for continued development of theory and prediction, and it should serve as a considerable stimulus to interdisciplinary work and exchange of ideas in the fields that are concerned with, or affected by, climatic change and its implications.

Dendroclimatic and snow/ice core studies should be extended to supplement direct records. Dendroclimatological work in the tropics (Africa and South America), especially near the alpine timberline, is particularly needed.

Further study is needed of the magnitude and spatial extent of fluctua-

tions for different climatic parameters, and of rates of change. These might offer confirmation, or otherwise, of the existence of various rhythms.

Advances in general atmospheric-circulation studies over the next decade should greatly improve our understanding of the way in which the atmosphere responds to internal and external forcing functions. If the present climatic deterioration in middle and high latitudes of the northern hemisphere *is* part of a 50- to 100-year fluctuation, research over the next decade would be critical in terms of our "engineering" ability to cope with it adequately.

Finally, analyses of air-sea feedback effects on various time-scales need to be undertaken.

Numerical Model Experiments — Model experiments should provide definitive information on the effect of such variables as pack-ice extent, snow cover, and sea-temperature anomalies on the heat budget and on atmospheric circulation patterns. Adequate sophistication will probably be available for this work within two to five years.

Work in progress should provide information on tropical-temperature and trans-equatorial links in the general circulation necessary to an understanding of spatial aspects of fluctuations. It is not yet clear, however, whether or not this work will clarify understanding of the way in which seasonal weather patterns commonly develop in different manners in different years. This is fundamental to the possibilities of predicting short- or long-term fluctuations.

Environmental Cyclic Behavior: The Evidence of Tree Rings and Pollen Profiles

One of the major problems to be faced before we can arrive at an understanding of environmental cyclic behavior is concerned with standard-

izing definitions. Attempts at worldwide standardization of terms in climatic studies are being made. The Commission for Climatology of the

World Meteorological Organization has published two suggested glossaries, one for various statistical characteristics of climatic change and the other for differentiating between the various time-scales of climatic change. Similar glossaries are needed for other aspects of the physical matrix making up the environment.

"Operational" definitions are used here. "Environment" is considered to be the physical matrix in which organized and unorganized matter exists. The term "cycle" refers to the complete course of events or phenomena that recur regularly in the same sequence and return to the original state; in this sense, a cycle has a true harmonic course. "Cyclic" (or "cycle-like") refers to something that only roughly approximates a harmonic.

Aside from "seasonal" patterns, no true harmonic behavior has been found in global or regional climatic patterns; the latter are cyclic patterns but they vary in duration and intensity. Several biological and natural processes reach such a degree of

harmonics that they are sometimes called rhythms, but these rhythms are generally tied to seasonal climatic changes.

Tree growth and pollen production are, in a certain sense, a physiological response to the climatic conditions prevailing at the time these processes occurred. A thorough understanding of these processes leads to a better understanding of the immediate environment, and when old samples of tree rings (the long chronologies) and pollen production (the pollen profiles) can be located and studied, past local environmental conditions can be determined for those specific areas. Publications are now appearing on climatic conditions over the past 15,000 years or so, as interpreted by various authors. Although cyclical patterns appear in many of these interpretations, the patterns are so obscure that little credence can be put on their meaning.

Tree Rings and Environmental Cyclic Behavior

Certain species of trees respond to physiological behavior by doing all of their yearly growth in a particular period of time. Thus, growth itself is harmonic. The *amount* of growth produced each year, however, varies in response to environmental changes. Trees in a uniform environment, or one that remains fairly constant year in and year out, produce tree rings of a uniform width over a given period of years. In contrast, trees growing in areas where environmental changes are quite pronounced will reflect those changes in variable ring-widths for a given period of years. (See Figure III-5) In areas where one growth-controlling factor assumes dominance over the others, this factor can be isolated; variations of ring-widths then permit study of this particular type of variable environmental condition. In certain areas the con-

Figure III–5 — PRECIPITATION PATTERNS FROM TREE RINGS

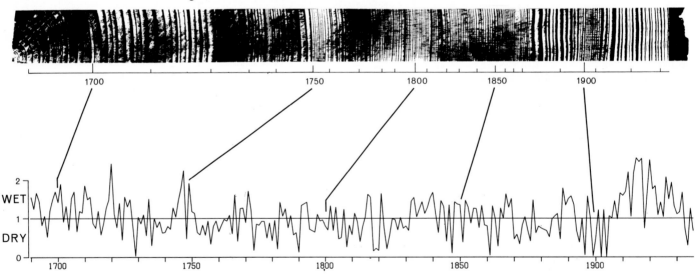

The photograph shows tree rings beginning about 1690 and ending about 1932. The rings were used to estimate whether the year was wet or dry; moisture was then computed to provide the graph in the lower part of the diagram. Since variations in atmospheric circulation cause periods of wetness and dryness, the ring-width records can be calibrated with surface pressure and used to map anomalies of the atmospheric circulation for periods of time in which few if any historical data exist.

trolling factor might be soil moisture, in others it might be summer temperatures, and in still others it might be solar radiation. If too many variables enter the picture, to a point where they cannot be isolated, the growth patterns become "confused"; in the present state of knowledge, they are of little value for this type of study.

Numerous studies are being conducted on tree growth. Those concerned with the bristlecone pine (*Pinus aristata* Engelen) in the White Mountains of eastern California are among the more important. Living bristlecone trees as old as 5,000 years or more have been studied and a good yearly growth chronology for that period of time has been developed. Bristlecone snags and other pieces of deadwood have enabled the chronology to be extended back for over 7,000 years. Similar but shorter chronologies have been developed in other areas throughout many parts of the northern hemisphere. Some work has been done in the southern hemisphere but none has yet attained the length of the bristlecone studies.

Although numerous studies on these tree-ring series have been made by meteorologists, climatologists, and statisticians, as well as dendrochronologists and others, no cyclic pattern has been detected in spite of the annual variation that exists. The non-uniform periods of good and poor growing conditions for the bristlecone show a cycle-like behavior. But because of the wide variation in intensity and duration, one can "screen" the data to find almost any cycle length desired, or even none at all. These data appear to be promising from the standpoint of cyclic be-havior, but at present they are of limited value.

Pollen Profiles and Environmental Cyclic Behavior

The number of pollen and spores recovered from any depositional sequence is the result of a wide variety of variable factors which are not yet well understood. Climatic factors are involved in the production and dispersal of pollen of the various wind-pollinated species; in addition, a differential is caused by preservation and recovery from the sediments. Experimental work is being done on almost every aspect of these wide variations, and there is hope that the future will see at least a reasonable solution to many of these problems.

Profiles represent a random count of various wind-pollinated species recovered from sediments. Seldom does the palynologist working with recent materials give an absolute pollen count of every grain present on the slide. These counts are treated in a statistical manner in an attempt to overcome bias caused by differential production (plants too close to the depositional area) or differential preservation (oxidation). Such profiles give only a gross representation of the true situation. Furthermore, no annual variation in past pollen production or preservation can be detected from such profiles unless the variation is frozen into annual deposits such as a varved clay sequence.

Pollen profiles are being interpreted as essentially representing the vegetative cover existing at the time the pollen was produced. The vegetative cover was, in turn, a response to envi-ronmental conditions during those periods, and those environmental conditions are interpreted as being of climatic significance.

Present Status

There is no question that, under certain environmental conditions, plants produce different amounts of growth in the annual layers of wood, and different amounts of pollen are produced and dispersed during the pollen-production seasons. Tree-growth and pollen studies are still, however, in what one could call a primitive state. We are only now learning what the problems actually are. As soon as the problems can be better defined, concentrated effort can be made toward their solution. At the present time, only trends can be detected in the various environmental conditions; no scientific prediction can yet be made from these trends.

In general, more physiological studies are needed regarding the connection between environment and tree-ring growth, especially in quantitative amounts. Such studies need to be made on a variety of species growing under a wide variety of conditions. Once these measurements are made and understood, considerable statistical work (computer analysis) will be necessary to reduce the data to usable forms. We are still in need of better knowledge on pollen production and dispersal, on pollen preservation and recovery, and on statistical (or computer) analyses of recovered grains. These studies will be of limited value, however, if we do not also have a much better understanding of all aspects of the physical matrix comprising the natural environment.

2. CAUSES OF CLIMATIC CHANGE

Basic Factors in Climatic Change

It is useful to introduce the problem of climatic change by considering the definition of climate. Practical definitions of the term "climate" vary in their specifics from one authority to another. All are alike, however, in distinguishing between climate and weather (and between climatology and meteorology) on the basis that climate refers to "average" atmospheric behavior whereas weather refers to individual atmospheric events and developments. On the face of it, then, it might seem that we are left simply with the decision of what time interval to choose over which to average the observed weather into "the climate." By "average" is meant average statistical properties in all respects, including means, extremes, joint frequency distributions, time-series structure, and so on.

Climatic Change as a Fundamental Attribute of Climate

Were atmospheric behavior to proceed randomly in time, the problem of defining climate would reduce to a straightforward exercise in statistical sampling. We could make our estimate of climate as precise as we wish merely by choosing an average interval that is sufficiently long. One difficulty arises immediately because our knowledge of past atmospheric behavior becomes less and less detailed (and less and less reliable) the further back in time we go. But there is another, more important difficulty: If our knowledge of past climates is imprecise, it is at least good enough to establish that long-term atmospheric behavior does *not* proceed randomly in time. Changes of climate from one geological epoch to another, and apparently also those from one millen-

nium to another, are clearly too large in amplitude to be explained as random excursions from modern norms.

When one examines modern reconstructions of the paleoclimatic record, one might be led to suppose that geological changes of climate—such as those associated with the alternating glacials and interglacials of the Pleistocene ice age—are smoothly varying functions of time, readily distinguishable from the much more rapid variability of year-to-year changes of atmospheric state. In other words, one might suppose that each part of a glacial cycle has its own well-defined climate, just as each season of the year is revealed by modern meteorological data to have its own well-defined climate. In such a case, the averaging interval needed to obtain a stable estimate of present-day climate should be long enough to suppress year-to-year sampling variability, but short in comparison to the duration of a glacial cycle.

If we succumbed to the foregoing rationale for defining climate, we would probably be living in a fool's paradise. The reason is simple enough: the apparent regularity of atmospheric changes in the geological past is only an illusion, attributable to the inadequate resolving power of paleoclimatic indicators. Most such indicators act to one degree or another as low-pass filters of the actual climatic chronology. If our more recent experience — based on relatively higher-pass filters such as tree-rings, varves, ice-cap stratigraphy, and pollen analysis applicable to post-glacial time — is any guide, the state of the atmosphere has varied on most, if not all, shorter scales of time as well.

In other words, the variance spectrum of changes of atmospheric state is strongly "reddened," with low-frequency changes accounting for relatively large proportions of the total variance (in the broadband sense). At the same time, important gaps in the spectrum of climatic change have yet to be identified and may not even exist. Taken together, these circumstances imply that *there may be no such thing as an "optimum" averaging interval, and therefore no assurance that we can define (let alone measure) a unique, "best" estimate of what constitutes average behavior of the atmosphere.*

To summarize, atmospheric state is known to vary on many scales of time, and it cannot be ruled out from present knowledge that it varies on *all* scales of time (from billions of years all the way down to periods so short that they are better defined as meteorological variability). Thus it can be argued that the very concept of climate is sterile as a physical descriptor of the real world as long as it adheres to the classical concept of something static. In any event, present-day climate is best described in terms of a *transient* adjustment of atmospheric mean state to the present terrestrial environment.

The Problem of Causes

If climate is inherently variable, as here suggested, different interpretations can be lent to the variability.

The "Slave" Concept — One interpretation is the conventional one, which can be called the "slave" concept of climatic change. This embodies the idea that the average atmospheric state is virtually indistinguishable from an equilibrium state, which in turn is uniquely consistent with the earth-environmental conditions at the time; in this view, the atmosphere requires a relatively short time to adjust to its new equilibrium state when the earth-environmental conditions change.

The "Conspirator" Concept — Another interpretation can be called the "conspirator" concept of climatic change. This concept considers that the average atmospheric state is influenced as much by its own past history as by contemporary earth-environmental conditions, that there may be more than one equilibrium state that is consistent with those environmental conditions, and that the choice of equilibrium state approximated by the actual atmospheric state at any given time depends upon the antecedent history of the actual state.

Sharp Distinctions — The distinctions between these two concepts is sharp for long-period climatic change, such as the change from Tertiary to Quaternary times. On such a timescale, the dynamic and thermodynamic time-constants of atmospheric processes are infinitesimal, even if one chose to include the oceans and the polar ice-caps as coupled "atmospheric" processes. As now seems plausible, earth-environmental changes included gradual sea-floor spreading and continental drift, together with a gradual increase of average continental elevation. It is usually assumed that the climate acted in keeping with the "slave" concept throughout and that, after a certain point in the course of continental drift was reached (perhaps when the Arctic Ocean was isolated), the equilibrium climate was transformed in a deterministic manner from a glacial-inhibiting pattern to a glacial-stimulating pattern.

On the other hand, it is possible to argue, following Lorenz, that the actual climate of the Quaternary was not necessarily preordained by its contemporary environmental state; that the evolution of climate to its Quaternary mode was not a deterministic evolution but a *probabilistic* one that *might* have turned out very differently under identical conditions of continental drift and other environmental change. The different Quaternary outcomes (two or more) would have followed from differences in the precise course of the climate itself, due either to transient environmental disturbances or perhaps to "random" excursions of atmospheric state along the way.

Subtle Distinctions — With regard to relatively rapid climatic change, however, the distinction between the "slave" and the "conspirator" concepts of change is much more subtle in character, and perhaps unrecognizable within present bounds of either theory or observation. The reason for this is to be found in the intimate dynamic and thermodynamic coupling that exists between the atmosphere and the oceans, and to a lesser extent in the coupling between the atmosphere, the oceans, and the polar ice-caps. These couplings introduce long time-constants into the changes of atmospheric state, and result in various forms of *autovariation* in the total system, on the time-scale of decades and centuries. In the course of such autovariation, the atmosphere itself may be said to obey the "slave" principle. But in a relatively limited period of years, the coupled atmosphere-ocean system would exhibit changes of state that are not independent of its initial state. In this case, the system is more properly described as obeying the "conspirator" principle. To complicate matters further, it is conceivable that the autovariation of the atmosphere-ocean system is riding on top of a transient of the Lorenz type already mentioned.

In the presence of Lorenz-type transients, the effect of systematic en-

vironmental changes on present-day climate (changes, for example, involving secular increases of carbon dioxide (CO_2) or other consequences of human activities) might be so badly confounded as to be totally unrecognizable. Even without such transients, however, atmosphere-ocean autovariation could effectively obscure the effect of systematic environmental changes that we are seeking to discover.

Rationale for the Isolation of Human from Natural Factors in Climatic Change

What rationale, then, are we to follow in establishing the climatic effects of systematic environmental change on the scale of decades and centuries? More specifically, how do we go about the task of isolating the contribution of man's activities to twentieth-century climatic change?

First of all, there seems no real possibility of detecting Lorenz-type transients in present-day climate, so we will have to proceed on the assumption that they are not now occurring nor are they likely to be induced in the foreseeable future by further environmental change from human activities.

Second, while we should not hesitate to use presently available estimates of the climatic effects of atmospheric pollution and other forms of environmental change as an interim guide in assessing the potential climatic hazards of various human activities, we should also remember that such estimates are highly tentative. We should take pains not to put undue confidence in them.

Shortcomings of the Present Data Base — In this connection, there are two important points to consider:

1. Most present estimates of the climatic impact of human activities are based on relatively

simple hydrostatic heat-balance models (as refined, for example, by Manabe and used by him to estimate the thermal effect of variable CO_2, stratospheric water vapor, surface albedo, and the like). Manabe himself has often stressed the limitations of such models, the most important of which are: that they do not take account of atmospheric dynamics other than purely local convective mixing; and that they do not take into account changes of atmospheric variables other than the variable that is explicitly controlled as a parameter of the calculation (plus water vapor in those experiments stipulating a constant relative humidity).

2. Climatic changes caused by natural agencies, and those possibly caused by human agencies, are not necessarily additive. For example, by analysis of past data on CO_2 accumulation in the atmosphere, roughly 50 percent of all fossil CO_2 added to the atmosphere appears to have been retained there. Using published United Nations projections of future fossil CO_2 production, together with a constant 50 percent retention ratio, it can be predicted that by A.D. 2000 the total atmospheric CO_2 load will have exceeded its nineteenth-century baseline by more than 25 percent. As pointed out by Machta, however, recent atmospheric CO_2 measurements at Mauna Loa and other locations indicate that the atmospheric CO_2 retention ratio has been dropping steadily since 1958, to a present value of only about 35 percent.

It may be significant that the 50 percent retention figure applied to a time when world average temperatures were rising, and that the observed decline since 1958 applies to a time when world average temperatures have been falling. It is conceivable, though certainly not proven, that the reversing trend of world climate in recent years has somehow altered the rate at which the oceans can absorb fossil CO_2. If this is the case, we are witnessing an interactive effect whereby climatic changes produced by one agency (presumably a natural one) are at least temporarily reducing the climatic impact of another agency (in this case, an inadvertent human one). Such interactive effects are very poorly understood, and yet they may be a very important element in the evolution of present-day climate.

The Use of Advanced Mathematical Models — To return to our question of what rationale we should follow in our study of contemporary climatic change and of human influences on climate, we are left with little choice. We have to rely on the development of advanced mathematical models of the global atmosphere that will be suitable for long-term integration to generate stable climatological statistics and will be capable of simulating many dynamic and thermodynamic processes in the atmosphere and at the earth's surface. Relatively sophisticated models of these kinds have already been developed, at least one of which has been expanded to deal with coupled atmosphere-ocean systems. Experiments with such models have begun to lay a solid foundation for a quantitative theory of global climate and have elucidated the climate-controlling influence of the general atmospheric and oceanic circulations. There appears to be no limit to the refinement possible in such models, other than the limits imposed by computer capacity and speed.

The manner in which such numerical experiments bear on the study of climatic change is essentially twofold:

1. The experiments verify that a wide range of environmental factors have a bearing on the global pattern of atmospheric circulation and climate. They confirm that the most important factors in this respect are: (a) solar emittance; (b) the geometry of the earth-sun system including the orbital and axial motions of the earth; (c) the distribution of oceans and land masses; (d) the state of the ocean surface which, along with the juxtaposed atmospheric state, governs the fluxes of energy, moisture, and momentum across the surface; (e) the state of the land surfaces with respect to albedo, thermal capacity, water and ice cover, relief, and aerodynamic roughness; and (f) the gaseous and aerosol composition of the atmosphere itself. To the extent that all of these factors may vary with time, either slowly or rapidly, in response to forces other than the contemporary atmospheric state itself, all such factors are automatically to be regarded as *potential* causes of climatic change.

2. In the numerical experiments, it is possible to simulate the behavior of circulation and climate as a function of arbitrarily chosen boundary conditions and atmospheric constituency, which enter the experiments as controllable parameters. This makes it possible to vary any of the environmental factors listed above and determine how the circulation and climate respond. In this way, various theories of climatic change can be tested in terms of their meteorological consistency. With the further refinement of joint atmosphere-ocean models, the more realistic modeling of continents and ocean basins, and the introduction of ice-cap interactions into the models, the range of factors in climatic causation that are amenable to this kind of study will eventually became almost exhaustive of all reasonable possibilities.

Figure III-7 — FACTORS IN THE RADIATION BALANCE OF THE EARTH

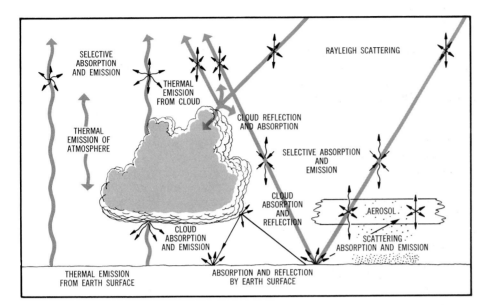

The diagram indicates the major components in the global radiation balance. The albedo, or reflectivity, is composed of the radiation reflected from the ground, clouds, aerosols, and other materials that might scatter incoming solar radiation.

reflectivity, in the unlikely event that all clouds were so affected, would have about the same effect as a 5 percent reduction in cloud amount.

Budyko, at Leningrad, and Sellers, at the University of Arizona, have taken this energy calculation one step further, arguing that a decrease of only 1.6 to 2.0 percent in the solar radiation available to the earth would lead to an unstable condition in which continental snow cover would advance all the way to the equator, with the albedo raised by the greater snow cover to the point where the oceans would eventually freeze. Lest this rather frightening calculation be taken too seriously, it should be mentioned that there is no evidence that a mechanism for a change of as much as 1.5 percent actually exists, or ever has in the history of the earth. The model nevertheless illustrates the delicacy of our planet's thermal balance.

Aerosols — The aerosols that fill the atmosphere — natural haze, dust, smoke, smog, and so on — probably play an important role in the radiation balance of the earth, but this is one of the great uncertainties in the theory of how the atmosphere behaves. Aerosols in cloudless air probably increase the albedo to some extent, and they absorb sunlight themselves. Also, as we have noted, they can change the reflectivity of clouds. We are quite certain that variations in the solar radiation absorbed by the earth's atmosphere and surface, due to changes in turbidity or total aerosol content of the atmosphere, are significant. Furthermore, as will be noted below, aerosols in the atmosphere can be greatly affected by man and volcanic activity.

Factors Affecting Loss of Terrestrial Heat — On the other side of the ledger by which we keep track of the amount of heat into and out of the atmosphere-ocean heat engine is the loss to space of terrestrial heat by infrared radiation. Over a period of a year or so, the amount of radiation lost by infrared radiation must almost exactly balance the amount of solar radiation absorbed by the earth and its atmosphere. If this did not happen, the earth would rapidly heat or cool.

As a general principle, any substance in the atmosphere that absorbs infrared radiation will slow the cooling of the surface. The reason for this is that the energy radiated from the surface is absorbed by the absorbing substance in the atmosphere, thus heating the atmosphere which in turn radiates back toward the ground. In effect, an absorbing layer acts as a radiation blanket, and its presence will result in a higher surface temperature.

An auxiliary effect of this absorbing blanket will be an increase in the stability of the lower part of the atmosphere, between the surface and the absorbing layer. This increase in stability will reduce convection in the lower layers. The ability of the atmosphere to stir itself by convection is a principal source of cumulus clouds, so that a decrease in convection would also decrease precipitation.

Infrared Absorbers — There are two main classes of infrared absorbers in the atmosphere: trace gases (water vapor and carbon dioxide (CO_2) being the most important in the lower atmosphere) and aerosols of all kinds, including clouds. Various estimates have been made of the effect of increasing CO_2 in the atmosphere, since man has in fact been able to raise the total amount through burning fossil fuels. Since 1900, the amount of CO_2 has increased an average of 10 to 15 percent, and this trend has usually been cited to account for the observed rise in the average surface temperature of 0.2° centigrade up to 1940. The theoretical calculations of Manabe and Weatherald indicate that a doubling of the CO_2 content in the atmosphere would have the effect of raising the temperature of the atmosphere (whose relative humidity is assumed to be fixed) by about 2° centigrade, an appreciable change.

The role of aerosols in the radiative balance cannot be calculated with anything like the certainty of that for carbon dioxide. Various estimates have been made of the effect of aerosols, with conflicting results. The principal effects of aerosols are to increase the scattering of sunlight in the atmosphere and also to absorb sunlight, the two effects being about equal. Thus, Robinson, in England, reports an average decrease of 25 percent in the amount of sunlight reaching the surface due to aerosols, and presumably at least half of this amount went into heating the atmosphere. In clear air, such as that found in the polar regions, the effect of aerosols is much less, but in the tropical zone the turbidity of the atmosphere, probably due primarily to natural haze from vegetation, is high all the time.

Man-Made Aerosols — Aerosols should be taken into account in any calculation of the radiative balance of the earth-atmosphere system, but the fact is that we do not yet know how to do this with certainty. Furthermore, there is the practical question of how man-made aerosols compete with natural aerosols.

The haze observed in many parts of the world far from industrial sources originates chiefly in the organic material produced by vegetation, with large contributions from sea salt from the ocean and dust blown from dry ground. At times, volcanic activity in the tropics produces a worldwide increase of the aerosol content of the high atmosphere. It is estimated by Budyko, for example, that the solar radiation reaching the ground after the 1963 eruption of Mt. Agung, in Bali, was reduced in the Soviet Union by about 5 percent, a significant attenuation whose total effect on the global radiation balance is not clear.

In contrast to these natural aerosols, man has overwhelmed nature in

certain parts of the world where industrial smog and smoke have an evident effect on the clarity of the atmosphere. Observations in a few cities, such as Washington, D. C., and Uccle, Belgium, have documented the increase in turbidity and the decrease in solar radiation reaching the surface over the past few decades, even though progress has been made in the United States and Europe in reducing the production of smoke from coalburning heat sources.

An additional complication, a possible effect of man-made contaminants in the atmosphere, is the observed reduction of the albedo of clouds due to contaminants absorbed in cloud droplets. This effect must also be taken into account in a complete calculation of the radiation budget and man's effects on it.

Needed Scientific Activity

In view of the uncertainties in the many factors involved in the radiation balance of the earth, and the possibility that man is significantly affecting the radiation balance by his introduction of aerosols and his increase in the CO_2 content, it is necessary to intensify our studies of the effects of these factors on the climate.

Models — The key to such studies is the development of adequate climatological models on which experiments can be run. One would, for example, study the change in the average temperature in various regions of the globe for certain changes in the optical characteristics of the atmosphere resulting from aerosols and carbon dioxide. There are many feedbacks in this system, and the model should take as many as possible into account. A major feedback, already referred to, is that due to changing ice and snow cover in the polar regions; another is due to change of cloud cover; the two probably react in the opposite direction to a change in average temperature.

Since the oceans are important in the long-term heat balance of the system, a climatic model must certainly include oceanic circulations, even though they are largely secondary to atmospheric circulations in the sense that the atmosphere drives the surface currents. Progress in modeling oceanic circulation has been made in a number of places, notably the Geophysical Fluid Dynamics Laboratory of NOAA, NCAR, Florida State University, and The RAND Corporation. The challenge, eventually, will be to combine the atmospheric and oceanic circulations in one model.

Monitoring — It is not sufficient to develop a theory without being aware of changes actually taking place in the real atmosphere. For this reason it will be necessary to continue to monitor the climate, as is being done in a number of stations throughout the world. In addition to the usual parameters of temperature, wind, and precipitation, the composition of the atmosphere and its turbidity need to be monitored better than they are now. This is not a simple task, since quantitative measurements of trace gases require fairly elaborate techniques, while measurements that describe the aerosol content of the atmosphere should provide information on the optical properties of these aerosols as well as their concentration. It is necessary to know how these aerosols affect incoming solar radiation and outgoing infrared radiation. This has not been done adequately, except on a few occasions using special equipment.

Satellites have been useful in many ways in obtaining new information about the global atmosphere, and they can contribute significantly to the monitoring task. Except for cloud cover, however, observations to date have not been sufficiently quantitative. Cloud cover can and should be monitored by satellites. Satellites can also monitor snow and ice cover, although there is a problem during the polar night when pictures cannot be taken in the usual manner. This situation is improving rapidly, since the High Resolution Infrared Radiometers, of the type used on the Nimbus-4 and ITOS-1 satellites, can obtain pictures by day or night and even provide an indication of the heights of cloud tops. Nimbus-F, scheduled for launching by the National Aeronautics and Space Administration (NASA) in 1974, may carry an absolutely calibrated radiation experiment that could mark the beginning of direct quantitative measures of the total heat budget of the earth. Measurements of lower atmospheric composition, or pollution, from satellites have been proposed, but at this time they seem to be further in the future. Ozone, a trace gas found mostly in the stratosphere and upper troposphere, has been measured, but this component may be of minor concern in the present context.

A Perspective on Man-Made Pollution — The possible change in the radiative characteristics of the upper atmosphere due to rockets can probably be dismissed, because even extreme assumptions about numbers of Saturn-class rockets being launched lead to negligible changes. The contribution of jets to water vapor and aerosols in the stratosphere may also be trivial. Recent studies by the National Academy of Sciences, by Manabe and Weatherald, and by others strongly suggest that it is. Contrails are likely to have a climatic influence only when they trigger the formation of extensive bands of cirrus cloud

which mature, with the passage of time, to a sufficient optical depth in the infrared to produce either significant blanketing or reduction of incoming visible solar radiation.

One cannot say for certain that, on the occasions when jet-airplane contrails produce cirrus clouds, the cirrus clouds would not have formed naturally. But there are many occasions, some lasting for several days, when major portions of the United States are crisscrossed by jet-airplane contrails that do not dissipate, but instead spread out until major fractions of the sky are covered by thin cirrus of sufficient intensity to be of radiative significance. What needs to be done is to conduct quantitative studies, in selected areas of the earth, of the radiative losses to space that occur with and without cirrus clouds. Then there needs to be a rather careful examination of the degree to which these cirrus can be artificially triggered. The stability of the large-scale circulation is an extremely important matter. We know that large trough developments occur in the 300-millibar circulation, particularly in the late winter and spring seasons, in a way that is difficult if not impossible to predict. It is quite conceivable that cirrus cloud formations at high latitudes over warm sources, as over the Gulf of Alaska, may be important in this regard.

The atmosphere-ocean system depends on the heat available to run it, and this is the result of a delicate bal-

ance between heat received from the sun and re-radiated to space. There are ways to disturb this balance, and the ice ages of the past are proof that nature sometimes does, in fact, alter it. Man might do the same, and this possibility deserves the most careful study. There has been much hand-waving of late by "prophets of doom." While virtually none of these people is a scientist, atmospheric scientists have not been able to make convincing rebuttals so far.

The earth actually has a remarkably stable life-support system, and man is unlikely to be able to move it far from its equilibrium. To mention a few examples: Aerosols, of the sort that man or nature creates, only remain in the atmosphere for about a week on the average. Thus, industrial pollution in the United States hardly has time to reach Europe before it is washed from the air. Furthermore, natural sources of contamination from vegetation, volcanoes, the oceans, and the deserts still far outweigh all of man's contributions, taken on a global scale. With respect to the balance built into our highly variable clouds, an increase in mean temperature would probably cause an increase in moisture and cloudiness, which in turn would reflect more solar radiation back to space. Such a negative feedback, forcing the situation back to equilibrium, is only one of several mechanisms that we are beginning to identify in the complex atmosphere-ocean system.

Climatic Change and the Effects of Civilization

A worldwide climatic change has been taking place for the past decade or two. Its reality has been established by scientists of the United States, the Soviet Union, and England.

The climatic amelioration that took

place between the late 1800's and 1940 has ended, and the mean temperature of the earth appears to have fallen since the middle of the present century. (See Figure III-8) Some dramatic environmental changes have followed — e.g., the return of mid-summer frosts in the upper Midwest,

record cold autumns in Ohio, rising lake levels in East Africa, and massive encroachment of sea-ice on the north shore of Iceland. With this change, the circulation patterns of the atmosphere also appear to have changed. Any such changes on an earth that is straining its capacity to

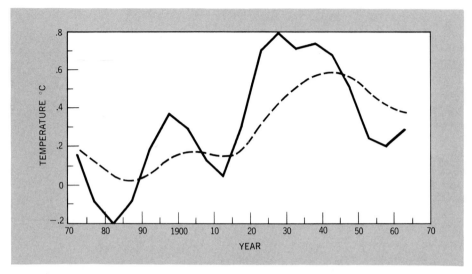

Figure III–8 — OBSERVED LAGGED TEMPERATURE
VARIATION OF THE NORTHERN HEMISPHERE

The observed temperature variation of the northern hemisphere has here been corrected (see solid line) for the time lag of the ocean-atmosphere-soil system and the system's response to factors that cause the variation of temperature. A half-response-time of ten years was used. The broken line is the smoothed curve of Figure III–4 repeated for comparison.

feed the human population are significant.

The theory of climate is so poorly developed that we cannot predict accurately whether the climatic trend will continue, or how the distribution of rainfall and frost will change if it does. Clearly this knowledge is a national and international need of high priority. Clearly, too, we must know whether any or all of the recent fluctuation in climate is man-made, and whether it can be man-controlled. Lacking an adequate theoretical basis for prediction, we can only look to the past to see what kinds of changes are possible, with what rapidity they may occur, and what the causal factors might have been.

Basic Balances

Although numerical models of the atmospheric circulation are still too crude to simulate the climatic pattern within an error small enough to be less than the occasional ecologically significant variations, certain basic

relations may be identified that can yield information on some of the factors important to climatic change.

Ultimately the sun drives the atmosphere. The fact that we have water in gaseous, liquid, and solid states in the proportions we do is dependent on our distance from the sun and the fraction of the sunlight that the earth absorbs. In the long run, there must be the same amount of heat re-radiated to space from the atmosphere as is absorbed by the earth.

The receipt of solar radiation occurs on the cross-sectional area of the earth, but re-radiation takes place from four times as large an area — i.e., the entire area of the globe. Thus,

$$S\pi R^2 (1 - a) = 4\pi R^2 I_t$$
where S is the solar constant,
R is the radius of the earth,
a is the albedo, or "reflectivity," of the earth,
and I_t is the mean outward infrared radiation flux from the earth to space.

Satellite data show that I_t is fairly uniform over the earth, on the annual average, and that the albedo of the earth is such that the above equation is approximately balanced. The outward radiation measured from space is smaller on the average than that emitted by the earth's surface, so that

$$S (1 - a) = 4 \overline{(\epsilon\sigma T_o^4 - \Delta I)}$$
where ϵ is the emissivity of the earth's surface,
σ is the Stefan-Boltzman constant,
T_o is the surface temperature of the earth,
ΔI is the difference between the heat radiated upward by the earth's surface and that leaving the top of the atmosphere for space — the "greenhouse effect,"
and the overbar on $\epsilon\sigma T_o^4$ indicates an average over the whole surface of the globe.

The above equation is crude, but it provides an insight into the factors that might affect the general temperature state of the earth. Clearly, fluctuations in solar intensity, the fraction of incoming solar radiation that is "reflected" or scattered away before reaching the ground, and the "greenhouse effect" are the major causes of variation in the mean temperature of the earth. A change of one or 2 percent in any one of these variables is enough to produce a significant climatic change, yet none of them is known with this accuracy except perhaps the solar intensity.

Albedo — The temperature of the earth is most sensitively dependent on the albedo of the earth-atmosphere system — an increase of a few percent would cool the earth to ice-age temperatures. This variable — reflectivity — can be measured by meteorological satellites, but not yet with sufficient accuracy. The albedo is also a variable that can be changed by human activity, primarily by changes in the transparency of the atmosphere resulting from particulate pollution. According to Angstrom, a 7 percent increase in the turbidity of the atmosphere will produce a one percent change in albedo and a 1°-centigrade change in world mean temperature.

The "Greenhouse Effect" — The other variable that can be changed by human activity is the "greenhouse effect." This depends on such things as the water-vapor content of the air, dustiness, cloudiness, and, especially, the carbon dioxide content. The carbon dioxide content of the atmosphere has risen 11 percent or so in the past century, and it is widely believed that the rise is due to human activity in the burning of fossil fuels and greater exposure of soil humus and the like to oxidation. (See Figure III-9)

In times past, changes in vegetation and land distribution and elevation affected the earth's albedo, as did short-time changes in cloud and snow cover. Volcanic activity, then as now, produced a variable input of particulates to the atmosphere, as did blowing dust from desert areas — which in turn affected the albedo. (See Figure III-10) In earlier times, the distribution of land and sea, volcanic activity, the elevation of the land and nature of the biota probably affected the magnitude of the greenhouse effect. The sun's intensity may also have varied, though there is no evidence. In addition, there are complex feedback mechanisms, such as additional water vapor in the air at higher temperatures, that increase the greenhouse effect which in turn increases the water-vapor content still more. While increased volcanic activity makes the atmosphere more turbid and thus tends to depress the temperature, it may also contribute to the greenhouse effect and thus tend in part to counteract the temperature effect. The complete equation for relating these effects is not known, but it appears that the effect of turbidity on the greenhouse effect is only about 10 percent of its effect on the albedo.

We do know, however, that there is something new under the sun — a population of humans sufficiently numerous to modify the whole albedo of the earth and the magnitude of the greenhouse effect through their sheer

Figure III–9 — LAGGED TEMPERATURE CURVE FOR THE NORTHERN HEMISPHERE CORRECTED FOR CO_2

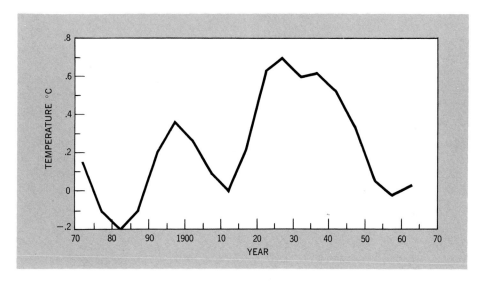

In this graph, the mean observed temperature variation for the northern hemisphere has been adjusted for the time lag shown in Figure III–8 and for the warming effect of carbon dioxide (CO_2). It can be seen that the increase of variation due to the "greenhouse effect" of CO_2 is small compared with the variation of temperature corrected for system lag. (Compare values of Figures III–8 with III–9) Only about 3 percent of the variance can be explained by the presence of CO_2.

Figure III–10 — LAGGED TEMPERATURE CURVE FOR THE NORTHERN HEMISPHERE CORRECTED FOR CO_2 AND DUST

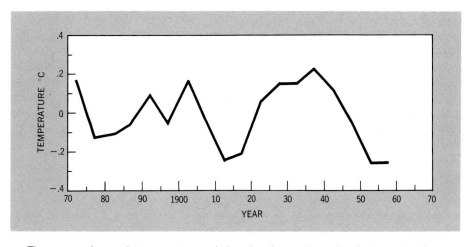

The mean observed temperature variation for the northern hemisphere has here been adjusted for the time lag of the system, the warming effect of CO_2, and the effect of both stratospheric (volcanic) and tropospheric dust. The dust effect explains 80% of the variance of the adjusted temperature, with 63% due to stratospheric and 17% due to tropospheric dust. The resulting curve shows what temperatures would be observed under conditions of direct solar radiation with cloudless skies, although some residual errors remain. (Compare Figures III–4, 8, and 9)

numbers and control of energy. Thus man can, and probably has, modified the climate of the earth.

The Climates of the Past Century

From late in the nineteenth century until the middle of the twentieth, the mean temperature of the earth rose. During this time the carbon dioxide content of the atmosphere rose enough to explain the global temperature rise — apparently the first global climatic modification due to man. At the same time, local production of particulate pollution was starting to increase rapidly due to mechanization and industrialization. By the middle of the twentieth century, these trends — amplified by a general population explosion and a renewal of volcanic activity — increased the worldwide particulate load of the atmosphere to the point where the effect of these particulates on the global albedo more than compensated for the carbon dioxide increase and world temperatures began to fall.

The total magnitude of these changes in world or hemispheric mean temperature is not impressive — a fraction of a degree. However, the difference between glacial and non-glacial climates is only a few degrees on the worldwide average.

Actually, it is not the mean temperature of the earth that is important, but rather the circulation pattern of the atmosphere. This is strongly dependent on the temperature difference from the tropics to the poles. The same man-modifiable factors that affect the mean temperature of the globe-albedo and carbon dioxide — even if applied uniformly over the globe — will have the effect of changing the meridional temperature gradient and thus the circulation pattern and resultant weather pattern. It is this change of pattern that is of prime concern. Dzeerdzeerski in the Soviet Union, Kutzbach in the United States,

and Lamb in England have all produced different kinds of evidence that the circulation patterns have changed in the past two decades. In turn, the local climates show change — some regions wetter, some drier, some colder, some warmer — though some remain unchanged.

The most striking changes have been where the effects of the change are cumulative, such as the slightly changed balance between evaporation and precipitation in East Africa which has caused the level of great lakes such as Victoria to rise markedly. Another case is the balance between ice wastage and production that has changed enough in the last decade to bring drift-ice to the Icelandic shores to an extent unknown for a century. It would be most useful to know what the cumulative ecological effect of these local or regional changes might be. Since biological selection in response to environmental changes usually requires a number of generations to show the total effect of the change, it is probably too soon to know the total ecological impact of the present change. Here we can only look to the past to see what is possible.

The Lesson of History

The advent of radiocarbon dating has given a new dimension to the study of the variety of paleobotany known as palynology. It is now possible to put an absolute time-scale on the record of environmental change contained in the pollen assemblages recovered from bogs and lake sediments. In the context of the present discussion, the most startling result is the rapidity with which major environmental changes have taken place.

If we examine the most carefully studied and best-dated pollen profiles, we find that the pollen frequencies often show a quasi-exponential change from, for example, an assemblage that might indicate boreal forest to an assemblage typical of mixed hard-

woods. Calling the time required for half the change to occur the *half-life* of the transition, it appears that such major changes in vegetation may have half-lives of a couple of centuries or less. (Greater specificity must await analyses with much finer time-resolution than has been generally used.) Since the plants integrate the climate, the half-life of the climatic change must be shorter still!

With the agricultural land use of the world still reflecting the climatic pattern almost as closely as the native vegetation did, a major shift in climatic pattern within a century could be disastrous. Unlike the past, migration into open lands is not possible: there are none, and forcible acquisition of agricultural land with a favorable climate is not acceptable. Only in a few nations would a combination of regional variety and advanced technology allow an accommodation to a major climatic change.

What We Need To Know

Faced with the possibility that we are well into a climatic change of appreciable magnitude, of man's making, there appear a number of questions to which answers are urgently needed.

Since in the past there have been rapid changes in climate due to natural causes, such as major changes in volcanic activity, what is the probability of increased volcanism in the next few decades adding to the pollution of the atmosphere made by man and thus speeding up the present climatic change?

How far will the present climatic change go? It appears that the change from a glacial climate to a nonglacial climate occurred with great rapidity. Would the opposite change occur as fast? What chance is there, on a relatively short time-scale, to control the sources of turbidity?

If we have reverted to the climate characteristic of the early 1800's, what displacements in the world agricultural pattern will occur in the next decade?

The answers to these and a host of related questions will require a much more sophisticated knowledge of climate and the man-environment system than we now possess. Time is short and the challenge to science is clear.

Environmental Change in Arid America

One of the great controversies in ice-age paleoecology is how to explain the virtually simultaneous coast-to-coast extinction of large mammals in North America around 11,000 years ago. We know, for example, that elephants once existed even in the presently arid lands of the West. Paleontologists have commonly recovered the bones of *Mammuthus columbi* in arid America, along with bones of other extinct large mammals, including horses, camels of two extinct genera, extinct bison, and ground sloth.

Did the climate change suddenly? Fossil elephants and the like inevitably provoke visions of a wetter climate and a more productive ecosystem than today's arid land will support. But the fossil-pollen record has indicated otherwise.

Fossil Pollen and Other Forms of Evidence

The technique of fossil-pollen analysis has proved of unique value in determining what the vegetation and, by implication, the primary productivity of arid America must have been during the period when this region, along with the rest of the continent, supported large numbers of native large mammals.

Pollen is a very popular fossil because it is produced in quantity by certain plants and, thanks to its acid-resistant outer wall or shell, is preserved in many types of sediments. Unlike fossils of larger size, pollen is usually dispersed evenly throughout a deposit rather than aggregated in one or a few distinct beds. Under relatively uniform sedimentation, as determined by closely spaced radiocarbon dates, one can estimate the intensity of the local pollen rain through time, as Davis has done in a study of vegetation history at Rogers Lake, Connecticut. Different vegetation zones shed different amounts of pollen — a tundra much less than a forest, for example. This is revealed by the fossil pollen extracted through hydrofluoric-acid treatment of lake muds.

In many deposits, especially in arid lands, absolute values cannot be estimated. The relative amounts of the dominant pollen types in a deposit can be compared with the pollen content of sediments presently being deposited in areas of natural vegetation. Literal interpretation of the relative pollen percentage cannot be made — i.e., 10 percent pine pollen does not mean that 10 percent of the trees in the stand were pines. But the pollen spectrum of all types identified in a fossil count *can* be matched, through computer programs or simple direct comparison, with the pollen rain of modern natural communities. This method works especially well in western United States, where there are extensive areas of relatively undisturbed vegetation. In this way, any major or increasing number of minor changes in vegetation through time can be detected.

As opportunity allows, the fossil-pollen record can be compared with other forms of evidence. Macrofossil remains of plants, including seeds and leaves, are found in certain lake muds. They have been reported in remarkable abundance in ancient wood-rat middens of certain desert regions by Wells. The oldest rat's nests studied by Wells are over 30,000 years in age, essentially older than can be determined by the radiocarbon method.

The Climatic Record of Western America

The fossil record of radiocarbon-dated deposits covering the last 30,000 years in western America indicates an initial cool, dry period becoming colder and wetter by 20,000 to 16,000 years ago. At this time, there were ponderosa-pine parkland and pinyon-juniper woodland at elevations about 3,300 feet below their present lower limits on western mountains. The fate of prairie, both short and tall grassland, is unknown. The present prairie region was occupied by spruce in the north and pine in the south. This suggests that arid America, like other regions, was affected by the late Pleistocene cooling associated with ice advance over Canada.

Around 12,000 years ago the climate changed rather rapidly, becoming warmer and drier, until conditions were only slightly cooler and wetter than now. Modern vegetation zones have occupied their present positions, with minor fluctuations, continuously for the last 8,000 years.

Thus, the record shows that the environment of western America inhabited by mammoth, camels, native horses, and bison at the time of their extinction 11,000 years ago was not vastly different from what we know at present. Why, then, did the animals die? Fossil pollen and other evidence from the radiocarbon dating of extinct Pleistocene faunas seem to indicate that no environmental defects will explain this phenomenon. One must look elsewhere. And the only new variable in the American ecosystem of the late-glacial period is the arrival of skilled Stone Age hunters. These events of thousands of years ago have major implications for modern-day range management.

Implications for Modern Range Management

In part, the concept of the West as a "desert" is based on the fact that grass production is indeed quite low. But the dominant woody plants found across the one million square miles of western America — the creosote bush, sagebrush, cactus, and mesquite — do yield large amounts of plant dry-matter annually. Primary productivity data on these western shrub communities are less abundant than one might wish. Nevertheless, such data as do exist indicate that shrub communities in southern Arizona may yield 1,400 kilograms per hectare a year, considerably more than adjacent grassland under the same climate (12 inches of precipitation annually).

Observers have overlooked or written off this annual production, perhaps because it is often avoided by domestic livestock. Indeed, fifty years of range management in the West has been aimed at destroying the woody plants to make way for forage more palatable to cattle. The effort has been singularly futile and should be abandoned.

The Future of Western Meat-Production — The dilemma faced by the range industry in arid America is that beef can be produced faster, more efficiently, and at less expense in the southeast or in feedlots. If this fact is accepted, one can make a case for keeping large areas of arid America as they are, at least until much more is known about primary production of the natural communities and until some value for Western scenery can be agreed upon. Some large, wealthy ranchers have already recognized this and have disposed of their cattle. More should be encouraged to do so. If a meat-producing industry is to be established in the marginal cattle lands in the West, it should be based on new domestic species, animals that are better adapted to arid environments than cattle and that are adapted for efficient browsing rather than grazing.

Potential New Domesticates — One obvious source for potential new domesticates is Africa, where arid ranges that barely sustain cattle are supporting thrifty herds of wildebeest, kongoni, zebra, giraffe, and kudu. In size and general ecology, the African species bear at least general resemblance to the extinct Pleistocene fauna of the Americas. They did not invade the New World during the ice ages because they failed to range far enough north to be able to cross the Bering Bridge, the only natural method of intercontinental exchange open to large herbivores. Many natural faunal exchanges of arctic-adapted herbivores did occur over the Bering Bridge in the Pleistocene. Some, but not all, of the invaders re-adapted to warmer climates of the lower latitudes.

In summary: (a) Studies of fossil pollen and other evidence of the last 30,000 years reveal no environmental defects that might explain the extinction of many species of native New World large mammals 11,000 years ago. (b) The only known environmental upset at the time of large animal extinction was the arrival of Early Man. (c) The cattle industry of western America is marginal, being maintained for reasons of its mystique, not for its economics. (d) If a more productive use of the western range is desirable, experiments with other species of large mammals should be begun now, as indeed they have been on certain ranches in Texas, New Mexico, Mexico, and Brazil.

PART IV

DYNAMICS OF THE
ATMOSPHERE-OCEAN
SYSTEM

1. OCEANIC CIRCULATION AND OCEAN-ATMOSPHERE INTERACTIONS

Oceanic Circulation and the Role of the Atmosphere

The ocean circulation is one of the primary factors in the heat budget of the world. The circulation is important not only internally to the ocean but also to the overlying atmosphere and, indeed, to the climate of the entire earth. Together the sea and the air make a huge thermal engine, and it is not possible to understand either without having some comprehension of the other. Any studies of ocean circulation must inevitably involve this coupling with the atmosphere.

The Present State of Understanding

Studies of ocean circulation have progressed a long way in the past fifty years. Measurements of the characteristics of the ocean at great depths have produced at least a general sense of the major deep circulations. And extensive theoretical developments over the same period have given us some glimmering as to why the circulations are what they appear to be.

Ocean Variability — Both the observational and theoretical studies have dealt mostly with a steady-state ocean or the long-term mean of an ocean. (See Figure IV-1) During the past few years, however, some data have been accumulated that allow us to speculate a bit about the variability of the ocean. Like mean circulation, variability is closely coupled to the atmosphere, and variations in ocean circulation may lead to, or stem from, variations in atmospheric phenomena. For example, one of the critical parts

Figure IV–1 — SEA-SURFACE TEMPERATURE

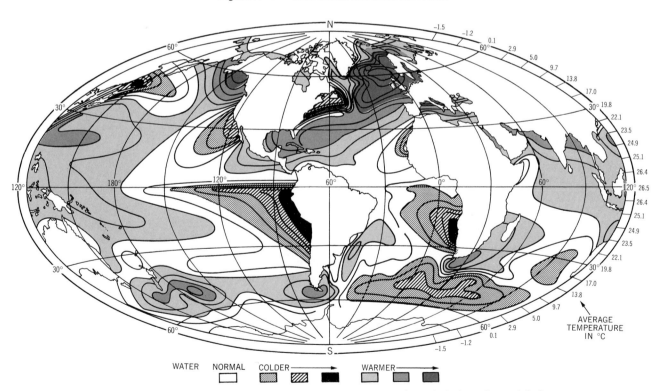

The figure shows sea-surface temperatures represented as deviations from global average values of the sea-surface temperature. The global average value for each 5° latitude band is marked at the right-hand edge of the world map. Note the extent of the cold equatorial water in the Pacific (from the coast of South America westward halfway across the Pacific) and the warm water west and north of the United Kingdom.

of the heat engine is the Norwegian Sea, an area where warm saline surface water from the Gulf Stream is cooled by contact with the atmosphere, made dense, and returned to the open Atlantic as dense deep water in such quantity as to create a recognizable subsurface layer extending throughout the Atlantic, Antarctic, Indian, and Pacific oceans. In this case, the power to drive this thermohaline engine comes from heat exchange with the atmosphere.

Warming of the surface waters in low latitudes and cooling in high latitudes creates easily recognizable effects on the circulation of the ocean. The effect of this exchange on the atmosphere is equally important, not just locally — in that the coast of Norway remains ice-free — but also in the larger sense of general effects on the world atmospheric climate. The budget of this heat exchange and the details of its various expenditures must be learned if the earth's climate is to be understood. Seasonal and nonseasonal variations of the heat exchange, and their causes and effects, must be studied.

The Gulf Stream is both a cause and an effect of this exchange. It would exist in any case as a consequence of the wind-driven circulation in the trade-wind and westerlies areas, as do, in a weaker form, its South Atlantic, North Pacific, and South Pacific counterparts. (The heat and water sink of the far North Atlantic requires a vaster flow in the Gulf Stream than in the other western boundary currents.) But variations in the strength of the Gulf Stream may be either causes or consequences of variations in heat exchange in the Norwegian Sea. Although the effects of these variations may be severely damped by the time the waters enter the immense reservoir of the abyssal ocean, there is no certainty that their effects on the far reaches of the ocean are negligible.

Some of the most interesting variations yet observed in the ocean are in the North Pacific, where bodies of surface water thousands of miles in diameter remain warmer or colder than their seasonal means for periods ranging from three months to over a year. Such features seem to be characteristic of the North Pacific. Thus, a typical map of surface temperature is not one that is very near the norm everywhere, with many small highs and lows; instead, the whole North Pacific may consist of three to five large areas of deviant temperature. Such features have been noted only in the past fifteen years. They are beginning to receive the attention of meteorologists, as well as oceanographers, since their consequences for the atmospheric climate cannot be discounted in attempting to understand and predict the world's weather.

Prediction — Our present understanding of the ocean is barely sufficient to account for the major circulations in a general way. Some preliminary attempts are now being made to predict specific features of ocean behavior, most of them being based on the persistence of deviations from the mean. That is, if an area shows an abnormally high surface temperature in one month, this anomaly is apt to endure or persist for several months more and to diminish to the norm slowly. Strictly speaking, this is not prediction but merely the extrapolation of a present feature. More ambitious predictions are being contemplated, but they are still in very early stages.

Advances in Instrumentation

Devices to measure ocean currents have improved greatly over the past ten years. They have been used to monitor changes in position of the Gulf Stream, to measure its deep flow, and to investigate some of the principal inferences about deep circulation in the Pacific and Atlantic oceans. Considerable improvement has also been achieved in instruments for measuring water characteristics.

Moored buoys of various kinds have been developed for deep-water use within the past decade. They are used for monitoring certain characteristics of the ocean and atmosphere, including wind, air, and sea temperature, subsurface temperature, waves, and, possibly, water velocity. These measurements can either be recorded and recovered by vessels or transmitted immediately by radio to appropriate shore bases.

The future may see interrogation and retransmission of signals by satellite. The advantages of such monitoring stations would include relatively inexpensive operation (compared to weather ships) and the ability to gather data from regions that are outside normal shipping lanes but may be extremely pertinent to ocean and weather studies.

Deficiencies in the Data Base

The data base for study of the ocean consists of measurements of water characteristics in various locations and depths at different times and measurements of currents, waves, tides, and ocean depths. In some areas and some seasons, this data base is adequate for a long-term mean to be established; it is not continuous enough in time, however, to allow for adequate study of variations from the long-term mean. In other areas and seasons, the data base barely exists. High-latitude areas in winter have hardly been explored. Our knowledge of the deep arctic is extremely limited. Some few winter data are available from the antarctic region. The deeper parts of the ocean may be better represented in the present data base than the surface parts, since the deeper parts show less time-variation than the upper layers.

Other parts of the data base involved in investigating ocean circulation include atmospheric-pressure observations and wind measurements, air temperature and the like. These, too, are limited both in time and space. Major shipping lanes are fairly well measured in many seasons. Among the more systematically measured areas are the North Sea, the California Current system, and the Kuroshio Current. But data from the areas that ships avoid, either because of bad weather conditions or because they do not represent profitable ship routes, are generally sparse. Not only is the arctic poorly represented even with atmospheric information, but also the South Pacific and large parts of the South Atlantic. Very few areas in the world are represented by a data base sufficient to allow for seasonal and nonseasonal variations. Numerical models of the ocean are also still in an early stage of development.

What is Needed

A proper understanding of air-sea interchange and of deep flow are among the most urgent tasks of oceanic circulation research. We need to determine which data are critical, obtain them, and use them in mathematical modeling of the ocean. Topics of practical importance to man, requiring urgent study, include fisheries production in the world ocean; this is related to ocean circulation, since the latter controls the availability of plant nutrients.

Better understanding of the Arctic Ocean is crucial to proper evaluation of its possibilities as a commercial route for surface vessels or submarines. Better knowledge of the deep circulation and the rates of exchange of ocean water — both from the surface to the bottom and from the deeper parts of one ocean to the deeper parts of another — is particularly important in the light of new concerns over contamination and pollution. While the ocean can act as a reservoir to absorb, contain, and reduce much of the effluent now being produced, it is not of infinite capacity nor can it contain materials indefinitely without bringing them back onto the surface.

Time-Scale — It is not possible to lay out a time-scale for many of the things that must be investigated. For the problem of describing the mean ocean, another ten or fifteen years might be sufficient. In that period of time, it would be feasible to collect the additional data needed without substantially expanding the facilities. In order to accomplish this, however, the various institutions capable of carrying out the requisite measurements would have to devote a greater part of their time to this subject — and this may not be desirable.

Developing a data base to study the time-variable ocean is a different sort of problem. Since our understanding of the nature of time-variations is still in a primitive stage, we must first learn how to observe the phenomena and then begin a systematic series of observations in the appropriate places. Progress has been made in learning how to do this from buoy deployments in the Pacific and Atlantic oceans. These are preliminary, however, and must be greatly augmented before we can really understand even the scale, much less the nature, of the anomalies being observed. Understanding of this kind usually advances step by step from one plateau to another, but the steps are highly irregular both as to height and duration, and a feasible timescale cannot be estimated.

Necessary Activity — On the one hand, the scale of the problems discussed here suggests large-scale, large-area, heavily instrumented research carried out by teams of investigators. On the other, the history of ocean circulation research has shown that some of the greatest contributions were made by individuals — e.g., Ekman transport, Stommel's westward intensification, Sverdrup transport. A balance is required between large-scale programs comparable to the space program and individual small-scale projects.

One of the first needs is to train people able to work on problems of both the ocean and the atmosphere. The two fields have been far too separated in most cases. People trained in mathematics and physics are available, but the average student finds it difficult to acquire a working background in both the oceanic and atmospheric environment; indeed, many people trained in physics and mathematics have limited backgrounds in either environment, relying on theory without adequate knowledge of the structure of the two systems.

On Predicting Ocean Circulation

Nonspecialists tend to think of ocean circulation systems as being primarily a matter of geographical exploration. We are not going to discover many new undercurrents, however. Nor will simple-minded "monitoring" of ocean currents teach us much. Twenty years of looking for — and not finding — relations between changes in patterns of applied wind stress and the total transports of currents like the Gulf Stream where it passes through the Florida Straits warn us that the chain of cause and effect in the ocean is rather complicated and that the primary problem is to make more profound our understanding of the ocean as a hydrodynamical phenomenon.

What We Know — and Don't Know

It has been pointed out that there has been a really effective growth of understanding of ocean surface waves only in the last decade. And ocean surface waves are probably the most easily observable and dynamically linear of ocean phenomena. Internal waves and oceanic turbulence are not so easily observable, and treatments of these phenomena are a thin tissue of preliminary theory largely unsupported by observation. Studies limited to rather high-frequency phenomena actually represent the kind most nearly duplicable in the laboratory.

There is a small body of theory concerning oceanic circulation, but it deals only with the climatological mean circulation. The role of medium-scale eddy processes in ocean circulation is completely unknown, although current measurements indicate that they can be very important — as, for example, they are in the general circulation of the atmosphere. A two-pronged development of mathematical modeling and fairly elaborate field investigation is going to be necessary to develop much further our understanding of the hydrodynamical interaction of these eddies and the mean circulation. (A working group of the Scientific Committee on Ocean Research of the International Council of Scientific Unions recommended a "Mid-Ocean Dynamics Experiment" (MODE).) Considering the three-dimensional detail of velocity structure and its development in time that such a measurement program will entail, it seems clear that a major input from the engineering community will be needed.)

Technological Limitations

Oceanography is not presently competent technologically to tackle the tasks of measurement that are necessary in trying to unravel the dynamical features of large-scale motions. The difficulty is simply that one needs to map variables like velocity rather densely in large volumes (perhaps 2 miles deep and 300 miles on a horizontal side) for rather long periods (perhaps a year) with sufficient accuracy that reliable statistics can be calculated for complicated functions like triple correlation products. Many different modes of motion are occurring simultaneously, and we need to be able to separate one mode from another in order to compute interactions. Therefore, a great variety of arrays of sensors need to be arranged in different configurations and on different scales for gathering the kind of data required from the ocean. Some test portions of the ocean will need to be heavily instrumented in a manner more sophisticated than present small-scale observational operations can achieve. It is safe to say that solutions of problems of internal waves, the general circulation and eddy processes, and such important local processes as coastal upwelling are simply going to have to wait until major new instrumental arrays become available.

There is a limit beyond which inferior technique cannot go. It needs to be made very clear what a helpless feeling it is to be on a slow-moving ship, with a few traditional measuring techniques like water bottles and pingers on hand, trying to keep track of a variable phenomenon like an eddy that won't hold its shape. A faint idea of the elusiveness of the phenomenon can be conveyed to anyone who has tried to pick up mercury with his fingers or who has watched a teacher trying to keep track of her pupils on an outing to a public park. But the ocean environment is so much larger, so much harder to see, that we don't bring many of "our children" home. Measurement in large-scale ocean physics illustrates this limit very well. Further theoretical development is simply going to have to wait upon adequate measurement technique. The theoretical difficulties are not serious; mathematical modeling can be worked by machine once sufficient insight has been gained as to what is actually going on in the ocean.

The Need for Mathematical Models

Some advances in climate control, pollution evaluation, and numerical weather forecasting might be achieved simply by extending present land-based meteorological networks into the ocean by means of buoys. Perhaps a superficial knowledge of temperature on a coarse grid in the upper 100 meters of the ocean will be useful to meteorologists. But this will not provide the basis for a quantitative, rational, ocean-prediction system.

In order to be able to predict the mechanism of the ocean it is necessary to have numerical-mathematical models that have been verified by comparison with actually observed case histories of oceanic motion. Because there are several modes of such motion, these experiments or comparisons have to be made on several different scales. But to date they have not been made. They are beyond our technical means.

Actually, it is too early to try to design an oceanic monitoring system; some experimental measuring systems are needed first — aimed squarely at providing input for mathematical numerical modeling of the basic hydrodynamical processes at work. Successfully tested models could evolve into successful prediction schemes. If sufficient resources were mustered to start a good crew of instrument engineers on a sample program of measurement, sufficient progress might be made in carrying out one sample comparison of theory and observation to catalyze progress on the other necessary experiments. One has the feeling that the science is locked in a dead-center position, and that a mighty shove is going to be needed to get it rolling.

Hydrodynamic Modeling of Ocean Systems

Waves and currents in the ocean can be organized into many different categories depending on horizontal dimension and the time-scale of variability. Some of these categories are strongly interconnected, others almost independent. In Figure IV-2 an attempt is made at classification, along with an indication of the principal ways in which each phenomenon has an impact on human activities. (The emphasis in this outline is on ocean-circulation phenomena; surface waves, tides, and storm tides are treated only briefly, although they are admittedly important subjects from the standpoint of practical disaster-warning systems.)

Present Status

Wind Waves and Tidal Waves — The numerical models presently used to predict surface waves are essentially refinements of earlier operational models developed by the U.S. Navy; they have proved valuable to shipping. New computer models, however, allow a much more detailed incorporation of the latest experimental and theoretical advances in the study of wave generation. Furthermore, orbiting satellites may soon be able to provide a good synoptic picture of the surface sea state all over the globe. Given an accurate weather forecast, computer models would then be able to predict future sea states. Indeed, it may turn out that the ultimate limitation to wave forecasting will involve the accuracy of the weather forecast rather than the wave-prediction model itself.

Operational models for predicting tidal waves (tsunamis) have been developed for the Pacific, where the danger of earthquakes is greatest. As soon as the epicenter of an earthquake is located by seismographs, the model can predict the time a tidal wave will arrive. Such warning systems are being developed by the National Oceanic and Atmospheric Administration (NOAA) and the Japanese Meteorological Agency.

Storm Surges and Tides — Most of the research in developing numerical models to predict storm tides has been carried out in Europe, in connection with flooding in the North Sea area. In the United States, storm surges caused by hurricanes approaching the Gulf Coast have generated the most interest. The results of these model studies appear promising. Graphs and charts based on the model calculations may be used by Weather Service forecasters in making flood warnings. The models will also be useful in the engineering design of harbor flood-walls and levees. In time, computer models will probably replace the expensive and cumbersome laboratory models of harbors now used by coastal engineers.

Figure IV–2 — CLASSIFICATION OF WAVES AND CURRENTS

Time-Scale	Local	Intermediate	Global
Short (minutes)	Surface Waves (shipping, shore erosion, offshore drilling)		Tidal Waves (tsunamis) (safety of shore areas)
Intermediate (hours/days)	Ocean Turbulence and Mixing (pollution, air-sea interaction	Storm Surges (safety of shore areas, hurricane damage)	Tides (navigation)
Long (months/years)	Near-Shore Circulation (pollution)	Circulation of Inland Seas (Great Lakes pollution, polar pack-ice models)	Circulation in Ocean Basins (long-range weather forecasting, fisheries, climatic change)

The chart classifies waves and circulations as functions of time and distance.

Ocean Circulation — Over the past decade, three-dimensional numerical models for calculating ocean circulation have been developed by the Soviet Hydrometeorological Service and NOAA. The methods used are similar to those of numerical weather forecasting. Given the flux of heat, water, and momentum at the upper surface, the model predicts the response of the currents at deeper levels. The currents at deeper levels in turn change the configuration of temperature and salinity in the model ocean.

Although active work in developing these models is being conducted at several universities, the only published U.S. calculations are based on the "box" model developed at NOAA's Geophysical Fluid Dynamics Laboratory. This model allows the inclusion of up to 20 levels in the vertical direction and a detailed treatment of the bottom and shore configuration of actual ocean basins.

Cox's calculation of the circulation of the Indian Ocean is perhaps the most detailed application yet attempted with the NOAA "box" model. Using climatic data, it was possible to specify the observed distribution of wind, temperature, and salinity at the surface as a function of season. The model was then able to make an accurate prediction of the spectacular changes in currents and upwelling in response to the changing monsoons that were measured along the African coast during the Indian Ocean Expedition of the early 1960's.

Application of the Model to Practical Problems — The numerical models designed for studying large-scale ocean circulation problems can be modified to study more local circulation in near-shore areas or inland seas such as the Great Lakes. Thus, numerical models may be useful for the many problems in oceanography in which steady currents play a role. A partial list includes: (a) long-range weather forecasting; (b) fisheries fore-casting; (c) pollution on a global or local scale; and (d) transportation in the polar ice-pack.

Needed Advances

The Data Base — Standard oceanographic and geochemical data provide a fairly adequate base for modeling the time-averaged, mean state of the ocean. The data base for modeling the time-variability of the ocean is extremely limited, however. Information on large-scale changes in ocean circulation as well as the small-scale variability associated with mixing in the ocean have not been gathered in any comprehensive way.

Future progress in ocean modeling will depend on more detailed field studies of ocean variability. Such studies will establish the data base for the formulation of mixing by small-scale motions which must be included in the circulation model. Information on large-scale variability will provide a means for verifying the predictions of the models.

Technical Requirements — The most promising approach appears to be the different arrays of automated buoys that have been proposed as part of the International Decade of Ocean Exploration (IDOE) program. Coarse arrays covering entire ocean basins, as well as detailed arrays for limited areas, will be required.

Another technical requirement for ocean modeling is common to a great many other scientific activities: the steady development of speed in electronic computers and the steady decrease in unit cost of calculations.

Manpower Training — Numerical models of currents have now reached a point where they can be of great value in the planning of observational studies and the analysis of data collected at sea. The models can be used in diagnostic as well as predictive modes. This is particularly true of the buoy networks proposed as part of the IDOE. In order to do this, however, more oceanographers will need to be trained to use the numerical models and to carry out the computations. This action will have to be taken quickly if numerical models are to have much signficance in IDOE programs.

Application of Ocean Modeling in Human Affairs

As pointed out by Revelle and others, a large fraction of the added carbon dioxide (CO_2) generated by the burning of fossil fuels is taken up by the oceans. However, few details are known concerning the ocean's buffering effect and how long it will continue to be effective. The ability of the ocean to take up CO_2 depends very much on how rapidly surface waters are mixed with deeper water. More detailed studies of geochemical evidence and numerical modeling are essential to get an understanding of this process. A start in numerical modeling of tracer distributions in the ocean has been made by Veronis and Kuo at Yale University and Holland at the NOAA Geophysical Fluid Dynamics Laboratory.

Another urgent task is to make an assessment of the effect of CO_2 and particulate matter in the atmosphere on climate. Present climatic knowledge does not allow reliable quantitative predictions of the "greenhouse effect" due to CO_2 or the screening out of direct radiation by particulate matter. Published estimates have been based on highly simplified models that treat only the radiational aspects of climate. But no climate calculation is complete without taking into account the circulation of *both the atmosphere and the ocean*. Some preliminary climatic calculations have been carried out with combined numerical models of the ocean and atmosphere. But greater effort is required to develop more refined ocean models if these climatic calculations are to be reliable enough to be the basis for public policy decisions on pollution control.

Time-Scale of Significant Advances — Since published papers on three-dimensional ocean circulation models have only recently begun to appear, rapid development should continue for at least another five years along present lines. In that time, ocean models should have reached about the same level of development as the most advanced atmospheric numerical models today. Within five years, at least the *feasibility* of application of numerical modeling to small- and large-scale pollution studies, long-range weather forecasting, and hydrographic data analysis should be well established. Another five years will probably be required to work out standard procedures for using numerical ocean circulation models in these applications.

Effects of Antarctic Water on Oceanic Circulation

Except for a relatively thin (slightly less than one kilometer) warm surface layer in the tropics and subtropics, the ocean is basically cold and fairly high in dissolved oxygen content. Ninety percent of the ocean is colder than 8° centigrade, with an oxygen content generally from 50 to 90 percent of the saturation level. This warm surface layer, because of its high stability, acts as an impervious cap over the cold abyssal water, blocking renewal (by the usual turbulent transfer methods) of the oxygen that has been consumed by various biological processes.

Why, therefore, is the bulk of the ocean so cold and highly oxygenated? In studying the relationship of temperature to salinity in the cold abyssal waters of the world ocean, one is struck by its similarity to that found in antarctic waters. This suggests that the oceanographic processes occurring in antarctic waters influence, in a direct way, the physical and chemical properties of much of the ocean's abyssal water. One may think of the antarctic region as a zone in which the abyssal waters can "breathe," renew their oxygen supply, and release to the atmosphere the heat received at more northern latitudes.

The Antarctic Water Masses

The basic circulation pattern along a north-south plane in antarctic waters is shown in Figure IV-3. The warm and low-oxygen-content circumpolar deep water (CDW) slowly flows southward and upward. Eventually, it reaches the near-surface layers at the wind-produced Antarctic Divergence. Here, the intense thermohaline alteration resulting from the sea-air interaction converts the CDW into "antarctic surface water" (AASW), which is cold (near freezing, −1.6° to −1.9° centigrade) and relatively fresh. Some of the CDW is converted by more intense thermohaline alterations due to ice formation into a fairly dense continental shelf water. At certain times, this shelf water drops to the sea floor where, on mixing with additional CDW, it forms the "antarctic bottom water" (AABW); neither the times nor the exact locations of the vertical motion are adequately known. The AABW has worldwide influence. It reaches far into the northern hemisphere in the western Atlantic and Pacific oceans.

Though we do not know how the shelf water is produced, three methods appear to be likely: (a) sea-ice formation; (b) freezing, melting, or a combination of these at the floating

Figure IV–3 — ANTARCTIC WATERS AND THEIR CIRCULATION

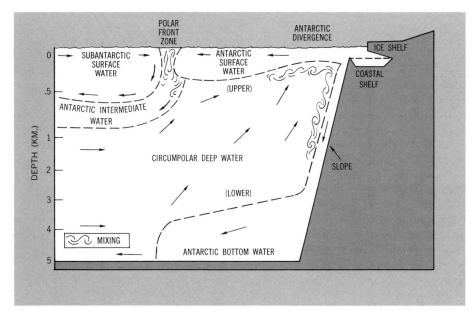

This figure shows the position, circulation, and interaction of the several water masses found in the antarctic region.

base of the extensive ice shelves of Antarctica; (c) rapid cooling and evaporation resulting from the outbreaks of cold, dry antarctic air masses. Recently, a fourth method was proposed which is based purely on molecular exchange of heat and salt between a warm salty lower layer and a cold fresh upper layer. Which of these methods is the dominant one is not known. Method (a) has generally been considered the key method; however, recent studies show that method (b) may be most important. It is probable that all the methods are active to a varying degree, depending on the location, and a variety of AABW types are formed.

The AASW flows slowly northward (see Figure IV-3); on meeting the less dense sub-antarctic water (near 55° S.), it sinks, contributing to the "antarctic intermediate water" (AAIW). The cold, relatively fresh AAIW flows northward at depths of nearly one kilometer. It reaches the equator in the Indian and Pacific oceans and up to 20° N. in the Atlantic Ocean.

The zone where the AAIW forms is called the "polar front zone," or Antarctic Convergence. The processes occurring within the zone are not understood; even the concept of a "convergence" process is questionable. The structure and position of the polar front zone varies with time. How, and in what frequency, and how it influences the AAIW formation are not known at all. The polar front zone should be subjected to much study in the coming years. It is of major importance to the overturning process of ocean waters and to climatic characteristics of the

southern hemisphere and perhaps the world. The only way to study this feature effectively is by multi-ship expeditions and/or time-series measurements from numerous anchored arrays of instruments.

Exchange of Water Masses — From salt studies, the general rate of meridional exchange has been determined. The CDW southward transport is 77 million cubic meters per second, of which only 15 million cubic meters per second have been derived from the sub-arctic regions (mainly from the North Atlantic). The rest is the return flow from the two northward antarctic components (AAIW and AABW). The CDW also brings heat into the antarctic region. It is calculated that 14 to 19 kilogram calories per cm² per year are released into the atmosphere by the ocean. This has a great effect in warming the antarctic air masses and, hence, in modifying the influence of Antarctica on world climate.

The exchange of CDW for AAIW and AABW has the important result of taking out the warm, low-oxygenated water and replacing it with cold, high-oxygen-content water. Were it not for this, the abyssal waters would warm considerably by geothermal heating and downward flux of heat across the thermocline. They would also become devoid of oxygen by organic decomposition.

Need for More Information

Though the gross features of the circulation pattern can be found, we do not know enough detail about the process of conversion of CDW into the antarctic water masses. In what regions does this conversion

take place? Is it seasonal or does it vary with another frequency? By what methods is the CDW converted into antarctic water masses?

To accomplish these tasks, long time-series measurements of currents, temperature, and salinity are needed along the continental margins of Antarctica and within the polar front zone. Multi-ship expeditions and satellite observations would also be useful in studying time-variations of the water structure. Geochemical studies of the isotopic makeup of the ice and sea water are necessary to yield information as to "residence" times within water masses and insight into methods of bottom-water production.

The antarctic waters are also of importance in that they connect each of the major oceans via a circumpolar conduit. The rate of the circumpolar flow is not known, though recent studies indicate a volume transport of well over 200 million cubic meters per second, making it the largest current system in the world ocean. A program of direct current observations is needed to study the circumpolar current. Satellite surveillance of drogues will be a useful method to study the current systems.

In short, scientists need to know in more detail the methods, rates, and location of the formation of the antarctic water masses. They can accomplish this task by hydrographic and geochemical observations in circumpolar waters using modern techniques. In addition, detailed time-series observations would be needed at particular points such as the Weddell Sea, Ross Sea, the Amery Ice Shelf, and other appropriate regions.

Tropical Air-Sea Rhythms

Tropical air-sea rhythms are best seen in the time-series of air and sea temperature at Canton Island, an equatorial island in the Pacific

(2°48'S. 171°43'W.); this is the only locality where temperature observations have been maintained uninterruptedly over a long period, 1950

through 1967. However, there is now no way of continuing this important time-series because the Canton Island observatory, with its modern equipment for aerological data-gathering, was abandoned in September 1967 for economy reasons.

Air-sea data from near-equatorial islands has great importance because the sea temperature in such localities is subject to fluctuations of much greater amplitude than in the adjacent trade-wind belts of either hemisphere. As a consequence, the heat supplied from the ocean to the atmosphere near the equator becomes the most variable part of the total tropical ocean-to-atmosphere heat flux, which in turn is the major control of the global atmospheric circulation. It is, therefore, logical to expect that ocean temperature fluctuations near the equator will influence atmospheric climate outside of tropical latitudes. This action by remote control through the global atmospheric circulation is here referred to as "teleconnections."

According to preliminary findings, the teleconnections from the Pacific equatorial air-sea rhythms are major factors — perhaps, in many cases, the dominant factor — in creating rhythms of climatic anomalies anywhere on the globe. Hence, these teleconnections must be understood before climatic anomalies can be predicted successfully.

General Characteristics

The following facts stand out from the Canton Island record. (See Figure IV-4)

1. Sea temperatures vary over a greater range than air temperatures.

2. In periods of cold ocean the air is warmer than the sea, whereas in periods of warm ocean the air is colder than the sea.

3. Heavy monthly rainfall occurs only during periods of warm ocean.

It is known from atmospheric thermodynamics that the heating of the atmosphere over a tropical ocean takes place mainly through the heat of condensation within precipitating cloud. Hence, the rainfall record is also a record of the major year-to-year variations of the atmospheric heat supply from the ocean. Those variations showed rhythms of about

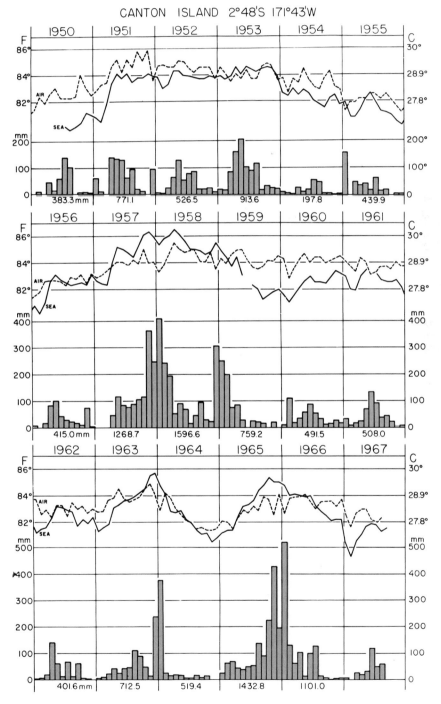

Figure IV-4 — CANTON ISLAND DATA

CANTON ISLAND 2°48'S 171°43'W

The figure shows a time-series of monthly air and sea temperatures and monthly precipitation amount as measured at Canton Island from 1950 through 1967.

two years' periodicity, especially during the 1960's; at other times the rhythms were less regular.

The mechanism of the equatorial air-sea rhythms is illustrated in Figure IV-5, which shows that a six-month, smoothed time-series of atmospheric pressure in Djakarta, Indonesia (6°S. 107°E.), exhibits the same long-period trends as the sea-surface temperatures measured at Canton Island and by ships crossing the equator at 165°W. When the barometric pressure in Djakarta is lower than normal, the equatorial easterlies heading for the Indonesian low become stronger than normal; this automatically intensifies the Pacific equatorial upwelling and cools the sea surface. The parallelism of the time-series of Djakarta pressure and Canton Island sea temperature is thereby assured.

If wind profiles are observed along the equator at two opposite phases of the air-sea rhythm, as exemplified by November 1964, with its cool ocean and aridity, and November 1965, with its warm ocean and abundant rainfall at Canton Island, it is

found that in November 1964 the equatorial easterlies swept uninterruptedly from South America past Canton Island toward a deeper-than-normal Indonesian low, whereas in November 1965 they stopped short of reaching Canton Island. The equatorial upwelling — a by-product of the equatorial easterlies — extended almost to Indonesia in November 1964, while being confined to a much smaller area east of Canton Island a year later. Concomitantly, the equatorial rainfall was confined to the neighborhood of Indonesia in November 1964; the following year it expanded from the west to beyond Canton Island, while Indonesia suffered serious drought.

The propulsion of the air-sea rhythms resides in the atmospheric thermally driven equatorial circulation over the Pacific, which has its heat source (by condensation) in the rising branch, and heat sink (by radiative deficit insufficiently compensated by scarce precipitation) in its descending branch near South America. The oceanic counterpart to this atmospheric circulation is, in part, the westward surface drift and

the subsurface return flow and, additionally, the circulation consisting of an upwelling thrust at the equator and sinking motion to the north and south of the equator. These ocean circulations are wind-driven and intrinsically energy-consuming, but they exert a powerful feedback upon the atmosphere by slowly varying the areal extent of warm water at the equator and thereby varying the thermal input for the global atmospheric circulation.

In November 1964, when cool upwelling water occupied almost the whole Pacific equatorial belt, the atmosphere received less heat than in November 1965, when the upwelling had shrunk back into a smaller eastern area. Consequently, the tropical atmosphere swelled vertically from 1964 to 1965. This swelling was most conspicuous over the Pacific at 160°W. longitude. Moreover, the swelling of the tropical atmosphere had spread all around the global tropical belt between 1964 and 1965, a global adjustment that is inevitable, since pressure gradients along the equator must remain moderate.

North and south of the swelling atmosphere in the tropical belt, the gradient of 200-millibar heights increased from November 1964 to November 1965, which indicated increasing westerly winds in the globe-circling subtropical jet streams. This can best be documented in the longitude sector from the area of Pacific equatorial warming eastward across North America and the Atlantic to the Mediterranean.

The corresponding change at sea level could be seen most dramatically over Europe, where the moving low-pressure centers abandoned their normal track by way of Iceland to Scandinavia and, instead, in November 1965 moved parallel to the strengthened subtropical jet stream and invaded central and southern Europe.

Other associated rearrangements involved the arctic high-pressure sys-

Figure IV-5 — WALKER'S "SOUTHERN OSCILLATION"

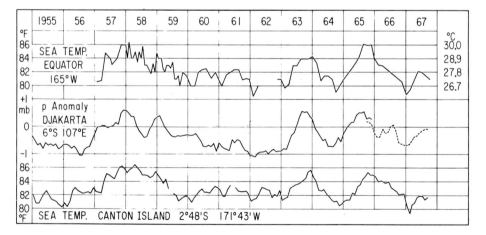

The diagram shows the similarities in trend of the time-series of sea temperature and pressure measured at and near the equator in the southern hemisphere. The dotted curve that follows that for Djakarta is based on data from Singapore. The rapid oscillations of the sea-temperature curve measured at the equator in 1958 and 1959 result from more frequent ship crossings—and hence a greater density of short-period detail—rather than from any unusual natural activity.

tem, which in November 1965 was displaced toward northern Europe and, consequently, on the Alaskan side of the pole left room for the moving low-pressure systems from the Pacific to penetrate farther north than normal.

So much for a description of the air-sea rhythms. Supporting evidence is available from a few other case histories. The motivation for continued research on the equatorial air-sea rhythms is the desire to develop skill in forecasting climatic anomalies.

Current Scientific Knowledge

The data base is, unfortunately, scanty. As mentioned earlier, Canton Island is the only place where a continuous record of the near-equatorial air-sea interaction was maintained; even there, scientific knowledge of the air-sea rhythms, extending vertically to great heights in the atmosphere, must be based mainly on a study of the years from 1950 through 1967.

Oceanographic cruises in the equatorial belt have been few and far between in space and time. The EASTROPAC Program, a series of internationally coordinated cruises in the eastern tropical Pacific and transequatorial cruises in the mid-Pacific, sponsored by the U.S. National Marine Fisheries Service (NMFS), Honolulu, has been the best oceanographic effort to date to explore air-sea interaction in the critical area where the air-sea rhythms originate. Less sophisticated, widely scattered observations are available from commercial ships. Those collected by the NMFS in Honolulu from commercial ships that ply the route from Hawaii to Samoa have provided a time-series of equatorial sea temperature at 165°W., together with the corresponding sea-temperature series at Canton Island. The two records agree rather well as far as the long rhythms are concerned.

Organized reporting of sea and air temperatures from commercial ships crossing the east and central part of the Pacific tropical zone is in good hands with the NMFS in La Jolla, California; the monthly maps issued by that institution are at present the best source of information on tropical air-sea rhythms.

The Status of Instrumentation — An important technical improvement in the ocean data reported from commercial ships will come soon. Selected ships will be equipped with Expendable Bathy-Thermographs (XBT) to enable them to monitor the varying heat storage in the ocean down to the thermocline.

Anchored buoys can provide the same information as XBT-equipped commercial ships and will have the advantage of delivery data for long time-series at fixed locations. The buoys that can be permanently financed should preferably be placed to fill the big gaps between frequented shipping lanes. Also, their locations should be selected where ocean temperatures are likely to vary significantly, for instance along the equator.

Infrared radiometers on satellites can be adjusted to record sea temperature in cloud-free areas, but the accuracy of such measurements cannot quite compare with careful ship- or buoy-based observations. The great contributions of the satellites to tropical studies are — presently and in the future — the TV-mapping of cloud distribution, the temperature measurements of the top surface of cloud, and, under favorable conditions, the movement of individual clouds and cloud clusters.

Fixed installations on tropical islands will continue to be important for research on ocean-atmosphere interaction. Aerological soundings, including upper wind measurements, are best done from islands; moreover, fundamental measurements like the time variations of the topography of

ocean level can only be done with a network of island-based tide gauges. The latter job does not call for very expensive equipment, and the tide gauges can be serviced as part-time work by trained islanders; the aerological work, on the other hand, calls for a technologically skilled staff on permanent duty.

Replacements for Canton Island as an aerological observatory would be relatively expensive, but yet cheaper than was Canton, if islands with stable native population were selected for observatory sites. The two British islands of Tarawa (1°21'N. 172°56'E.) and Christmas (1°59'N. 157°29'W.) would be ideal choices.

Mathematical Modeling — A crude modeling of an asymptotically approached "steady state" of an equatorial ocean exposed to the stress of constant easterly winds has been produced by Bryan, of the Geophysical Fluid Dynamics Laboratory, NOAA. A corresponding, quickly adjusting atmospheric model of the equatorial circulation, such as observed over the Pacific, was described in 1969 by Manabe, also of the Princeton NOAA team.

Presumably, the ocean and atmospheric models can soon be joined for a simulation of the equatorial air-sea rhythms. Even without mathematical formulation, the rhythm can be crudely visualized to operate as follows:

The cooling phase of the rhythm begins when the equatorial easterlies of the eastern Pacific start increasing and thereby start intensifying the upwelling. This increases the temperature deficit of the eastern end of the oceanic equatorial belt compared to its western end. The associated feedback upon the atmosphere shows up in an increased east-west temperature contrast, which produces an increment of kinetic energy in the equatorial atmospheric circulation. This, in turn, feeds back into increasing upwelling and ocean-cooling over an increasing area.

A corresponding chain reaction can be visualized for the phase of the rhythm characterized by decreasing easterly winds, decreasing upwelling, and increasing equatorial ocean warming. Hence, a slow vacillation between the two extreme phases of equatorial atmospheric circulation, rather than a stable steady-state equatorial circulation, becomes the most likely pattern.

Simulation experiments are presently being planned on a global basis, encompassing both ocean and atmosphere; they will bring more precise reasoning into the explanation of the equatorial air-sea rhythms and, hopefully, into the interpretation of their teleconnections outside the tropics. Both the Princeton team, under Smagorinsky, and the team at the University of California, at Los Angeles, under Mintz and Arakawa, are progressing toward that goal.

Requirements for Scientific Activity

Continued empirical study of the tropical air-sea rhythms, in past and in real-time records, should accompany and support modeling efforts of theoretical teams. The knowledge gained on tropical air-sea rhythms and their extratropical teleconnections so far rests on the study of only a limited number of case histories. Much more can be learned by studying the whole sequence of years 1950-67, during which Canton Island was available as an indicator of the air-sea rhythms. These years include the International Geophysical Year period, which happened to exhibit some extreme climatic anomalies and also had better-than-normal global data coverage.

Such investigations are relatively cheap. The main expense goes into the plotting and analysis of world maps of monthly climatic anomalies in several levels up to the tropopause. Such a system of climatic anomaly maps would be the empirical tool for tracking the mechanism of the teleconnections. Liaison with EASTRO-PAC and other post-1950 Pacific tropical oceanographic research would become a natural outgrowth of the "historical" study.

The 1970's is to be the era of the International Decade of Ocean Exploration (IDOE) as well as that of the Global Atmospheric Research Program (GARP). The study of tropical air-sea rhythms belongs within the scope of both of these worldwide research enterprises and, indeed, will serve to tie the two together. The ultimate goal of IDOE-plus-GARP should be to model the atmosphere and the world oceans into one comprehensive system suitable for electronic integration. That endeavor should produce meaningful progress toward climatic forecasting by the end of the 1970's.

2. ATMOSPHERIC CIRCULATION

Modeling the Global Atmospheric Circulation

An understanding of the structure and variability of the global atmospheric circulation requires a knowledge of:

1. The quality and quantity of *radiation* coming from the sun.

2. The *atmospheric constituents*— not only the massive ones, but also such thermodynamically active components as water vapor, carbon dioxide, ozone, and clouds as well as other particulates. Furthermore, one must understand the process by which these constituents react with the circulations and their radiative properties — i.e., absorption, transmission, scattering, and reflection.

3. The processes by which the atmosphere interacts with its *lower boundary* in the transmission of momentum, heat, and water substance over land as well as sea surfaces. The behavior of the atmosphere cannot be considered independent of its lower boundary beyond a few days. In turn, the lower boundary can react significantly. Even the surface layers of the oceans have important reaction times of less than a week, while the deeper ocean comes into play over longer periods. Hence, the evolution of the atmospheric circulation over long periods requires consideration of a dynamical system whose lower boundary is below the earth's surface.

4. The interactions of the large-scale motions of the atmosphere with the variety of *smaller-scale motions* normally present. If these smaller scales have energy sources of their own, as is the case in the atmosphere, the nature of the interactions will be considerably complicated.

In principle, mathematical models embodying precise statements of the component physical elements and their interactions provide the means for numerically simulating the natural evolution of the large-scale atmosphere and its constituents. Successful modeling would have potential applications in a number of areas: long-range forecasting; determination of the large-scale, long-term dispersion of man-made pollutants; the interaction of these pollutants in inadvertently altering climate; the influence of intentionally tampering with boundary conditions to artificially modify the climate equilibrium. No doubt there are a variety of other applications of a simulation capability to problems that may not yet be evident.

Current Status

Efforts to model the large-scale atmosphere and to simulate its behavior numerically began more than twenty years ago. As additional research groups and institutions in the United States and elsewhere became involved, steady advances in model sophistication followed. These came from refinements in numerical methods as well as from improved formulations of the component processes.

Today's multi-level models account for a variety of interacting influences and processes: large-scale topographic variations; thermal differences between continents and oceans; variations in roughness characteristics; radiative transfer as a function of an arbitrary distribution of radiatively active constituents; large-scale phase changes of water substance in the precipitation process; interactions with small-scale, convectively unstable motions; the thermal consequences of variable water storage in the soil; and the consequences of snow-covered surfaces on the heat balance. More recently, combined models have taken into account the mutual interaction of the atmosphere and ocean, including the formation and transport of sea-ice.

Although many of these elements are rather crudely formulated as cogs in the total model, it has been possible to simulate with increasing detail the characteristics of the observed climate — not only the global wind system and temperature distribution from the earth's surface to the mid-stratosphere, but also the precipitation regimes and their role in forming the deserts and major river basins of the world. Attention is beginning to be given to the simulation of climatic response to the annual radiation cycle.

Detailed analyses of such simulations in terms of the flow and transformation of energy from the primary solar source to the ultimate viscous sink show encouragingly good agreement with corresponding analyses of observed atmospheric data. Such models have also been applied to observationally specified atmospheric states in tests of transient predictability. Even within the severe limitations of the models, the data, and the computational inadequacies, it has been possible to simulate and verify large-scale atmospheric evolutions of the order of a week. These advances give promise that, as known deficiencies are systematically removed, the practical level of the large-scale predictability of the atmosphere can converge on a theoretical deterministic limitation of several weeks.

Models have also been used in some, more limited applications. For example, an attempt was made to simulate the long-term, large-scale dispersion of inert tracing material, such as radioactive tungsten, which had been released at an instantaneous source in the lower equatorial troposphere. The results were surprisingly good. Only limited attempts have been made to apply extant models to test the sensitivity of climate to small external influences. The reason is that one normally seeks to detect departures from fairly delicately balanced states. It is often beyond the current level of capability to simulate an abnormal response that is comparable in magnitude to the natural variability noise level.

Observational Problems

The present large-scale data base is essentially dictated by the extent of the operational networks created by the weather forecast services of the world. The existing network is hardly adequate to define the northern-hemisphere extratropical atmosphere; it is completely inadequate in the southern hemisphere and in the equatorial tropics. For example, there are only 50 radiosonde stations in the southern hemisphere in contrast to approximately 500 in the northern. The main difficulties arise from the large expanses of open ocean which, by conventional methods, impede determination of the large-scale components of atmospheric structure responsible for the major energy transformations. This critical deficiency in the global observational data store makes it difficult to define the variability of the atmosphere in enough detail to discern systematic

theoretical deficiencies. Furthermore, the data are inadequate for the specification of initial conditions in the calculation of long-range forecasts.

Recent dramatic advances in infrared spectroscopy from satellites promise significant strides in defining the state of the extratropical atmosphere virtually independent of location. (See Figure IV-6) However, the motions of the equatorial tropical atmosphere lack strong rotational coupling, making the observational problem there more acute. Independent

wind determinations may be needed as well as the information supplied by a Nimbus 3 (SIRS sensor) type satellite. It is not yet known to what extent balloon-borne instrumentation or measurements from ocean buoys will be needed to augment satellite observations, especially in the lower troposphere. This will depend on just how strongly the variable characteristics of the atmosphere are coupled. A more precise knowledge would permit relaxing observational requirements for an adequate definition of its structure.

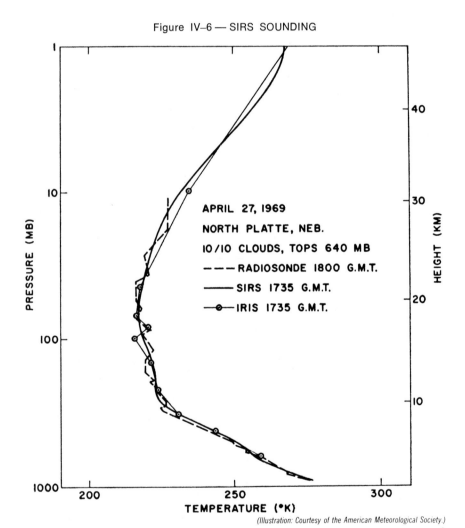

Figure IV–6 — SIRS SOUNDING

APRIL 27, 1969
NORTH PLATTE, NEB.
10/10 CLOUDS, TOPS 640 MB
- - - RADIOSONDE 1800 G.M.T.
——— SIRS 1735 G.M.T.
—⊙— IRIS 1735 G.M.T.

(Illustration: Courtesy of the American Meteorological Society.)

This figure shows the broad similarities between simultaneous temperature soundings obtained by radiosonde equipment and satellite-borne SIRS (Satellite Infrared Spectrometer) and IRIS (Infrared Interferometer Spectrometer) systems. The latter systems, however, are able to provide far broader and more continuous coverage than conventional equipment. Further work is in progress to overcome the difficulties of the present instruments in predominantly overcast areas.

There is some controversy as to the inherent deterministic limitations of the predictability of the atmosphere—say, for scales corresponding to individual extratropical cyclones. The span of controversy ranges from about one to several weeks. Moreover, it is not known at all whether longer-term characteristics of atmospheric variability are determinate. For example, is it inherently possible to distinguish the mean conditions over eastern United States from one January to another in some deterministic sense? In the equatorial tropics there is very little insight as to the spectrum of predictability.

Needs for Future Improvements

Broadly, there are three areas that require intensive upgrading, the first two of which are essentially technological:

Technological Requirements — The need for establishment of an adequate global observing system has already been discussed. In addition, computers two orders of magnitude faster than those currently available are needed to permit the positive reduction of mathematical errors incurred by inadequate computational resolution. Faster computers will also permit more exhaustive tests of model performance over a much larger range of parameter-space to assess the sensitivity of simulations to parameterizations of physical process elements of the model. Faster computers will also provide an ability to undertake the broad range of applications implied by a more sophisticated modeling capability.

Scientific Requirements — The scientific requirements stem from the necessity of refining the formulation of process elements in the models. To cite a few: boundary-layer interactions — to determine the dependence of the heat, momentum, and water-vapor exchange within the lower kilometer of the atmosphere as a function of the large-scale structural characteristics; internal turbulence — to determine the structure and mechanisms responsible for intermittent turbulence in the "free" atmosphere, which is apparently responsible for the removal of significant amounts of energy from the large scale and may also play a role in the diffusion of heat, momentum, and water vapor; and convection — to determine how cumulus overturning gives rise to the deep vertical transport of heat, water vapor, and, possibly, momentum.

We still do not know the consequences of particulates, man-made or natural, either directly on the radiative balance or ultimately on the dynamics.

In the tropics, we have yet to completely understand the instability mechanisms responsible for the formation of weak disturbances or the nature of an apparent second level of instability which transforms some of these disturbances into intense vortices, manifested as hurricanes and typhoons. Without an understanding of the intricacies of the tropics, it is impossible to deal comprehensively or coherently with the global circulation, particularly with the interactions of the circulation of one atmosphere with that of the other.

Most of these critical scientific areas of uncertainty require intensive phenomenological or regional observational studies. These will provide the basic data as foundations for a better theoretical understanding.

Any one of the general scientific and technological categories listed above may at any one time provide the weakest link in the complex required to advance a modeling and simulation capability. Obviously, then, they must be upgraded at compatible rates.

Prospects

A comprehensive look at the status, needs, and implications of an understanding and simulation capability of the global circulation is embodied in the Global Atmospheric Research Program (GARP), which was established several years ago as an international venture under the joint auspices of the World Meteorological Organization and the International Council of Scientific Unions. In the United States, GARP is overseen by a National Academy of Sciences committee that has produced a planning document for U.S. national participation. Almost all the problem areas discussed above have come to the attention of the U.S. Committee for GARP. The international timescale for major field experiments extends into the late 1970's. Concomitantly, national and international research programs to support and derive results from the field programs will be established. The time-scales governing GARP planning imply that one can expect the necessary elements to be systematically undertaken over about a ten-year period. The first GARP tropical experiment will take place in 1974 in the eastern equatorial Atlantic and the first GARP global data-gathering experiment is scheduled for 1976 or later. GARP is the research part of the World Weather Program (WWP). The other part of the WWP is the World Weather Watch (WWW), whose objective is to bring the global atmosphere under surveillance and provide for the rapid collection and exchange of weather data as well as the dissemination of weather products from centralized processing centers. GARP will rely heavily on data obtained from the WWW. (See Figure IV-7)

FIGURE IV–7 — AVAILABILITY OF UPPER AIR DATA

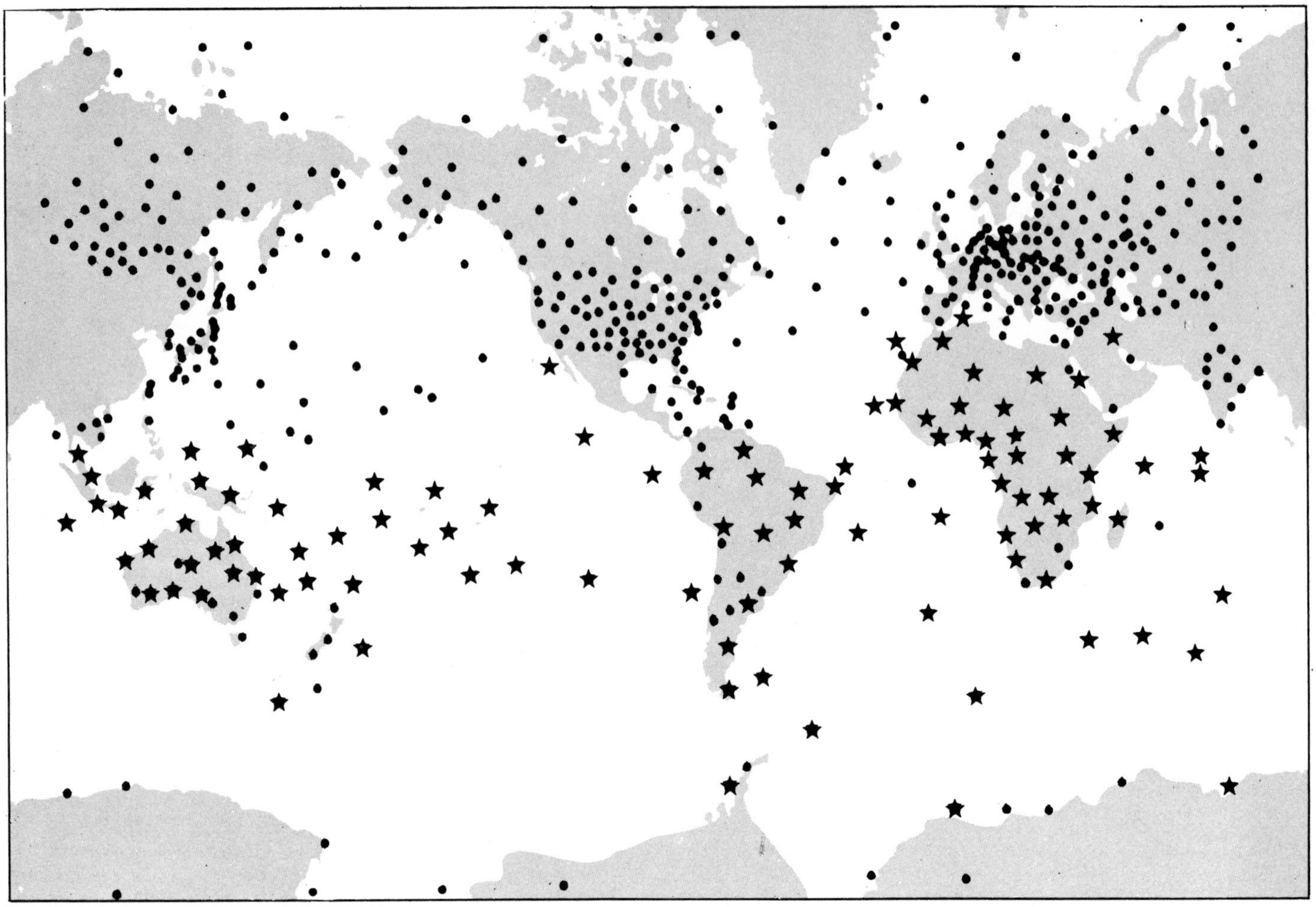

The map shows the current and planned global radiosonde network. The current network is adequate only over Europe, central Asia, and the United States. The planned additions will add greatly to our knowledge of the southern hemisphere; they are part of the first phase of the World Weather Watch.

3. WEATHER FORECASTING

Short-, Medium-, and Long-Term Forecasting

The effects of weather on human activities and the importance of accurate weather predictions and timely weather warnings for human safety and comfort hardly need stating. The farmer, the seafarer, the aviator, the man on the street all share a common concern for the weather. Hurricanes, tornadoes, floods, heavy snows, and other severe weather phenomena take a heavy toll of lives and cause billions of dollars loss in damage and disruption each year. The cost would be even greater were it not for weather warnings and forecasts.

As the science of weather prediction grows, it touches an ever wider range of human problems. Today there is much concern about air pollution and the possible effects of pollutants on weather and climate. The mathematical models used in numerical weather prediction provide the best known means of determining how pollutants are spread over large distances and how they might affect weather patterns. Furthermore, mathematical modeling has reached the stage where interactions of the atmosphere with the ocean can be taken into account. This development opens up the possibility of predicting changes in the physical state of the upper layers of the ocean, which might prove useful to the fishing industry and other marine activities.

Although of great economic value, present-day forecasts fall well short of perfection. Even modest improvements in accuracy would result in substantial additional benefits. With the new tools now available, especially the meteorological satellite, opportunities exist for increasing the accuracy of forecasts at all ranges — short, medium, and long.

The Nature of Weather Prediction

It is customary, and for some purposes useful, to divide the subject of weather prediction into three categories: short, medium, and long term. These categories are generally understood to refer to time ranges of 0-24 hours, 1-5 days, and beyond 5 days (e.g., monthly and seasonal forecasts), respectively. While it is often convenient to discuss the forecast problem under these headings, it is important to realize that they do not necessarily represent logical divisions of the subject in terms of methodology employed, concepts involved, or phenomena treated.

Weather prediction, as presently practiced, is actually a highly complex subject. It deals with such diverse phenomena as thunderstorms, tornadoes, hurricanes, and cyclonic storms, and with a wide variety of weather elements — wind, temperature, and precipitation, to name a few of the more important. Moreover, it involves the use of an assortment of techniques, some based on human judgment, others founded on physical law and numerical computation. Weather forecasting is still a mixture of art and science, but a mixture in which the scientific ingredient is becoming increasingly dominant as fundamental understanding of the atmosphere grows and more and more application is found for numerical methods.

In the following sections we will review the principal elements involved in prediction at different ranges, dividing the subject according to the pertinent phenomena. Figure IV-8 shows the geographical range, both latitudinally and in height, of data needed for forecasting. To aid in the discussion, it is desirable first to summarize briefly the methods employed in weather prediction.

Prediction Methods

Numerical Weather Prediction — This is the term applied to forecast methods in which high-speed digital computers are used to solve the physical equations governing atmospheric motions. In order to compute the future state of the atmosphere accurately, the initial or present state must be specified by observation. Numerical methods are most successfully applied in predicting the behavior of the synoptic-scale disturbances (cyclones, anticyclones, jet streams) of middle and high latitudes.

Extrapolation — In this method, successive positions of the feature being forecast, for instance a low-pressure center, are mapped, and the future position is estimated by continuing past displacements or trends. Since the advent of numerical weather prediction, this method has fallen into disuse in predicting motions of synoptic systems, but it is still useful in other connections, for example, in predicting movements of individual thunderstorms seen on a radarscope.

Steering — In the steering method, a smaller-scale weather system or feature is assumed to move with the direction and speed of a larger-scale current in which it is embedded. Thus, a hurricane may be displaced according to the broad-scale trade-wind current in its vicinity. The accuracy of the method depends on how well the basic steering assumption is satisfied and how accurately the steering current is known or predicted.

Figure IV-8 — DATA REQUIRED FOR FORECASTS

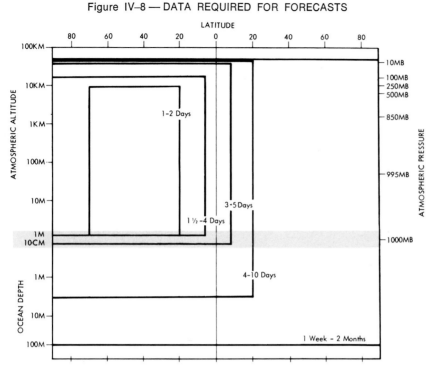

The diagram gives an indication of the data necessary for forecasts in the middle latitudes for varying lengths of the forecast period. It is important to note that both atmospheric and oceanographic data are needed for all forecast periods.

ena selected on the basis of their practical importance: severe local storms (thunderstorms, hailstorms, and tornadoes); hurricanes; and synoptic disturbances (cyclones, anticyclones, and fronts and their associated upper-level troughs, ridges, and jet streams).

Severe Local Storms — These storms develop with extreme rapidity and seldom have lifetimes of more than a few hours. On the basis of the large-scale temperature, moisture, and wind fields, and their expected changes, it is possible to delineate areas in which severe storms are likely to occur 6 to 12 hours in advance, or sometimes even longer. But there is at present no way of predicting when and where an individual storm will develop. Once a storm has been detected, extrapolation and steering methods can be used to predict its motion with fair accuracy, but in view of the short lifetime of the typical storm, the forecast rarely holds for more than a few hours.

Weather radar is the most valuable tool in severe-storm detection, and it is only since the introduction of radar that adequate monitoring of severe storms has been possible. Geostationary satellites also have great potential usefulness in identifying and tracking these systems. Until there is full radar coverage of the United States and permanent surveillance by geostationary satellite with both visual and infrared sensing capability, short-range prediction of severe storms will not have reached the limits of accuracy allowed by the present state of the art.

Ultimately, one may hope that the methods of numerical weather prediction used so successfully with larger-scale storms will be applied to thunderstorms and other small-scale phenomena. But there seems no clear way of achieving this hope in the foreseeable future. To forecast these phenomena by numerical methods requires observations of the basic meteorological variables — wind, tem-

Statistical Forecasting — Though statistical methods have wide application in forecasting, the term, as applied here, refers to any of a number of techniques in which past data samples are employed to derive statistical relationships between the variable being forecast and the same or other meteorological variables at an earlier time. The statistical method is particularly valuable in forecasting local phenomena that are too complex or too poorly understood to be treated by numerical or physical methods but that experience has shown to be related to identifiable, antecedent causes.

The Analogue Method — The aim of this method is to find a previous weather situation which resembles the current situation and to use the outcome of the earlier case to determine the present forecast. The method has the advantage of simplicity, but its usefulness is extremely limited since sufficiently close ana-

logues are difficult to find, even when long weather records are available.

Mixed Methods — Combinations of the foregoing methods are quite common. Thus, surface temperature is customarily forecast by a combination of numerical and statistical techniques in order to obtain better predictions than would be obtained from use of the numerical method alone.

Short-Range Prediction

The problems encountered, methods employed, and the time period for which accurate predictions can be made differ according to the phenomenon or scale of motion being forecast. It is therefore convenient to discuss the subject on the basis of different types of weather systems involved. To keep the subject within reasonable limits, the discussion will be limited to the following phenom-

perature, and moisture — at spatial intervals of less than a kilometer and nearly continuously in time (cf., present spacing of about 400 km. and time intervals of 12 hours). Economically, this is a prohibitive requirement, quite apart from its practical feasibility in terms of the instrumentation and observing systems currently envisaged.

Despite the present hopelessness of straightforward applications of physical-numerical methods to the prediction of small-scale phenomena, there is no doubt that opportunities exist for improved forecasting through properly directed research efforts. New developments in instrumentation and measuring systems — doppler and acoustic radars and the geostationary satellites, to mention the most promising — utilized in conjunction with special observing programs planned for the future, offer great opportunities for advancing understanding of severe storms. From this understanding, improved techniques are bound to emerge. For instance, it has been found that, unlike the typical thunderstorm, very large thunderstorms tend to move to the right and slower than the steering current. A better physical understanding of the cause of this behavior would undoubtedly lead to superior forecast techniques.

Hurricanes — Hurricane prediction has improved steadily during the past decade or two. The improvement has been brought about by the use of aerial reconnaissance, radar, and, more recently, meteorological satellites to detect and track the hurricanes and by the development of better techniques for predicting their movement. Skill is still largely lacking in forecasting their development, but fortunately they form sufficiently slowly and usually far enough away from land areas that the development problem is seldom critical.

In the past, extrapolation and steering methods have been the mainstays in predicting hurricane movement.

Currently, the most accurate method is a statistical one that uses past weather records to derive regression equations relating future movement to previous movement and to various measures of the large-scale atmospheric structure in the region surrounding the hurricane. With this method, hurricane positions can be predicted 24 hours in advance with an average error of about 100 nautical miles. While this figure leaves considerable room for improvement, there can be no doubt about the enormous value of current forecasts in terms of lives saved and property damage reduced.

Further refinement of the statistical method and better observations of the broad-scale features of the hurricane environment could lead to some improvement in hurricane prediction, but it seems likely that the statistical method has already approached its limits of accuracy. Development of numerical prediction methods would seem to hold the key to further progress in this area. Methods of numerical prediction have already been tried which forecast the large-scale steering flow in the vicinity of hurricanes and thereby allow better use of the steering principle. These methods have met with some degree of success, yielding errors comparable to, or slightly larger than, the statistical method.

More significant and promising for the future has been the development in recent years of theoretical models which, starting from assumed initial conditions, are able to simulate many important features of hurricanes. These models have reached the stage where they could be tested routinely in the atmosphere if the proper initial data — i.e., observations of wind, temperature, and humidity at sufficiently close intervals to resolve the atmospheric structure in and near the hurricane — were available. The interval required is 100 kilometers or less, well beyond present observational capability. However, it is conceivable that geostationary satellites

with visual and infrared sensors, including sounders, could go a long way toward providing the type of information needed for carrying out physical-numerical prediction of hurricane formation, movement, and intensity.

Despite these promising theoretical and observational developments, it would be premature to enter on a crash program of hurricane prediction. Emphasis now must be put on improving the physical basis of hurricane models and on developing the full potential of the geostationary satellite as an observing platform. Tropical field experiments planned as part of the Global Atmospheric Research Program (GARP) will assist theoretical studies of hurricanes by providing data suitable for investigating the nature of the interaction of mesoscale convective phenomena with the larger-scale flow patterns of the tropics.

Synoptic Systems — During the past decade or two, thanks to the introduction of high-speed computers and the development of numerical weather prediction, remarkable progress has been made in predicting the genesis and movement of high and low pressure systems and tropospheric circulation features in general. Prognostic weather maps prepared by computer now surpass the efforts of even the most skilled and experienced forecasters.

Despite these successes, short-range forecasts of specific weather elements often leave much to be desired. In part, the shortcomings are due to small-scale phenomena which, as explained earlier, are not predictable, except in a statistical sense, more than a few hours in advance. But, in considerable measure, they can also be attributed to deficiencies or limitations in the numerical prediction models. The models are most successful in predicting pressure and wind fields; they are less successful in predicting cloud and precipitation amounts and patterns and in answering such critical problems as whether precipitation will be in the form of rain or snow. These problems, involving interactions of wind, temperature, and moisture fields, are of a different order of difficulty. Short-range predictions also suffer somewhat from data deficiencies, particularly in oceanic and adjoining regions. Satellite observations have, however, alleviated the data deficiencies to a considerable degree in recent years.

There are several avenues for advancing the science of short-range prediction of synoptic-scale phenomena; all of them are being actively pursued and deserve encouragement. First, fine-grid scale models are being developed which accept data at grid intervals of half or less the current standard mesh length of about 400 kilometers. Use of a finer grid permits better resolution and more accurate depiction of the synoptic patterns and improves the accuracy of the computational procedures. Unfortunately, the presently available observations are not ideally suited for fine-grid computation. Though a network of surface observations exists which makes it possible to represent surface weather features more precisely than is presently done in numerical prediction, no corresponding closely spaced upper air observations are available. High-resolution, scanning radiometric sounders aboard satellites offer a promising means of overcoming this gap, and every effort should be made to speed their development and application. Data from more advanced satellites can also be expected to improve further the quality of ocean analysis, and thereby contribute to better short-range forecasts over ocean areas and adjacent coastal regions.

Another important avenue for advancing short-range prediction is through continued efforts at improving the physical basis of the prediction models. Such efforts can be carried out in part by theoretical means, using presently available knowledge of the physical processes.

But they will also almost certainly require the acquisition of special data sets of the sort planned under GARP and other large observational programs. Better modeling of the physical processes will not only widen the scope of the phenomena that can be forecast successfully by objective means but will result in greater accuracy of the forecast as a whole.

A final important new direction in short-range prediction is in modeling of the near surface layer. This is the layer that affects man most directly. Accurate predictions of its structure will contribute to successful predictions of the dispersal of pollutants in the atmosphere, and of fog and other visibility- and ceiling-reducing factors that hamper aircraft operations. Modeling of this layer is a difficult undertaking, since its characteristics and behavior are controlled in large measure by turbulent processes. Both theoretical work and field observational programs will be required to advance this effort. We are still a long way from being able to make surface-layer prediction a part of the routine prognosis.

Medium-Range Prediction

During the past dozen years, the greatest gains in forecast skill have probably occurred at medium range (1-5 days). These gains are the direct outcome of the development and application of numerical prediction models capable of forecasting the formation and movement of synoptic-scale weather systems. The method differs in no way from that described in connection with short-range prediction; it is simply extended for a longer period.

Surface weather predictions are now quite satisfactory for periods of about 48 hours. Upper-level prognoses show some degree of skill for periods as long as three to five days. Again, pressure and wind patterns are better forecast than such elements as precipitation. At medium ranges

it is still possible to infer likely areas of convective activity — thunderstorms and the like — but prediction of individual small-scale disturbances is completely beyond the realm of possibility.

Numerical experiments conducted as part of GARP suggest that it is possible, in principle, to forecast day-to-day weather changes for periods as long as two to three weeks in advance — though some critics feel this is an excessive figure in terms of what the public would judge to be successful forecasting. In any event, there is good reason to believe that useful forecasts can be made by numerical methods for periods well in excess of the present three-to-five day limit.

The main obstacles in the way of increasing the time range of forecasts (and thereby also their accuracy, even at shorter ranges) are the lack of an adequate observational network on a worldwide basis and deficiencies in the physical formulation of the prediction models. A principal aim of GARP is to overcome these observational and physical shortcomings.

A number of areas or industries have been identified in which more accurate predictions in the five- to twenty-day range would result in great economic benefit. Among these are agriculture, transportation, public utilities, and the construction and fishing industries.

Long-Range Prediction

Long-range prediction is a controversial subject. Its proponents make a variety of claims, ranging from the ability to forecast a given day's weather weeks or months in advance to the ability to forecast, with some small degree of skill, departures of temperature or precipitation from their monthly or seasonal means. Skeptics contend that the whole business is a waste of time, either that we do not know how to make long-range predictions or that long-range prediction is an impossibility. Where does the truth lie?

First we might ask: Are there valid grounds for attempting long-range prediction? Here the answer is definitely "yes." If weather changes were due exclusively to migratory synoptic- or smaller-scale weather systems, it is known from the GARP experiments cited previously that prediction would not be possible beyond two or three weeks. But it has long been recognized that there are larger-scale patterns in the atmosphere which tend to persist or recur over periods of weeks, months, or seasons. Drought episodes and prolonged spells of warm or cold weather may be cited as examples of such patterns. They are associated with abnormal features of the circulation—unusual displacements of the jet stream, the semi-permanent high and low pressure centers, and so forth.

Theories of Causation — The cause of long-period weather changes is a debatable subject. Many investigators have sought to connect them to extraterrestrial events — to variations of solar radiation, in particular — but the evidence in favor of an extraterrestrial origin is not impressive. Other investigators have suggested that they are caused by complex feedback mechanisms within the atmosphere. This hypothesis cannot be discounted. In laboratory experiments with rotating fluids, it has been found possible to generate long-period (on the time-scale of the model) circulation fluctuations even when external conditions are kept rigidly constant.

A final theory, which has steadily gained support, attributes long-period weather variations to interactions of the atmosphere with surface features. Anomalies of sea-surface temperature and of snow cover are examples of conditions that are believed capable of producing and perpetuating abnormal weather situations.

Forecasting Methods — Though some physical reasoning may enter into the formulation of a long-range forecast, the methods currently in use do not have a physical basis. The numerical methods applied at shorter ranges are not, as presently formulated, appropriate to long-range prediction.

Thus, main reliance is put on extrapolation, statistical, and analogue methods of forecasting, and human judgment plays a heavy role. The results obtained from these methods show at best only slight skill, and there seems little or no hope of significant improvement through their continued use and development. However, in view of the great economic importance of long-range prediction and the growing evidence that a meaningful physical understanding of long-period atmospheric variations can be achieved, it is essential that efforts to derive more suitable quantitative methods of prediction be continued and strengthened.

Needed Scientific Activity — Activities of two types deserve particular encouragement in this respect. First are programs to acquire the kind of global data needed for establishing the physical basis of long-range prediction. Such programs will have to endure for a long time and will not only have to measure the usual meteorological variables employed in numerical prediction but will have to measure additional parameters such as sea-surface temperature, snow cover, and the like. It is apparent that observations from satellites will be the key element in a global monitoring effort.

A second type of activity that merits vigorous support is experimental work in numerical modeling of the general circulation, of the sort now practiced by a number of groups in the United States. From such experiments, it may well be possible to discover the underlying causes of long-term weather and climatic anomalies. In fact, the modeling experiments are essential to the observational effort, for without them we can never be sure, until perhaps it is too late, that the proper variables are being measured.

Long-Range Weather Forecasting

Scientists who work in long-range weather forecasting encounter great difficulties, not only in the intricacies of their chosen field but also in getting across to other scientists and the lay public the essential nature of their problem and the reasons for their painfully slow progress in the modern-day milieu of satellites, computers, and atomic reactors. When solar eclipses can be predicted to fractions of a second and the position of a satellite pinpointed millions of miles out in space, it is not readily understandable why reliable weather predictions cannot be made for a week, month, season, or even a year in advance. Indeed, eminent scientists from disciplines other than meteorology, underestimating the complexity of the long-range problem, have tried to solve it only to come away with a feeling of humility in the face of what the late von Neumann used to call "the second most difficult problem in the world" (human behavior presumably being the first).

And yet, the potential economic value of reliable long-range forecasts probably exceeds that for short-range (daily) forecasts. Many groups need as much as a month or a season or more lead-time to adjust their plans. These include such diverse types as manufacturers (e.g., summer suits, raincoats, farm implements), fuel and power companies, agriculturalists, construction companies, and commodity market men, to say nothing of vacationers. Aside from this, long-range forecasting, by setting the climatic background peculiar to a given month or season, is of distinct value to the short-range forecaster. For example, it can alert him to the likelihood of certain types of severe storms, including hurricanes, intense extratropical cyclones, and even broad areas most frequently vulnerable to tornadoes.

Most of the needs of these groups for long-range forecasts cannot presently be met, however, because of the low skill level of predictions or the inability to predict anomalous weather at ranges beyond a month or season. Why is the problem so intractable?

The General Problem

In the first place, long-range forecasting requires routine observations of natural phenomena over vast areas — and by vast we mean at least hemisphere-wide coverage in three dimensions. More probably, the entire world's atmosphere, its oceans and its continents, must be surveyed because of large-scale interactions within a fluid that has no lateral boundaries but surrounds the entire earth. In contrast to the physicist, the meteorologist has no adequate laboratory in which to perform controlled experiments on this scale, although some recent work with electronic computers holds out hope for useful simulation.

Inadequate Observational Networks — When the immense scale of the atmosphere is realized, it becomes clear that the present network of meteorological and oceanographic observations is woefully inadequate. Even in temperate latitudes of the northern hemisphere, relatively well covered by surface and upper-air reports, there are "blind" areas of a size greater than that of the United

States. The tropics are only sparsely covered by reports, and the data coverage in the southern hemisphere is poorer still.

In the southern hemisphere, a moat thousands of miles in diameter separates the data-rich antarctic continent from the temperate latitudes, making it virtually impossible to get a coordinated picture of what is occurring now, let alone what may occur in the future. The "secrets of long-range forecasting locked in Antarctica" — a cliché often found in press articles — are indeed securely locked. Of course, cloud and radiation observations from satellites are assisting to an ever increasing degree, but better methods of determining the atmosphere's pressure, wind, and temperature distribution from satellite and other types of observations are urgently needed.

Inadequate Understanding — Even if every cubic mile of the atmosphere up to a height of 20 kilometers were continuously surveyed, however (and there are 2,500 million such volumes), reliable long-range forecasts would still not be realizable. Regardless of their frequency and density, observations are not forecasts; they merely provide "input data" for extended forecasting. Meteorologists have yet to develop a sufficient understanding of the physics of the atmosphere and the ocean to use these input data effectively in long-range forecasting, although this understanding is unlikely to come about in the absence of such data.

The Present Situation

The Data Base — Today the data and facilities for making long-range forecasts, inadequate as they may be, are far better than ever. In addition to about 25,000 surface weather reports (22,000 over land and 3,000 over sea) available each day at a center like Washington, there are 900 balloon observations of wind direction and speed, and 1,500 radiosonde observations of upper air pressure,

temperature, and humidity and, frequently, wind. In the same 24-hour period about 1,300 aircraft reports, dozens of indirect soundings of upper air temperatures made by the Nimbus-SIRS satellite system, and hundreds of satellite cloud photographs are received.

While these figures are impressive they are inadequate, especially because they represent a most uneven geographical array of observations and neglect proper surveillance of the ocean. The vast blind areas are, unfortunately, located in important wind and weather system-generating areas, like the northern Pacific Ocean, the tropics, and parts of the southern hemisphere. These systems, once generated, soon influence weather in distant areas around the world, their complex effects often traveling faster than the storms themselves. Hence, if an area is especially storm-prone during a particular winter, the storms will persistently influence other areas thousands of miles distant, sometimes leading to floods or droughts. Obviously, if the wind and weather characteristics in the primary generating area are imperfectly observed one cannot hope to predict the distant responses.

As pointed out earlier, data alone, regardless of how extensive in space and how frequent in time, are not sufficient to insure reliable long-range forecasts. It does appear, however, that more data of special kind and accuracy are required if a successful solution is to be obtained. The kinds of data required and a rough estimate of the density will be discussed later.

State of the Art — Forecasts can be made for future days by using elaborate numerico-dynamical methods and high-speed computers. In these methods, one predicts various meteorological elements at many levels for successive time-steps. The approach always begins with the initial conditions observed at many levels at a certain time over a large area like the northern hemisphere and forecasts for time-steps of about 15 minutes. Each iteration starts from the last prediction, and the forecast is carried forward for many days.

Numerical predictions of this kind form the basis for the extended (5-day) forecasts made by the National Weather Service, an additional component being supplied by the experience of the forecaster. How accurate are they?

The skill of the final pressure-pattern predictions made by the present "man-machine mix" from two to six days in advance is shown in

Figure IV-9 by the curve marked "Present." Without going into details, 1.00 on the vertical scale implies perfect forecasts, and 0 indicates forecasts that are no better than maps randomly selected from the same month of past years. As can be seen in Figure IV-9, extended forecasts deteriorate rapidly from day to day; by the sixth day, one might as well use the initial day's map as a forecast ("persistence"). Even at the fourth day, the skill is low enough to be of marginal economic value. Assuming, however, that the present accuracy of forecasts for the fourth day are economically valuable, we might ask

how good the two- to six-day predictions would have to be to give us accuracy equal to the four-day figure at two weeks, or 14 days in advance. These computed values are shown in the upper curve marked "Future." Thus, we see that a six-day forecast will have to be about as good as a two-day forecast is now. A six-day forecast will have to be about 25 times better than at present (ratio of the squares of the six-day correlations for "Present" and "Future"), a four-day forecast about 10 times better.

Prospects — These are tremendous strides that will have to be made, especially if one considers the frustratingly slow rate of progress in improving short-range weather forecasts over the past twenty years. The situation suggests that some major breakthrough in understanding, and in the density and quality of observations, must come about before detailed predictions in time and space out to two weeks or more will be realized. There is controversy in the meteorological community as to whether forecasts of this type will ever be possible.

Yet the potential for economically valuable long-range predictions is not as bleak as might be gathered from this discussion. While the forecast for a given day well in advance may be greatly in error using the above method, the general weather characteristics of a period — say, the average of computerized forecasts for the second or third week in advance — may turn out to contain economically valuable information. There is still no evidence this is so, but the hope exists that better and more observations combined with more knowledge of atmospheric modeling will result in this advance. Numerical modeling may make a major spurt forward because of the development of a first model aimed at coupling air and sea.

What Needs To Be Done

In order to bring about this progress and raise the level of the "Pres-

Figure IV–9 — FORECASTING SKILL

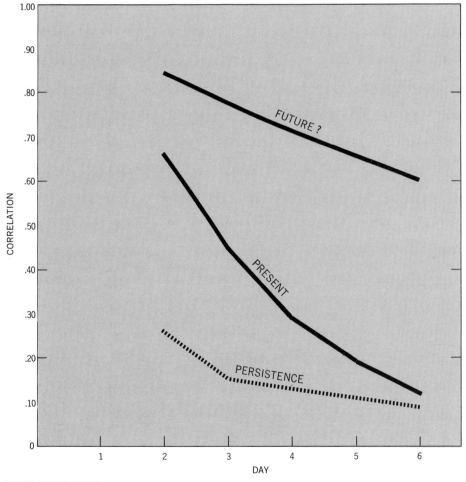

BASED ON 156 CASES

The graph shows the accuracy — and limitations — of National Weather Service forecasts of the pressure pattern for North America for the period March 1968 to February 1969.

ent" curve in Figure IV-9, a vast World Weather Watch (WWW) program to acquire an adequate network of observations has been set in motion by the WMO (World Meteorological Organization) and a companion research arm, GARP (Global Atmospheric Research Program), under ICSU (International Council of Scientific Unions) and WMO. The aims, rationale, and scope of these undertakings have been well documented in many reports and will not be reiterated here; suffice to say that a satisfactory solution of long-range forecasting problems is not likely to come about without them.

Statistical Aggregation—Nevertheless, the future of long-range weather forecasting does not and should not depend solely on the possibilities inherent in the iterative approach described earlier. Virtually every group of meteorologists that has attacked this problem over the past century has done so by working not with short time-step iterations but, rather, by studying statistical ensembles and the evolution of average wind and weather systems — e.g., from month to month and season to season. The long-range forecasting services of the Soviet Union, England, Japan, and the United States operate with statistical aggregates as well as physical methods. In the statistical approach, it is taken for granted that the average prevailing wind and weather patterns for one month, together with the associated abnormalities of sea temperatures and land surfaces (e.g., covered or free of snow), largely determine how the general weather patterns are going to develop during the following month under the influence of the solar radiation appropriate to time of year. A small effort in numerical modeling using this philosophy has begun.

How good are long-range predictions by conventional non-iterative methods? This is a question of scientific as well as practical importance, because any positive skill over and above climatological probability im-

plies knowledge that ought to funnel into further research and thereby lead to more reliable prediction. The present skill at forecasting departures from normal of average temperature at 100 cities over the United States for 5-day, 30-day, and experimental seasonal forecasts may be roughly given as 75, 61, and 58 percent, respectively, if chance is defined as 50 percent. Similarly, for precipitation, 5-day, 30-day, and seasonal forecasts average roughly 59, 52, and 51 percent, respectively. While these skills are far from perfect they do indicate, particularly for temperature, that the methods contain some knowledge of long-term atmospheric behavior. The 5- and 30-day forecasts that are released to the public appear to be of definite economic value, judging from hundreds of comments by users and also from their reaction when the forecasts are not received on time.

Despite the work and performance of many groups around the world along these practical lines and the fact that their forecasts show some small but definite skill in long-range prediction (contrasted with the utter failure, up to now, of dynamical iterative models at periods up to a month), the statistical-physical-synoptic (synoptic here meaning an over-all view with the help of maps) approach has been relatively neglected by meteorologists in the United States.

The Role of Oceanography— Oceanographers may see the long-range problem more clearly than meteorologists as one in which statistical aggregates play an important part — both in forecasting general thermal conditions in the sea and in forecasting its long-period interaction with the atmosphere. Perhaps this is because large-scale changes in the sea take place much more slowly (about ten times more slowly) than in the atmosphere and the reasons can therefore provide a sort of memory bank for the atmosphere.

In the past decade, research has shown that the thermal state of the

oceans, especially the temperatures in the upper few hundred meters, varies considerably from month to month and year to year, and that these variations are both cause and result of disturbed weather conditions over areas thousands of miles square. By complex teleconnected processes, the effects of these disturbed conditions are transmitted to areas thousands of miles distant. Thus, the prevailing wind systems of the globe — the westerlies, the trade winds, and the jet streams — may be forced into highly abnormal patterns with concomitant abnormalities of weather. Because these reservoirs of anomalous heat in the ocean are deep, often up to 500 meters, and may last for long periods of time, the atmosphere can be forced into long spells of "unusual" weather, sometimes resulting in regional droughts or heavy rains over periods ranging from months to seasons, and even years or decades.

Potential Lines of Action — The interface between meteorology and oceanography is thus a promising area which should receive more attention. Several items are needed:

1. A network of observations for both air and sea measurements over the world's oceans, or at least over the Pacific Ocean where much of the world's weather appears to be generated. This network can be a mix of ocean weather ships, specially equipped merchant ships, and — particularly — unmanned, instrumented buoys which have now been demonstrated to be feasible. A network of observations about 500 kilometers apart would be adequate as a start; later, the data gathered could indicate whether a finer or coarser grid is necessary. Satellite measurements can supplement but cannot replace these observations, particularly the subsurface ones which monitor the heat reser-

voirs of the sea and give information on the ocean currents.

2. "Air-sea interaction" should be more than a catch phrase. It is a subject which must occupy the efforts of the best young men in geophysics today. Equally important is meteorologist-oceanographer interaction. These men must not be steered only into narrow avenues where they lose sight of the big problems that lie at the heart of long-range prediction. Special seminars and inclusion into academic curricula of large-scale air-sea problems on long time-scales (months, seasons, and decades) are necessary despite the imprecise knowledge relative to short-period phenomena and short-range numerical weather prediction.

3. Special attempts are needed to bring meteorologists and oceanographers together more fre-quently in universities and laboratories where they can analyze oceanographic and meteorological data in real time, conduct joint discussions of what went on and is going on, and try to predict what *will* go on in subsequent months. This will involve computers and much research, but the research effort will be sparked by the satisfaction of seeing one's predictions verified. This type of stimulus has been largely missing in the oceanographic community, where oceanographers have had to work on restricted problems mainly with data months or years old or with series of observations embracing a small area.

These same observations and procedures, and their exploitation, will assist in most of ocean-air inquiry, whether iterative or non-iterative methods are employed. The ultimate long-range prediction scheme will probably be a combination of all three facets — physical, statistical, and synoptic.

Whether science will be able to achieve appreciable skill in long-range weather prediction should be known in the next ten to twenty years, providing enough trained people are efficiently employed and adequate data, as suggested by the WWW and GARP programs, become available. If, however, an unbalanced program is embarked upon, with little or no use made of statistics and synoptics, it is unlikely that good, practical long-range forecasts will be achieved. Considering the rate of progress already achieved despite the complexity of the problem, the small number of scientists who have attacked it, and the inadequacy of data and tools in the pre-computer age, the outlook is optimistic, particularly in view of the WWW and GARP programs. General forecasts for periods up to a year in advance are quite within reach; even the general character of the coming decade's weather may be foretold in advance.

Short-Term Forecasting, Including Forecasting for Low-Altitude Aviation

Substantial progress has been made during the past two or three decades in the nonclassical, exotic areas of the atmospheric sciences and their applications. From a state of almost no knowledge of the characteristics of the atmosphere between 10 and 30 kilometers, rawinsonde networks and high-flying, instrumented aircraft have enabled us to produce excellent analyses and prognoses over most of the northern hemisphere. Rocketsonde programs are greatly expanding our knowledge of the atmosphere from 30 to 100 kilometers. Meteorological satellites promise to enable the meteorologist to expand his charts to cover the globe. Furthermore, the speed and capacity of the electronic computer make it possible for his charts to be prepared in time for practical use. The machines produce upper-air wind and temperature fields that are as accurate as those of an experienced meteorologist.

These and similar advances have great practical value. For example, sophisticated climatic techniques permit introduction of the weather factor into construction planning and other operations. Twenty years ago, Fawbush and Miller, in Oklahoma, began what is now a successful national program of advising the public of threatening weather such as tornadoes and hailstorms. Weather-modification programs at military airfields near Spokane and Anchorage have all but eliminated air-traffic delays due to wintertime supercooled fog at those locations.

Air-pollution research and operations promise to benefit planning for industrial and residential areas, warning the public of impending high pollution levels, and locating pollution sources. Simulations of atmospheric circulation features and weather-modification efforts are beginning to enable atmospheric scientists to assess, quickly and relatively economically, the effects of deliberate or inadvertent modifications in the structure or dynamics of meteorological features through a wide range of scales.

Progress has also been great with respect to sheer volume of output in both the classical and exotic areas of the atmospheric sciences, thanks both to the electronic computer and other modern methods of communication and to improvements in organization and management.

Evaluation of Forecast Performance

The "bread and butter" products of the meteorologists, however, are the hour-to-hour and day-to-day forecasts of rain, snow, and temperature for the general public and of airfield and low-level flying weather. These have not fared so well. Reliable figures to demonstrate improvement of accuracy over the past few decades are not available for scientific judgment of the performance of the meteorological community. Statistics do exist for a large number of forecast targets (cities, airports) for a limited time period and for a few selected targets for two or three decades. However, this sparse data sample (which may be quite misleading) and subjective evaluations over the years suggest that, in an over-all sense, short-period forecasts have demonstrated little improvement for several decades.

Routine Forecasts of Temperature and Precipitation — Between 1942 and 1965, for example, the Chicago office of the National Weather Service (NWS) showed a steady improvement in their combined weather and temperature forecasts of about .33 percent per year. Large temperature-forecast errors (10°F. or more) made by the Salt Lake City office decreased from one such error every 6 days to one each 14 days. (Statistics for the over-all temperature-prediction capability of this office are not available.) A study of 260 NWS stations discerned no noticeable change in the ability to forecast rain "today" during the first half of the 1960's, but did note an increase of about 3 percent in the number of accurate predictions of rain "tonight" and "tomorrow." Scattered data such as these suggest that the accuracy of routine, classical forecasts of tem-

perature and precipitation has increased — but only very slowly.

Hurricane and Typhoon Positions — Forecasts for special types of weather events in some, if not most, cases have fared better. For example, from 1955 to 1965, the NWS's 24-hour forecasts of hurricane positions improved from an average error of about 125 nautical miles to one of about 110 nautical miles. With regard to similar forecasts for typhoons in the western Pacific, made jointly by the Air Force and Navy weather services, errors diminished from nearly 170 nautical miles in the mid-1950's to about 110 in 1969.

Winds — Forecasts of winds for high-flying aircraft are in the "new" and specialized area. Between the early and late 1960's, wind-prediction errors at 20,000 feet dropped from over 15 to under 11 knots. With regard to similar forecasts for low-flying aircraft (e.g., at 5,000 feet) which, although part of a specialized activity, can hardly be classed as exotic, the reduction was about one-half that for the higher level.

Visibility and Cloud Cover — The predictions of airfield ceiling and visibility made by the Air Weather Service (U.S. Air Force) are representative of those made by other services. Their statistics for the period January 1968 through January 1970, compiled from the records of 200-odd airfields, show a small improvement, not necessarily representative of performance improvements of previous years. The accuracy increased between 3 and 4 percent for forecasts with time ranges of 3, 6, 12, and 24 hours. By 1970, the forecasts were better than persistence (no change from "time of observation") by nearly 4 percent at 3 hours and nearly 8 percent at 24 hours. Statistics for predictions of low-level, in-flight clouds and weather are not available, but are likely to be about the same as those for airfield conditions.

Verification systems used for the kinds of forecasts discussed above necessarily vary considerably. Opinions of atmospheric scientists regarding the representativeness of the data, and the value of the methods, also differ widely. On the whole, however, it can be said that the status of forecasting is about the same for cities, airfields, and low-level flying — on the average not bad, on occasion seriously deficient, and improving very slowly.

Factors Responsible for Improvements in Forecasting

The Norwegian Theory — The Norwegian air-mass and frontal theory, developed around 1920, began to influence meteorological research and application on a large scale by the late 1930's. It represented a scientific and conceptual revolution that substantially improved the capabilities of the atmospheric scientist. The Norwegian theory was largely subjective, and its application relied on the individual skill and imagination of trained and experienced practitioners. A large part of the theory was concerned with the distribution and intensity of rain, surface temperature and wind changes, and cloudiness — elements that directly influence man in his daily activities.

The Rossby Theory — A second revolution in concept was initiated by Rossby in the 1940's. In contrast to the Norwegian theory, Rossby's approach emphasized the importance of upper-level wind and temperature patterns, whose influences on sensible weather were broad and ill-defined. The theory was objective and lent itself to mathematical calculation. Almost at the outset, after refinements by a number of atmospheric scientists, Rossby's basic theory began to produce usable prognoses of upper-level wind and temperature fields. Further refinements produced relatively large-scale fields of vertical air-movement from which it has become possible to predict broad areas of cloud and precipitation with measurable skill. At first, the necessarily large volume of data was processed manually; with the arrival of electronic computers in the mid-1950's, processing could be completed in a few hours.

This approach to research and prediction caught the fancy of most modern atmospheric scientists. Their fascination with an objective system that really worked — together with, in a sense, a commitment to large, expensive computer systems — has brought into being a breed of scientist different from those of pre-Rossby days. This new approach has strengths, but it also has weaknesses. On the one hand, real progress has been made in predicting for high-altitude jet aircraft and even, hopefully, in forecasting large-scale atmospheric features several days ahead of time. On the other hand, de-emphasis of the Norwegian theory has, if anything, degraded the meteorologist's ability to deal with the small-scale atmospheric patterns associated with weather at or near the earth's surface.

The current approach has made some inroads on the short-range, small-area problem. In the past three or four years, programs employing closer grid networks and more attention to the vertical variation of low-level meteorological elements have increased the detail of computer-produced prognoses. In recent tests, three-dimensional air-trajectory computer programs have increased the accuracy of forecasts of airfield weather by a few percent in selected geographic areas.

Technological Contributions — Most of the small increases in short-period weather forecasts of the past decade or so are not attributable to the atmospheric sciences, however. Thus, speeded-up communications and computer-operations systems have brought the "data-observation time" closer to the "forecast time";

since short-period forecasts are more accurate than long-period ones, an improvement has been gained. Networks of observation stations have gradually been augmented, beneficially realigned, and provided with improved instrumentation. New kinds of data, such as those from weather radar, have helped especially in very short period forecasting (minutes to hours) of clouds, precipitation, and severe weather. Improved Air Weather Service and other weather-reconnaissance planes have strengthened the National Weather Service's diagnostic capability; they have been vital in pinpointing hurricane locations and specifying their intensities. Judicious use of various stratifications of past weather data (climatology), again a technique requiring no meteorological skill in its applications, has helped to reduce large errors in local forecasts. There have also been advances in management practices, such as grouping specialized meteorologists at locations where they can work uninterrupted by telephonic or face-to-face confrontations with their public or military customers.

Satellites — The meteorological satellite is the most significant innovation in the atmospheric sciences since the computer. By far its greatest contribution to date has been to provide the meteorologist with cloud-cover information on a global basis. Research on the use of infrared data obtained by satellite is growing; these data have real potential, but they have not yet contributed to improvement in routine short-period prediction.

The satellite has vastly increased day-to-day knowledge of existing cloud cover, which in turn has improved subjectively derived circulation patterns that embrace fronts, major storm centers (including hurricanes), and other large-scale tropical features, and even some of the larger thunderstorms. It is sometimes feasible to deduce upper-level winds from observed cloud features.

The satellites assist the forecaster to make predictions for areas such as the oceans and regions of the southern hemisphere, where data cannot be obtained by conventional means. In special cases — e.g., in overseas military operations and in flights over regions of the United States not covered by conventional data-gathering systems — they can be of much, occasionally vital, aid to the weather forecaster. Without rapid access to good-quality, recent satellite read-outs, however, the value of the data for short-period forecasting drops quickly.

It must be remembered that satellites describe *present* conditions; the atmospheric scientist is still confronted with the classical problem of predicting how conditions will change. Furthermore, satellites do not measure parameters beneath the tops of clouds (except for thin cirrus).

Actions to Improve the Value of Forecasts

As noted earlier, an adequate data base for evaluating weather forecasting does not exist. A satisfactory evaluation program also does not exist with respect to the community of atmospheric scientists. There are sporadic evaluation programs, but statistics for one kind of forecast do not necessarily apply to other kinds and proper assessments for long periods of years are not available. Further, forecast-verification programs are normally conducted by the agencies that make the forecasts themselves, leaving open the question of objectivity.

Operational Data Transmission — Over data-sparse areas such as remote oceanic regions, airlines and other flying agencies are already testing the use of rapid, automated transmission of operational data via satellite to management centers. Selected meteorological data should be included and made available to appropriate weather-forecasting stations. Similarly, in-flight weather data over the continental United States should be made available on call to stations making short-period predictions for the public, for airfields, and for low-level flying activities. The large numbers of aircraft in U.S. airspace constitute existing platforms with the potential for providing much valuable data for short-period forecasting.

As a general rule, the shorter the period of a forecast, the more detailed and dense (in three dimensions) should be the data used in the prediction process and the smaller the required area to be represented by the data. The current rawinsonde network over the United States is excellent for long-period forecasts, but as the period decreases to half a day or less the density of observations begins to leave much to be desired. Further, upper-air wind analysis and prognoses prepared by the computer and used by the forecaster are smoothed in the computational process.

Computer Models — Efforts to produce lower-troposphere computer models with finer and finer meshes should be expanded, since work done to date has already shown some gain. Development of adequate display techniques should accompany these efforts.

Radar and Satellite Data — Increased emphasis should be placed on better utilization of radar information, including digital processing and use of interactive graphics to display data and to integrate them with other kinds of information.

Greatly increased research should be conducted to apply meteorological satellite data to the short-term forecast problem.

The Man-Machine Mix — Considerably greater effort should be directed toward the man-machine mix in forecasting. There should be greater exploitation of the valuable — albeit subjective — Norwegian theory of air masses and fronts. Digital graphics offer significant potential.

Microminiaturization should be emphasized in the development of new sensing and processing equipment in the interests of reducing lag times of sensors as well as of reducing the weight of equipment that must be borne on aircraft, rockets, or balloons.

Regardless of research directed at improving short-period forecasting, however, progress will almost inevitably be slow (except for new kinds of applications) because of the chaotic nature of smaller-scale atmospheric phenomena and because meteorologists are required to state certain kinds of prediction in probabilistic terms. In some areas the state of the art appears to have reached a plateau; if this is so, what are needed are breakthroughs.

4. CLEAR AIR TURBULENCE

Clear Air Turbulence and Atmospheric Processes

Understanding of atmospheric processes appears to decrease rapidly with decreasing scale or typical size of the phenomena considered. Thus, it has only recently been recognized that turbulence in clear air in the upper troposphere and lower stratosphere is an important part of the energy cycle of the atmosphere.

Although motions in the atmosphere at scales less than a kilometer are often turbulent to some degree, the occasional outbreaks of moderate or severe turbulence that have plagued aviation for the past decade or more have important implications for the study and prediction of large-scale atmospheric motion.

These motions are a result of differential heating. In the process of attempting to restore a uniform distribution of heat in the atmosphere, the motions and processes of the atmosphere create narrow layers in which both wind and temperature variations are concentrated. The sharpest of these occur in the boundary layer, in the fronts associated with weather systems, and in the vicinity of the jet stream near the tropopause.

In each of these regions of strong gradients, turbulence typically occurs when the gradients become strong enough. The turbulent motions cause mixing and tend to smooth the variations of wind and temperature. In the process, a considerable amount of heat and momentum may be transported from one region to another, and with all turbulence there is a conversion of kinetic energy to thermal energy.

The basic cycle of events in the atmosphere may thus be viewed as a sequence in which:

1. Large-scale gradients created by differential heating result in large-scale motions.

2. The large-scale motions concentrate the variations caused by this differential heating into narrow zones which now contain a significant fraction of the total variation.

3. As the degree of concentration increases, turbulence arises in these zones, destroying the strong variations and thus modifying the larger-scale structure of the atmosphere.

In this sense, turbulence in the zones of concentrated variation is an essential part of the thermodynamic processes of the atmosphere.

Atmospheric scientists have long known that both the transport of heat and momentum and the dissipation of kinetic energy were strong in the boundary layer and in frontal regions. The importance of these same processes in clear air turbulence near the jet stream is a recent discovery.

Perhaps the most important practical implication of this development concerns the feasibility of long-range numerical weather prediction. Such predictions cannot be reliable for extended periods unless the computer models correctly simulate the energy budget or energy cycle of the atmosphere. It now appears likely that this cannot be done without taking account of the role of clear air turbulence — a phenomenon of too small a scale to be revealed by present standard sounding techniques or to be represented directly with the data fields used in the computer models.

The importance of clear air turbulence in the energy budget is illustrated by its contribution to the rate of dissipation of kinetic energy in the atmosphere. Although the exact value is subject to some controversy, the total dissipation rate probably will be somewhere in the range 5 to 8 watts per square meter, of which 2 to 3 watts per square meter probably occurs in the boundary layer. Studies of dissipation by Kung, using standard meteorological data, and by Trout and Panofsky, using aircraft data, both arrive at an estimate of 1.3 watts per square meter for the dissipation in the altitude range 25,000 to 40,000 feet near the tropopause.

Thus, despite the present uncertainty of these estimates, it appears that the region near the tropopause contributes on the order of 20 percent of the total dissipation of the atmosphere. The rate of dissipation in severe turbulence is about 400 times as large as that in air reported smooth by pilots and about 20 times as large as that in light turbulence. The estimates of Trout and Panofsky show that the light and moderate turbulence contributes the major fraction of the total dissipation in the layer near the tropopause; furthermore, their estimates show that about equal fractions of the dissipation in this layer are probably due to the severe clear air turbulence and to the smooth air. (It should be noted that the estimate of the contribution of severe turbulence is undoubtedly too low, because pilots attempt to avoid it if at all possible.)

Available Observational Data

Most of what is known about the structure of clear air turbulence and the regions in which it occurs results from investigations motivated by its impact on aviation. Clear air turbulence has caused injuries to crew members and passengers on commercial airlines, loss of control, and damage to aircraft structures. For these reasons, two main types of investigations have been carried out.

Pilot Reports — In the first type, reports of civil and military pilots are used in conjunction with standard weather data in an attempt to derive a gross climatology of both the frequency of occurrence of clear air turbulence and its association with wind and temperature fields. These data are biased because pilots try to avoid clear air turbulence; furthermore, the pilot reports are subjective and not uniform, due both to varying pilot temperament and to varying aircraft response to characteristics.

Instrumented Aircraft — In the second, aircraft specially instrumented to measure the gust velocities comprising the clear air turbulence are flown into such regions. The resulting data have been analyzed in a variety of ways. These programs have contributed significant and valuable information about the internal physics of the turbulent motion and about certain aspects of its statistical characteristics. The data are biased, however, by the fact that turbulence was being sought by pilots; thus, they cannot be used directly to establish the frequency of occurrence of clear air turbulence.

A more serious defect, from the scientific standpoint, is that these programs were conceived on the basis of the needs of aviation and aeronautical engineering; they were not designed to reveal information about the physics of turbulence or its details or interactions with larger-scale flows. Nevertheless, the available data could be used for scientific purposes more extensively than they have been.

In the past few years, attempts to conduct scientific studies of the physics of clear air turbulence with specially instrumented aircraft (in some cases with simultaneous use of ground-based radars) have been started in the United States, Canada, England, and the Soviet Union. Although the preliminary results from these programs appear both promising and encouraging, no definitive body of knowledge has yet emerged. The problem is that the accuracy of data required for scientific study of the physics of clear air turbulence and its interactions with the environment leads to requirements for basic sensors that severely test, or even exceed, current instrumentation capabilities.

Theoretical Knowledge

Despite these deficiencies in the collection of empirical data about clear air turbulence, there does appear to have been recent theoretical progress. Atmospheric scientists have long suspected that clear air turbulence is primarily a result of a particular mode of fluid-flow instability that occurs when there is weak density stratification relative to rapid vertical variation in the flow velocity. This phenomenon has been modeled in the laboratory by Thorpe, seen under water in the Mediterranean by Woods, and the characteristic shape has appeared on the scopes of radars used in turbulence studies by Hardy, Glover, and Ottersten as well as in a few photographs taken when the process was made visible by clouds. The hypothesis that clear air turbulence is indeed a manifestation of this particular fluid-flow instability provides an important conceptual basis for planning the structure of empirical investigations.

Recent work has also suggested that internal gravity waves in the atmosphere may be linked with the formation of clear air turbulence. An interesting possibility is that the waves may be absorbed in shear layers, and thus may act as a trigger for the outbreak of turbulence. The fact that gravity waves are often generated by flow over mountains may explain why clear air turbulence occurs more frequently in mountainous regions.

Basic Equations — Although the basic laws that govern clear air turbulence are the same mechanical and thermodynamic ones that apply to all fluid motion and can be expressed mathematically, there has been little success in applying the equations to the problem. The main reason is that mathematical theories that provide solutions to these equations do not seem to exist. The essential difficulty is that turbulence is a distinctly nonlinear process, and interactions on different scales are a crucial part of the physical phenomenon.

It is precisely this that makes clear air turbulence important to the energy cycle of the atmosphere. The kinetic energy destroyed by the turbulence comes from the kinetic energy of much larger-scale flows — those that we attempt to predict with numerical methods. The equations used in the computer models apply to averages of the variables over quite a large region, and should include terms that express the effect of smaller-scale motions within the region of averaging upon the averaged variables. Here again, the mathematical form of the correct equations is known, but some practical method must be found for representing in the models the contributions to these terms from the intense processes occurring in both clouds and clear air.

This probably can be accomplished for clear air turbulence only when a great deal more is known about its characteristics and its interactions with the large-scale processes. The most pressing need is for a thorough empirical study with aircraft, radar, and other means (perhaps laser techniques). Such a study has been recommended by the U.S. Committee for the Global Atmospheric Research Program.

Specific Questions About Clear Air Turbulence

The major questions concerning clear air turbulence now requiring answers fall into three groups:

First, questions concerning the origin or onset of clear air turbulence:

1. Is clear air turbulence generally the result of a particular fluid-flow instability? If so, what are the crucial parameters of the instability?

2. What are the typical atmospheric features in which clear air turbulence occurs and how is their structure related to the parameters of fluid instabilities? (Of particular interest are the relationships to vertical wind shear, horizontal temperature gradients, and the Richardson number.)

3. Are other small-scale processes, examples being gravity waves or local heating, important in the formation of clear air turbulence?

Second, questions concerning the evolution of clear air turbulence:

1. What is the precise evolution of the atmospheric variables at various scales during an outbreak of clear air turbulence?

2. How can this evolution be most economically summarized or depicted?

3. What are the temporal characteristics of the transport of momentum and heat, the flux and dissipation of energy, and the stress imposed on the larger-scale flow during an outbreak of clear air turbulence?

4. What are the relationships between processes occurring in one part of a patch of clear air turbulence and those of another? Are there relationships between apparently distinct patches of turbulence?

5. What characterizes the termination of an outbreak of clear air turbulence? What scars does turbulence leave in its environment?

Third, questions concerning the implication of clear air turbulence:

1. How often do patches of clear air turbulence of various sizes and intensity actually occur in various regions of the atmosphere?

2. What is the usual intensity of turbulence in the free atmosphere in regions in which flight is sensibly smooth?

3. How important is clear air turbulence — quantitatively — in the atmosphere's energy cycle compared to regions with the usual intensity of turbulence in air smooth for flight?

4. How large are the terms expressing the effects of clear air turbulence in the usual meteorological equations (used for numerical prediction) compared to other terms?

The urgent needs of aviation and aeronautical engineering for information on clear air turbulence and for reliable predictions of its occurrence will be finally and completely satisfied only when a full scientific understanding of the phenomenon is obtained. The same understanding will permit accurate determination of whether the effects of clear air turbulence must be incorporated in an attempt at extended numerical weather prediction. If this is necessary, and successful methods can be found, it will mark the crossing of a long plateau in attempts to understand the interactions of large- and small-scale motions.

The economic and social benefits that would accrue from a capability for long-range weather prediction and the needs of aviation make it imperative that the importance and characteristics of clear air turbulence in the general circulation of the atmosphere be investigated and comprehended.

Prediction and Detection of Wave-Induced Turbulence

The phenomenon of "clear air turbulence" is of particular importance to man's activities within the atmosphere because: (a) it is both a hindrance and hazard to aviation and (b) it accounts for roughly 20 to 30 percent of the total dissipation of the atmosphere's energy. The latter fact, only recently discovered, relates directly to our attempts to predict the global circulation weeks in advance. Without an adequate appraisal of this significant portion of the total energy budget, it will be impossible to model and predict the future state of the atmosphere.

Dimensions of the Problem

The name "clear air turbulence," or "CAT," has conventionally been used to refer to turbulence occurring several kilometers above the earth's surface and in air that is free of clouds and strong convective currents. But our understanding of CAT processes, which reached a new climax only in 1969-70, strongly implies that identical mechanisms also occur within clouds and storm systems.

Cumulative evidence is sufficiently persuasive to conclude that CAT occurs in internal fronts or layers in which the air is statically stable and across which there is strong shear of the wind either in speed or direction. Such conditions commonly prevail at both warm and cold fronts marked by clouds and precipitation. Increasingly abundant aircraft incidents, some of them fatal, also suggest that the CAT mechanism occurs at such frontal boundaries. The fact that the process has not been clearly identified as such is due to the general assumption by pilots and meteorologists that turbulence within clouds or storms is more commonly due to convective- or thunderstorm-like activity. But this assumption is untenable when no direct meteorological evidence of convective activity exists and when aircraft undergo forced maneuvers that can only be associated with waves and breaking waves; the latter are now recognized to be the primary, if not the sole, origin of what we have previously called "CAT."

Newly Recognized Features — Because it now seems clear that severe turbulence of the nonconvective variety also occurs within clouds and storms, it is fallacious to continue the usage "clear air turbulence." And since turbulence in both clear air and clouds and storms owe their origin to breaking waves, it has been proposed that such turbulence be renamed "wave-induced turbulence," or "WIT." Unless we recognize these important facts, we shall fail to appreciate the full dimensions of the problem. For example, while CAT generally occurs at relatively high altitudes, thus allowing the pilot time to recover from a turbulence-caused upset, severe WIT within frontal

storms may occur at very low altitudes without the possibility of safe recovery. Indeed, it is now reasonable to suppose that many previously unexplained fatal and near-fatal aircraft accidents owe their origin to WIT. Until this phenomenon is fully appreciated both by pilots and meteorologists, aircraft will continue to encounter potentially fatal hazards without warning.

Another deceptive aspect of the acronym "CAT" is its exclusion of wave-induced turbulence near cloud boundaries. This may have unfortunate consequences, since it is well known that cloud tops commonly occur at the base of temperature inversions, and the latter, when marked by sufficiently strong wind shear, are the seat of wave-induced turbulence. Indeed, there is reason to believe that the presence of clouds below the inversion will enhance the chance of WIT above. This is because radiative and evaporative cooling from cloud tops induces convective overturning and this decreases the wind shear below the inversion while enhancing the shear in and above the inversion. Similar arguments suggest that cloud bases may also be preferred regions of WIT.

Finally, recent radar observations (both ultra-high-resolution acoustic and microwave) of stable and breaking waves indicate that WIT is an almost ubiquitous feature at the low-level nocturnal inversion and the marine inversion. On occasion, therefore, especially in association with the low-level nocturnal jet, we may expect moderate to severe turbulence at low levels. These situations would be excluded from the present definition of CAT, which is restricted to turbulence at heights above the middle troposphere. Equally important, however, is the recognition that WIT plays a role in the mixing processes at the top of the boundary layer. This may have significant consequences for the metamorphosis of the boundary layer, and thus upon air-pollution meteorology.

Hazards and Cost Implications — All this is by way of indicating that WIT is far more widespread than is presently recognized. The associated hazards are also greater; and the consequences, both in terms of basic atmospheric processes and of ultimate operational predictability, are more far-reaching. This is so simply because our present classification of CAT excludes the many occurrences at low levels that might be confused with ordinary boundary-layer turbulence, and those within and near clouds and precipitation that are often misinterpreted as convectively produced turbulence.

Statistics on CAT occurrence, and its associated hazards and cost to aviation, must therefore be viewed as gross underestimates of the broader, but identical, phenomenon of WIT. Even so, the statistics compiled by the National Committee for Clear Air Turbulence indicate that damage to aircraft may have cost the Department of Defense $30 million from 1963 to 1965, to say nothing of crew injuries or the effect of turbulence in reducing combat effectiveness. The committee reported a study that showed the cost to commercial aviation in 1964 to have exceeded $18 million, of which a major portion was the increased expense caused by diversions around areas in which turbulence was forecast or had occurred.

The WIT Mechanism and Its Predictability

Our knowledge of the WIT mechanism is substantial — at least compared to the state of knowledge before 1968. A great deal more needs to be learned, however. Newly developed observational tools promise major advances in understanding the WIT mechanism which should open the way to a more realistic appraisal of the climatology of WIT and the physical conditions under which it occurs. Together, the instruments and the increased understanding should lead to improved predictability, although some of our new knowledge implies clear-cut limitations in this respect.

The Origin of WIT — Classical theory concerns the rapid growth of perturbations on an internal front (inversion) in a fluid, called Kelvin-Helmholtz instability, which leads to large-amplitude Kelvin-Helmholtz (K-H) waves. The rolling-up of these waves under the action of wind shear, and their subsequent breaking, like ocean waves breaking on the shore, produces turbulence.

The process may be described simply, as follows: Suppose that we have two fluids of different density and that we arrange them in a stable stratification with the lighter one on top. Then we set the fluids in motion, with one of the two moving faster than the other, or in the direction opposite to the other. If the density change across the interface is strong enough and the shear is not too great, smaller perturbations will be damped out and the interface will come back to rest. But when the shear is strong relative to the density gradient, the situation is unstable and the perturbations will grow rapidly with time; vortices are created, as though a tumbleweed were being rolled between two streams of air.

The condition leading to unstable K-H waves and turbulence is that the ratio of buoyancy forces (working to damp vertical perturbations) to shearing forces (working to enhance them) should be less than 1. One-fourth of this ratio is the gradient Richardson number, Ri, which is defined as

$$ \mathrm{Ri} = \frac{g}{\theta} \; \frac{\partial \theta}{\partial z} \Big/ \left(\frac{\partial V}{\partial z} \right)^2 \qquad (1) $$

where g is the acceleration of gravity, θ is potential temperature, $\partial\theta/\partial z$ is the vertical gradient of θ (positive whenever the atmosphere is more stable than in the neutrally buoyant or adiabatic case), V is the horizontal wind velocity, and $\partial V/\partial z$ is the wind

shear. A result obtained in 1931 that the critical Ri leading to K-H instability is 1/4 has been confirmed. More precisely, Ri > 1/4 is sufficient for stability, and Ri ≤ 1/4 is necessary, but not sufficient, for instability.

The entire process has been demonstrated by Thorpe in laboratory fluid experiments and by Woods in thin, hydrostatically stable sheets in the summer thermocline of the Mediterranean Sea. Both of these experiments show the development of beautifully formed billows, or K-H waves which roll up into vortices and finally break. And both demonstrate the general validity of the critical Ri ≤ 1/4.

Evidence from the Atmosphere — Ludlam has observed the existence of the K-H instability mechanism in the atmosphere by the presence of billow clouds, but only rarely are the combination of cloud and stability conditions just right to produce the lovely roll vortices in the clouds that are seen in the laboratory and the sea. The observation of their common presence in the atmosphere has awaited the use of ultrasensitive radars capable of detecting the weak perturbations in refractive index (due to temperature or humidity perturbations) which mark sharp inversions. Using three powerful radars at Wallops Island, Virginia, Atlas and his colleagues first reported the radar detection of clear air turbulence at the tropopause; Hicks, Angell, Hardy, and others have reported K-H waves and turbulence in clear air layers marked by static stability, large wind shear, and small Richardson number.

Undoubtedly the most striking evidence of the K-H process as a cause of WIT, and of its common occurrence at interval fronts, are the observations made possible by the use of a unique new ultrasensitive FM-CW (Frequency Modulated Continuous Wave) microwave radar at the Naval Electronics Laboratory Center, San Diego. This radar is capable of one-

meter vertical resolution, roughly a hundredfold increase over that previously available with radars of comparable sensitivity. With this new tool, it has been reported that K-H waves are a virtually ubiquitous feature of the marine inversion over San Diego at altitudes up to about one kilometer. Indeed, the atmospheric K-H waves observed in this manner are commonly as beautiful in form as those produced in the laboratory and observed in the sea. (See Figure IV-10) It is worth noting that the unexpectedly classical form of the waves, and their great frequency of occurrence within the marine inversion, recommends the southwest coast of the United States as an atmospheric laboratory for studies of WIT.

What the Data Show — The fact that the observed K-H waves are frequently restricted to exceedingly thin layers, sometimes only a few meters in depth, and rarely with amplitudes as large as 100 meters, explains why the previously available high-sensitivity radars of poor resolution could not identify them. In other words, the K-H wave structure was simply too small to be seen and the echoes appeared merely as thin, smooth layers marking the base of the inversion.

The new data also indicate that, though K-H wave activity may be in progress, the associated turbulence will not be intense unless the waves grow to large amplitude prior to breaking. This has been demonstrated by the erratic perturbations of the height of the radar-detected layer, indicative of moderate turbulence, which resulted from the breaking of K-H waves of 75-meter amplitude. In general, waves of significantly smaller amplitude appear not to produce appreciable turbulence.

Work now in progress shows that the turbulent kinetic energy following the breaking of the roll vortex of a K-H wave is directly proportional to the kinetic energy of the vortex im-

Figure IV–10 — WAVES AND TURBULENCE IN THE CLEAR ATMOSPHERE

Height (m)

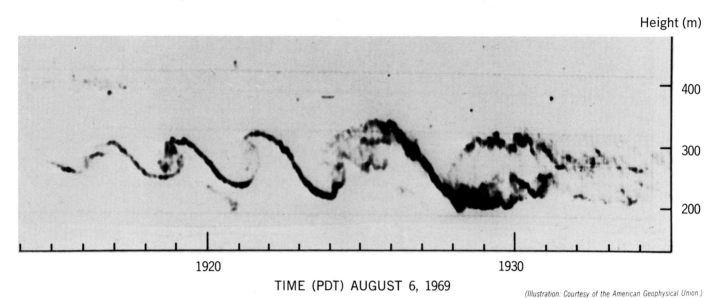

400

300

200

1920   1930

TIME (PDT) AUGUST 6, 1969

(Illustration: Courtesy of the American Geophysical Union.)

Radar echoes from the clear atmosphere reveal a group of amplifying and breaking waves in the low-level temperature inversion at San Diego, California, as observed with a special FM-CW radar. Waves are triggered by the sharp change of wind speed across the interface between the cool, moist marine layer and the warmer, drier air aloft. They move through the radar beam at the speed of the wind at their mean height, about 4 knots, so that crests appear at successive stages of development. In the second wave at 1919 PDT, cooler air from the wave peak drops rapidly as the breaking begins. By 1929 PDT the layer has become fully turbulent, and the radar echo subsequently weakens. Note, too, the secondary waves near the crests at 1919.5, 1922, and 1926 PDT; these secondary waves give rise to microscale turbulence, which causes the echo layers to be detected. The resulting turbulence would be weak, as detected by an aircraft. Waves of this type occur regularly in the low-level inversion, and are believed to be similar to those which cause the severe turbulence occasionally encountered by jet aircraft at high altitude.

mediately prior to breaking. The r.m.s. velocity of a vortex,

$$v_{rms} = 0.707 \, A\omega$$
$$= 0.707 \, A(\partial V/\partial z) \quad (2)$$

where A is the amplitude of the roll or wave, ω its angular rotation rate or vorticity, and $\partial V/\partial z$ the wind shear, thus provides a simple estimate of the expected turbulence; preliminary tests support this hypothesis. Moreover, it is of particular interest that the high-resolution radar data provide direct measures of A and its rate of growth as well as of $\partial V/\partial z$, the shear. Similarly, the turbulence intensity may be deduced from the r.m.s. perturbations in the echo-layer height subsequent to breaking. (As yet, the inherent doppler capability of the FM-CW radar, which would provide direct measurements of both vertical motion and roll vorticity, has not been implemented.)

Unresolved Problems — If Equation (2) is validated by experiments now in progress, we may contemplate the prediction of WIT from measurements and predictions of maximum wave amplitude and shear. But this assumes that we shall be able to predict the latter. At this writing, the relationship of the maximum wave amplitude to the thermal and wind structure of the environment is not understood. Present K-H wave theory is limited to small-amplitude waves and their initial growth rates; clearly, the theory needs to be extended to finite-amplitude waves. But rapid progress is more likely to come from experiments in the real atmosphere, such as those already mentioned, which involve somewhat more complex wind and temperature profiles and interactions than are likely to be tractable in finite-amplitude theoretical models.

In this regard, it should also be noted that the critical Richardson number, $Ri_c < \frac{1}{4}$, which might be regarded as a predictor of WIT, refers only to the initial growth stage of K-H instability. Since the high-resolution radar shows breaking K-H waves with amplitudes as small as 5 meters (with negligible resulting turbulence) and as large as 100 meters (with appreciable turbulence), a serious question is raised as to the vertical scales over which thermal stability and shear—and so Ri—need to be measured. Surely, the present data imply that Ri must be observed on scales of a meter or less to account for the small-amplitude waves. But it is not so clear that measurements with resolution of 10 to 100 meters or more, such as those available from present-day radiosondes, would be adequate to predict the occurrence of larger-amplitude waves. What, for example, happens to a growing unstable wave in a thin stratum when it reaches a dynamically stable layer in which Ri is significantly greater than ¼? We do not know. This is one of many important questions that needs to be answered by further research.

Other aspects of the new radar observations that are relevant to flight safety as well as to aircraft investigations of WIT and to its predictability, are: (a) the sharp vertical gradations in turbulence intensity (i.e., sometimes the turbulence is restricted to a stratum no more than a few tens of meters thick) and (b) the intermittancy of K-H waves and turbulence.

It is not surprising that one aircraft experiences significant turbulence while the next one encounters none in the same region. While the radar observations demonstrate that the base of the inversion and subsidiary sheets within it are the seat of K-H wave activity, their breaking is self-destructive in that the shear and stability to which they owed their origin are decreased, and Ri thus increased above its critical level. Accordingly, the breaking action acts as an escape valve to release the pressure for K-H activity, and turns the waves and turbulence off. On the other hand, the larger-scale atmospheric processes work to restore the initial conditions, and new K-H waves are triggered.

All this speaks to the difficult questions of aircraft experiments directed to observing the initial conditions for WIT, the energy budget involved, and, indeed, its entire life cycle. Precisely where and when should the measurements be made and how are they to be interpreted in the light of WIT's great spatial and temporal variability? Clearly, such experiments should preferably be conducted simultaneously with a radar capable of "seeing" the waves and turbulence directly.

Prospects for Prediction — The prior discussion raises serious doubts as to the ultimate achievement of pinpoint forecasts of WIT in either space or time. While one may expect, eventually, to be able to predict the medium- to large-scale processes that work to develop and sharpen internal fronts and shear, many presently unobservable small-scale phenomena (gravity waves, orographic lifting and tilting, convective motions, and such) will operate to reduce Ri to its critical value locally and trigger wave activity here and there. Accordingly, while we may expect significant improvements in the predictability of the heights of internal surfaces, and thus in the heights at which WIT is likely, and probably in the predicted intensity as well, the actual forecast will probably remain a probabilistic one for many years to come. We should therefore direct a good share of our attention to the remote-probing tools that are capable of detecting both the internal surfaces and the occurrence of waves and turbulence. As in the case of radar detection of thunderstorms, such observations are likely to provide the best short-term predictions of WIT for the foreseeable future.

Instrumentation for Detecting WIT

Although we have spoken extensively of the capability of ultrasensitive high-resolution radar techniques in detecting WIT, a few additional remarks need to be made concerning actual warning devices.

Ground-Based Devices — High-resolution FM-CW microwave radar is an obvious candidate for this task. At present, however, it is limited to a detection range (based on over-all sensitivity in detecting clear air inversions) of about 2 kilometers. An increase of range to 15 kilometers is attainable with available state-of-the-art components. This would accomplish the detection of clear-air WIT throughout the depth of the tropo-

sphere. A network of such stations across the nation, with fixed, vertically pointing antennas, is economically feasible. Fortunately, the significant internal fronts at which WIT occurs are horizontally extensive, so that detection of waves and turbulence at one or more stations would indicate the layers affected and the likelihood of WIT at the same height (or interpolated height for sloping layers) in between stations. (Note that we emphasize the need for observations with a high degree of *vertical* resolution, capable of detecting the suspect layers and measuring the amplitude and intensity of breaking waves.)

Airborne Radar — With regard to the use of high-resolution FM-CW microwave radar on board aircraft for purposes of detecting and avoiding WIT along the flight path, the 15-kilometer range capability would be inadequate to provide sufficient warning even if a high-gain antenna of the required dimensions (10′ to 15′ effective diameter) could be accommodated in the aircraft. Moreover, since the vertical resolution in such a use-mode would correspond to that of the beam dimension rather than the available high-range resolution, the radar could not discern wave amplitude and heights with precision. However, the use of such a radar in both downward- and upward-looking directions (from large antennas fitted within the fuselage structure) does appear feasible. Clear-air WIT could then be avoided by detecting the heights of internal surfaces and K-H wave activity above and below flight level and assuming continuity of layer slope. Whether or not such a system should be adopted depends on cost/benefit/risk ratios. The installation of a $100,000 radar seems warranted when aircraft carry more than 200 passengers. Certainly, it should be adopted for experimental purposes in connection with WIT research. The potential benefits of airborne high-resolution radar to both military and commercial aviation could then be better evaluated.

High-Resolution Acoustic Radar is another candidate for clear-air WIT detection from ground-based stations. Such radars have detected thin internal surfaces and stable and breaking wave activity to heights of 2 kilometers. The potential to reach 15 kilometers in the vertical direction can probably be realized, although the effect of strong winds aloft on the refraction of the acoustic beam remains an open question. Unfortunately, acoustic radar cannot be used on board fast-flying aircraft because of the slow speed of sound and the high acoustic noise levels.

Future Technology—Finally, a real hope still remains for the development of a coherent laser radar (or LIDAR) sufficiently sensitive to detect the small background concentrations of aerosols in the high troposphere and capable of measuring turbulence intensity through the doppler velocities. Although a theoretical feasibility study of such a device in 1966 indicated that the then available LIDARs could not accomplish the task, more recent developments in laser technology may now make such a system feasible. The National Aeronautics and Space Administration is presently conducting research and development along these lines.

A Note on Acoustic Monitoring

As is well known, the propagation of sound waves through the atmosphere is strongly affected by wind, temperature, and humidity. The possibility therefore exists that measurements of the propagation of sound waves could be used to derive information on important meteorological parameters.

The potential of these methods has been analyzed and some experimental results published. It has shown that acoustic echoes can readily be obtained from the atmospheric turbulence and temperature inhomogeneities always existing in the boundary layer of the atmosphere. The equipment required is relatively simple; it involves a radar-like system in which pulses of acoustic signal, usually about 1kHz in frequency, are radiated from an acoustic antenna, with echoes from the atmospheric structure obtained on the same or on a second acoustic antenna.

This field of acoustic echo-sounding of the atmosphere is very new and appears to hold considerable promise for studies of the boundary layer of the atmosphere—i.e., the lowest several thousand feet. Specifically, research is now being undertaken to identify its usefulness for the quantitative remote measurement of wind, turbulence, humidity, and temperature inhomogeneity. If, as expected, the technique is shown capable of measuring the structure of the boundary layer and the vertical profiles of these meteorological parameters, it will represent a major breakthrough in remote measurement of the atmosphere, which should be of great value to meteorological observations and research. Its primary application is likely to be in the monitoring of meteorological parameters in urban and suburban areas, for use by air-pollution and aviation agencies. In addition, it is already providing the research worker with totally new insight into the detailed structure and processes controlling the atmospheric boundary layer in which we live.

5. URBAN EFFECTS ON WEATHER AND CLIMATE

Urbanization and Weather

For centuries, man has speculated that major battles, incantations, large fires, and, lately, atomic explosions could affect weather, although he made no serious scientific attempts to modify weather until 25 years ago. Except for a few localized projects involving precipitation increases and fog dissipation, however, man's intentional efforts have yet to produce significant, recognized changes. Rather, the major means whereby man has affected weather have been inadvertent—through his urban environment.

Growing Awareness of the Problem

As long ago as 700 years or more, London had achieved a size great enough to produce a recognizable effect on its local weather, at least in terms of reduced visibility and increased temperature. Since major urban areas became prevalent in Europe following the Industrial Revolution, Europeans have directed considerable scientific attention to this problem of urban-induced weather change. Now that major urban-industrial complexes exist in many countries, world-wide attention has grown rapidly, particularly in the United States, where the growth of megalopolitan areas during the past ten to thirty years has brought with it increasing public and scientific awareness of the degree and, in some cases, the seriousness of urban effects on weather. Recent studies documenting significant urban-related precipitation increases in and downwind of Chicago, St. Louis, and industrial complexes in the state of Washington have further focused scientific and public attention on the urban-weather topic and its considerable potential.

Certainly, even the casual observer is aware that visibility is more frequently restricted in a major urban complex than in rural areas, and that this has come from smoke, other contaminants, increased fog, and their additive, smog. Most Americans are now aware that the temperature within a medium-to-large city is generally higher at any given time of the day or season than it is in rural areas. This temperature effect has been recognized and measured for many years, since its measurement, at least at the surface, is relatively easy. "Heat islands" for many cities of various sizes have been well documented.

Urban areas also act as an obstacle to decrease winds near the surface, to increase turbulence and vertical motions above cities, and to create, occasionally, a localized rural-urban circulation pattern. There have been enough descriptive studies, furthermore, to reveal that many other weather conditions are also being changed, often dramatically, by urban complexes. Although available results indicate that urban-induced weather changes are restricted to the cities and their immediate downwind areas and have little effect on macroscale weather conditions, the "urban flood" and advent of the megalopolis could conceivably lead to significant weather changes over large downwind regions.

Value Judgments — The question of desirability of the weather changes wrought by urbanization has only recently been considered. The fact that many of the urban-induced changes have occurred gradually has not only made them difficult to measure quantitatively within the natural variability of weather, but has also made

them less obvious and, therefore, unwittingly accepted by the urban dweller. Now that urbanization is nearly universal, American citizens have suddenly become aware of many of the urban-induced weather changes. In general, such changes as increased contaminants, higher warm-season temperatures, lower winds, added fog, increased thunder and hail, added snowfall, and decreased visibility are considered undesirable. Certain urban-related weather changes are desirable, however, including warmer winters and additional rainfall to cleanse the air and to add water in downwind agricultural areas.

In summary, then, with respect to their effects on weather, urban areas sometimes act as volcanoes, deserts, or irregular forests; as such, they produce a wide variety of weather changes, at least on a local scale, and these changes can be classed as beneficial or detrimental depending on the locale and the interests involved.

Type and Amount of Weather Change

The changes in weather wrought by urbanization include all major surface weather conditions. The list of elements or conditions affected includes the contaminants in the air, solar radiation, temperature, visibility, humidity, wind speed and direction, cloudiness, precipitation, atmospheric electricity, severe weather, and certain mesoscale synoptic weather features (e.g., it has been noted that the forward motion of fronts is retarded by urban areas). (See Figure IV-11)

The degree of urban effect on any element will depend on the climate,

Figure IV-11—WEATHER CHANGES RESULTING FROM URBANIZATION

	Annual	Cold season	Warm season
	(percent)	(percent)	(percent)
Contaminants	+1000	+2000	+500
Solar Radiation	−22	−34	−20
Temperature	+3	+10	+2
Humidity	−6	−2	−8
Visibility	−26	−34	−17
Fog	+60	+100	+30
Wind Speed	−25	−20	−30
Cloudiness	+8	+5	+10
Rainfall	+11	+13	+11
Snowfall	±10	±10	—
Thunderstorms	+8	+5	+17

The table summarizes changes in surface weather conditions attributable to urbanization. Changes are expressed as percent of rural conditions.

nearness to major water bodies, on topographic features, and city size and components of the industrial complex. Furthermore, the amount of effect on the weather at any given time depends greatly on the season, day of the week, and time of day. Thus, urban solar radiation is decreased much more in winter than summer; is decreased on weekdays; and is decreased more in the morning than in the afternoon. Temperature increases resulting from the heating of urban structures are much greater in winter than in summer; hence, the average urban air temperature in winter is 10 percent higher than that in rural areas, whereas in summer it is only 2 percent higher. However, urban temperatures during certain seasons and weather conditions can be as much as 35 percent higher or 5 percent lower than nearby rural temperatures.

It should be emphasized that opposite types of changes in certain weather conditions are produced at different times. For example, fog is generally increased by urbanization, although certain types of fogs are actually dissipated in large cities. Wind speeds are generally decreased, but they increase in some light wind con-

ditions. Snowfall is generally increased by urban areas, but under certain conditions the city heat actually melts the descending snow, transforming it into rain.

Current Scientific Status

Most studies of urban effects on weather have been descriptive and based on surface climatic data. Furthermore, only a few studies have attempted to investigate the causative factors and the physical processes involved in urban-produced weather changes. Without careful investigations of the processes whereby urban conditions affect the weather, there is little hope for developing an adequate understanding and, hence, predictive capabilities.

Data Base — The present data base is woefully inadequate for studies of most urban-affected weather elements. Two-dimensional spatial descriptions of urban effects on weather elements are now adequate only for temperature patterns. Data for weather changes in the vertical are totally inadequate for temperature as well as for all other weather elements.

Descriptive types of urban-weather studies based on existing historical records tend to be seriously limited in their spatial information. For instance, studies of urban-rural fog differences have typically been based on surface values from a point in the central city and one at the airport; although these may indicate a 30 percent difference, they fail to describe the horizontal distribution of fog over the urban or rural environs.

Unfortunately, adequate descriptions of the surface weather changes are not available for most metropolitan areas of the United States. Study of the urban-weather relationships in the United States has been much more limited than that in Europe because the surface weather-station networks in and around American cities have been too sparse. Information useful for such practical problems as city planning can be developed for major U.S. metropolitan centers only on the basis of thorough comparative studies of data from denser urban-rural surface networks than currently exist around most American cities.

Instrumentation — Satisfactory tools to perform needed monitoring and study of urban-induced weather changes are available. Major advances in the development of airborne equipment to measure meteorological variables and aerosols provide the potential for obtaining the vertical data measurements needed to develop time-dependent, three-dimensional descriptions of the weather elements around cities. Field studies of the airflow and vertical temperature distributions at Cincinnati and Fort Wayne, Indiana, have used these new instruments and techniques in pioneering research.

Theory and Modeling — The basic theoretical knowledge and formulas exist for understanding the atmospheric chemistry and physics involved in urban-weather relationships. Ultimately, studies of the urban factors that affect weather elements will provide the inputs needed to model the urban-weather system. However, this will require three-dimensional, mesoscale numerical models (not currently available) and computers (soon to be available) with the capacity to handle them.

Practical Implications of Urban-Induced Weather Change

Regional Planning — The factors that produce undesirable weather changes clearly need to be assessed, and hopefully minimized, in planning and building new urban areas and redeveloping old ones. For instance, the ability of large urban-industrial complexes to produce thunderstorms, heavy rains, and hailstorms in and downwind of the complexes has particular importance in hydrologic design for urban storm drainage and in agricultural planning.

Pollution — Knowledge of the urban-induced wind and rainfall changes apt to occur with various weather conditions is also required for determining whether these changes will materially affect pollution levels. The generally expected decrease in winds and poorer ventilation are certainly undesirable, but urban-increased rainfall is beneficial in this connection. Such knowledge would also help in improving local forecasting, thus enabling man to do better planning of his outdoor activities.

Weather Modification — Study of the exact causes of various urban-produced weather changes can also be expected to help man in his efforts to modify weather intentionally. In particular, the study of the conditions whereby urban complexes affect precipitation processes could generate needed information about the weather conditions appropriate for seeding, the types and concentrations of effective seeding materials, and potential rainfall changes expected beyond the areas of known urban-related increases. Continuing disagreements over evaluation of man-made changes

and the types of physical techniques and chemical agents of modification reveal the need for proper study of these aspects during urban field investigations and analyses.

The economic aspects of this problem are hard to assess but are surely significant. Reduced visibility, more fog, and added snowfall directly and indirectly restrict human activity. The damages to health, property, and crops resulting from added contaminants, less sunshine, higher temperatures, and less ventilation can be serious. National economic losses attributable to urban-induced weather changes are inestimable.

Requirements for Scientific Activity

The interactions of urban-produced weather changes with such matters as agriculture and hydrology, and with ecology, are only partly understood, since the inadvertent aberrations are frequently within the limits of natural variability of weather. For instance, the increase in crop yields resulting from urban-increased rainfall could be easily and accurately assessed, whereas the effect on crop yields of increased deposition of urban contaminants into soils cannot currently be assessed without special studies. Our knowledge and understanding of the interactions of weather changes with man and society are almost totally lacking. The legal and social ramifications are barely understood, although the threats of damage to property, crops, health, and safety from such changes as increased contaminants, more fog, less sunshine, and higher temperatures are now clear. Certainly, the responses to inadvertent weather changes provide an opportunity to study and assess potential human reaction to planned weather modification. The only means of fully assessing the urban-modification effect of each weather element in a given locale, however, is to measure all elements in three dimensions.

Adequate measurement and understanding of the interactions between urban factors and atmospheric conditions that produce, for example, a 10 percent rainfall increase in one urban complex should lead to reasonably accurate predictions of the precipitation changes in most comparable cities where routine measurements of the urban factors exist or could easily be performed. Indeed, major projects to study the urban conditions that change weather elements are sorely needed at several cities, each of which should be representative of basically different North American climates and urban complexes so that the results could be extrapolated to other cities. A minimum national effort would consist of a thorough field project in one city that is representative in size and climate of several others.

Such a project would be more meaningful if relevant interdisciplinary projects involving the physical and social sciences were conducted simultaneously.

To achieve meaningful, three-dimensional measurements of weather and urban conditions will require marshalling of instrumentation and scientific effort to create dense networks of surface instruments heavily supplemented by vertical measurements obtained by aircraft, balloons, and remote probing devices. The scientific skills, personnel, and facilities necessary to explain and predict most facets of this topic exist, but they have yet to be focused on it. Answers exist in relation to several basic questions concerning the urban-weather topic, but more concentrated study is needed in the next five years. No serious effort has been made to describe the interaction between urban-induced weather changes and man, and this, too, is urgently needed. If performed, these studies should provide information adequate to modify some of the undesirable weather changes within ten years.

The Influence of Urban Growth on Local and Mesoscale Weather

The fact that large human settlements change the atmospheric conditions in their immediate vicinity has been recognized for over a century. Up to very recently, however, it was considered that these influences were strictly local in character. Analysis in depth has shown that this may not be the case at all and that urban influences on the atmosphere may well reach considerably beyond the urban confines.

The causes for effects of towns on weather and climate are easily traced. First, human activities, especially combustion processes, produce heat. In some cities in northern latitudes during the winter this added energy may be a sizable fraction of the solar energy impinging on the same area. In recent years, airconditioning has also been adding heat to the air in summer by dumping the excessive indoor heat into the surrounding atmosphere.

The energy balance is further altered because urban surfaces replace vegetation of low heat capacity and heat conductivity with stony surfaces of high heat capacity and heat conductivity. These same urban surfaces also alter the water balance. Rain runs off rapidly, diminishing the natural system of evaporation and evapotranspiration, not only further altering the energy balance by reducing evaporative cooling but also throwing great burdens on drainage and runoff systems at times of intense precipitation.

Compact areas of buildings and dwellings also alter the natural air flow. They create considerable aerodynamic roughness. This may cause changes in the low-level wind profiles up to several thousand feet in the atmosphere.

Most important, probably, is the effect of cities on atmospheric composition, not only locally but even for many dozens, if not hundreds, of miles downwind. Literally hundreds of different chemical compounds from industrial and combustion processes are blown into the atmosphere. The blind faith of the past trusted that friendly air currents would dilute and dispose of them harmlessly. Yet many of these admixtures have become semi-permanent residents of the atmosphere, where they undergo further chemical change through the impact of solar radiation and by interaction with the water vapor in the atmosphere.

Meteorological Changes and their Consequences

Many of the meteorological alterations in urban areas have been quantitatively assessed. Most of them are universally agreed to. In enumerating them we proceed from the simpler to the more complex and, almost in parallel, from the noncontroversial to the controversial aspects of the problem.

The Water Balance — It is perfectly obvious that, by replacing the naturally spongy vegetative surface with impervious roofs, parking lots, and streets, any falling rain will quickly run off. Indeed, urban drainage systems are designed to carry the waters rapidly into streams and rivers. The consequence is that flood waters may gather more rapidly and, in case of excessive rainfalls, not only increase crests but also cause rapid flooding of low-lying districts in urban areas. The lag time of flood runoff may be cut in half by the impervious areas.

Heat Islands — The excess energy production of a city and its altered heat balance, because of changes in albedo and heat characteristics of the man-made surface, creates one of the most notable atmospheric changes in urban areas. It has been given the very descriptive label "heat island." This term designates a temperature excess that covers the urban area. It is most pronounced in the sectors of highest building and population concentrations; on calm, clear nights it can reach or even exceed 10° Farenheit compared with rural surroundings. (See Figure IV-12) Recent experiments have shown that a single block of buildings will produce a measurable heat-island effect. At the same time, the reduced evaporation caused by rapid runoff and reduced vegetation as well as this temperature increase reduces the relative humidity at the surface.

Wind Circulation — The previously mentioned increase in surface roughness causes decreased wind speed at the surface. The heat island also induces wind convergence toward the urban area. In daytime, the highly overheated roof and black-top surfaces create convective updrafts, especially in summer. The updrafts induce a higher degree of cloudiness over the city and contribute to the release of showers over the city. At night, inversions of temperature form over the rural and suburban areas while temperature-lapse conditions continue in a shallow layer over the city core. This temperature distribution induces a closed circulation system within a metropolitan area, which in turn contributes to concentrations rather than dispersion of pollutants when the general wind circulation is weak.

Solar Radiation — Pollutants act in an important way on the incoming solar radiation. The aerosol absorbs and scatters the solar radiation, affecting principally the shorter wavelengths. This means that the long-wave ultraviolet radiation is radically weakened and its possible beneficial effects as killer of germs and activator of vitamin D in the human skin

Figure IV–12 — HEAT ISLAND EFFECT

The figure shows the isotherm pattern for 2320 PST on 4 April 1952 superimposed on an aerial photograph of San Francisco. The relation between the air temperature measured 2 meters above the surface and urban development is evident. A temperature difference of 20°F. was observed on that calm, clear night between the densely built-up business district (foreground) and Golden Gate Park (left rear).

are reduced or eliminated. At the same time, these actinic rays cause a large number of photochemical reactions in the welter of pollutants. Many of them lead to obnoxious secondary products such as ozone, which irritates mucous membranes, and other equally undesirable products. They cause notable reduction in visibility, which is not only aesthetically objectionable but often detrimental to aviation. Increased haze and fog frequency, compared with the natural environment, is a man-made effect, a fact that becomes impressive because it is demonstrably reversible. In some cities (e.g., London) where the number of foggy days had gradually increased over the decades, a

determined clean-up of domestic fuels and improved heating practices led to immediate reduction in the fog frequency.

Precipitation — Much less certainty exists about both the local and more distant effects of city-created pollutants on precipitation. The already mentioned increased shower activity in summer has probably little or nothing to do with the pollutants. It is primarily a heat effect, with water-vapor release from combustion processes perhaps also playing a role. But we do have a few well-documented wintertime cases when isolated snowfalls over major cities were obviously induced by active freezing

nuclei, presumably produced by some industrial process. There is no incontestable evidence that over-all winter precipitation over urban areas has increased, but most analyses agree that total precipitation over cities is about 5 percent to, at most, 10 percent greater than over rural environs, even if all possible orographic effects are excluded. More spectacular increases observed in the neighborhood of some major industrial-pollution sources are probably the effect of sampling errors inherent in the common, inadequate rain-gauge measuring techniques.

Even so, there is major concern about the very possible, if not already probable, effects of city-produced pollutants on precipitation processes. One of them can be caused by the high emission rates of minute lead particles from the tetraethyl-lead additive to gasoline. Some of these particles combine with iodine brought into the atmosphere primarily from oceanic sources to form lead-iodide. This compound has been shown to form very efficient and active freezing nuclei, which can trigger precipitation processes in only slightly sub-cooled cloud droplets. The lead particles are so small that they will stay in suspension for long distances and thus trigger precipitation at places far removed from the sources of the lead. Even more ominous could be the swamping of the atmosphere by condensation nuclei. These are produced in urban areas in prodigious amounts in concentrations surely two orders of magnitude higher than in uncontaminated air. There are literally hundreds of thousands of these nuclei in a cubic centimeter, and even the most hygroscopic of them competes for the available moisture in the air. The more nuclei there are, the more likely it is that the cloud droplets that form will be very small because of the large number of competing centers around which condensation occurs. Small cloud droplets have more difficulty in coalescing and forming rain than large droplets. Hence it is quite possible, although not proven beyond doubt, that in some urban areas or downwind from them a decrease in rainfall could occur. This is one of the effects requiring careful watch in future research.

Atmospheric Stagnation — When weather conditions favor slight winds and surface temperature inversions,

air layers in metropolitan areas become veritable poison traps. These can lead to the well-known health-endangering pollution episodes. With a number of metropolitan areas in close proximity, a slight ventilation will waft pollutants into the next series of settlements within a few hours or days and aggravate the situation there. This type of accumulation has not been adequately investigated either. But the whole area of the United States east of the Appalachians from northern Virginia to southern Maine may be affected by cumulative pollution effects. There are also other megalopolitan areas in the country that may need similar attention. Computer simulation of such atmospheric-stagnation periods has made some progress but is still severely restricted by the inadequacy of the mathematical models and the lack of sufficient actual observations.

Many of the micrometeorological alterations brought about by urbanization have been well documented in a number of cities. They have recently been followed, stey by step, in a rural area that is in the process of becoming urbanized — the new town of Columbia, Maryland, where population density has increased from a few hundred to a few thousand inhabitants and will increase to a hundred thousand in the current decade. Many of the characteristic changes in temperature, wind, humidity, and runoff are already observable. This continuing study in a planned, growing community may greatly further our knowledge of the micrometeorological changes.

Implications for Town Planning

It is proper to ask whether we can

turn this knowledge to use in future town planning and redevelopment of older cities. The answer is affirmative. Natural environments characteristically have a varied mosaic of microclimatic conditions, most of which are destroyed by urbanization. The detrimental effects are primarily introduced by compact construction with few interruptions, creating an essentially new surface of roofs at which energy interactions take place. In many urban areas, vegetation has been sharply diminished or even completely eliminated. Reversal of this trend will bring about a desirably diversified pattern of microclimate. Two tall buildings with large green and park areas surrounding them are far preferable to the typical row house or walk-up slum configuration. The open construction characteristic of suburban areas has caused little climatic deterioration of the environment.

Air pollution will remain a problem. There is some merit in using tall stacks for the effluents from stationary sources. Appropriate location, predicated on the general regional airflow patterns, is indicated for industrial sources of pollutants. There is little substantive knowledge on possible amelioration of pollutants from mobile sources through highway routing, construction, elevation, or other engineering techniques. Control at the source seems to offer the only tenable solution over the long run.

Too little is yet known about the sinks of pollutants in urban areas, although shrubbery and insensitive plants seem to offer some help by intercepting particulates.

Urban Effects on Weather—the Larger Scales

The possibility that human activities might be modifying large-scale weather patterns or even the global

climate has received much publicity. The present state of atmospheric science does not allow either firm support or confident refutation of any of the effects which have been postulated.

There is no doubt that cities modify their own weather by the local production of heat and addition of material to the atmosphere. "Material" includes water vapor (H_2O) and carbon dioxide (CO_2) as well as the gases and particulates commonly classed as pollutants. City temperatures exceed those of similarly exposed rural areas, particularly at night, but the most noticeable change is in the solar radiation reaching the ground, which is typically about 10 percent below that of upwind surroundings. In considering the extent to which effects on weather may overstep the city boundaries, it is convenient to look at three scales — local, regional, and global. "Local" refers to effects downwind of the city at distances up to about 100 miles; "regional" to subcontinental areas of the order of 1,000 square miles; and "global" to the whole world.

Local Effects

Local effects include deterioration of visibility and reduction of solar radiation, which are not in question. At 100 miles distance, in New England, one knows when the wind is blowing from New York City. This does not, in general, have repercussions on the other weather factors that are large enough to be established by examining weather records. If there are such effects they are small and probably lost in the general variance, although no very sophisticated search has been made — for example, among satellite cloud pictures — to verify that speculation.

In two or three instances, it has been claimed that an increase of precipitation downwind of cities has been established. The best known example is at La Porte, Indiana, where an apparent considerable excess of precipitation over surrounding areas has been associated with industrial activity (particularly steel mills) in the Chicago and Gary, Indiana, areas. This seemed to be a clear-cut case,

but the skill and/or objectivity of the one observer whose record established the effect has recently been questioned (with supporting evidence) by other climatologists. In the other cases that have been discussed, including recent claims of an increase of shower activity downwind of pulp plants in Washington state, the statistical evidence offered in support of the hypothesis of modification is less convincing than that for La Porte. Physically, there is doubt whether any precipitation increase that might occur would be an effect of cloud seeding by particulate pollutants or of the increased triggering of convection by the heat and moisture sources of the city. The latter explanation is gaining favor.

Regional Effects

On the regional scale there is general agreement that atmospheric turbidity — a measure of the extinction of solar radiation — has increased over the past fifty years in western Europe and eastern North America, even in locations as remote from cities as can be found in these areas. Again, there is no indication that the reduction in solar radiation reaching the ground has had any effect on other weather elements. Such connections are extremely difficult to establish, for reasons which will be discussed later when we consider global effects.

There is, however, one possible regional effect of pollution that is causing international concern, though it would not traditionally be considered a "weather" phenomenon. This is the deposition in precipitation of pollutants transported hundreds of miles from their source, perhaps across international boundaries. The best-known case is the occurrence in Scandinavia of rainfall with an unusual degree of acidity which has been attributed to the transport of pollutants emitted in Britain and Germany. A similar geographical and

meteorological situation exists in the northeastern United States, where the situation might repay investigation. Persistently acidic rain or snow might have long-term effects on forest ecology and lead to reduced productivity in forest industries. The connection between the observation and its presumed cause is simply the fact that no other explanation has been conceived. Statistical or physical links have not been demonstrated — indeed, our current ignorance in the fields of atmospheric chemistry and microphysics precludes a convincing physical link. This is potentially one of the most serious of the currently unsolved scientific environmental problems.

Global Effects

The possible modification of climate by industrial effluents has been under serious scientific discussion for more than thirty years and the extent, nature, and intractability of the underlying problems is now becoming evident. It was postulated in the 1930's, and it is now clearly established, that the atmospheric CO_2 content is increasing as a result of combustion of fossil fuel. Radiative transfer calculations indicate that if the CO_2 content increases, and nothing else changes, temperature at the earth's surface will increase. No one ever seriously suggested that "nothing else changes," but it was noted that during the first forty years of this century recorded surface temperatures did increase. The connection with CO_2 increase was noted and extrapolated. There were prophecies of deluge following melting of the polar ice. However, by 1960 it was clear that surface temperatures were falling, and at the same time the continent-wide increase in turbidity was noted. (A global increase cannot be established because a network of suitable observations does not exist.) The obvious connection, on the hypothesis that solar radiation at the surface had decreased and nothing else had changed, was made. The extrapolators moved in, and there were prophecies of ice ages.

Statistical and physical explanation of the problem of climatic change can be conceived, but each approach has fundamental difficulties. In the first case, existing series of climatic statistics based on instrumental readings are short — about 250 years is the longest reliable record. The statistics of these long series are not stationary; there is variance at the longest periods they cover. Historical and geological evidence indicates greater fluctuations of climate than the instrumental record. Statistics indicative of climate are not stationary. There can be no test of significance to separate climatic change that might be associated with man's activities from the "natural" changes associated

perhaps with internal instabilities of the ocean-atmosphere system or perhaps with extraterrestrial change. The physical approach leads to similar conclusions, as Lorenz, in particular, has pointed out. The equations governing the ocean-atmosphere system certainly have innumerable solutions, and it may be that sets of these solutions exist with very different statistics — i.e., that the earth may have many possible climates with its present atmospheric composition and external forcing function. At most, changing the composition of the atmosphere (e.g., by adding CO_2) might change the nature of the inevitable change of climate.

Indicated Future Research

Present activity is in two directions — confirming and extending our

knowledge of the changes of atmospheric composition due to industrial activity by monitoring programs, and developing physical models of the climate. This latter is one of the major scientific problems of the age, and we do not yet know whether it can be resolved to any useful extent. The requirement is for a model, similar to existing models of the global atmosphere and ocean but completely independent of any feature of the present climate. The most complex existing models incorporate a forcing function specified in terms of the current climatological cloud distribution and ocean surface temperature. The output of these models can, therefore, at best only be consistent with the existing climate. The requirement is for a model which will generate its own cloud distribution and ocean-surface temperatures.

PART V

SEVERE STORMS

1. HURRICANES

The Origin of Atlantic Hurricanes

Atlantic hurricanes are uncommon events by comparison with the frequency of the storms that parade across the temperate latitudes of the United States each month. In terms of their deadly, destructive potential, however, they are, individually, the greatest storms on earth and the most important natural phenomena to affect the welfare of the United States. A single event may visit more than a billion dollars of damage and result in hundreds of lives lost, mainly due to drownings. In addition to carrying sustained winds that sometimes exceed 150 miles per hour and hurricane tides that may rise more than 20 feet above mean sea level, this massive atmospheric storm often carries with it families of tornadoes running ahead of the highest tides and strongest winds. For example, in Hurricane Beulah, which moved into the lower Texas coast in 1967, a total of 49 verified tornadoes was reported.

The quest for a better understanding of the hurricane, for means of increasing the accuracy of forecasts, and, ultimately, for reducing the extent of hazard has focused attention on the source regions of the seedling disturbances from which hurricanes grow, and on the environmental structure of the equatorial trough and the trade winds which control the forces promoting hurricane development. This quest has been greatly assisted by a new tool of observation, the meteorological satellite, which maintains a continuous global surveillance of cloud groups produced by disturbances and storm systems.

Surveillance and Prediction of Hurricane Seedlings

On average, more than 100 hurricane seedlings move westward across the tropical Atlantic during the course of a hurricane season, June through November. These seedlings are initially benign rain storms which move westward in the flow of the trade winds. Less than one-fourth of the seedlings develop circulation eddies with discrete centers of low pressure, and an average of only 10 per year intensify enough to sustain gale-force winds and earn a girl's name as a tropical storm. On average, 6 of the 10 tropical storms reach hurricane intensity at some stage in their lifetime and 2 of these cross the U.S. coastline.

For many years, meteorologists have known that some hurricanes seem to have their origin near the west coast of Africa. Not until the meteorological satellite provided daily information on storm systems around the globe, however, was it apparent not only that hurricane seedlings could be traced back to the African coastline in many instances, but also that they seemed to stem from a source region near the Abyssinian Plateau of eastern Africa. They march in great numbers across arid portions of Africa before reaching the Atlantic Ocean, where they begin absorbing the moisture necessary to drive a vigorous storm system.

A census of the hurricane seedlings that occurred in 1968 is presented in Figure V-1, which diagrams the sources and movement of disturbances and their evolution into tropical storms. The parade of disturbances, mainly from Africa westward across the Atlantic and Caribbean, extends across Central America into the eastern Pacific. Approximately three-fourths of the eastern Pacific storms are spawned by seedlings whose origin is on the Atlantic side of Central America.

It is noteworthy, however, that not all hurricanes form from seedlings which had sources in Africa. Indeed, not all hurricanes form in the tropics. Almost every year one or two hurricanes develop from temperate-latitude systems. Typically, the trailing edge of an old worn-out cold front, while losing its temperature contrast, acquires a rich influx of moisture from the tropics. The process causes a circular storm to form and to develop the structural character of the hurricane. Since this process frequently takes place in close proximity to a U.S. coastline, it poses a particularly challenging warning problem.

Surveillance — The surveillance of hurricane seedlings and of hybrid disturbances that may become hurricanes is done mainly by satellite cloud photography. Figure V-2, for example, shows a series of hurricane seedlings in the tropical Atlantic and a hurricane that is lashing the Texas coast — in this case, Hurricane Beulah, September 18, 1967. Two tropical storms are also visible in the eastern Pacific Ocean. In such photographs, the satellite looks down essentially on the exhaust product of the heat engine that generates the clouds.

At present, inferences about the efficiency of the engine and the energy that is being released must be drawn empirically and indirectly. However, second-generation satellites, and techniques for analyzing the movement of cloud segments from successive pictures, will soon provide more direct means of assessing the changes in horsepower that the heat engine develops.

The tracking and prediction of hurricanes cannot be done with meteoro-

Figure V–1 — A HISTORY OF HURRICANE SEEDLINGS

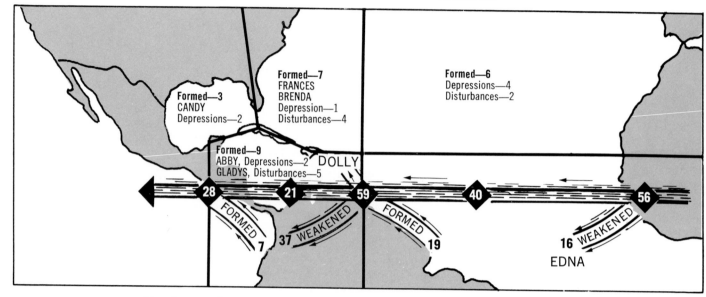

The diagram shows areas of formation and decay of hurricane seedlings during 1968. Although the African continent appears to be important in the development of seedlings, some form in other parts of the Atlantic and the Caribbean. A hurricane may develop from any of the seedlings. Surveillance and tracking is much easier with satellites, but the question of why one seedling develops into a hurricane and another does not remains unanswered.

Figure V–2 — HURRICANE BEULAH, 1967

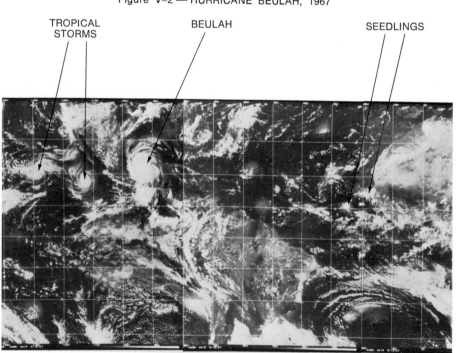

This cloud mosaic from September 18, 1967, shows Hurricane Beulah before it struck the Texas coast. The mosaic was compiled from pictures taken on eleven successive passes by the polar orbiting satellite, ESSA–3. Polar orbiting satellites pass over a given area twice per day, once during daylight hours and once at night.

logical satellites alone. Judicious deployment of aircraft reconnaissance is also required to probe the storm center directly. The delicate balance of forces that usually exists within a hurricane and determines its destiny can be measured only by direct sensing, and the only practicable tool in sight for this purpose is the reconnaissance aircraft.

Numerical Modeling — The problem of modeling numerically the movement and development of hurricane seedlings, and especially the movement of full-blown hurricanes, is more complicated than that of modeling temperate-latitude frontal storms. The large-scale temperate-latitude storm derives its energy mainly from the sinking of large amounts of cold air, a process that can be described in terms of temperature contrasts on a scale of many hundreds of miles. The tropical storm, in contrast, develops in an environment where lateral temperature constrasts are absent.

The release of energy in a developing tropical storm involves a number of links in a chain of actions, each of which must unfold in a timely and effective manner if the storm is to develop. First, the environment must be structured to support the spin that tries to develop locally in the wind circulation when pressure first begins to fall. Second, the environmental winds must be able to distribute systematically the heat released by the large cumulus clouds that spring up near the area of maximum spin. It is the systematic distribution of this heat, not its release *per se*, which generates fresh kinetic energy for intensification of the storm system.

As the tropical storm intensifies further and approaches hurricane force, the system depends uniquely on a continuous flow of heat energy from the sea to the air. These processes involve a subtle interaction between the scales of motion characteristic of temperate-latitude storms and those characteristic of cumulus clouds only a few miles in diameter. This interaction is difficult to model, as is the flow of heat energy from the sea to the air. The primary purpose of project BOMEX (Barbados Oceanographic and Meteorological Experiment) conducted from May through July of 1969, was to gain better understanding of the exchange processes across the ocean/atmosphere interface.

The modeling problem, especially in connection with the tracking of undeveloped disturbances, is further complicated by the fact that in the tropics there is essentially a two-layer atmosphere, with disturbances in the lower layer sometimes traveling in a direction opposite to those in the upper layer.

Because of all these complications, no model yet exists that can predict in real-time the moment and development of hurricane seedlings. A number of diagnostic models have been produced which seem to simulate, in a research environment, many of the physical processes that occur during this development and that characterize the behavior of the full-grown hurricane. However, forecasting procedures for tropical disturbances and storm systems still depend primarily on the identification, description, tracking, and extrapolation of the observed movement of the system.

Present-Day Techniques — Fortunately, the digital computer provides the forecaster with rapid data-processing which enables him to assess the immediate behavior of storm systems and how this may reflect on the future movement and development potential. Because of the increasing use of machines for data-processing, it is now possible to make more extensive use of analogues to compare the present storm system with similar systems from historical records and thereby compute the probable movement and intensification to be expected.

Figure V-3 is an example of one such method developed during 1969 at the National Hurricane Center. In this case, the computer is required to search historical records for all storms that were similarly located and whose characteristics were comparable to the storm system for which a forecast must be made. From the historical record, a most-probable track for periods up to 72 hours is determined and a family of probability ellipses is computed showing expected deviations from the most-probable track (50% and 25% probability areas). This family of ellipses is used to identify the area of the coastline to be alerted initially to the threat of a hurricane.

Other more sophisticated tools, using statistical screening techniques, are also used by the forecaster to guide his judgment in predicting hurricane movement.

Figure V–3 — PROBABILITY FORECASTS FOR HURRICANES

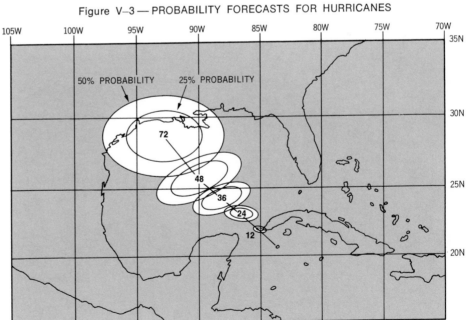

In this relatively crude warning technique, a computer searches historical data to find a hurricane situation with similar characteristics to the one under observation. It then prognosticates future positions for 12, 24, 36, 48, and 72 hours, as shown in the figure, based on the history of the earlier hurricane. The size of the probability ellipses indicates the magnitude of error that is involved in the use of this technique.

Development of still more sophisticated prediction models depends on a better means of observing the interactions between large and small scales of motion. The major emphasis of the Global Atmospheric Research Program's first tropical experiment, scheduled for the Atlantic Ocean in 1974, will be to describe and understand cloud clusters. The results of this investigation should provide valuable guidance in modeling the interaction between meso- and synoptic-scale motions. For the immediate future, however, the emphasis will probably have to remain on development of numerical methods that will minimize errors in predicting tropical disturbances and storms. Unless vast resources are devoted to the problem, sophisticated prediction models are not apt to become available in less than five to eight years, if then.

The median error in predicting the landfall of hurricanes along a U.S. coastline continues to decrease slowly, although it varies from year to year. This progress is due not so much to advances in modeling hurricanes numerically as it is to the availability of better facilities to track and observe disturbances at each stage of development and of modern technology that provides rapid processing of data from the storm area and environment. These facilities permit us to apply diagnostic tools of reasoning in an objective fashion, though we have only scratched the surface in the development of such tools. Apart from any progress that might be made in modeling the behavior of hurricanes, there is good reason to estimate that the median error for predicting hurricane movement near our coastlines, now about 110 nautical miles for a 24-hour movement, can be reduced by 30 to 40 percent. This depends, however, on exploiting information from the meteorological satellite to obtain *numbers* — rather than impressions — concerning the physical character of the environment in which the hurricane or its seedling moves.

Basic Understanding of the Hurricane System

While much has been learned about the hurricane, its structure, and the energetics that cause a seedling disturbance to develop, there remain notable gaps in the fundamental understanding of the hurricane system. The first is the puzzle of why so few hurricanes manage to develop from the abundance of seedlings that parade across the tropical scene. Secondly, the hurricane is basically an unstable system varying in intensity from day to day and even from one six-hour period to the next, but the reasons for these variations are not understood. The whole concept of weather modification in hurricanes may depend on a better understanding of the natural instabilities in this delicately balanced system.

Answers to these questions will probably depend on a concerted program of field experimentation and numerical modeling. To pursue the problem only through numerical modeling is risky for the simple reason that, in so complex a system, the modeling problem becomes intractable unless there are extensive uses of approximations, parameterizations, and other mathematical simplifications which, while yielding interesting results, may only crudely simulate the real atmosphere. Experience has shown that the best results come from a two-pronged program which, in step-wise fashion, produces a model for one facet of a development and then verifies the result of this simulation by field exploration in the real atmosphere.

Prospects for Reducing the Hurricane Hazard

Ideally, one would like to find some means to prevent all hurricane seedlings from developing into severe storms while retaining the useful rainfall carried by these disturbances. Although many suggestions have been made for cloud-seeding or other cloud-modifying measures to curb the formation of hurricanes, none has comprised a physical hypothesis that has considered both the cloud processes and the circulating properties of the cloud environment.

It appears more and more likely that the formation of a hurricane is something of an accident of nature, at least with regard to the particular cluster of clouds in which the event occurs. In general, a storm center tends to form somewhere in an envelope of rain clouds spread over hundreds of miles. But there is still no reliable means of predicting which particular cluster nature will pick to foster the growth of a storm center. Therefore, even if one knew precisely what modification techniques to apply to a cluster of clouds (no more than 25 or 30 miles in diameter, for example) — and one does not know this yet — it would be impossible to know where to send the aircraft to conduct the seeding or take other preventive actions.

Cloud Seeding: Project STORM-FURY — As for curbing the fury of the hurricane, it must be conceded that, at present, the only hope lies in identifying, and hopefully treading on, the "Achilles heel" of a delicately balanced storm system — its ability to release latent heat under certain circumstances. That is precisely what the Project STORMFURY hypothesis seeks to accomplish.

While scientists do not yet fully agree on the benefits to be expected from systematically seeding hurricanes or seeking in other ways to upset the balance of forces in the storm, those who have followed the STORMFURY experiments cannot help but be excited about the very encouraging results obtained in 1969 from Hurricane Debbie. If the same order of response from cloud seeding is obtained in one or two additional experiments, it will be possible to demonstrate beyond a reasonable doubt that a significant reduction can be made in the destructive potential of hurricanes, including the damage due to hurricane tides, by strategic seeding of the eye wall.

This is the most exciting prospect in all geophysical research and development, both because of the immediate potentialities for reducing property losses and saving lives in hurricanes

and because the insight gained from this experiment should open the door to more far-reaching experiments aimed at modifying other threatening large-scale storms.

A Report on Project STORMFURY: Problems in the Modification of Hurricanes

Damage to property in the United States caused by hurricanes has been increasing steadily during this century. Hurricanes caused an average annual damage in the United States of $13 million between 1915 and 1924. By the period 1960 to 1969, this figure had soared to $432 million. Hurricane Betsy (1965) and Hurricane Camille (1969) each caused more than $1.4 billion in damage. Even after adjusting these values for the inflated cost of construction in recent years, there remains a *650 percent* increase in the average annual cost of hurricane damage in less than 50 years. Since Americans are accelerating construction of valuable buildings in areas exposed to hurricanes, these damage costs will probably continue to increase.

The loss of life from hurricanes has been decreasing about as dramatically as the damages have been increasing. This decrease in number of deaths can be attributed largely to improvements in hurricane warning services and community preparedness programs. The reduction in loss of life is especially notable considering that the population has been increasing in hurricane-vulnerable areas just as rapidly as the value of property. Figure V-4 illustrates the trends with time in damages and loss of life in the United States caused by hurricanes.

When warnings are timely and accurate, lives can be saved by evacuating people to safe locations. Property damages can be reduced only by building hurricane-resistant structures or by reducing the destructive

potential of hurricanes. But the first solution may be quite expensive.

Extreme destruction may result from any one of three different attributes of a hurricane: (a) the storm surge, associated ocean currents, and wave action along the coast; (b) the destructive wind; and (c) rain-created floods. The hurricane winds that

Figure V–4 — HURRICANE LOSSES BY YEARS

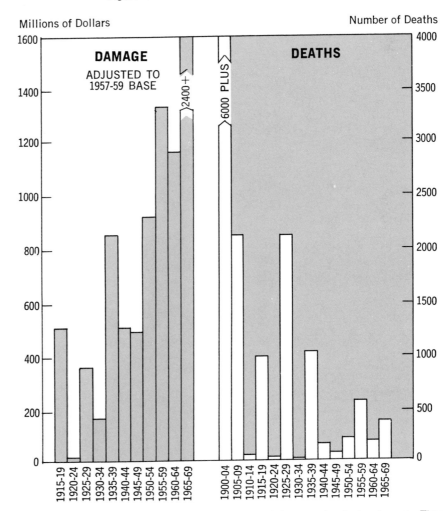

The bar graph shows the trends in loss of life and damage due to hurricanes. The damage figures have been adjusted to eliminate inflationary and other fluctuating trends in the cost of construction.

sometimes approach 200 miles per hour may cause storm surges of 20 to 30 feet or so, the development of strong coastal currents which erode the beaches, and the onset of mountainous waves. Once the latter three elements are in being, they are far more destructive than the winds and are usually responsible for the greater damage. Their destructive power varies directly with the speed of the winds.

Damage due to sea forces and to winds is concentrated along and near the seacoast; even the damage attributed to winds alone usually drops off drastically within a relatively few miles of the coast when a hurricane moves inland. Damage from rain-caused floods, on the other hand, may extend far into the interior and is particularly acute in mountainous regions traversed by the remnants of a hurricane. This is especially true in situations where rain-induced floods originate in mountains near the coast and arrive at the coastal plain before the ocean waters have receded. In view of the difficulty of building structures to resist all these destructive elements, efforts have lately concentrated on reducing the destructibility potential of hurricanes.

If the present program for modifying hurricanes to reduce their intensity should prove effective, the potential benefit/cost ratio could be of the order of 100:1 or 1,000:1. It should be emphasized that the modification program has no intention of either "steering" or completely destroying hurricanes. The rainfall from hurricanes and tropical storms is an essential part of the water budget of many tropical and subtropical land areas, including the southeastern United States. The hope is to reduce a hurricane to a tropical storm by a reduction in the speed of the concentrated ring of violent winds near the center, leaving the rainfall and total energy release of the over-all storm essentially unchanged.

Details of the Project

The groups active in Project STORMFURY, a joint effort of the U.S. Navy and the National Oceanic and Atmospheric Agency (NOAA), conducted experiments on hurricanes in 1961, 1963, and 1969. In each case, the objective was to reduce the maximum winds of the hurricane. The technique called for seeding a hurricane with silver iodide crystals in order to cause supercooled water drops to freeze and release their latent heat of fusion. In the earlier years, the experiments consisted of seeding a hurricane one time on each of two days. The results appeared favorable but were inconclusive, since the changes were of a magnitude that often occurs naturally in hurricanes.

In August 1969, the STORMFURY group seeded Hurricane Debbie five times in a period of eight hours on the 18th and 20th of the month, with no experiment on the 19th. Following the seedings, maximum winds at 12,000 feet decreased within six hours by 31 percent on the 18th and 15 percent on the 20th. The storm regained its original intensity on the 19th. While changes of this magnitude have happened in hurricanes on which there was no experiment, they have been quite rare. When one considers the entire sequence of events in 18-20 August, one can say that such a series of events has not happened in previous hurricanes more than one time in 40. Thus, while we cannot state that the Debbie experiments proved that we know how to modify hurricanes, the results were certainly very encouraging.

Along with the experimental program, there has been an intensive effort to develop models which simulate hurricanes. The best of these models now reproduce many features of a hurricane quite well. One developed by Rosenthal has been used to simulate seeding experiments, including the one performed on Debbie. The STORMFURY experiment was simulated by adding heat at appropriate radii at the 500 and 300 millibar levels (approximately 19,000 and 32,000 feet, respectively) over a period of ten hours. The amount of heat added was believed to be comparable to the amount of latent heat that can be released by seeding a hurricane. Within six hours after cessation of the simulated seeding, the maximum winds at sea level decreased about 15 percent. The time-scale for the decrease in maximum winds was roughly the same as that in the Debbie experiments.

Evaluation of Results

The net results of the various field experiments and the implications from modeling experiments give strong reason for believing that at least some degree of benefical modification was achieved in the Debbie experiments. Unfortunately, however, we cannot say the matter is proved nor can we claim the results are statistically impressive at some high level of significance.

The modeling results are most interesting and highly suggestive, but there are certain deficiencies in the model which require that one be cautious in interpreting them. First, a highly pragmatic parameterization of cumulus convection is used. Substantial improvements in this area must await increased understanding of both cumulus convection and its interaction with larger scales of motion. Second, the major simplifying assumption of circular symmetry used in the model precludes direct comparison between model calculations and specific real tropical cyclones. Real cyclones are strongly influenced by interaction with neighboring synoptic systems, and these vary markedly in character and intensity from day to day.

When one looks at parameters other than the winds for further verification of seeding effect, either the data were not collected in Hurricane Debbie or insufficient data are available from previous storms to provide a clear definition of the natural variability of the parameter. These points can be illustrated by discussing the various measurements that should be made.

The following are either assumed by the modification hypothesis or are implied by results from the modeling experiments:

1. In hurricane clouds, large quantities of water substance exist in the liquid state at temperatures lower than −4° centigrade.

2. Introduction of silver iodide crystals into these supercooled clouds will cause the water droplets to freeze and release the latent heat of fusion.

3. If the heat is released in the annulus radially outward from the mass of relatively warm air in the center of the storm, it should cause a temperature change that will cause a reduction in the maximum temperature gradients in the hurricane.

4. A reduction in the mean temperature gradients must result hydrostatically in a reduction of the maximum pressure gradient in the storm.

5. A reduction in the pressure gradients should cause a reduction in the maximum winds in the storm.

6. The belt of maximum winds should migrate outward after the seeding has had time to affect the storm. This action presumably would be accompanied by development of a larger eye, with the eye wall at a larger radius, or, possibly, a change in structure of the wall cloud.

All of the above suggest certain measurements that should be made

in the storm. If the changes in these parameters occur at the right time, in the right sequence, and with proper magnitudes, the cumulative evidence that the experiment was a success could be very convincing. Efforts were made to collect all of these data in Debbie. In some cases, however, the efforts were unsuccessful or the data do not permit conclusive deductions.

An aircraft was equipped to make measurements of the character and amount of water substance in the lower levels of the supercooled layer in Hurricane Debbie. While attempting to make the first pass across the storm at the 20,000-foot level, a supercharger malfunctioned and the aircraft was no longer able to maintain that high an altitude. There are, however, some qualitative observations which suggest there was a change in character of the water substance from predominantly supercooled water to a mixture of ice and water. These observations are not at the right level or of sufficient detail and quality to document incontrovertibly that the seeding accomplished a major transformation in the liquid-ice budget of the clouds. This should not be interpreted to mean that the seeding failed to accomplish the desired effect, however. There are just insufficient data to convince a skeptic that the effect was actually achieved.

Very detailed and frequent observations of the temperature, pressure, and winds were made along diameters across the hurricane at the 12,000-foot level. From these data we can compute changes with time in the parameters of their gradients at any point along the diameter. The changes in the maximum wind speed have already been mentioned.

The changes observed in temperatures and temperature gradients are not conclusive enough to support the above hypotheses. On the other hand, if the release of latent heat was in the layers above 18,000 feet,

one should not expect dramatic changes in the temperature and its gradient at 12,000 feet. We have inadequate temperature measurements in the layer between 18,000 feet and 30,000 feet, since lack of properly instrumented aircraft precluded the acquisition of the type and quantity of data needed. Furthermore, results from the seeding simulation experiment conducted with the model suggested that the added heat is rapidly dispersed and dramatic changes in the temperatures are not likely to occur.

The changes in the pressure and pressure gradients measured at 12,000 feet do give some support to the success of the seeding and some indication that results conformed to the hypothesis. But the great amount of noise in the variations of this parameter and lack of adequate knowledge concerning natural variations in hurricanes make it impossible to say the case is proved. Once again, the indications are positive but inconclusive.

Intensive efforts were made to get continuous coverage of the structure of the storm by airborne radar and by the ATS-3 satellite. This was done with the hope that these data would reveal the nature and time of changes in the cloud structure that might be caused by the seeding. The radar pictures suggest that the eye size did become larger after the seedings; the changes in size even appeared to have a periodicity similar to that of the seedings: about an hour and a quarter after several of the seedings there was a rapid increase in the area encompassed by the wall cloud.

One must be cautious, however, in placing too much emphasis on this evidence. The eye wall was pulsating during most of the time the STORM-FURY crews were monitoring it, so there were many changes in size, shape, and character of the eye before, during, and after the seeding. There were also many problems with the data. No single radar monitored the storm during the entire seeding operation, and it was necessary to use various radars to obtain a continuous time record of the eye area. After considering the many problems of interrelating various radars, calibrating ranges, distortions, etc., one can only conclude that there is some evidence that the seeding did indeed affect the hurricane clouds around the eye in the manner hypothesized, but that the data are of such a heterogeneous nature as to be inconclusive in themselves.

Pictures of Hurricane Debbie were taken by ATS-3 each day of the period, 17-21 August. Normally, processed pictures do not reveal much detail of the seeded areas. Although enhanced pictures were made along lines suggested by Fujita, they have not yet been developed. Work with a small sample of these pictures suggests that we will obtain some interesting information about changes in the cloud structure of the storm, though it is unlikely that these pictures will be adequate for determining with confidence whether the seeding had a major effect on the changes.

Wind-field measurements did show that the radius of maximum winds increased following the seeding.

Requirements for Future Activity

The use of theoretical models to study the modification hypotheses was discussed in the previous section. Some deficiencies of the present models were also mentioned. We should use the present models to learn as much as possible about the interactions and potential instabilities of hurricanes, but we should also continue experiments to develop further information as to how well the models simulate actual hurricanes. At best, they can do this only in a mean sense. We should also continue work to remove the restrictive assumptions; these relate to circular symmetry, interaction between the hurricane and synoptic-scale features in the environment, dynamics of cumulus clouds, and interactions between the hurricane scale of motion and circulations of smaller scale. The matter of parameterizing cumulus processes in the model must be re-examined and carefully compared with cumulus models and observations. A more closely spaced grid should be used in the eye-wall region. And, finally, the outer radial boundary (now at 440 km) should be moved outward and other outer boundary conditions investigated to make sure they are not determining or markedly affecting the solutions following the "seeding."

When the field experiments are repeated, every effort should be made to obtain data that will permit verifying various steps related to the seeding hypotheses. These were discussed in the preceding section. Facilities and manpower are not available at the present time to obtain all of these data.

In summary, the present status of our scientific knowledge suggests quite strongly that techniques presently available are adequate to achieve beneficial modification of mature hurricanes. Data from experiments and theoretical studies support each other, but in each case there are gaps in our knowledge which suggest we should be cautious in making extreme claims. What is clear is that we should repeat the Debbie-type experiments on other hurricanes as soon as possible to see if we can duplicate the Debbie decrease in wind speeds and to document details of the effects. We should continue our theoretical investigations to remove some of the limiting assumptions.

With losses from hurricanes in the United States currently averaging over $400 million per year and loss of life still a threat, action should be taken as soon as possible. Since the prospects seem good that we can reduce the destructive power of hurricanes, the need for additional experiments becomes much more urgent.

If present techniques are adequate for modifying a hurricane, it is quite likely that we can collect enough information during the next one or two years to justify application of the experiments to storms expected to affect the coastline. If present techniques are inadequate, we have several other approaches which should be explored. The time needed to develop and test better hypotheses or to improve and exploit the present hypotheses suggests that we should plan five to ten years ahead.

The Scientific Basis of Project STORMFURY

Project STORMFURY is concerned with the problem of devising experiments to modify hurricanes and tropical cyclones. Because the design and evaluation of such experiments depends essentially on understanding the structure and behavior of "natural" hurricanes, the close association of the project with the National Hurricane Research Laboratory of the National Oceanic and Atmospheric Administration is appropriate. The impetus for such experiments arises primarily from the large potential benefits, in the form of reduced property damage and loss of life, which could be realized from relatively small modifications of the intensity or motion of these storms.

During the past decade, increased understanding of hurricanes, based on both descriptive and theoretical studies, has suggested at least two possible avenues of achieving beneficial modification. Utilization of the approach with the sounder basis of scientific understanding has so far been precluded by logistic considerations. The second approach, which involves complex but feasible logistics, has been used in experiments on three hurricanes with encouraging but not yet definitive results even though the detailed physical basis for the approach is not completely understood.

Present Scientific Status

Special observational efforts and more intensive theoretical studies during the past twenty years have led to important advances in the understanding of the physics of hurricanes, but significant gaps remain to be filled. Preliminary efforts at constructing mathematical models of the hurricane have been encouraging, but serious defects remain.

Data Base — For hurricanes in the mature stage and in dissipating stages over land, the descriptive data base is good in the *qualitative* sense. The principal data deficiencies consist of *quantitative* measurements of such items as: the distribution of water in all phases as a function of temperature in the storm; the fluxes of heat and water vapor from the sea to the air under the extreme conditions present in the hurricane; and the natural variability of various meteorological parameters in the inner regions of the hurricane as a function of time-scales ranging from an hour to a day or two.

Basis for Modification — The most significant addition to our scientific knowledge of hurricanes in recent years has been the convergence of both theoreticians and empiricists on the concept that the hurricane is the complex result of the interaction of physical processes on several distinctly different scales. It is now agreed that these storms, whose space-scale of a few hundred kilometers and lifetime of a few days typify the synoptic-scale of atmospheric systems, depend critically on *microscale* (1 to 10 meters) turbulent motions of the surface boundary layer for the addition of heat and water vapor from the sea surface, and on *mesoscale* convective clouds, primarily organized in the annular ring surrounding the eye, for release of the latent heat of water vapor as the primary driving mechanism of the storm. Furthermore, the combined processes on these scales are influenced by interactions with much larger scale systems of the atmosphere.

It is this dependence on microscale turbulence and mesoscale convection that has suggested the two avenues to modification. Reduction of the evaporation associated with the former would certainly result in reduction of hurricane intensity, but this approach to modification has been prevented by insurmountable logistic problems. Redistribution of the latent heat release associated with the latter through the use of cloud-seeding techniques shown to influence the structure and dynamics of convective clouds is logistically feasible and has been employed in experiments on a small number of hurricanes. There are residual uncertainties and disagreements as to the correct seeding techniques and the interpretation of the experimental results.

Theoretical models of the hurricane incorporating the various scales discussed above with varying degrees of simplification have been developed. Results of computer simulations based on these models indicate qualitative success in modeling the physical processes responsible for the formation and maintenance of the hurricane. But significant quantitative uncertainties remain. Furthermore, present models cannot contribute significantly to problems of hurricane motions.

Interactions — Our present scientific knowledge and understanding of the interaction of hurricanes with other aspects of the atmospheric general circulation, with other environmental systems such as the ocean, and with man and society are qualitative and inadequate. For example, it is known that rainfall associated with hurricanes is often of considerable economic benefit, but it can also lead to disastrous floods. We do not know how the atmospheric circulation would change if hurricanes did not exist. Nor is it decided who in society is to decide when and where hurricane modification should be attempted.

Requirements for Scientific Activity

Significant scientific controversy exists with respect to the following aspects of hurricane modification:

1. Can the effects of seeding experiments be unequivocally detected against the large natural variability of hurricanes?

2. How, exactly, does cloud seeding redistribute latent heat release and how is this redistribution responsible for decreases in hurricane intensity?

3. Are the present mathematical models and associated computer simulations of hurricanes sufficiently realistic to serve as indicators of differences in expected behavior of natural and seeded hurricanes?

4. Are the amounts of supercooled liquid water necessary if seeding techniques are to result in significant redistribution of latent heat release actually present in the correct portions of the storm, and is this water actually frozen by the seeding?

The most urgently needed scientific advances fall into two categories: observations and theoretical modeling. Observations are needed to document more thoroughly the natural variability of hurricanes; to determine the distribution of water in all its phases in the inner portions of both natural storms and before, during, and after seeding in experimental storms; and to quantify further the interactions among physical processes on the various scales important to hurricanes. Theoretical models and associated computer simulations need: (a) to be improved in the way in which smaller-scale processes are treated implicitly through parameterized relationships; (b) to be generalized such that the effects of internal processes on the motion of the storm can be treated; and (c) to utilize improved observations as varying boundary and initial conditions for the models.

Time-Scale — The urgency of satisfying these needs is undoubtedly relative. In terms of clarifying the scientific basis for Project STORM-FURY, the need is very urgent. To substantiate the encouraging, but inconclusive, results from past experience and, thereby, provide a solid foundation for modification experiments on storms threatening inhabited coastlines, their importance cannot be overemphasized.

These advances in scientific background are needed within one to two years. Instrumentation and observational platforms needed to fill most of the known gaps in the scientific data base for both natural and experimental hurricanes are available. Similarly, significant improvement in computer simulation is possible with existing computers.

Legal Implications — The greatest potential policy problems associated with hurricane modification will arise from the legal questions that will be raised at both national and international levels when modification experiments are carried out on storms which shortly thereafter affect inhabited coastal regions or islands. When and if we are able to predict what will result from such modification attempts, who will make the decisions? A study of these problems is sorely needed.

A Note on the Importance of Hurricanes

Necessity

Our understanding of the physical laws governing the behavior of the atmosphere has not advanced to the point where we can deduce from these laws that hurricanes, or any tropical circulation systems resembling hurricanes, *must* occur. It is just reaching the stage where we can deduce theoretically that systems of this sort *may* occur. Recent numerical experiments aimed at simulating hurricanes have produced cyclonic circulations of hurricane intensity from initial conditions containing weak vortices. Other experiments aimed at simulating the global circulation have produced concentrated low-pressure centers within the tropics, but the horizontal resolution has been so coarse that it is impossible to say whether the models are trying to simulate hurricanes.

Nevertheless, from our general knowledge of atmospheric dynamics together with the observation that hurricanes do occur and continue to occur year after year, we can safely conclude that hurricanes not only may but must occur if nature is left to its own devices. We could make a similar statement about other atmospheric motion systems (e.g., tornadoes) that occur repeatedly.

Such reasoning does not apply to everything that is observed in nature. It would be incorrect to conclude, for example, that a particular species of animal is necessary simply because it exists. If we should destroy all members of the species, there is no assurance that evolutionary processes would ultimately create the same species again. However, hurricanes are not a species; new hurricanes are not ordinarily born of old ones. On the contrary, they, or the weaker tropical disturbances that mark their origin, appear to be spontaneously generated when the proper distributions of atmospheric temperature, moisture, wind, oceanic temperature, and probably certain other quantities occur in the tropics on a worldwide or ocean-wide scale.

Strictly speaking, therefore, we should modify the statement that hurricanes are necessary by saying that they are necessary only if the larger-scale conditions characterizing the tropical environment are maintained over the years. The absence of hurricanes in the southern Atlantic Ocean is presumably due to the local absence of favorable large-scale conditions, as is the relative scarcity of hurricanes in other oceans during the winter season.

What If Hurricanes Could Be Destroyed? — Assuming that the tropical environment is favorable to the formation of hurricanes, the latter, in forming, will exert their own effects on the environment. Hurricanes, by virtue of the active cumulonimbus clouds that they contain, are effective in transporting large amounts of heat and moisture upward to high levels. They may also carry significant amounts of heat, moisture, and momentum from one latitude to another. In any event, they act to alter the environment; in the long run, their effect on the environment must be exactly canceled by that of other processes.

Suppose, then, that nature is not allowed to take its course. Suppose that we possessed the means, not for directly altering the large-scale conditions that favor the development of hurricanes, but for destroying each hurricane individually during its formative stages, soon after its initial detection. In the hurricane-free world that we would have temporarily created, the effects of hurricanes on the environment would no longer cancel the other effects and the environment would proceed toward a different state of long-term statistical equilibrium.

Very likely, the new environment would be more favorable for the natural development of hurricanes than the old one. This would be true if one of the natural effects of hurricanes is to remove from the environment some of its hurricane-producing potential, as would be expected if the hurricane is an instability phenomenon. Perhaps a super-hurricane would then try to form to do the work of the ordinary ones that were suppressed; perhaps it would not. In any event, the task of artificially removing the hurricanes one by one, if such a task can be visualized at all,

would become even more difficult than it had originally been.

Beneficial Effects

The most frequently cited beneficial effect of hurricanes is probably the rainfall that they supply to certain areas, with its obvious value to agriculture. A familiar example of such an area is the southeastern United States, where a fair fraction of the total annual rainfall is supplied by tropical storms. Yet even if this region were deprived of all its hurricanes, there would still be ample rainfall left to support other crops not presently raised in this region. This leads us to suggest that the principal beneficial effect of hurricanes may be to help preserve the climatic *status quo* — a *status quo* which the hurricanes themselves have helped to create.

To appreciate the value of preserving the *status quo*, let us suppose that two regions of the United States, each possessing a reasonably satisfactory

climate, could somehow suddenly exchange climates with one another. The climatic statistics of the United States as a whole would then be unaltered. Yet the average climate of the United States would be worse, because the climate would be "worse" in each of the two regions in question. That is, the new temperature and rainfall regime in each region would presumably be unfavorable to the plant and animal life existing there, especially to the crops, and very likely also to many aspects of human culture. The new climates would favor new flora and fauna, and after a sufficient number of years those in one region might become effectively interchanged with those in the other. But during the period of adjustment there would be a net loss.

Since hurricanes exert a modifying influence on the larger-scale tropical environment, a further effect of hurricanes is to help preserve the climatic *status quo* throughout the tropics, even in those areas not frequented by heavy hurricane rains or violent hurricane winds. Here, too, the effect may be beneficial.

Geomorphological Effects of Hurricanes

The morphologic changes induced by hurricanes are concentrated along seacoasts and the shores of large estuaries. As they move inland, few major tropical cyclones encounter atmospheric conditions necessary to maintain their destructive violence for as much as 100 miles. Only rarely are they capable of retaining their structures when crossing land areas, as from the coast of the Gulf of Mexico to New England or to the Canadian border.

Hurricane Camille (1969) — shown in Figure V-5 — reached the Gulf Coast as the most intense hurricane ever reported, breaking records for barometric depression and wind velocities and bringing tragic devastation to the coast of Mississippi. It

retained its identity for an exceptional distance, causing excessive rainfall and flooding that did considerable damage in West Virginia and southwestern Virginia the day after leaving Mississippi. And yet, Camille caused few morphologic changes of any consequence. It effected many short-lived, minor physical changes on islands in Louisiana and Mississippi, but in comparison with losses in human and animal life and with destruction of property, the physical changes were trivial.

Effects of Differing Coastal Characteristics

Morphologic changes resulting from hurricanes depend mainly on

the physical characteristics of the coasts involved. Three examples will illustrate the relationships:

Plum Island, Massachusetts, experienced the impact of Hurricane Carol (1954). A detailed line of levels had been surveyed across the marshes behind the island, the coastal dunes, and the island's beach. This survey was completed the day before Carol arrived. On the morning following, the beach was broadened and reduced as a result of wave erosion to a level well below that determined by the instrumental survey. Three days later, however, most of the beach had been restored, and within a few days following its profile had returned essentially to its pre-hurricane condition.

Figure V–5 — HURRICANE CAMILLE, 1969

Hurricane Camille on August 17, 1969, in addition to being very intense, covered an extremely large area as shown in this segment of a satellite picture from the geostationary satellite ATS–3. A geostationary satellite is fixed relative to the earth and so is able to photograph the same area once every 25 minutes. Camille was first observed as a large area of cloudiness over the Lesser Antilles. It was tracked for over a week before it hit the Mississippi coast with 190-mph winds and 30-foot tides. Even though adequate warnings were given, many people were killed as a result of coastal flooding.

compared on a basis of pre-hurricane, a-few-months-later, and three-years-later investigations. The photographs and other comparisons demonstrated very minor physical changes, an immense upset in the exotic flora, and the rapid recovery of endemic vegetation.

Louisiana, in June 1957, experienced the direct impact of Hurricane Audrey, a storm that caused the greatest loss of life and property damage of any early-summer hurricane on the Gulf Coast. The coastal marshes were flooded to almost record depths of as much as 13 feet. The surge of sea water removed practically all beach sand and shell for about 100 miles along the coast of western Louisiana. Loss of this thin, protective armor exposed readily eroded marsh sediments to wave erosion, which was responsible for accelerated coastal retreat for as long as four years, after which effective beaches accumulated.

In 1953, a field party had been engaged in the study of a coastal mudflat that began to form in 1947. The party had implanted 25 monuments as reference points for that number of surveyed cross sections. Most of these survived the onslaught of Audrey and were used to monitor coastal retreat at several-month intervals.

The most spectacular geomorphic event related to the hurricane was the lifting, shifting, and deposition of two huge masses of mudflat sediment during the storm surge. These deposits were separated by about 19 miles. The western mass had a maximum length of 12,350 feet; the eastern deposit, 11,350 feet. The respective widths were 1,050 and 1,000 feet. Each overlapped the shore and extended inland about 2,051 feet, with an original thickness of 11 inches. Several months later, after drying, each mass had formed a sharply bounded, dense sheet of gelatinous

Mauritius, during the southern-hemisphere summer of 1960, felt the effect of Hurricane Alix, which passed close to its west coast in January, and the full impact of Hurricane Carol in February. Carol was accompanied by the lowest barometric depression and most violent winds, as well as the greatest economic loss, ever experienced in the southwestern part of the Indian Ocean. The path of Carol was such that the 1,200 square mile area of Mauritius was completely covered by the passing eye of the storm.

It happened that six months earlier a field party of the Coastal Studies Institute of Louisiana State University had completed an intensive study of the vegetation, landforms, and beaches of the entire coast. Following Carol, field parties returned in 1960 and again in 1963 to assess changes. As a great number of photographs had been taken during the first visit, an opportunity was afforded for taking subsequent photographs from identical positions with the original camera. Many individual plants were re-located, and their conditions were

clay up to 6 inches thick; they are permanent additions to the marsh deposits.

Some Generalizations

The three specific examples given here justify several generalizations that can be substantiated by many other case histories:

1. Catastrophic as they are from human, biological, and economic standpoints, in most instances hurricanes result in only minor and ephemeral geomorphic changes, and these are confined to coasts.

2. A coast where durable rock is exposed to the violence of storm attack (Mauritius example) suffers negligible physical change.

3. A coast flanked by deep water close to the shore (Plum Island and Mauritius examples) is affected mainly by high seas. Unconsolidated materials such as beaches and sand dunes experience abrupt changes, but these last for only short periods of time.

4. A coast flanked by a broad, gently inclined continental shelf, with a long fetch across shallow bottoms, suffers changes associated with flooding (Louisiana example).

Hurricane Carol (Mauritius) brought a storm surge that registered only about 33 inches above expected level on the tide gauge at Port Louis. The island is surrounded by deep water. Hurricane winds generated high seas along all shores, however, and it was these that accounted for physical and biological changes. Much the same experience was associated with another Hurricane Carol (Plum Island). At Plum Island, the 10-fathom isobath hugs the shore closely, and a depth of 50 fathoms

lies only 6 miles out. In contrast, in southern Louisiana the 10-fathom isobath lies about 43 miles from the shore, and the 50-fathom depth lies some 118 miles out. Hurricane surges are low over open ocean and are not significant aboard ship, but they rise to 15 feet or more when their rate of forward advance is reduced by shear or friction, creating greater and greater turbulence and more vigorous internal waves as they travel across wide, gently rising bottoms, especially at shallow depth.

Although not much coastal change ordinarily occurs when water attains a depth of more than 5 fathoms within a short distance, too much dependence should not be attached to this relationship. With gently inclined bottoms, offshore surges may grow to proportions that create extensive flooding. These surges continue for long distances, both across shallow bottoms and adjacent coastal lowlands. Even in the extensive and shallow area east of New Orleans, local inhabitants identify channels in the marsh and cuts across linear islands as having resulted from hurricanes in 1915 and 1925. A popular resort on Isle Derniere, south of New Orleans and landward about 27 miles from the 10-fathom isobath, was wiped out with tragic consequences in 1856, when the position of the low sandy spit on which it was built was shifted westward.

Hurricane Protection: Problems and Possibilities

An individual hurricane arrives as a possibly catastrophic event, one that is likely to be considered unique in the minds of people affected. The fact is, however, that the storm is but one of a recurring series that reach the region at highly irregular intervals. Hurricane arrivals are as uncertain as those of impressive earthquakes. Although the present state of the art does not justify exact forecasts concerning either, except for short terms in the case of hurricanes,

both meteorologists and seismologists recognize that there are definite hurricane- and earthquake-prone regions. Eventually, it may be possible to educate people living in them to recognize that they must protect themselves against potential catastrophes.

Most hurricanes reaching the United States originate either between the Azores and Cape Verde Islands or else in the Caribbean. There is no evidence that any originate within 6° of the equator. In most cases they are first identified in latitudes between 10° and 20° north. The shores of the Gulf and Atlantic coasts, from Brownsville, Texas, to Lubec, Maine, are everywhere vulnerable to hurricane attack. Tracks are particularly concentrated near Puerto Rico and Florida, but extreme damage has occurred around all parts of the Gulf of Mexico and up the Atlantic seaboard at least as far as Cape Cod.

Defense against events such as hurricanes, tornadoes, earthquakes, and destructive volcanic activity is most effective in places where disaster strikes most frequently. Cyclone cellers have undoubtedly saved many lives in the American Middle West. The Japanese have done well in designing structures that withstand intense earthquake tremors.

Practically all serious damage resulting from hurricanes is caused by human mistakes. Protective beaches are mined for sand, shell, or gravel. Sand dunes, among nature's most effective coastal protectors, are bulldozed away to level land for building sites or even to enhance seascape views. A trip along any part of the Atlantic coast between Florida and Cape Cod soon after a hurricane will demonstrate gross variations in damage, depending on whether beaches or dunes had been altered seriously. Cities and towns suffer most, not only because they are concentrations of people and buildings but also from the fact that they have introduced many more "improvements" that destroy or upset natural conditions. Intervening rural areas are left relatively untouched, particularly if their coastal sand dunes have been left intact.

It is difficult to convince people that hurricanes bring most disastrous results to places near disturbed beaches and sand dunes, and that substantial buildings reduce losses of life immensely. Hurricane Camille evidenced tremendous contrasts between the minor damage to substantial buildings and the destruction of shoddy structures, however nicely adorned. Great loss of life occurred in hotels and motels with inadequate framework, the buildings being held together mainly by wallboard or insufficiently bonded partitions of thin concrete blocks. Surges up to twenty feet high did relatively little damage, however, to buildings with adequate frames, whether of wood or steel. Trailer courts were wiped out, even several blocks back from the shore, while old homes with good construction withstood the surge much better even where they were located on or near the Gulf of Mexico.

While the number of seashore buildings anchored on effective pilings often increases for some years after a hurricane, this is not always true. After Hurricane Audrey, nearly all new houses were built on concrete slabs at ground level, following the dictates of a current style rather than in anticipation that the buildings will probably be flooded by several feet of seawater within a decade or two. People appeared to assume that Audrey would be the last hurricane to strike the coast of southwestern Louisiana.

The National Weather Service performs an invaluable service in providing hurricane watches, alerts, and warnings, each of which becomes progressively more specific about time of arrival and width of dangerous impact as the storm nears the mainland coast. But to what extent has public confidence been created? For some reason the people in a small but active community on Breton Island (east of the Mississippi River Delta) heeded a hurricane warning in 1915. The buildings in the community were totally destroyed, and have not been rebuilt, but every inhabitant was evacuated before the storm struck, without the loss of a single life. In 1957, on the other hand, few people heeded timely, adequate warnings of the approach of Hurricane Audrey toward the Louisiana coast. Many hurricanes had brought storm surges to the area, but all had been lower than the elevation of the higher land in the vicinity (about 10 feet). Hurricanes were an old story. Most of the people remained at home and were totally unprepared for vigorous surges that swept as much as three feet across the highest land in the vicinity, causing tremendous loss of life and property. On several occasions during the past thirteen years people have evacuated the region as soon as early warnings have been issued, but in no case did a dangerous surge occur. Will these experiences result in destroying confidence in warnings by the time that the next potential disaster appears?

Awareness of danger is almost impossible to maintain for disasters that recur a generation or more apart. Probably the most effective hurricane-protection measures result from legal actions, at state and local levels, such as the formulation and enforcement of adequate building codes, provision for rapid evacuation, maintenance of reserve supplies of fresh water for domestic use, well-constructed sanitary systems, and the availability of carefully planned health and emergency facilities.

Needed Scientific Activity

In their pristine condition, factors associated with the destructive effects of hurricanes are in reasonable equilibrium with those that resist geomorphic change. Scientific knowledge about hurricane origins, mechanics, physics, and behavior slowly increases, as does knowledge concerning the destruction or alteration of shoreline landforms and the accumulation and transport of near shore sediment. The effects of upsetting natural environmental conditions may be forecast with considerable qualitative precision.

In order to understand more completely the relations between hurricanes and their physical effects on coastal lands, the following suggested activities appear to be pertinent:

1. Accelerating the Weather Service's program of hurricane tracking and its ability to forecast the intensity and time of arrival of individual storms and to designate the coastal areas most likely to suffer.

2. Encouragement of studies by coastal morphologists to identify areas where physical changes are imminent, with emphasis on man-induced causes, in the hope that they may become expert in assessing the results of undesirable practices.

3. Creation, on a national level, of a group charged with monitoring proposed activities of U.S. Army and other coastal engineers from the standpoint of assessing probable long-term changes that designs of defenses against the sea are likely to induce. This should be a cooperative, rather than strictly policing, activity. There is tremendous need for better communication between scientists and engineers. Scientists need to be better informed about engineering design practices, and engineers need better understanding of the conclusions of basic scientific research.

2. TORNADOES

Status of Tornado Research

Tornadoes are among the smallest in horizontal extent of the atmosphere's whirling winds, but they are the most locally destructive. Although they are occasionally reported from many places, it is only in the United States that very intense tornadoes occur frequently. A typical intense tornado accompanies an otherwise severe thunderstorm, lasts about 20 minutes, and damages an area a quarter of a mile wide along a 10-mile path toward the northeast. The maximum winds (never accurately measured) are probably between 175 and 250 miles per hour, but damage is caused as much by a sudden drop of pressure, amounting in extreme cases to about 0.1 of the total atmospheric pressure, or 200 pounds per square foot. Especially when structures are poorly vented, roofs and walls are moved outward by the higher pressure within; then, as their moorings are weakened, they are carried off horizontally by the wind.

During the past 15 years, about 125 persons have been killed annually by tornadoes. Average property damage has been about $75 million. These figures may be compared with estimated losses owing to lightning, hail, and hurricanes as shown in Figure V-6.

The high tornado death rate in relation to property loss is attributable partly to our inability to warn effectively against impending tornadoes. A tornado is a very destructive phenomenon, but it usually exists for only a short time and affects only the thousandth part of a region covered by tornado-spawning thunderstorms. Extreme variability is an essential characteristic. Most tornado losses are associated with just a few storms that utterly destroy the structures in significant portions of urban areas or in whole small communities. These events, sudden and never foreshadowed more than a few hours in advance, leave the survivors stunned amid desolation; they call for a sudden focused response, of a magnitude akin to that demanded in war, by the affected community and by state and national governments.

Tornado Prediction

We have noted that the typical tornado accompanies an otherwise severe thunderstorm. Severe thunderstorms are themselves hazards and demand public forecasts, and the possibility of tornadoes is usually indicated when severe thunderstorms are predicted.

Our forecasts, which must start from a description of the present state of the atmosphere, are less specific than we would like. This lack of specificity is associated in part with a lack of knowledge, but also with observations that are too sparse to describe atmospheric variability on the scale of tornado or thunderstorm phenomena. Thus, the extent of a severe thunderstorm is 10 to 20 miles and the lifetime of a storm system is generally about six hours. But the distance between first-line surface weather stations is about 100 miles, and between upper air stations about 150 miles. Observations are made hourly at the surface stations (more often under special conditions) but usually at only 12-hour intervals at the upper air stations. Therefore, even if our knowledge were otherwise adequate to the task, the observing system would limit us to indicating the probability of thunderstorms in regions much larger than the storms themselves.

At present, tornadoes are foreshadowed from one to six hours in advance, for periods of about six hours and in regions of about 25,000 square miles. About 50 percent of such predictions are correct, with the

Figure V–6 — COMPARATIVE LOSSES DUE TO SEVERE STORMS AND HURRICANES

Type of Storm	Average Annual Deaths in U.S.*	Average Annual Property Damage in U.S.*
Tornado	125	$ 75 million
Lightning	150	100 million
Hail	—	150 million
Hurricane	75	500 million

*Based on data from 1955-1970

Loss of life is almost four times greater from severe storms than from hurricanes, while property damage is less than one-half as great.

incorrect forecasts being nearly divided between cases without tornadoes and cases with tornadoes outside, but near, the predicted regions. It should be noted that the climatological expectancy of tornadoes during six hours in a randomly selected 25,000-square mile area in eastern and central United States is only about one in 400. Plainly, then, present forecasts give evidence of considerable skill in identifying the meteorological parameters associated with severe storms and tornadoes and in correctly anticipating their development.

Briefly stated, the storm-forecasting parameters are warmth and moisture in a layer about 5,000 feet deep near the earth's surface, with a cool dry region at intermediate levels, strong winds in the upper atmosphere, and a trend toward intensification rather than diminution of these conditions. The prediction of all the necessary features is based on objective techniques, rooted in statistical and dynamical evaluations and modified by the judgment of experienced forecasters.

Forecasts of severe storms and tornadoes one to six hours in advance are considered "watches." In view of the wide area covered by the forecast relative to the area likely to be affected, the public is encouraged by a "watch" merely to remain alert to further advisories. The forecasts are disseminated by teletype from the National Severe Storm Forecast Center in Kansas City, Missouri, to local offices around the country. Occasionally, a local National Weather Service office may issue a modified local forecast which takes special account of peculiar local conditions. Since subscribers to the teletype service include most elements of the communications media, storm indications are quickly brought to the attention of the radio and TV public.

Tornado Warning

Severe storms are observed as they develop by Weather Service offices,

local government authorities, and private persons. When the Weather Service, through its own action or a report by a private observer, becomes aware that a severe storm or tornado exists, a warning to communities in the extrapolated path of the storm is issued by teletype, or immediately by radio and television if the situation warrants. The public in the threatened communities may be warned by various actions of local authorities, including the sounding of sirens. The few minutes' warning thus provided is credited with a twofold reduction in loss of life. The greatest loss of life from a tornado is often to be found in the first community visited by a storm, downstream locations having the benefit of longer warning time.

These days, observer reports are valuably augmented by radar observations. The primary radar network of the National Weather Service has stations spaced 200 to 250 miles apart. When severe storms threaten, the radar screens are monitored continuously. The more intense echoes are associated with heavier precipitation and a greater likelihood of hail, strong straight-line winds, and tornadoes. Severe tornadoes are often associated with a hook-shaped appendage on the echo. Thus, the forecaster's observation of the intense radar echoes provides a continual check on visual sightings and damage reports, and provides for timely warnings to communities lying in the projected path of a storm.

Tornado Research

Observations — Accurate description of tornado vortices and of the atmospheric conditions preceding and accompanying tornadoes is essential for improved understanding and prediction of tornadoes, and for the possible development of practical means for influencing tornadoes beneficially. But scientific observation of tornadoes is made difficult because of their random occurrence, brief

duration, small size, and great violence.

In an attempt to study tornado vortices directly, the National Severe Storms Laboratory has maintained a network of 30 to 60 conventionally equipped surface stations during the past seven spring seasons in an area where tornadoes are relatively frequent. Only two of the stations, however, have been directly affected by the winds of a tornado vortex during this period. The network density would have to be increased by a factor of 100 to obtain detailed data on the wind distribution in tornado vortices. For detailed information on the vortices, therefore, we are forced to rely on chance observations, engineering analysis of damaged areas, eyewitness accounts, and on the results of efforts to obtain data remotely by photography and by indirect probes such as radar.

Our information indicates that the tornado is characterized by an inner region where the winds decrease toward the center, as in solid rotation, and an outer region where the winds fall off with increasing distance. Many other tornado features are highly variable. The tornado cloud, presumed to be the surface of constant reduced pressure at which the well-mixed subcloud air is cooled to saturation, varies in size and shape. In some photographs it appears as uncommonly smooth, suggesting laminar flow, in others as highly irregular, suggesting strong turbulence. Such differences are quite important from the point of view of tornado dynamics. Since the less fierce waterspouts are usually cylindrical and smooth-walled, we are led to search for significant variability in surface roughness or atmospheric conditions over land to account from the apparent variability of turbulence and shape of tornadoes.

The electrical properties of the tornadoes also appear highly variable. Finley's report on 600 tornadoes, published in 1882, lists the observation of thunder and lightning in 425 associated rainstorms. In 17 cases, luminosity of an apparently electrical origin was noted in the tornado funnel itself, while in 49 cases the absence of any electrical indication in the cloud was specifically reported. More recently, interest in electrical theories was stimulated when Jones reported unusual 100-kHz radiation from a tornadic storm. Vonnegut presented an electrical theory of tornadoes; Brook has reported on the magnetic anomaly observed during touchdown of a tornado near Tulsa; and Weller and Waite have proposed that tornadoes are associated with intense electromagnetic radiation at television frequencies. On the other hand, Gunn measured the electrical activity of the tornadic storm that devastated Udall, Kansas, on May 25, 1955, and found it to be "more or less typical of exceptionally active storms." Rossow has measured magnetic fields over numerous waterspouts and found little disturbance. Kinzer and Morgan located the position of sferics sources in the tornadic storm in Oklahoma on June 10, 1967, and reported no obvious connection between areas of cloud lightning and tornado locations.

In a sense, the tornado itself is only an important detail of the circulation and energy balance of the larger thunderstorm. By virtue of its larger size and greater frequency, the typical parent thunderstorm lends itself much more to detailed examination. Therefore, present research is concentrated on identifying details in atmospheric structure associated with formation of tornadic and non-tornadic storms, with the variable behavior of different storms that form in the same general area, and with the evaluation of the way forces manifested in the storm environment combine to produce major features of the in-storm motions. To this end, experimental networks of closely spaced surface and upper air stations are used along with quantitative radar and specially instrumented aircraft.

We have learned that severe and enduring tornadoes form near the small low-pressure areas associated with the hook-shaped radar echo marked by the arrow in Figure V-7. Within the last decade the combination of observations and data gathered by many sensors at one place has taught a great deal about major features of thunderstorm circulation and, indeed, has revealed important but hitherto unidentified distinct storm classes.

Mathematical Modeling — All present-day mathematical models of weather represent extreme simplifications of the natural phenomena. We are still especially far from simulating realistically and in combination the many factors associated with the development of local storms.

Most adequate for their purpose are the models of atmospheric behavior on the scale of the global circulation and large weather systems. In use at the National Meteorological Center in Washington, D. C., such models predict the general patterns of horizontal wind, moisture, and vertical currents; they provide useful guidance to the thunderstorm forecaster, who combines their indications with his knowledge of the distribution of features specifically associated with local storms — and with his judgment — to forecast the probable location of storms. Models that forecast directly the parameters known to be important to thunderstorm development are just beginning to come into operational use. Some incorporate both dynamical and statistical methodology and provide somewhat more detailed spatial distributions over the United States than has been available heretofore.

Figure V–7 — RADAR VIEW OF A HOOKED ECHO

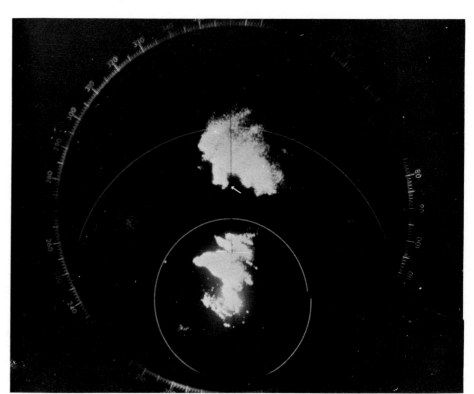

The picture is of a Plan Position Indicator (PPI) presentation of a severe storm over Oklahoma City on May 26, 1963. Range marks denote intervals of 20 nautical miles. North is toward the top. The radar is located at the center of the range circles. The arrow points out the location of the tornado.

Local convective phenomena are significantly affected by a greater variety of processes and factors than widespread weather, and are correspondingly more difficult to model realistically. To date, we have some two-dimensional models that incorporate simplified formulations of precipitation-related processes and of entrainment. These show some skill in predicting, for example, the maximum height to which a cloud tower rises with specified ambient conditions. The most comprehensive of today's models, however, is probably less detailed by a factor of at least 100 than one that would illustrate significant features of the asymmetric horizontal and vertical structure.

Today's mathematical models of the tornado itself treat cylindrically symmetric cases. At the edge of knowledge, we find steady-state models such as Kuo's, which appears to describe essential features of observed tornadoes in terms of an unstable vertical stratification and an ambient field of rotation. The fact that these features are often present when tornadoes are absent, however, serves to emphasize that we still have very far to go in our modeling and observing to identify the factors responsible for concentrating angular momentum in the developing tornado.

Experiments — The control of parameters afforded by laboratory conditions recommends the experimental approach to identification and analysis of factors responsible for the growth of tornadoes. Such experiments have been conducted for many years, often in conjunction with theoretical investigations, and realistic-appearing vortices have been produced in various liquids and in air under a considerable variety of experimental conditions. The very ease with which tornado-like vortices can be produced experimentally has made it difficult to progress much beyond theoretical implications regarding the development of swirling motion in converging fluid at the base of a ris-

ing column, and the important influence of boundaries.

Concurrent with the recent development of numerical analysis of large-scale atmospheric circulations, however, has come appreciation of the importance of similarity both in theoretical and experimental modeling. Similarity in flows on different scales is said to exist when the ratios of various quantities involving inertia, viscosity, rotation, and diffusion are the same. Considerations of similarity, and increased attention to such natural observations as are available, are leading to design of models more revealing of the effects of natural conditions.

Thus, Turner and Lilly have constructed physical models of vortices driven from above to simulate the convection in a cloud, and have found rising motion in the vortex core with descending motion in a surrounding annulus. Ward, noting that no tornado vortex can be indefinitely long, has ingeniously separated a fan from the vortex it creates in controlled inflow beneath. In this model, his control of the inflow angle and depth of the inflow layer represent the most important influences in the creation of a vortex, its intensity and diameter, and, in contrast to earlier models, the development of a central downdraft.

The problems of developing theoretical and experimental models indicate the importance of observations on even gross characteristics of tornado circulations. Is the flow upward or downward in the funnel core? How is tornado behavior, such as funnel-skipping, related to the roughness of underlying terrain? What is the wind inflow angle and air pressure at various distances from the visual funnel? How does the wind vary with height in the vicinity of tornadoes? If we could better answer these questions for atmospheric cases, we could design experiments accordingly, and rationally extend our search for influential parameters of the flow.

Comments on Investigational Techniques

We have surveyed observational, theoretical, and experimental aspects of tornado investigations. The variety and complexity of processes implicit in tornado development and maintenance, and the rarity, relatively small scale, and intensity of the natural phenomena have been sources of great difficulty. Let us briefly consider the helpful technological advances that may reasonably be anticipated and whose development should be encouraged.

Emerging Observational Techniques — With regard to observations, no available prototype technique seems practical for measuring details of the distribution of velocity and other parameters in a tornado vortex. With the encouragement of severe-storm study programs, however, greater numbers of observations — including useful motion pictures — should become available, and we may reasonably expect an opportunity in the next few years to extend the important study of the Dallas tornado of April 2, 1957, made by Hoecker and his colleagues.

Emphasis should be placed on observing the circulations around severe storms, since it is certain that the intensity of a storm and the occurrence of tornadoes is greatly controlled by the storm environment. In addition to encouraging existing programs having this objective, we may put special emphasis on two emerging tools. One is meteorological doppler radar, which in units of two or three can map the distribution of precipitation velocity with unprecedented detail. The development of an improved doppler capability would have value both for fundamental research and for research on an improved warning system, the latter by providing bases for evaluating the distinguishing features in a storm velocity field characteristic of an impending tornado. Doppler capability for clearer tornado identification needs to be assessed. Although some meteorological doppler radars are presently in use and other systems are under development, the pace of work seems slow.

The second emerging technique is satellite infrared spectrometry, which is providing new detail on the vertical thermal stratification of the atmosphere at intervals of about 30 miles. Further development of the satellite system should result in better analysis of severe thunderstorm precursor conditions over the United States and refinement of our forecasting ability.

Computers — With regard to mathematical modeling, greater realism will be possible as computers become larger and faster and as theoretical models are revised in light of observations and experimental results. Of course, many techni-sociological forces are already encouraging the development of improved computers. We may emphasize here that no conceivable computer can ever solve meteorological problems in such a way that careful scientists will not be an essential part of problem preparation; indeed, theoretical interpretation of data from observational and experimental programs will be increasingly required to develop reasonably posed mathematical formulations.

Physical Models — With regard to physical modeling of thunderstorms and tornadoes, the difficulties inherent in modeling significant atmospheric processes such as condensation and precipitation, in diminishing the effect of container sidewalls to levels consistent with the atmosphere's lack of sidewalls, and in simulating the vertical density gradient and diffusion processes characteristic of the atmosphere will continue to represent serious obstacles. These problems have been less serious with respect to interpretation of the more essentially two-dimensional flows representative of atmospheric circulations on larger scales. Nevertheless, experimental methods should

continue to be important for testing tornado hypotheses and suggesting new lines for observational and theoretical study.

The General Status of the Operational System for Severe Storm Prediction and Warning

Present-day severe-storm forecasts are immensely valuable, but we wish they were more precise and more accurate. Although numerical methods have been used for forecasting large-scale weather patterns for over ten years, the development of mathematical models relevant to the smaller scale of local storm complexes is still in its infancy. Basic improvements in the quality of severe-storm forecasts depend on the development of new understanding of storm structure and dynamics, the interaction between severe local storms, and the larger patterns of air motion that establish the general conditions favorable for storm development. As previously indicated, such improved understanding can be expected to evolve only as the insights provided by more detailed observations are assessed by careful scientists with the aid of more powerful computers. Eventually, methods will be developed combining such detailed data as that provided by radar and satellites with other weather parameters in dynamical storm models; appropriate ways to use such detail in operational forecast preparation should then become clear.

At present, we can strive to hasten the preparation and distribution of such forecasts as we have. To this end, hand analysis of patterns significant to local storm development is being significantly replaced by computer techniques. The radar network, which is the backbone of the system used for severe-storm warning, also lends itself to significantly advanced automation. Displays like that shown in Figure V-7 can be replaced by contour-mapped echo representations. (See Figure V-8) A correspond-

ing digital array can be produced simultaneously (see Figure V-9) as a basis for automatic preparation and dissemination of extrapolation forecasts. In midwestern United States, the Weather Service is presently starting to develop an operational test of advanced radar systems in order to evaluate the probable costs and benefits of various system designs for nationwide application.

Prospects for a Measure of Tornado Control

The energy production involved in one severe local storm is comparable to the total power-generating capacity of the United States. Thus, the control of severe-storm phenomena clearly requires an ability to direct far greater amounts of energy than those locally applied by man at present. This will depend on developing knowledge of how to modify the processes by which nature's supply is utilized. For example, silver iodide and a few other chemicals are used to stimulate the freezing of water drops that otherwise remain liquid during cooling to temperatures somewhat below their melting point; the artificial release of the latent heat of fusion thus achieved can raise the air temperature enough to enhance significantly the growth of some clouds and to hasten the dissipation of others. Conceivably, this kind of process could be applied to alter nature's choice for rapid growth among a host of nearly identical clouds.

Other means for modifying tornadoes might involve alteration of the earth's topography and roughness to decrease the probability of tornadoes over inhabited areas, and the direct application of heat at a point in time and place where such application would beneficially modify the course of subsequent events. It must be plain from the foregoing discussion, however, that we are still very far from having a reasonable basis even for estimating the likelihood that such efforts could ever be successful.

Figure V–8 — CONTOUR-MAPPED PPI DISPLAY

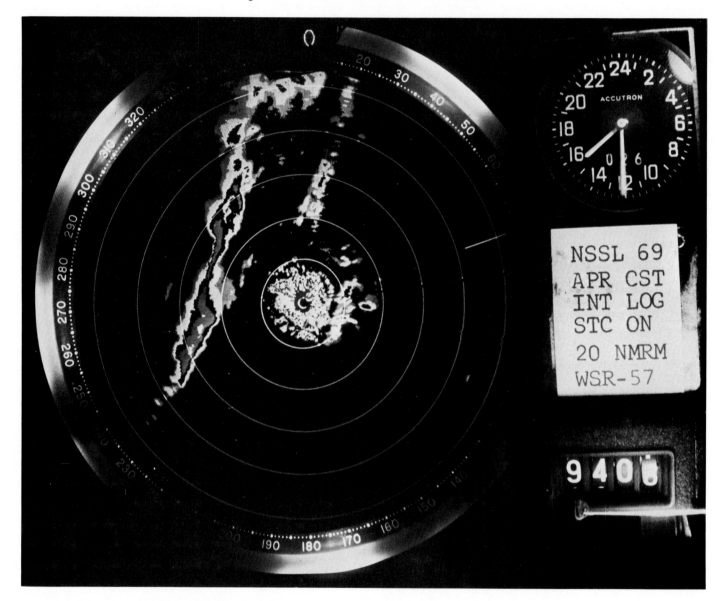

The figure shows the PPI-scope of the 10-centimeter WSR–57 radar at the National Severe Storms Laboratory in Norman, Oklahoma on April 26, 1968. Differences in shading indicate intervals of a factor of 10 in received echo power. From such an electronic display it is possible to determine the most dense part of a storm. Range marks are at intervals of 20 nautical miles. North is at the top of the figure.

Figure V-9 — CONTOUR-MAPPED DIGITAL DISPLAY

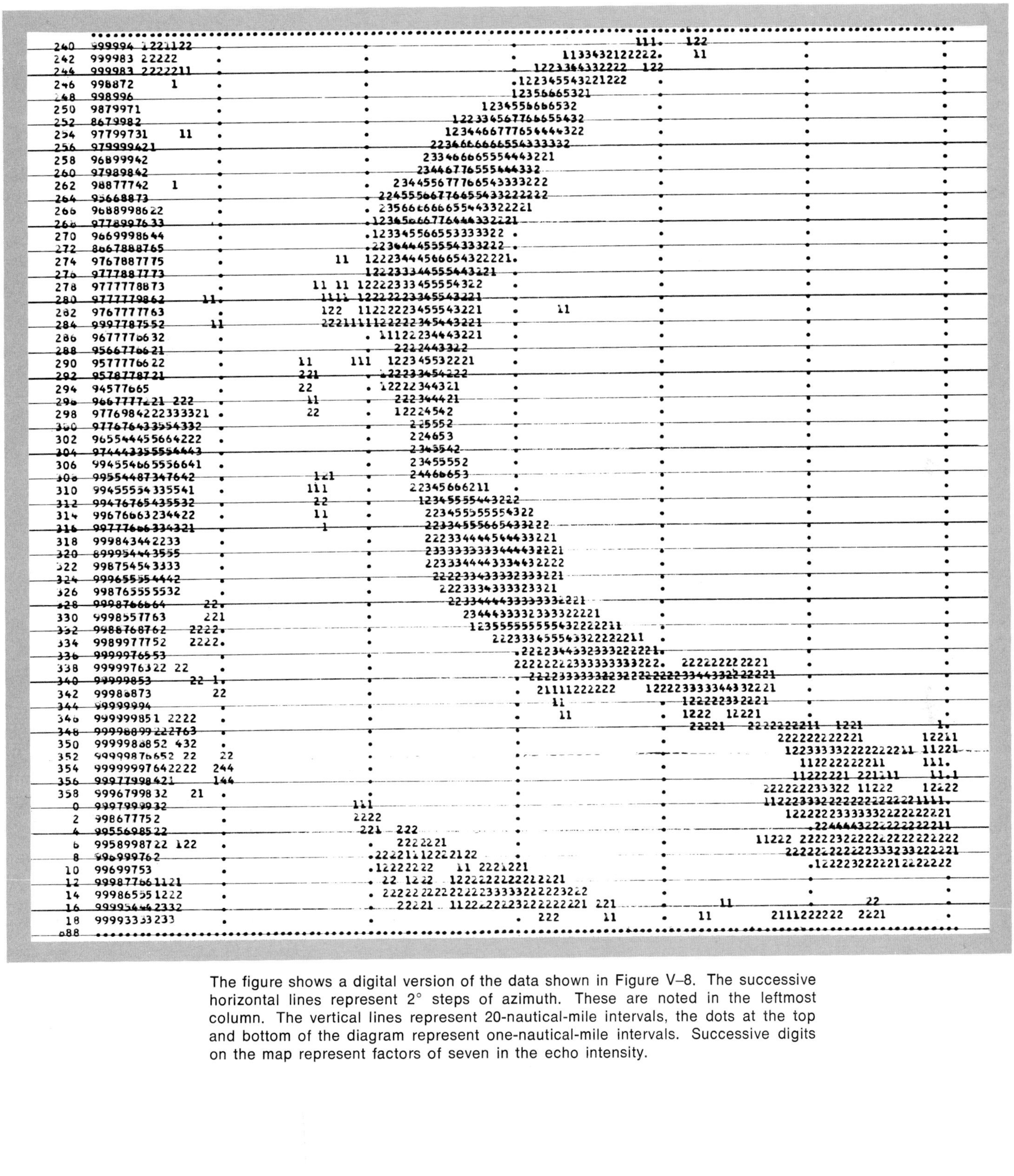

```
240  999994 1221122                                            111. 122
242  999983 22222        .                .                1133432122222.      11
244  999983 2222211                       .              1223364332222  122
246  998872    1         .                .             .122345543221222       .
248  998996             .                .               12356665321
250  9879971             .                .              1234556666532          .
252  8679982            .                .             122334567766655432
254  97799731    11      .                .             1234466777654444322
256  979999421                          .              2236666665554333332
258  96899942            .                .             23346666555444321
260  97989842                           .              23446776555444332
262  98877742    1       .                .            234455677766543333222
264  95668873            .                .           224555667766554332222222
266  9688998622          .                .          2356666666655443322221
268  9778997633      .                             .12345066776444332221
270  9669998644          .                .         .123345566553333322  .
272  8667888765                            .       .22364445555433322 . .
274  9767887775          .              11  1222344456665432221.
276  9777887773          .                .      122233344555443221 .
278  9777778873      .             11 11 122223333455554322    .
280  9777779862     11.           1111 12222223345543221
282  9767777763          .       122  11222223455543221   .      11
284  9997787552     11          222111112222234543221   .
286  9677776632          .         . 11122234443221   .
288  956677b621                       222443322    .
290  95777766 22         .       11    111 122345532221   .
292  9578778721                 221  .22223454222
294  94577765            .      22   . 1222234321      .
296  966777221 222             11     222344421    .
298  9776984222333321 .        22    . 12224542      .
300  977676433554332   .              225552       .
302  965544455664222        .        224653        .
304  9744433555544643    .            234542      .
306  994554665556641   .              23455552    .
308  9955448734 7642          121     24466653    .
310  99455554335541    .      111     22345666211   .
312  99476765435532   .        22  .  1234555543222
314  99676063234422   .       11  .   223455555554322
316  9977766334321   .          1    .2233455665433222
318  999843442233      .             222334444544433221
320  899954443555     .             2333333333444432221
322  998754543333      .             223334444334432222
324  999655354442      .             2222334433332333221
326  998765555532      .             222333433332333221
328  9998766664     22.             2233444433333332221
330  9998557763     221            2344433332333322221
332  9988768762    2222.            12355555555554322222211
334  9989977752    2222.            2223334655543322222211  .
336  9999976553                   .222233443323332222221.
338  9999976322 22     .          22222223333333333222.         222222222221
340  99999853    22 1.            .22223333333323222222223344332222221
342  99986873      22             . 21111222222    12222333334432221
344  99999994                     .            11     . 122222332221
346  999999851 2222    .          .            11    . 1222  12221
348  9999989 9 222763 .                         .      .  22221  222222221 1221
350  9999998852 432    .                                     222222222221         12211
352  9999987b652 22    22                   . .                12233333222222222211 11221
354  99999997642222    244                        .             112222222211     111.
356  99977998421    144                                     .    11222221 221 11  11 1
358  9996799832    21 .            .             .        .     222222233322 11222    12222
0    9997999932        .           111.                  .     112223332222222222221111.
2    998677752         .          2222                  .       122222233333322222222221
4    9955698522        .          221  222                    .2244443222222222211
6    9958998722 122    .          2222221                    11222 222222322222222222222
8    996999762         .         .22221112222122   .         22222222222333233222221
10   99699753          .          .12222222 11 2221221            .1222232222212222222
12   999877661121                 .  22 1222 12222222222221    .          .     .
14   99986555 1222    .            2222222222222233333222223222    .
16   999954442332     .            22221  1122.22223222222221 221     .11         22  .
18   99993333233     .               .222   11    .  11    2111222222  2221    .
088  ............................................................................................
```

The figure shows a digital version of the data shown in Figure V–8. The successive horizontal lines represent 2° steps of azimuth. These are noted in the leftmost column. The vertical lines represent 20-nautical-mile intervals, the dots at the top and bottom of the diagram represent one-nautical-mile intervals. Successive digits on the map represent factors of seven in the echo intensity.

Tornadoes — Their Forecasting and Potential Modification

A tornado, also called cyclone or twister, is defined as a violently rotating column of air, pendant from a cumulonimbus cloud, and nearly always observable as a funnel. The shape of a funnel varies from a cone to a rope; its lower end does not always touch the ground. A confirmed small tornado could be characterized by a damage area of 10,000 square feet, while the swath of a giant tornado covers more than 30 square miles. Thus, a giant tornado could be 50,000 times larger than a tiny one in terms of potential damage area.

The annual tornado frequency changed from a minimum of 64 in 1919 to a maximum of 912 in 1967, which represents a ratio of 1:14. This *does not* mean that tornado frequency increased by at least one order of magnitude. Instead, reporting efficiency — related to the reporting system, urban development, population density, and such — probably increased the apparent tornado frequency. It is preferable, therefore, to evaluate the potential danger of tornadoes according to damage areas rather than their number of occurrences.

Damaging Tornadoes

When a tornado warning is issued, the general public will be looking for the nearest storm shelter for protection of life. Statistics show, however, that 50 percent of the total tornado damage area is produced by only 4 percent of the tornadoes. This means that half of the potential damage area can be warned efficiently if the top 4 percent of tornadoes are predicted with great accuracy. If the top 10 percent of tornadoes can be predicted, their damage area would cover 75 percent of the total damage area. Although these statistics do not suggest that only large tornadoes should

be predicted to the neglect of others, accurate prediction of large tornadoes would be of great value to local residents.

Small Tornadoes — The origin of large, long-lasting tornadoes seems to be quite different from that of the tornadoes at the small end of the size spectrum. Small tornadoes and waterspouts are so similar in dimension and appearance that the former can be regarded as waterspouts traveling over land. These small storms, although they make up a large number of all storms, are very difficult to predict. They may form within a local shear line associated with growing cumulus clouds that may or may not become thunderstorms. Small tornadoes last only a few minutes, leaving a damage swath of only a few miles.

Hook-Echo Tornadoes — Large tornadoes frequently last 30 to 60 minutes. Furthermore, in many cases several tornadoes of similar size and intensity appear one after another, thus forming a family of large tornadoes. When radar pictures of proper gain and of low elevation angles are examined, almost all tornadoes in such a family are related to a thunderstorm echo with rotational characteristics—i.e., a rotating thunderstorm is a spawning place for one to several large tornadoes.

When the view is unobstructed, a rotating thunderstorm can be photographed at large distances as a bell-shaped cloud with an over-all diameter of 5 to 25 miles. The same cloud would appear in a plan-position-indicator (PPI) radarscope as a "hook echo," with an eye at the rotation center and several echo bands spiraling around the eye-wall circulation. Despite the fact that a family of tornadoes comes from a rotating thunderstorm, not every rotating thunderstorm or hook echo spawns a tornado during its lifetime. It is likely

that only a maximum of 50 percent of hook echoes spawn tornadoes — usually large ones. Hook-echo tornadoes are responsible for more than half of the damage areas caused by all tornadoes.

Detecting Large Tornadoes — The above evidence leads to the conclusion that large tornadoes spawn from mesoscale vortex fields identified as rotating thunderstorms, hook echoes, or tornado cyclones. The outermost diameter of such a vortex ranges between 5 to 25 miles. The eye, surrounded partially or totally by a hook-shaped echo, rotates at the rate of 20 to 40 miles per hour at its outside edge and is 1 to 3 miles in diameter. The central pressure of a tornado-bearing mesoscale vortex or tornado cyclone is only 2 or 4 millibars lower than its far environment. An impractically large and expensive network of barograph stations would be required for detecting tornado cyclones. Unless a doppler radar network becomes available in the future, PPI-scope pictures in iso-echo presentation with better than one-mile resolution will provide the only means of detecting tornado cyclones within some 10 minutes after their formation.

Early detection of tornado cyclones is the key to a warning within a narrow zone in which there is a chance of tornado formation. Such an alley is only 5 miles wide and 50 miles long on the average, while a tornado watch area extends 50 x 100 miles, some 20 times larger than one alley area.

Maximum Tornado Windspeed

Windspeed is an important parameter, necessary for the design of tornado protective structures. When settlers first experienced the impact of tornadoes in the Midwest, they estimated maximum windspeed to be in excess of 500 miles per hour. Some even estimated a supersonic speed.

Damage investigation since then has reduced general windspeed estimates to between 300 and 500 miles per hour. If these maximum-speed estimates are accurate, they would, where combined with the storm's pressure reduction, make it impossible to construct tornado-proof structures at reasonable cost.

Fujita's study of tornadoes during the past ten years, however, has now led to the conclusion that the maximum windspeed of tornadoes is much less than previously thought. Maximum rotational windspeeds, as estimated from scaling motion pictures and characteristic ground marks, are about 200 miles per hour. The translational motion of the storm must be added to the right side and subtracted from the left side of the rotating core. If a tornado travels at its average speed of 40 miles per hour, the maximum combined speed above the frictional layer would be 240 miles per hour. Some tornadoes, such as the ones on Palm Sunday, 1965, traveled eastward at 62.5 miles per hour. For these storms, the maximum combined windspeed would be 260 miles per hour. Inside the boundary layer, the gust speed must be added to the mean flow speed, which decreases toward the ground. Under the safe assumption that the peak gust speed could overpass the decrease in the flowspeed toward the ground, a maximum gust speed of 300 miles per hour seems to be quite reasonable. Thus, one has:

Maximum rotational speed....200 mph

Maximum traveling speed..... 70 mph

Maximum gust speed.........300 mph

It should be noted that the higher estimated speeds were obtained by assuming the cycloidal ground marks were produced by one rotating object. Fujita's study has indicated that there are 3 to 5 spots which produce cy-cloidal marks. Thus, the speed for any one tornado of a family must be reduced by one-third to one-fifth.

Minimum Pressure Inside Tornadoes

As in the case of tornado windspeed, in earlier days pressure reduction at the center of tornadoes had been overestimated to be a near vacuum or 2,000 pounds per square foot. Since then, meteorologists have tended to agree that the pressure reduction at the storm center is between 200 and 400 millibars.

It should be noted that a building will suffer also from differential pressure from its form resistance. A 300 miles per hour wind will produce a positive stagnation pressure of about 90 millibars at its windward side. Over the roof, however, the pressure may be negative, with the result that the roof is lifted. (The lifting force cannot be estimated unless the complete shape of the building is given and a wind-tunnel test is performed.)

Potential Tornado Protection and Modification

As a result of more recent windspeed and pressure estimates, criteria for designing tornado-resistant structures have now become feasible. Such structures could be expensive, although future designs and improved material could reduce costs to a level where at least public buildings in a tornado alley could be built to withstand tornado wind and pressure.

Tornadoes vary in both shape and size. The most commonly observed four shapes are:

Cone shape: Large tornadoes drop down in the shape of a cone; as the storm develops, the tip of the cone reaches the ground.

Column shape: A tornado or a large waterspout takes the shape of a large trunk.

Chopstick shape: This is a typical shape of weak tornadoes and waterspouts with small diameters.

Rope shape: When tornadoes become very weak, they change into a rope which often extends miles in a semi-horizontal direction.

Although tornadoes have such different shapes, all tornadoes and waterspouts are characterized by a core circulation surrounded by a circle of maximum wind. Outside this circle, the tangential windspeed decreases in inverse proportion to the distance from the circulation center.

Chopstick- or rope-shaped tunnels may be considered axially symmetric. When the core diameter increases, as in the case of the cone and trunk shapes, there are several spots of strong suction around the edge of the core; thus, they are no longer axially symmetric. These spots of strong suction rotate around the funnel at the speed of the funnel rotation.

Three ways of modifying tornado windspeed may be considered. They are: (a) a reduction of the circulation energy; (b) an increase in the core diameter without changing the circulation intensity; and (c) reduction of the windspeed near the ground.

Reducing the Circulation Energy —This possibility depends on the counteracting energy that can be created artificially. The total kinetic energy of a tornado is on the order of 10^7 kilocalories, which is just about 1/1,000 of a small, 20-kiloton atomic bomb. The energy of even the largest of tornadoes is comparable only to 1/100 of the energy in a small atomic bomb. Atomic bombs obviously cannot be used to modify a tornado. We might however, investigate such power sources as an artificial jet in order to learn more about how the relatively small and concentrated energy of a tornado might somehow be dispersed.

Increasing the Core Diameter — This definitely reduces the maximum tornado windspeed that occurs just outside the core. Modification of hurricanes through eye-wall seeding is based on the similar principle in which the release of latent heat around the eye wall will literally expand the eye diameter, thus reducing the extreme pressure gradient around the eye. In the case of tornadoes, it might be possible to cool the lowest portion of the core circulation. If we inject water droplets into the core at a certain level between the ground and the cloud base, they will evaporate as they slowly centrifuge out, thus cooling the core to increase the descending motion inside the core. The lower portion of the core will then expand, reducing the maximum windspeed.

Contrary to older reports, a tornado cannot suck up a body of water beneath its core. Investigation of

ground marks has revealed that the suction power of a tornado is weaker than a suction head of a household vacuum cleaner placed closed to the surface. It is, therefore, necessary to deliver a large amount of water in drop form into the core.

Reducing Windspeed Near the Ground — This could be achieved by constructing a number of deflectors to the west and southwest of an important structure such as an atomic power plant. The deflectors should be oriented in such manner that they change the southeast winds on the advancing side of a tornado to a northeast wind or possibly to a north-northeast wind, thus creating a flow converging toward the tornado center. The net effect of the convergence will be to reduce the speed near the surface. Design of deflectors should be made through aerodynamic calculations and a wind-tunnel test.

Other Activity

Methods of estimating tornado windspeed should be explored and tested whenever feasible. Direct measurement is desirable if "maximum wind indicators" are to be designed to stand against tornado wind. Measurement of object motion inside the tornado does not always give the air motion. Especially when an explosion of a structure is involved, the initial object velocity is likely to be overestimated. The designing of a low-priced "minimum-pressure indicator" for placement over the area of expected tornado paths is also recommended.

Basic research on tornado modification also needs to be carried on through various model experiments and theoretical studies. Furthermore, although the probability of tornadoes is small, some important structures must be protected against severe destruction.

Tornado Forecasting and Warning

Tornado frequency within the United States varies from 600 to 900 per year, with the major concentration through the Central Plains. Ninety percent of all tornadoes have a path-length between 0.5 and 50 miles and path-width between 40 and 800 yards. The median tornado has a path-length of 5 miles with a path-width of 200 yards. The median destructive period is less than 30 minutes. Less is known about tornado velocity profiles, but one can estimate that 90 percent of the peak speeds are between 100 and 225 miles per hour, with a median peak velocity of 150 miles per hour. Unfortunately, the upper limit appears to be around 300 miles per hour.

Thus, the problem is to forecast the occurrence of a rare meteorological event which has median dimensions of one square mile over a 30-minute period, and to forecast it

sufficiently far in advance to allow effective use of forecasts by all interested parties. There should be suitable differentiation for tornado classes based on width, length, and peak velocity. None of the above is possible at this time for areas of less than several thousand square miles and for more than one hour in advance.

Matters Contributing to the Forecast Problem

Data Network — The average distance between full-time surface reporting stations is 100 miles. Reports are made every hour, oftener when special criteria are met. Unless the special report is taken and transmitted near a free time-period in the teletype schedule, it is quite probable that the report will be delayed 10 minutes in reaching the user. Thus,

the spacing and frequency of reports taken with the standard data network is not adequate to fully describe the severe weather events taking place within the confines of the data network.

The average distance between upper air stations is 150 miles — and slightly more than that in the areas of high tornado incidence. Rawinsonde releases are scheduled only every 12, and on occasion every 6, hours. But the 1200 Greenwich Mean Time (GMT) release is made in the Midwest at 6 a.m. Central Standard Time (CST), a minimum thunderstorm period, while the midnight GMT release is made at 6 p.m. CST, a maximum thunderstorm period. Effectively, this produces only one useful report per day per station. These reports are not adequate to fully describe the temperature, moisture, and wind patterns within the troposphere. This is due partly to their spacing and frequency and partly to errors inherent in the equipment.

In addition, there are data voids in the areas surrounding the United States, such as the Gulf of Mexico, the Atlantic waters adjacent to the east coast, and portions of Mexico and Canada. All of these contribute to serious lateral boundary problems, the most pressing being the Gulf of Mexico. Texas, Louisiana, Mississippi, Alabama, Florida, and Georgia are all high-incidence areas for destructive tornadoes, and the lack of any direct meteorological data over the Gulf of Mexico has made objective analysis and prediction difficult.

To augment the conventional surface and upper air networks, use has been made of radar and satellite photographs. The processing and display of either method is still in its infancy; considerable experimentation will be required to obtain continuous readout of radar- and satellite-produced information. At present, neither the radar nor satellite output is woven into conventional analyses in a systematic and objective manner.

Forecast Methods — Present methods are largely subjective, drawing heavily on case studies and the experience of the individual forecaster. This is slowly being replaced by objective, computer-oriented methods, partly dynamical and partly statistical. (See Figure V–10) Considerable improvement is needed for either method. The most promising avenue for dynamical methods concerns the development of a fine-mesh primitive equation model for multi-layers. Such a model would be of limited value at this time because of the data limitations noted, but it will become increasingly important as the average spacing between stations is reduced. The statistical approach involves a search for predictors through the use of multiple-screening regression techniques. It has not been possible to gather all of the possible predictors

Figure V–10 — SEVERE WEATHER WARNING

TIME OF CLOSEST APPROACH	ECHO 2 EST. VEL. AT 2115CST=256/23		
	AIRPORT	DIST. AND DIR.	3 SIGMA TIME LIMITS
2139	CUSHING	12.5 N	2125 2154
2148	STROUD	23.5 N	2131 2205
2148	PAWNEE	12.4 S	2131 2205
2152	HOLDENVILLE	18.0 N	2133 2210
2200	ATOKA	21.3 N	2140 2221
2217	BRISTOW	25.2 N	2152 2242

The table illustrates an experimental severe weather warning of a thunderstorm cell moving from 256° at 23 knots. The warning gives the time of closest approach to airports near the forecast path. It also gives the distance and the direction of the echo from the airport. Finally, it estimates potential error of the forecast in terms of the time period of closest approach. This warning was prepared automatically by a computer using statistical properties of radar echoes such as those measured in Figures V–8 and V–9.

along with tornado occurrences, so this approach will require further work.

Research and Development — Comparatively little research on forecasts is being performed in this country. In allied fields, considerable research and development is under way on hail suppression, doppler radar, LIDAR (light detection and ranging), and remote-sensing techniques. Improved equipment and techniques will have application to the warning problem.

Modeling

Several theories have been advanced to explain the Great Plains tornado. These theories do not, however, explain the hurricane-induced tornado, the western U.S. tornado, or the waterspout. A great deal more work is needed in modeling tornado formation.

Prediction Techniques

The same problems apply to the warning as to the forecast. A vast majority of reported tornadoes do not

come close enough to any of the reporting stations to be detected, either visually or by instruments.

Radar Detection — The radar network is being expanded throughout the United States, using 10-centimeter radar. This is effective to 125 nautical miles in defining severe thunderstorms capable of producing tornadoes, but even a highly skilled radar operator cannot clearly identify a tornado by radar or give a 15-minute forecast that a certain cloud will produce a tornado. Certain characteristic shapes provide some information on the probability of tornadoes, but the pattern is not present for every tornado.

Instrument Detection — There are no mechanical methods at this writing that can make an objective distinction between the pressure fall or rise produced by a strong squall line and that produced by a tornado. Even if there were such a device, the spacing required to insure its usefulness would be prohibitively expensive.

Volunteer Spotters — Most warning is based on a combination of radar detection and visual spotting, usually performed by volunteers. This gives uneven results at best, since the ability of the spotter is as much a function of his zeal as anything else. The timeliness of the warning is a function of the spacing of the spotters.

To be of maximum value a warning should be as specific as possible with regard to area and time. More work is needed on "steering methods" for tornadoes once they are known to exist. No work at all has been done to determine how long a tornado will be in contact with the ground once it has been detected.

3. HAIL

Hailstorm Research and Hail Suppression

Hailstorms belong to those atmospheric phenomena whose life history originates and terminates in the mesoscale range — i.e., their size ranges from about 1 to 100 kilometers. Phenomena of this scale present great difficulties for observation and description, and the means and instrumentation for that purpose are only now being developed.

Radar, the oldest tool of mesoscale observation, has been somewhat disappointing when quantitative data are required. A system that combines airborne radar with data derived from the aircraft's doppler navigation system has proved to be a powerful tool for storm studies. The radar helps to delineate the precipitation echo of the storm while the doppler system provides the wind vector at flight level. Thus, on circling the storm, the line integrals for divergence and vorticity can be solved, and these yield the inflow into the storm throughout its life history.

The improved means of storm observation have de-emphasized the classical approach to storm research. This approach attempts to find, through observation and deduction, one valid storm model that satisfies all hailstorms. The last such model was derived by Browning from radar observations of one storm in England. It was characterized by a slanted updraft and an echo-free vault — i.e., an area where the main updraft speed was concentrated and where, due to the high updraft speed, no large particles accumulated that would cause radar reflections.

Hailstorm Characteristics

Nowadays we know that hailstorms appear in many manifesta-

tions. The energy source is always the latent energy of condensation, but in the exploitation of that energy the vertical wind profile appears to assume an important role. Over the Great Plains of the U.S., hailstorms usually travel from west to east. They can grow and form new cells from the leading (eastern) edge or from their trailing (western) edge; thus, they can actually grow from the rear. It appears that their updraft is usually upright and not slanted even under conditions of strong wind shear; more and more, they are regarded as aerodynamic hindrances in the large-scale atmospheric flow regime, with the wind going around and over the storm. Thus, the updraft tower may be eroded on the outside by the horizontal wind but remain undisturbed in the interior.

The air intake into a growing cell is of the order of 10 cubic kilometers per minute. High wind velocity in the anvil level appears to be the mechanism that prevents early decay of the cell, since precipitation and liquid water are carried away from the cell and, consequently, do not fall back into and "suppress" the updraft. It has been shown that hailstorms occur with special frequency in jet-stream regions of the United States, Europe, and India and that the combination of convective storms and jet stream can produce a very efficient and abundant precipitating cloud system. There are indications that the effectively producing hailstorm is characterized by high latent instability, inflow from the right rear quadrant, and strong wind shear aloft.

Very poorly understood is the way hailstorms become organized. As yet, we do not know under what conditions many small storms or a few

big ones form, what causes the storms sometimes to align themselves in rows and sometimes to form in clusters. It has been speculated that differences of surface temperature between sunlight and shadowed areas may cause local seabreeze-type circulations which contribute to the organization of inflow areas.

Some conditions lead to self-enhancement of storm intensity. For example, when the storm moves over its own precipitation area and entrains moist air, the base level is lowered, which in turn increases the buoyancy. This will increase the inflow into the storm, which then leads to an increased diameter of the updraft column. This causes an increase of updraft speed for the same latent instability because the ratio between buoyancy forces and drag forces has shifted in favor of the buoyancy force.

Theoretical Studies

Theoretical studies of the dynamics of storms extend in two general directions:

Analytical Studies — These studies deal with the influences of buoyancy and water-loading on updraft speed and radial divergence when the buoyancy term is compensated by the weight of the cloud and precipitation water. Essentially, this research aims at appraising the existence of an "accumulation level" of cloud water in the upper regions of the storm.

According to Soviet scientists, the accumulation level is characterized by a high liquid-water content, since the local derivative of the updraft speed versus height is negative $\left(\dfrac{\partial w}{\partial z} < 0\right)$ above that level and positive below it. As long as the maximum updraft speed is greater than 10 meters per second, water drops will neither descend below the accumulation level nor ascend much above it. Therefore, liquid water may become trapped at a certain layer and provide conditions for the rapid growth of hailstones. While the existence of such a level is possible, the rapidly increasing water-loading will, for continuity reasons, cause a strongly divergent flow that discharges the accumulating water content radially in a short time.

Numerical Studies — Several attempts are under way to expand one- or two-dimensional numerical cumulus-cloud models into convective storm models. Even two-dimensional models, however, are much too primitive for the simulation of a phenomenon as complex as a hailstorm. The best model to date appears to be a time-dependent, two-dimensional model developed by Orville; however, even this model puts severe strains on computer capacity and memory. There can be no question that these attempts are only first steps and that much research and data collection is required to make them realistic.

Microphysical Studies

Microphysical studies aim, particularly, at an explanation of hailstone structure and the application of hailstone features to explain the conditions under which it has grown. It is hoped that hailstones can be used as aerological sondes which eventually may reveal their life history and, consequently, the environmental conditions inside the hail cloud. (See Figure V-11)

Here the investigator is confronted with complexities related to greatly varying growth conditions of ice due to accretion of supercooled water. The most thoroughly conceived theory has been developed by List from actual growth conditions in a hail wind tunnel. However, List gives consideration only to the accretion of supercooled cloud water; ice structures resulting from the accretion of a mixed cloud (ice crystals and water droplets) or of aggregation of smaller hail or graupel have not been studied.

The following general statements may be made with caution:

Hailstone Structure — Most hailstones show a hail embryo in their

Figure V–11 — STRUCTURE OF HAILSTONE EMBRYOS

1

2

3

At the heart of almost every hailstone there is a distinct growth unit 5–10 millimeters in diameter known as the embryo. The illustration shows the three most common types: (1) Conical embryos consist of opaque crystals larger than 2 millimeters in diameter, indicating formation between −20°C and 0°C. These embryos fall in a stabilized position, blunt end downward, so they collect droplets on only one surface. This category represents about 60% of the hailstones studied. (2) Spherical embryos of clear ice (25% of the hailstones studied) consist of large crystals or a single crystal, indicating growth in clouds with temperatures above −20°C. Many of these embryos have cracks caused by the freezing of internal liquid water. (3) Spherical embryos of opaque ice (10% of the hailstones studied) have crystals of intermediate size and air bubbles showing no particular arrangement. They may have had a more complicated origin than other embryos, involving partial melting and refreezing or even collection of snow crystals. Because they tumble as they fall, they collect droplets equally on all surfaces.

growth center. This embryo is conical or spheroidal. It can be opaque or clear ice. It is usually well recognizable against the shell structure of the remaining stone.

One may conclude that the life history of a hailstone can be organically subdivided into two major periods: (a) growth in a hail embryo during the development cloud stage of the hail cell, and (b) growth in a hail shell during the mature-hail-cell cloud stage. It is conceivable that the former occurs during the development phase of the cumulonimbus or hail cell, the latter when the penetrative convection has been established and a strong supporting updraft has formed.

Environmental Growth Conditions — On the basis of List's theory it is possible to derive four environmental growth conditions from typical hailstone properties:

1. It is unlikely that hailstones are usually grown in the high water content of an accumulation level; if that were true, one should observe soft, spongy hailstones much more frequently.

2. It can be shown that hailstones with many alternating layers of clear and opaque ice may have grown at high levels in the cloud; at these levels, small altitude variations cause large variations of the growth conditions.

3. Hailstone structures that are homogeneous over a large part of the shell indicate that they have grown in an updraft with continuously increasing updraft speed.

4. The natural hailstone concentration is of the order of 1 to 10 per cubic meter. This concentration effectively depletes the cloud water content, as was shown in 1960 by Iribarne and dePena, which gives hope

that hailstones could be made smaller and less damaging through a slight artificial increase in the concentration of about two orders of magnitude. Amounts of seeding material needed to accomplish this are moderate.

Hail-Suppression Experiments

The problem of hail suppression is economic as well as scientific. One of the questions to be answered is: Does agriculture suffer sufficiently from hailstorms that prevention is necessary? Some people believe that, as long as we have a farm surplus and pay farmers for not planting certain crops, we do not need hail suppression. While this may be true now, in coming years we may need every bushel of farm crop for our food supply. This appears to be a good time, therefore, to begin a hail-suppression research program. Research must be emphasized, since too little is known about the hail mechanism to permit a realistic hail-suppression program to be conceived. Also, little is known about the relative damage that is done by hail, water, and wind during a storm.

The research phase need not be completed, however, before modification experiments can be thought of. On the contrary, the problem should be considered as a field program in experimental meteorology, where a well-conceived experiment with hail clouds is carried out with the potential of observing a cause-and-effect relationship. Some hail clouds are more suited to such an experiment than others; for example, hail clouds growing from the rear edge should have a basically simpler structure than hail clouds that grow from the leading edge. Such clouds are also easier to observe, as they are not usually obscured by an overhanging anvil.

The National Hail Research Experiment (NHRE) attempts to ac-

complish exactly this balance of research objectives and suppression operations — namely, to use aircraft, radar, and surface networks for a thorough study of the hailstorm simultaneously with a well-designed aircraft seeding program to which the storm's reaction is observable. The latter program cannot be conducted entirely without statistical control.

Hail Suppression: Soviet Union

Much information has been obtained from the operational hail-suppression experiments in the Soviet Union, specifically in the Caucasus. Several books have been published, and exchange visits between Soviet, American, and Canadian scientists have taken place, with many fruitful discussions, although it has not been possible to obtain a clear appraisal of the validity of the claims made by Soviet scientists.

It appears that two major efforts are under way in the Soviet Union which differ basically in the means of delivering the seeding agent into the cloud. In one, guns and shells are used; in the other, rockets. While the guns have greater range and altitude and deliver 100 to 200 grams of the seeding agent (AgI or PbI_2) by explosion of the "warhead," the rockets can carry a larger amount of the agent and deliver by burning a pyrotechnic mixture (3.2 kg). The rockets are somewhat more versatile in delivery either on a ballistic curve through the storm or vertically inside the cloud when descending by parachute.

One of four current projects in the Soviet Union is carried out through the Academy of Sciences of the Georgian S.S.R. in the Alazani Valley of the Caucasus, with Kartsivadze as the chief scientist. Another is conducted by the Hydrometeorological Service in Moldavia by Gaivoronskii and others. The third, and largest, project seems to be conducted by the High Altitude Institute of the Hydrometeorological Service in Nalchick, under the direction of Sulakvelidze. This project consists of hail-suppression expeditions in the northern Caucasus, Azerbaidjan, and Armenia. The fourth is also in the Georgian S.S.R. and is under the direction of Lominadze. Rockets are used in the first two projects; guns are used exclusively in the last two. The Ministry of Agriculture furnishes the hardware and crews for the field projects.

Scientific Bases — All of these efforts are based on the validity of the relationship

$$R_S = R_N \left(\frac{N_N^{1/3}}{N_S} \right)$$

where R_S is the mean-volume hailstone radius after seeding,

R_N is the mean-volume hailstone radius without seeding,

N_N is the hailstone concentration without seeding,

and N_S is the seeded hailstone concentration.

A physical justification for the validity of this relationship was given by Iribarne and dePena and confirmed more recently by List and Lozowski. The most important finding of this theoretical work is that the water content of a hail cloud becomes effectively depleted by a small number of hailstones, of the order of 10 per cubic meter, so that even modest artificial increases of their concentration by two orders of magnitude can be expected to decrease their size sufficiently to prevent damage. It is this recognition that brings hail-suppression experiments into the realm of physical realization and economic benefit.

All experiments in the Soviet Union seem to be designed in similar fashion: hail forecast, radar analysis, identification of the hail-spawning area in the cloud, and delivery of the seeding agent into the hail cloud. Forecasting skill has been developed to the degree that special experiments can be carried out to *prevent* the development of impending hail, while others are conducted to stop hail already falling.

Reported Results — Soviet scientists state that more than one million hectares (3,900 square miles) were protected in 1966. Hail damage in the protected area was 3 to 5 times smaller than in the unprotected area, which means that the cost of protection amounts to barely 2 or 3 percent of the value of the crops involved. For 1966, the total expenditure for protection was 980,000 rubles, and the computed economic effect was a saving of 24 million rubles.

Gaivoronskii and others have also reported on hail-suppression experiments in Moldavia, near the Bulgarian eastern border. These experiments utilize "Oblaka" rockets, a type that has a caliber of 125 millimeters, weighs 33 kilograms, holds 3,200 grams of PbI_2 as a pyrotechnic mixture, and delivers a total of 3×10^{16} nuclei at $-10°$ centigrade. Maximum range and height are 12 and 9.5 kilometers, respectively. The authors state that, in 1967, only 551 hectares out of 100,000 hectares of crop were damaged compared with 4,784 hectares in the control area. A similar effort with rockets is being carried out by Kartsivadze.

Evaluation — It appears from the literature that the work in the Soviet Union is already past the research phase and well into the operational stage. As tests in the research phase were not randomized, however, a firm statistical significance has not been established. It is possible that the discovery by Changnon of the occurrence of individual, short hailstreaks rather than long hailswaths may invalidate some of the conclusions made by the experimenters. Thus, a hailstreak may terminate by itself, rather than as a result of the seeding action, before reaching the boundary of the protected area, and since there are no means of knowing this beforehand such a case is counted as a positive seeding result. These conditions clearly point to the great complexity of designing a randomized experiment that would yield a unique result in a relatively short time.

There can be little doubt that the basic approach of the Russian scientists, to treat each hailstorm as an individual case, is appealing; at the least, it eliminates the great uncertainty of the diffusional process from surface generators to the storm.

Hail Suppression: Switzerland

The GROSSVERSUCH III hail-suppression experiment was conducted in Switzerland from 1957 to 1963 in the Canton Ticino. The experimental area appears to have been larger than the canton, since generators and raingauges were distributed over roughly 10,000 square kilometers, but the size of the area instrumented with 24 surface AgI generators (type unspecified) was only a minor part of about 4,000 square kilometers, one-half of which were in Italy.

After many years of careful freezing-nuclei measurements in and downwind from AgI generator sources it was concluded that, in order to be effective, seeding from the ground must be concentrated in *the regions* and at the moment in which storms form. It would appear, however, that the analysis should only be performed for the area coinciding with the generator network. Since this was not done, conclusions reached in the experiment — to the effect that "there is little doubt that seeding has been very effective in increasing the number of hail days" — seem to be not entirely valid.

Hail Suppression: France

French efforts in operational hail suppression are also continuing. Dessens gives a 22.6 percent decrease of hail falls as an average over the eight-year period since the experiment began. The French scientists are using surface AgI-acetone generators, of which 240 are distributed over 70,000 square kilometers. The generators are lighted 6½ hours before the expected outbreak of hailstorm activity in order to load the air sufficiently with good freezing nuclei, which may not normally be possible.

The operations in Switzerland (GROSSVERSUCH III) can be related to those in France in regard to the density of the generator network. The results for GROSSVERSUCH III show an increase of the number of days of hail (and an increase of rain amount per seeded day), while Dessens reports a decrease in hail damage. Of course, "days of hail" and "hail damage" are two parameters that need not be directly proportional.

Hail Suppression: Kenya

Final results are available for the hail-suppression experiment carried out from 1963 to 1967 in Kericho, Kenya. It was based on the firing of Italian antihail rockets from 13 firing positions within the Kitumbe Estate. In 1968 the rocket network was expanded to neighboring estates to a total of more than 30 stations. The rockets contain 800 grams of TNT and no AgI; their burst occurs at 2,000 to 2,400 meters above ground or at about the +2° centigrade level. Rocket-firing begins when hail starts falling and continues until hail stops. In Kitumbe nearly 5,000 rockets were fired during 60 hail storms.

Because of the consistency of the reduction of damage on Kitumbe during both periods, it seems unlikely that this was due to chance. (See Figure V-12) Five mechanisms have been suggested to explain why the experiment should work: (a) cavitation, (b) shock-induced freezing, (c) freezing due to adiabatic expansion, (d) introduction of ice nuclei, and (e) introduction of hygroscopic nuclei.

Continuing Experimentation — Preliminary results have been obtained from continued experiments over tea estates in Kericho. Seeding was done at cloud base with pyrotechnic devices dispersing between 6 and 30 grams of AgI per minute; 247 seeding flights were carried out on 225 operational days. In the first season, 58 hail reports from within the tea groves were obtained from 670 seeded cells, against a historical background of 360 hail reports from 686 nonseeded cells. Damage per hail instance was 2,929 pounds with seeding and 7,130 pounds without seeding. The great frequency of storms seems to make this area an excellent natural laboratory.

Hail Suppression: Italy

The effort in Italy proceeds along two avenues. The first approach is scientific in character and entails a study of the hail phenomenon rather than of hail prevention. The project is carried out by the Institute for Atmospheric Physics of the National Research Council. The second approach has been developed by farmer associations and the Ministry of Agriculture and Forests. The largest effort is that of exploding rockets inside the clouds when the hailstorm is overhead. The rockets carry 800 grams of TNT to altitudes of 1,000, 1,500, or 2,000 meters. In 1968, 96,000 of these rockets were fired in Italy. Plans are being made through the National Bureau of Electrical Energy for a project employing ground-based silver iodide burners of the type used by Dessens in France.

Hail Suppression: United States

In the United States, plans for a National Hail Suppression Field Test proceed slowly, while theoretical and applied research on the structure of hailstorms and the hailstone mechanism progresses more rapidly. Project HAILSWATH, a loosely coordinated field experiment, was organized in the summer of 1966 in Rapid City, South Dakota. Twenty-three institutions participated in this endeavor, whose outstanding purpose was to explore the feasibility of a large joint operation involving, at times, as many as 12 aircraft. Hailstorms were seeded with dry ice and silver iodide according to a target-control area approach on 10 experimental days, but the results lack statistical significance.

A review of various hail-suppression projects in the United States makes it apparent that American hail-suppression activities can hardly be called successful.

Figure V-12 — HAIL SUPPRESSION AT KERICHO, KENYA

	Control Period	July 63 to Aug 65	Sept 65 to Sept 67
All estates without rockets	20	22	24
Kitumbe	18	3	4
Other rocket firing estates	24	22	11

The table shows the decrease in the average loss per hailstorm in kilograms per hectare at Kitumbe estate compared with other estates in the nearby area.

Current Status of Hail Prevention

Hail losses in the United States, including damage to property and agricultural crops, have been estimated at $200 million to $300 million annually. While damage from hailstorms can occur in nearly every state, major hail losses are concentrated in a belt extending from western Texas through the High Plains into Alberta, Canada.

Most property owners respond to the hail risk by buying insurance, since damages by hail are typically covered in a homeowner's comprehensive policy. However, insurance coverage is less satisfactory for agricultural crops, because of the high premiums required in regions of high hail hazard. Crop hail insurance premiums in the Great Plains can range up to 22 percent for a standard policy.

During a period of crop surpluses, it may be debatable whether crop losses from hail justify any substantial research effort. However, from the point of view of the effects of hailstorms on society, and considering the trauma of a hailstorm loss and the fact that destruction of property by hail is a net economic loss, investigation of artificial hail prevention deserves attention.

In regions of high hail hazard, it appears likely that an ability to reduce hail damage by as little as 5 or 10 percent would provide a net economic benefit. It is anticipated that hail reduction of 50 to 75 percent should be possible, with a resulting higher net economic benefit.

Data Base: Large-Scale Field Experiments

Attempts to prevent hail by cloud seeding were initiated shortly after the early experiments of Schaefer and Langmuir in the late 1940's. The projects were based mostly on the concept of reducing hailstone size through increases in the number of hailstone embryos. Silver iodide was the most common seeding agent and was frequently released from networks of generators on the ground. The early projects in this country suffered from numerous handicaps, including a lack of knowledge of cloud processes and of resources for any significant evaluation studies.

The early hail-suppression projects in the United States were conducted for commercial sponsors and employed little or no statistical design. Some randomized experiments using ground-based generators were carried out in Argentina, Switzerland, and Germany. They yielded evidence that silver iodide could affect hailstorms, but that the effect could be unfavorable as well as favorable.

Throughout the 1960's, understanding of hail-formation processes was advanced through a number of extensive observational programs of hailstorms in the United States and abroad. The work carried out in the Soviet Union during this period is especially noteworthy, but observational programs carried out in northeast Colorado also deserve mention.

Improved understanding of hail growth processes led to more sophisticated systems for treatment. Seeding was increasingly carried out from aircraft and represented attempts to influence specific parts of a hail-bearing cloud rather than attempts to increase ice-nucleus concentrations throughout large volumes. This localization of the seeding treatment reached its apex in the development in the Soviet Union of a system to introduce seeding agents into special regions within a cloud by means of artillery shells.

There is increasing evidence that the seeding treatment used throughout the 1960's has been effective in eliminating hail from certain storms and reducing hail damage in other instances. Review of the evidence from a number of hail-prevention projects leads to the conclusion that the projects were successful in some instances. More recent results indicate substantial success in hail prevention in the United States, East Africa, France, and the Soviet Union. Indeed, a leading Soviet scientist is quoted as saying that "the problem of hail control is successfully solved."

Mathematical Modeling

During the past five years, substantial advances have occurred in mathematical models of cumulus clouds. An ability to create realistic mathematical models of hailstorms would provide the basis for a better understanding of hail-formation processes and mechanisms for hail prevention.

Initial cloud-modeling attempts utilized relatively simple one-dimensional steady-state models. These simple models were helpful as forerunners of more complex models which now simulate realistically the life history of a large rain shower.

In addition to modeling the dynamics and life history of the large cumulonimbus clouds, greater attention has been given to the mathematical simulation of individual hailstone growth. Early efforts at development of a mathematical formulation of hailstone growth are being continued. More recent work has given greater insight into the hailstone growth process, and shows that the primary region of hailstone growth appears to be in the higher and colder parts the hail-bearing clouds. (See Figure V-13) This information, derived from the mathematical analysis, is consistent with field observations. It is of particular importance since it implies a basis for success in hail prevention by cloud seeding through the mechanism of drying out the region of the cloud in which hailstones form.

Although unresolved problems remain concerning the position of hail growth with respect to the updraft maximum and the liquid-water concentrations in hail-growth regions, a picture is beginning to emerge of a physically reasonable system for hail growth and hail prevention that is consistent with observations obtained from field projects.

Prevailing Scientific Controversy

There is no general agreement on the effectiveness of hail-prevention techniques. Skepticism concerning the claims of success in the Soviet Union and concerning the reality of apparent reductions in hail damage on hail-suppression projects in this country loomed large in the development of current plans for hailstorm research in the United States. This is illustrated by the following extract from a planning document for the National Hail Research Experiment (NHRE):

. . . This document is almost entirely concerned with a discussion of the need to complete successfully a Hail Suppression Test Program, since it appears to us that a National Hail Modification Program is now premature. We must first determine if hailstorms can indeed be modified, and then learn if it is worth the effort.

This point of view (that so little is known about hailstorms that the primary hail research effort should be so directed) is in conflict with the point of view that current knowledge

Figure V–13 — A MIDWEST THUNDERSTORM

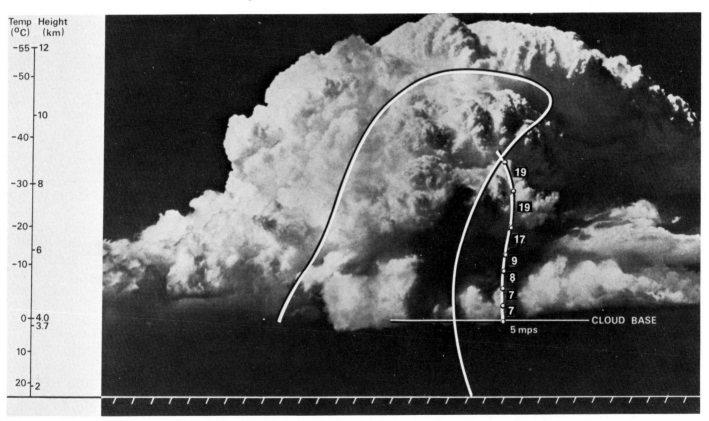

The figure shows a single, mature convective storm of the midwestern U.S. which is apt to produce hailstones. A temperature and height scale are along the lefthand margin. Note the base of the cloud at 3.7 kilometers. The vertical wind speed profile is plotted over the cloud and indicates a maximum wind speed of 19 meters per second near the middle level of the cloud. If the maximum speed of the updraft exceeds the terminal velocity of the largest stable droplet, an accumulation zone of supercooled water forms because of the chain-reaction mechanism triggered by droplet breakup. The heavy line in the center section of the cloud is the 35-decibel contour as seen by radar. The accumulation zone is within this area. It is this area into which seeding material should be placed to be effective.

provides a valid basis for initiating programs for application of current technology to hail prevention.

Requirements for Scientific Activity

Instrumentation — Current hail-research plans call for a substantial effort to develop sophisticated instrumentation to attempt to obtain the detailed life history of hail-bearing clouds. This is considered necessary to create a complete physical model of such storms. Development of the instrumentation for this task will require a major effort. The NHRE five-year program involves large expenditures for radars, specialized aircraft, and large numbers of field personnel.

The instrumentation and equipment required for a more modest effort at suppressing hail in a pre-designated target area would be less. Such an approach could provide a means of testing various hail-suppression techniques, would provide a basis for attaining knowledge to answer extant scientific questions, and would also partially satisfy the view that attempts should be made to apply current technology without further delay for scientific investigation, which should continue concurrently.

Applied Technology — Development of hail-suppression technology involves not only basic research, as is being planned under the current NHRE effort, but also efforts to apply the technology. Needs for basic research on hail appear to be covered adequately in present plans for NHRE. However, efforts in the development and application of hail-suppression technology are badly needed.

An advantage of having several applications projects under way simultaneously is that they can provide additional testing opportunities and opportunities for learning. An essential requirement for optimum learning is to have a number of untreated cases, randomly selected, reserved as "control" cases. In several locations, local groups primarily concerned with applications and benefits from weather modification projects have agreed voluntarily to forgo treatment of a limited number of storm situations to provide such control cases. This willingness sets the stage for an opportunity for increased learning.

However, local groups that have organized to apply hail-suppression technology have sometimes expressed the opinion that the scientific community is more interested in perpetual programs of research than it is in application. Such groups may be inclined to proceed on their own with premature operational programs that involve not only improper techniques but also foreclose future opportunities for associated research efforts. It is, therefore, rather urgent that steps be taken to develop mechanisms for cooperation with such local groups while the opportunity to reserve some untreated control cases still exists. If local groups begin hail-suppression programs from which they believe benefits are being obtained, the opportunity for cooperation and continued learning will disappear, since pressures will exist for treatment of all cases.

Approximate Time-Scale — If the present NHRE program begins its activities on schedule in 1972, it should produce useful inputs to hail-suppression technology within approximately five years. In addition, if steps are taken to work with local groups, useful inputs to hail-suppression technology can also be anticipated within three to five years of the start of such programs.

Considering the time-scale for both basic research and applications programs, it should be possible to obtain adequate knowledge to carry out hail-reduction efforts economically and routinely by the end of this decade.

4. LIGHTNING

Basic Processes of Lightning

About 2,000 thunderstorms are in progress over the whole earth at any given time. These storms produce a total of about 1,000 cloud-to-ground and 500 intracloud lightning discharges each second. It follows that there are over 8 million lightning discharges each day to earth, and about 5 times as many discharges within the clouds.

Lightning is essentially a long electric spark. (See Figure V-14) The total electrical power dissipated by worldwide cloud-to-ground lightning is roughly equal to the total annual power consumption of the United States, about 500 billion watts. On the other hand, the energy from a single lightning flash to ground is only sufficient to light a 60-watt bulb for a few months. It is the high worldwide rate of lightning flashing that provides the high power levels.

The electrical energy that generates lightning is transformed to sound energy (thunder), electromagnetic energy (including light and radio waves), and heat during the discharge process. The radio waves emitted by the hundreds of lightning discharges per second provide a worldwide noise background. The level at which many communications systems can operate is limited by this background noise level. The radio waves emitted by a single close (say, closer than one mile) lightning discharge can also cause malfunction of sensitive electronic systems (particularly solid-state systems) such as are used in modern guided missiles.

The heat generated by the lightning channel sets forest fires, ignites flammable materials, and can be a cause of individual death. Of the over 8 million discharges that hit the earth daily, very few cause damage. For example, most lightning to wooded areas does not cause forest fires. Still, there are about 10,000 forest fires a year in the United States attributable to lightning; and about 2,000 rural structures, roughly half of which are barns, are destroyed by lightning-induced fires each year.

Lightning strikes about 500 U.S. commercial airliners per year. Most

Figure V–14 — LIGHTNING

(1)

(2)

(1) This photograph shows a normal cloud-to-ground lightning flash near Mount San Salvatore, Lugano, Switzerland. Note how the streamers from the main lightning strokes branch downward. (2) In this photograph, a tall tower on Mount San Salvatore has triggered a lightning flash. Note how the streamers branch upward, indicating a reverse situation from the normal lightning flash.

strikes produce little if any damage, the lightning being confined to the plane's metal skin. Sometimes, however, potentially serious structural damage, such as the melting of large holes, does occur. There have been two cases of the total destruction of aircraft which the Federal Aviation Administration has attributed to ignition of the aircrafts' fuel by lightning. The most recent case was that of a Pan American Boeing 707, which exploded over Elkton, Maryland, in December 1963 after being hit several times by lightning.

In addition to the radio waves and heating effect produced by lightning, the direct electrical effects of lightning are often deleterious. They can, for example, result in the disruption of electrical power, as is often the case when lightning strikes a power-transmission line or a power station. Direct electrical effects can also result in malfunction or destruction of critical electronic equipment in aircraft and missiles. A spectacular example of the foregoing was the lightning-induced malfunction of the primary guidance system of the Apollo 12 moon vehicle. Further, individual deaths from lightning, about 200 per year in the United States, are primarily due to electrocution.

Control of Lightning

What can we do to control lightning? Are there possible harmful consequences of such control? Let us look at the second question first and attempt to answer it by two examples. Suppose technology were advanced enough that we could stop lightning from occurring. What would the result be to forests and the atmosphere?

1. If there were no lightning, would the incidence and destructiveness of forest fires decrease? In many cases, forest fires would be less common, but those that did occur would be more destructive. Lightning-induced forest fires and the forests have lived together in some sort of equilibrium for a a long time. (The oldest archeological evidence of lightning is dated at 500 million years ago.) There is now some evidence to indicate that frequent forest fires will keep a forest floor clean so that the fires that do occur are small and will not burn the trees. Further, in some cases, relatively clean forest floors may be necessary for the germination of new trees. For example, Sequoia seedlings can germinate in ashes but are suppressed under a thick layer of needles such as would cover an unburned forest floor. Thus, it is not obvious that blind control of forest fires is desirable.

2. If the frequency of lightning were diminished, would there be an effect on the atmosphere? Nobody knows. Lightning currents and other electrical currents flowing in the atmosphere during thunderstorms deliver an electrical charge to the earth. An approximately equal charge (a balancing charge) is thought to be carried from the earth to the ionosphere in areas of fair weather by the ambient fair-weather electric field between the earth and the ionosphere. Changing the lightning frequency might upset this charge-transfer balance with a resultant effect on the fair-weather field. The change in the fair-weather field might trigger further reactions.

The study of the effects of lightning on the environment is in its infancy. The control of lightning is not necessarily desirable unless the full consequences of that control are evaluated.

Now, let us look at lightning control. When "control" is mentioned it is reasonable to think either of (a) stopping lightning or (b) harnessing its power. To harness appreciable power from lightning would require a worldwide network which could tap energy from a reasonable fraction of the world's total discharges. Even if science were to devise an efficient way to tap energy from a lightning stroke (which it has not yet done), the construction and maintenance of some sort of worldwide network appears at present to be impractical. On the other hand, stopping lightning from a given storm, or at least decreasing its frequency, is certainly a practical goal, and some initial steps in this direction have been taken. For example, it has been experimentally demonstrated, although not to the satisfaction of everyone concerned, that cloud seeding can sometimes decrease the number of lightnings produced by a thundercloud.

Understanding of Lightning

A number of photographic, electrical, spectroscopic, and acoustic measurements have been made on lightning. From these we have a reasonably good idea of the energies, currents, and charges involved in lightning, of the electromagnetic fields (radio waves, light, and so on) generated, of the velocities of propagation of the various luminous "streamer" processes by which the lightning discharge forms, and of the temperature, pressure, and types of particles comprising the discharge channel. In short, we have available both an observational description of how lightning works (e.g., the discharge is begun by a luminous leader which is first seen at the cloud base and moves toward ground in steps, as shown in Figure V-15) and most of the data needed for routine engineering applications (e.g., power-line design and lightning protection).

A good deal of what we know about lightning has been determined in the United States in the past fifteen years. However, the total number of U.S. researchers primarily studying

Figure V–15 — THE INITIATION OF A LIGHTNING STROKE

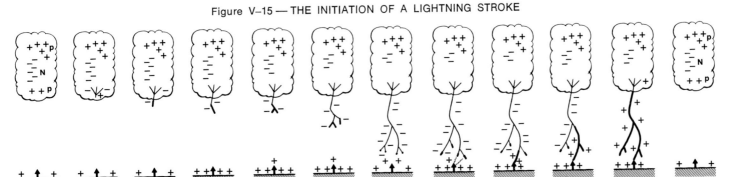

(Illustration Redrawn with Permission, BEK Technical Publications, Inc., Carnegie, Pa.)

The drawing shows the initiation of a stepped-leader from a cloud base. The time involved is about 50 millionths of a second. As the downward-moving leader gets close to the ground, upward-moving discharges meet it. A return stroke then propagates from the ground to the cloud. The time for the return stroke propagation is about 100 millionths of a second. Propagation is continuous until the charges are dissipated.

lightning at any given time during this period has been only about ten, of which perhaps half have contributed to our understanding of lightning. As an example of the general lack of scientific interest in lightning phenomena, the first technical book on lightning was not published until 1969.

While we have available a number of observational "facts" about lightning, we do not understand lightning in detail. Areas of particular ignorance are: (a) the initiation of lightning in the cloud and (b) propagation of lightning from cloud to ground. Unfortunately, these are just the areas in which a detailed understanding is essential if lightning control is to be practiced.

It is important to know what we mean by a "detailed understanding." A "detailed understanding" implies a mathematical description or model of the lightning behavior. The mathematical model is adequate when it can predict the observed properties of lightning. The mathematical model can then be used to determine the effects on the lightning of altering various parameters of the model. For the case of lightning initiation, these parameters might be the ambient temperature, ambient electric field, number of water drops per unit volume, etc. The predictions of

the mathematical model must be tested by experiments. The results of these experiments can suggest changes in the model or can verify its validity. It follows that experiment and theory must advance together to achieve a complete description of the lightning phenomenon.

The physics of lightning initiation and propagation is exceedingly complex. Some idea of its complexity can be gauged by noting that the processes involved in electrical breakdown between a rod and a flat plate in the laboratory (an electric spark) are at present only vaguely understood. It appears that, despite about thirty years of experimental work, a real understanding of the laboratory spark will not be available until a mathematical description of the spark is forthcoming. Only recently have digital computers become available in a sufficient size that a mathematical solution to the spark problem is in principle possible.

The Future

Significant progress in our detailed understanding of lightning could probably be made in the next ten to fifteen years, although given the present level of scientific activity and ability in the lightning area, it is unlikely that this will be the case.

Lightning research has been neither glamorous enough nor quantitative enough to attract the attention of many good graduate students or senior scientists. Several excellent experimentalists are presently working in the lightning area, and their work needs to be continued and enlarged. More important to the goal of detailed understanding of lightning, however, is the need for mathematically oriented scientists to become involved in the problems of lightning initiation and propagation. The mathematically oriented scientists and the experimentalists should work closely together in both the construction of suitable mathematical models and in the planning and analysis of experiments.

In studying lightning, the time-scale on which meaningful results can be expected is relatively long. From an experimental point of view, the necessity of staying in a given location for a long enough time to observe enough lightning to be able to compile statistically significant results determines the time-scale of any particular lightning research program — generally, several years. The mathematical approach to lightning is exceedingly complex and thus must also take place on a time-scale of several years. With a *coordinated* work force of perhaps five senior theoreticians and fifteen senior experimentalists (assuming, of course, that these researchers are equipped with the necessary skills), one might expect significant progress in our detailed understanding of lightning in the next ten to fifteen years. There is certainly no assurance of success in any lightning research. It is clear, however, that a successful effort to understand lightning must be a long-term effort.

Reduction of Lightning Damage by Cloud Seeding

Lightning is an important cause of forest fires throughout the world and especially in North America. In an average year, about 10,000 forest fires are ignited by lightning; in a severe season, the number may rise to 15,000. The problem is particularly acute in the western states, where lightning ignites over 70 percent of the forest fires. Here, hundreds of fires may be ignited in a single day, many of them in remote and inaccessible regions. These peaks in occurrence, along with existing heavy fire loads, tax fire-suppression agencies beyond reasonable limits of manpower and equipment. Fire-suppression costs can be very high; direct costs may approach $100 million per year while losses of commercial timber, watersheds, and other forest resources may be several times this amount. In addition to loss of human lives, lightning fires constitute a growing threat to homes, businesses, and recreational areas.

Potential Modification Techniques

What steps could be taken in weather modification to alleviate the lightning-fire problem? The most obvious is to reduce the number of cloud-to-ground discharges, particularly during periods of high fire danger. Those characteristics of discharges most likely to cause forest-fire ignition might be selectively modified to decrease their fire-starting potential. Also, the amount of rain preceding or accompanying lightning could be increased in order to wet forest fuels and thus decrease the potential for fire ignition and spread.

A Seeding Experiment — The large losses in natural resources each year caused by lightning-ignited forest fires has prompted the Forest Service of the U.S. Department of Agriculture to perform a series of experiments in the northern Rocky Mountains which are aimed at reducing fire-starting lightning strokes by massively seeding "dry" thunderstorms over the national forests. Following is a summary of results of the studies of lightning-fire ignition and lightning modification.

The first systematic program of lightning modification was conducted in western Montana in the summers of 1960 and 1961. This two-year pilot experiment was designed to test the effect of seeding on lightning frequency and to evaluate lightning-counting and cloud-seeding methods in mountainous areas. Some 38 percent fewer ground discharges were recorded on seed days than on days when clouds were not seeded. Intracloud and total lightning were less by 8 and 21 percent, respectively, on seed days during the two-year period. Analysis of these data by a statistical test showed that, if seeding had no effect, differences of this magnitude would occur about one in four. Also, the experiment confirmed the need to develop a continuous lightning-recording system that could resolve the small-scale details of individual lightning discharges. Subsequently, a continuous lightning-recording system and improved cloud-seeding generators were developed.

Building a Data Base

A new lightning-modification experiment was begun in 1965, with the first phase to last for three summer seasons. The objectives were to gain additional information on the frequency and characteristics of lightning from mountain thunderstorms and to determine if there is a significant difference in the occurrence and character of lightning from seeded and unseeded storms. It was not designed to confirm or reject a single mechanism by which lightning is modified by seeding. Rather, a primary objective was to build a body of observations of lightning from both seeded and unseeded storms and to use these data to build appropriate hypotheses and models for testing in future experiments. Appropriate statistical tests were included in the design of the experiments as a basis for evaluating differences attributable to treatment.

Analysis of data on the basis of the life cycle of individual thunderstorms occurring in 1965-67 (14 no seed, 12 seeded storms) gave the following results at the given level of significance for two-tailed tests:

1. Sixty-six percent fewer cloud-to-ground discharges, 50 percent fewer intracloud discharges, and 54 percent less total storm lightning occurred during seeded storms than during the unseeded storms.

2. The maximum cloud-to-ground flash rate was less for seeded storms. Over a 5-minute interval, the maximum rate averaged 8.8 for unseeded storms and 5.0 for seeded storms; for 15-minute intervals, the maximum rate for unseeded storms averaged 17.7 as against 9.1 for seeded storms.

3. There was no difference in the average number of return strokes per discrete discharge (4.1 unseeded *vs.* 4.0 seeded).

4. The average duration of discrete discharges (period between first and last return stroke) decreased from 235 milliseconds for unseeded storms to 182 milliseconds for seeded storms.

5. The average duration of continuing current in hybrid discharges decreased from 187 milliseconds for unseeded storms to 115 milliseconds for seeded storms.

Inferences

The results from the seeding experiments to date strongly suggest that lightning frequency and characteristics are modified by massive seeding with silver iodide freezing nuclei. While the physical mechanism by which massive seeding modifies lightning activity is not fully understood, there is evidence that the basic charging processes are altered by the seeding. Further, it has been established on the basis of direct measurements that hybrid discharges (lightning strokes that contain a continuing current) may be responsible for most lightning-caused forest fires. Thus, a substantial reduction in the duration of the continuing-current portion of the hybrid discharge may have a large effect on the ability of an individual discharge to ignite fuels or to cause substantial damage. This change in the nature of the discharge may be more important than a change in the total amount of lightning that is produced by the storms.

PART VI

PRECIPITATION AND REGIONAL WEATHER PHENOMENA

1. DROUGHT

The Causes and Nature of Drought and its Prediction

Drought is one of the manifestations of the prevailing wind patterns (the general circulation). A few special remarks may clarify this manifestation, and suggest further work necessary to understand and predict droughts.

Virtually all large-scale droughts (like the Dust Bowl spells of the 1930's or the 1962-66 New England drought) are associated with slow and prevailing subsiding motions of air masses emanating from continental source regions. Since the air usually starts out dry, and the relative humidity declines as the air descends, cloud formation is inhibited — or, if clouds are formed, they are soon dissipated.

The atmospheric circulations that lead to this subsidence are certain "centers of action," like the Bermuda High, which are linked to the planetary waves of the upper-level westerlies. If these centers are displaced from their normal positions or are abnormally well developed, they often introduce anomalously moist or dry air masses into certain regions of the temperate latitudes. More important, these long waves interact with the cyclones along the polar front in such a way as to form and steer their course into or away from certain areas. In the areas relatively invulnerable to cyclones, the air descends, and if this process repeats time after time, a deficiency of rainfall leading to drought may occur. In other areas where moist air is frequently forced to ascend, heavy rains occur. Therefore, drought in one area is usually associated with abundant precipitation elsewhere. For example, precipitation was heavy over the Central Plains during the 1962-66 drought in northeastern United States.

After drought has been established in an area, it seems to have a tendency to persist and expand into adjacent areas. Although little is known about the physical mechanisms involved in this expansion and persistence, some circumstantial evidence suggests that numerous "feedback" processes are set in motion which aggravate the situation. Among these are large-scale interactions between ocean and atmosphere in which variations in ocean-surface temperature are produced by abnormal wind systems, and these in turn encourage further development of the same type of abnormal circulation. Then again, if an area such as the Central Plains is subject to dryness and heat in spring, the parched soil appears to influence subsequent air circulation and rainfall in a drought-extending sense.

Finally, it should be pointed out that some of the most extensive droughts, like those of the 1930's Dust Bowl era, require compatibly placed centers of action over both the Atlantic and Pacific oceans.

In view of the immense scale and complexity of drought-producing systems, it is difficult for man to devise methods of eliminating or ameliorating them. However, given global data of the extent described previously, and the teamwork of oceanographers, meteorologists, and soil scientists, it should be possible to understand the interaction of continent, ocean, and atmosphere sufficiently so that reasonably accurate estimates of the beginnings and endings of droughts are possible.

Ability to predict droughts would be of tremendous planning value. Unfortunately, encouragement for drought research comes only after a period of dryness has about run its course, because the return of normal or abundant precipitation quickly changes priorities to more urgent matters. Without continuing in-depth drought studies, humanity will always be unprepared to cope with the economic dislocations induced by unpredictable long dry spells.

It has long been known that the general circulation of the atmosphere is such that alternating latitude belts of wetness and dryness tend to dominate the world system of climates. (See Figure VI-1) In connection with droughts, the important belts are:

1. The equatorial belt of wetness associated with ascending currents in the zone where the trade winds from the southern and the northern hemisphere meet;

2. The subtropical belt of dryness associated with descending air motions in the so-called subtropical anticyclones;

3. The mid-latitude belt of wetness associated with traveling depressions and storms that develop in the zone of transition between warm and cold air masses — i.e., the "polar front."

While the equatorial belt of wetness is more or less continuous around the world, the subtropical belt of dryness is disrupted by monsoon-like winds in the warm seasons and by polar-front disturbances in the cold season. As a result, rainfall is generally adequate along subtropical east

Figure VI-1 — ANNUAL WORLDWIDE PRECIPITATION

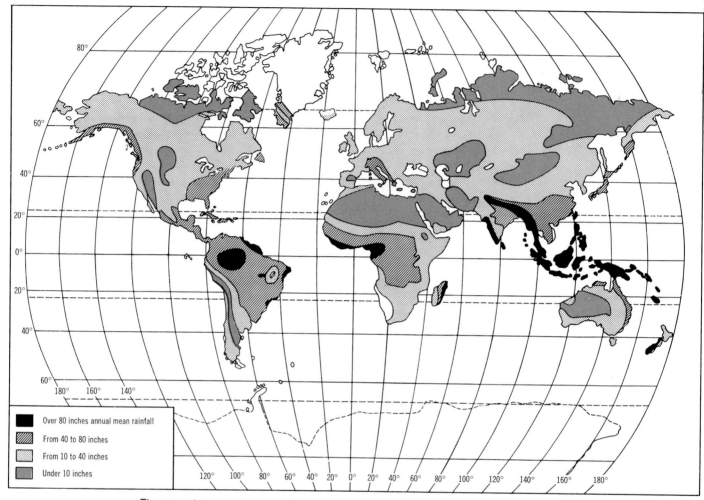

■	Over 80 inches annual mean rainfall
▨	From 40 to 80 inches
░	From 10 to 40 inches
▓	Under 10 inches

The map shows annual precipitation over the world compiled from land-station data and some ship and island observations. Isopleths over the ocean areas, which show large "dry" patches off western continental coastlines, are best guesses.

coasts (e.g., Florida), while dryness typically prevails along subtropical west coasts (e.g., southern California) and in adjacent continents. Finally, the mid-latitude belt of wetness will be disrupted where mountain ranges (e.g., the Rocky Mountains) provide shelter against rain-bearing winds from nearby oceans.

Between the semi-permanent climatic patterns, which do not change perceptibly, and the rather lively short-term patterns associated with traveling disturbances and storms, there exist regimes of long-lived anomalies superimposed on the gen-

eral circulation. These anomalies are quasi-stationary or move very slowly, and their duration and intensity may vary within wide limits. Anomalies of this kind are always present, and when their duration and intensity exceed certain limits of dryness, they become recognized as droughts. Most national weather services have established definitions of drought; although these are useful for record-keeping, administrative actions, and such, they do not reflect scientific principles. In the following, the word *drought* will be used in the meaning of *an extensive period of excessive dryness.*

Research Findings

There is some indication that certain time-lag relationships exist. For example, Namias found that many summer droughts in the United States appear to be associated with changes in the upper atmosphere that begin to develop in the foregoing spring. There is a need here for more research to determine whether reliable two-way statistical relationships exist and are applicable to independent sets of data; if this should prove to be so, techniques for predicting the onset of individual droughts might be developed.

166

The factors that determine the duration of droughts have not been well explored and no predictive capability exists. The droughts that have received most attention are those that have affected agricultural operations — i.e., late spring and summer droughts. Some of these have been unable to survive the hardships of the winter following, but others have shown a tendency to recur the next spring or summer, and these prolonged droughts are of great interest economically as well as scientifically.

There is evidence to indicate that drought-producing systems tend to develop in families (rather than as individuals), though each member may not qualify as a drought according to official definitions. For example, Namias found that drought-producing anticyclones over the agricultural heartland of North America have companion anticyclones on the Pacific as well as on the Atlantic. Drought-producing anticyclones in the lower atmosphere appear to be associated with distortions of the flow patterns through deep layers. Our knowledge of these conditions is meager; much firmer information could be provided through special analyses of existing data.

Although an official drought may cover a relatively small region, the associated atmospheric processes must be studied in the context of the general circulation of the atmosphere, including the principal sources of heat and moisture.

The Causes of Drought

The above-mentioned findings — that drought-producing systems tend to occur in families and that individual droughts may span one or more annual cycles — are of considerable scientific significance and hold out hope of progress toward prediction. These findings point toward the physical processes that create the large-scale anomalies of which droughts are manifestations. Since extraterrestrial influences can safely be ruled out, it is clear that the forces, or energy sources, that bring about these anomalies must develop within the earth-atmosphere system itself. Furthermore, since an individual drought in middle and high latitudes (where the annual variation is large) may outlast an annual cycle, it is plausible that the underlying energy sources are rooted in the equatorial belt (where the annual change is small).

Bjerknes has recently produced selected analyses that indicate, with a high degree of certainty, that the general circulations of the atmosphere in middle and high latitudes respond readily and significantly to energy inputs resulting in variations in the ocean-atmosphere interactions in low latitudes. Of special importance is the transfer of heat and moisture from the oceans, and the freeing of latent heat by condensation in the air. The major site of interactions resulting in varying inputs of energy is the equatorial belt from the west coast of South America to beyond the date line. Significant impulses can also be traced to the Humboldt Current, the Indian Ocean, and other areas.

Bjerknes found that the upwellings of cool water, resulting from the varying convergence of the trade winds, undergo changes that may be large at times, and these affect the rate at which energy is supplied to the atmosphere in the equatorial belt. These inputs are, in turn, exported via upper air currents as various forms of energy to the mid-latitude belt, where they bring about distortions of the flow patterns, dislocations of the storm tracks, and regional anomalies of different kinds. Of particular interest in connection with droughts is the tendency for more or less stationary offshoots from the subtropical belt of dryness to disrupt the mid-latitude belt of wetness. Bjerknes' findings are of great interest and raise hopes for progress in long-range prediction and other applied areas.

Research Aspects — It is clear from the foregoing discussion that our knowledge of drought is fragmentary and that much work remains to be done before adequate descriptions of individual or typical droughts can be provided. An individual drought must be recognized and described as a member of a family of anomalies, and its characteristics must be related to the evolution of these anomalies. Undoubtedly, such descriptive studies will lead to greater insights into the underlying general mechanisms as well as the many local or regional factors that determine the severity of droughts. In the past, research on droughts has been conducted on an *ad hoc* basis, with emphasis on local or regional conditions. A concerted effort, making full use of available data and data-processing facilities, seems justified in terms of national requirements as well as available talent.

Although the broad aspects of the causes of droughts appear to be understandable on the basis of Bjerknes' findings, much work remains to be done to relate the evolution and the characteristics of atmospheric anomalies to specific variations in the appropriate ocean-atmosphere interactions. Empirical studies should be matched with construction of models to simulate the behavior of the atmosphere in response to observed or inferred ocean-atmosphere interactions.

It is clear that the research opportunities in this general area are highly promising. Data are available to support analyses of many cases, with extensions to longer time-spans. The present recognition of a need for improved understanding of our environment and better management of our natural resources is likely to stimulate application. The research is likely to appeal to young talent in several disciplines. And the research is likely to provide important inputs to the co-operative schemes of the International Decade of Ocean Exploration and the Global Atmospheric Research Program.

The Prediction of Drought

The National Weather Service issues monthly general forecasts of large-scale patterns of temperature and rainfall, and from such forecasts the likelihood of onset of drought during the month concerned may be inferred in general terms. At the present time, no specific techniques for predicting drought exist. It is possible that a study of time-lag relationships for large areas could provide useful guidance. It is possible, too, that running analyses of the conditions within the Pacific section of the equatorial belt and related studies of the responses of the mid-latitude atmosphere would provide useful prediction aids. Finally, the results of the above-mentioned studies are likely to be considerably sharpened through numerical experiments with dynamical simulation models.

2. PRECIPITATION MODIFICATION

Artificial Alteration of Natural Precipitation

The scientific basis of all efforts to modify precipitation artificially rests on manipulating the rates of reaction of natural precipitation mechanisms. Our *qualitative* understanding of natural precipitation mechanisms is in rather good shape. (See Figure VI-2) But our knowledge of the *quantitative* aspects of these processes is generally quite poor. There are several reasons for this state of affairs:

1. The process rate coefficients are inadequately known.

2. Several of the processes are competitive, so that small initial differences may give one of them an ever widening advantage.

3. The initial and boundary conditions are known to be important but are poorly understood and difficult to measure.

Figure VI-2 — PRECIPITATION PROCESSES

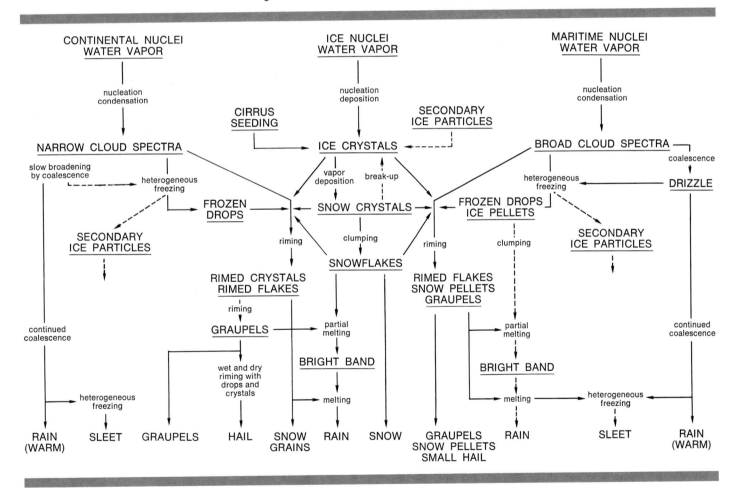

In this flow chart, the precipitation process is seen to begin with water vapor and one of several different types of nuclei. Through various processes, the nuclei obtain vapor and grow. The final form of the precipitation depends on the environment through which the precipitation falls. The various forms of precipitation that are observed in nature are listed at the bottom of the chart. By tracing their path upward through the chart, it is possible to determine the conditions necessary for their production.

4. There are several feedback loops whereby a change in the microphysical character of a cloud parcel, as a result of precipitation development, feeds back into the energetics of the cloud and thereby alters the boundary conditions in which the precipitation processes operate. These feedback loops are largely unexplored. They range in scale from the release of heat of phase change, causing a small cloud parcel to accelerate upward, thereby increasing its condensate load, to large-scale, long-range effects whereby a major change in the cloud system at one point induces adjustments in the atmosphere tens or hundreds of cloud-diameters away.

Natural Nuclei and their Relation to Weather Modification

Almost all U.S. efforts to change precipitation through cloud seeding (whether to increase, decrease, or redistribute either rain or snow) rest on the observation that the normal behavior of a cloud can be altered through the introduction of large numbers of suitable nuclei.

There are two types of natural nuclei, serving two different functions, in natural clouds:

1. *Cloud nuclei* (small soluble particles of the order of 0.1 to 3 microns in diameter), which serve as condensation centers for liquid cloud droplets.

2. *Ice nuclei* (probably clay minerals about 1 micron in diameter, although the exact nature of these particles is still in question), which serve as centers of initiation of ice particles either by freezing drops or directly from the vapor.

Ice nuclei are necessary for snow production. Snow generated aloft may melt inside a cloud on its way to the ground and land as rain. Rain may also be initiated by a few specially favorable cloud nuclei acting through an all-liquid process.

The relative importance of the two known precipitation mechanisms is not fully worked out. However, it appears that the all-liquid process is more important in warmer seasons and in maritime air masses, whereas the ice-crystal mechanism is probably more important in colder seasons and in continental weather events.

The ice-crystal mechanism of precipitation development was the first precipitation process proposed. It appeared to explain most available observations until the late 1940's, when meteorologists began to make measurements inside clouds and to examine them with radar. The all-liquid precipitation mechanism was essentially unknown before about 1950; even today its relative importance is **not** clear.

The common occurrence of supercooled clouds was taken as evidence to show that concentrations of natural ice nuclei were often insufficient for effective precipitation production. Proponents of seeding thus argued that, through the addition of artificial nuclei, one could enhance the efficiency of the ice-crystal mechanism and thereby increase rain at the ground.

Technology quickly provided efficient tools for releasing large numbers of artificial ice nuclei. Present-day seeding generators, burning an acetone solution of silver iodide (AgI), yield effective ice nuclei concentrations of about 10^{13} to 10^{14} crystals per gram of AgI at $-10°$ centigrade, increasing to about 10^{15} crystals per gram of AgI at $-20°$ centigrade. This means that a single gram of AgI, *if completely and properly dispersed*, would be capable of seeding 100 cubic kilometers. Technology has not yet, however, produced adequate tools for measuring the concentrations of natural ice nuclei.

A more realistic, more scientific approach to cloud seeding for altering precipitation is beginning to emerge. This approach recognizes, and attempts to relate, several interdependent factors:

1. There are two known precipitation mechanisms, only one of which depends on ice nuclei and only one of which is readily accessible through present-day seeding technology.

2. The concentrations of natural nuclei, both cloud and ice particles, and the internal structure of clouds of any given type differ importantly from time to time and place to place. For example, a substantial difference between cloud spectra in maritime and continental cumuli is recognized as due to differences in the cloud nuclei; basically, it is this difference in drop spectra that gives maritime clouds their propensity for warm rain. As a consequence of such differences, natural clouds differ markedly in their response to seeding.

   Not all responses to seeding are desirable. To give an example, Project WHITETOP found that AgI seeding of summertime cumulus clouds in Missouri may have decreased the rainfall by as much as 40 to 50 percent on days with south winds.

3. The development of precipitation takes considerable time, in many cases about the same as the lifetime of the cloud parcels that nurture the precipitation development. Thus, most seeding efforts attempt to alter the time required for precipitation development relative to the life of the cloud, or, alternatively, attempt to extend the life of the cloud by activating feedback loops between changes in cloud microstructure and cloud

energetics. The seeding of small cumuli over Florida and over nearby ocean areas aims at complete glaciation of the clouds to secure the maximum release of latent heat of fusion, which in turn might cause greatly expanded cloud development.

4. The *optimum* number of ice particles (hence the seeding requirement, if any) depends in a complex way on the detailed nature of the cloud and the desired end product. For example, the Bureau of Reclamation project in Colorado aims at regulating the number of snow crystals in the clouds to be the minimum required in order that their combined growth rate just uses up the liquid water of the cloud by the time the cloud reaches the crest of the mountain divide. A lesser number would permit cloud liquid water to pass over the divide and be evaporated. A larger number, and slower growth, might result in individual crystals being too small to fall out before crossing the divide.

Requirements for Scientific Cloud Seeding

The modern approach to cloud seeding is to couple the treatment method to the end object through specification of the target cloud and a knowledge of the intermediate physical processes. To accomplish this requires elaborate systems for real-time measurement of deterministic meteorological factors, and real-time computer modeling of the physical processes of the clouds to permit objective decisions as to when, where, and how to seed.

Data Base and Related Technology — The data base on which to develop a scientific approach to cloud seeding is uneven. In some areas it is fairly good, in others almost totally lacking.

The physical properties of cloud and precipitation particles, and the particle-interaction coefficients, though incomplete, are sufficient for most purposes. Given an initial specification of cloud properties, one can make usable estimates of the growth of a limited number of precipitation particles contained therein. Once the precipitation particles become sufficiently numerous to interact appreciably, or in the ever present case of the interaction of cloud drops, the bottleneck is not so much the lack of physical data as one of computer capability and mathematical devices to allow one to keep track of the large number of possible interactions.

A more serious difficulty is the general lack of data on the internal microstructure of clouds as a function of cloud type, season, geography, and meteorological situation. Instruments for measuring ice and cloud nuclei are essentially laboratory devices and really not suitable for routine field use. Only recently have tools been developed for routine measurement of cloud-particle spectra. We have many measurements of nuclei and cloud-particle spectra from research projects, but we still lack appropriate concepts for generalizing them in ways to permit useful extension to the unmeasured cloud situation.

Interactions and Downwind Effects — The feedback loops between the physics of particles inside clouds and the energetics of those clouds is almost totally unexplored. One can perceive a definite effort in this area in cloud physics today. Important advances are likely to come quickly in terms of the interactions inside single clouds. But the equally important problem of interaction between clouds and cloud systems on the mesoscale seems much more difficult. Such interactions are well known for the case of natural clouds. One should suspect them — indeed, there are signs pointing to them — in the case of clouds altered by seeding. For example, measurements on Project WHITETOP indicated strongly that changes in

rainfall due to seeding were accompanied by changes of opposite sign 50 to 100 miles downwind.

Water and Energy Budgets of Clouds — An area of general meteorology of great importance to cloud seeding, and still inadequately explored, concerns the water and energy budgets of clouds and cloud systems. Seeding to change precipitation presumes to alter the water budget of the target cloud system, yet studies of the water and energy budgets of mesoscale weather systems are almost totally lacking. Braham carried out such a study for thunderstorms in 1952. A study of the water budget of the winter storms involved in the Bureau of Reclamation seeding project in Colorado is presently under way. Virtually no other mesoscale weather system has been so studied. The reasons for this are primarily the inadequacy, for this purpose, of data from the National Weather Service and the great cost of obtaining additional data specifically for such studies. Yet cloud seeding can never be soundly based until we know in considerable detail the water budgets of both the natural and treated storms.

Looking to the Future

The preceding paragraphs are concerned mainly with topics in physical meteorology concerned with seeding clouds to alter the amount of precipitation at the ground. There are a number of other matters that must be resolved before such seeding can be adequate for public purposes. Some of these are scientific in nature, others are issues of economics, sociology, and public policy.

Unanswered Questions — Among the most important issues to be faced are four unanswered scientific questions:

1. Under what specific meteorological conditions (including microphysics and energetics of clouds) will a particular treat-

ment technique result in a predictable cloud response?

2. Which of the various possible cloud responses would be useful to society, in what ways, and under what conditions?

3. Given that a useful cloud response can be predicted from a particular treatment of some specific set of initial cloud conditions, are our abilities and tools for diagnosing the occurrence of these conditions sufficient to permit exploitation of such treatment? In what time-space scale? In what economic framework?

4. What is the proper division of resources between:

   (a) basic research, where the sought-for end product enhances knowledge about clouds and their physical response to seeding;

   (b) pilot projects, where the chief objective is assessment of the economics of a particular cloud-modification scheme; and

   (c) field operations, where the

principal aim is to maximize the field of a changed weather element?

Projected Scientific Activity — Because of the complexity of the atmosphere and our limited knowledge about modifying it, it is likely that the skill in recognizing seeding opportunities can be developed only from the results of a number of carefully designed experimental projects aimed at testing seeding hypotheses in various types of weather situations in different parts of the country. Project WHITETOP and the Bureau of Reclamation Upper Colorado Pilot Project are examples of what these projects might look like, each of which will require from three to ten years. Until such studies are carried out, scientists will probably be unable to specify how much precipitation can be changed, under what conditions, and how often these conditions occur. Technology is already at hand and scientific principles of experiment design are known. We must, however, be prepared to accept disadvantages as well as advantages to the underlying population.

Economic and Social Implications — The interactions of cloud seeding with society are clearly enormous, but they are hard to detail because we lack

firm information as to how much and how often precipitation can be modified, and also because most studies have emphasized the scientific aspects with little regard for the economic, social, and political issues.

Since there are few places in the United States where the economy is tied to a single economic enterprise, almost any change in precipitation is likely to disadvantage some while working to the advantage of others. We sorely need studies to learn the full scope of public cost and public benefit of changes in weather. We can start by using the natural variability of weather and determine just how a departure of weather from long-term normality works its way through the economy of a region. Such studies—involving the collective effort of sociologists, economists, and meteorologists—should be encouraged.

Even with such knowledge, one comes ultimately to the thorny issues of how we decide when and where to practice weather modification, and how the disadvantaged are to be compensated. Will insurance companies, for example, "pay off" in a region of cloud seeding if evidence develops that increasing rainfall also increases hail?

The Status of Precipitation Management

Research and operational weather-modification programs since the late 1940's have served to identify procedures that appear related to precipitation increases. At the same time, these results have indicated areas where real understanding and competence are insufficient.

A number of cloud-seeding techniques have been developed. Ground-based seeding with silver iodide (AgI), whose crystal structure resembles that of ice (see Figure VI-3),

is the most common technique, especially for winter storms in mountainous terrain. The seeding material is carried aloft by vertical motion resulting from the instability of the air or from the lift due to the mountain barrier. One remaining fundamental problem involves diffusion of the seeding material. Proper seeding procedures require (a) that the proper number of nuclei reach the effective level in the cloud, and (b) that the effect of the seeding will be felt in the desired location on the

ground. The diffusion process is a rather complex function of vertical temperature distribution and the three-dimensional wind field.

Airborne seeding with silver iodide or crushed dry ice is frequently employed with summer convective storms. The primary limitation of aerial operations is whether or not the aircraft can fly in weather conditions where seeding will be effective.

Various experimental designs and statistical evaluation procedures have

Figure VI–3 — LATTICE STRUCTURES OF AgI AND ICE

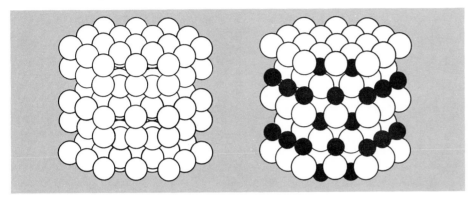

The models show the crystal structures of ice and silver iodide (AgI). In the model of AgI, the white spheres are iodide ions and the black spheres silver ions. Although the crystal structures of both molecules are similar, the lattice constant of AgI is 1.5% larger than that of ice. Partial compensation for the difference can be made by coprecipitating silver bromide (AgBr) with AgI and substituting Br for as many as 30% of the I atoms in the AgI crystal structure, which will produce a unit cell up to 0.5% smaller than that of pure AgI.

been used. In retrospect, some of them were inadequate. Nevertheless, the early programs did show that cloud seeding has a tremendous potential.

While the bulk of the activity in precipitation augmentation involves seeding clouds with artificial nuclei, other procedures have been proposed and are being studied. Modification of radiation processes is an example. If a large area (several acres or more) is covered with asphalt, the increased heating of the air immediately over the area can lead to strong convective currents, sufficient under some circumstances to stimulate the precipitation process. Another possibility involves increasing the humidity high in the air so that more water would be available for the natural precipitation processes. Several ideas have been offered for extracting water from coastal stratus clouds.

The obvious goal for weather-modification research, considered as a whole, is to find the best system for any given situation. However, the wide variety of conditions under which clouds and storms occur, coupled with the different types of topography over which these clouds develop, show that several, perhaps

many, procedures must be available to get the best results from every situation. It is unlikely that the real world will ever see a truly "best" system for all conditions. A reasonable procedure, short of finding the absolute "best" way, is to put the available techniques, equipment, and instrumentation together in such a way that, under the existing conditions, the desired effect is maximized. In other words, optimize the available systems.

What Constitutes a Precipitation Management System?

A true precipitation-management system, even a crude and inefficient one, will have four major components: (a) a component to analyze present and expected water needs and water sources, as well as the anticipated effects of precipitation management on such factors as the economy and ecology of the area in question, and arrive at a decision to employ precipitation-management techniques; (b) a component to recognize a weather situation where the application of precipitation-management techniques would result in the desired effect and also, hopefully, those situations in which the result

would be deleterious; (c) a component to select the proper treatment material and delivery system for the situation at hand; and (d) a component to assess the actual results of the treatment in terms of useful water on the ground, economic benefits and disbenefits, and environmental consequences.

Analyzer Function — The first activity of an operational system is to determine when the application of precipitation-management techniques could contribute to the resolution of a water problem of a particular area. After the specific need is defined, the various potential sources of additional water (e.g., the atmosphere, water mining, re-use) are examined to find the best way to fill the need. The effects of the application of precipitation-management techniques on the economics, ecology, and sociology of the area are examined.

Another important consideration is whether or not the increased precipitation would fall where a substantial portion of it would eventually be usable. There are also legal questions that must be looked at, such as ownership of the land being affected, ownership of the moisture being withdrawn, licensing and indemnification procedures, and reporting procedures.

When all the available information has been considered, a decision is made. Precipitation-management techniques may be inappropriate for a variety of reasons, or they may be the only techniques available. Usually, however, precipitation management will be used in addition to other methods of acquiring additional water.

Recognition — Once a decision has been made to use weather modification in the solution of a problem, treatable situations must be identified. Many of the necessary conditions for successful weather modification are known, at least qualitatively, but we do not yet know if these are sufficient conditions.

One important factor in determining whether or not a given weather situation is treatable is the number of natural nuclei. Nuclei are needed to convert vapor into liquid; other nuclei are needed to convert liquid into ice. The presence of ice crystals is considered critical to precipitation formation in most clouds that occur in the middle latitudes. If liquid droplets are present at temperatures below freezing, a nuclei deficit is implied. Such a deficit in an otherwise suitable cloud can be overcome by the addition of artificial nuclei. The additional nuclei will convert some of the droplets into ice crystals, which will grow at the expense of the liquid droplets until they are large enough to fall out, thereby initiating or increasing precipitation. There are few routine observations of natural nuclei numbers, and most counts are made at the surface, not aloft where the clouds are. We have only rather crude notions of how many nuclei are needed in any given situation.

Some of the other factors of importance in the treatability of a weather system are temperature structure, wind, liquid water content of the cloud, and cloud-droplet size spectra. Again, we have fairly good qualitative understanding of the role of each factor, but we do not completely understand all the links in the physical chain of events leading to the desired result of the modification attempt. In addition, some of the pertinent factors are difficult to measure. Still other factors may be important in cloud treatability, but our knowledge of them in real cloud situations is too meager even for qualitative statements.

In some situations, theory and empirical evidence have been united in mathematical models. These models simulate the atmosphere and can predict the response of the cloud to a given treatment. While the models available today are comparatively crude, they play a valuable role in enabling scientists to recognize treatable situations.

Treatment — After a situation is identified as treatable, the appropriate materials and techniques must be chosen. The most frequently used materials for weather-modification activities are AgI and dry ice, but many other substances have been used experimentally (salt, lead iodide, calcium chloride, and a host of organics including metaldehyde, phloroglucinol, urea, and 1,5-dihydroxynaphthalene). The temperature at which each of these agents becomes effective is fairly well known (see Figure VI-4), as is the particle-size requirement (for AgI, on the order of 0.1 micron).

Clouds can be classified into two categories, cold and warm. Cold clouds are those with temperatures wholly or partly at or below 0° centigrade. Warm clouds are those everywhere warmer than 0° centigrade. Materials that affect cold clouds rarely have any effect on warm clouds. Thus, the treatment material must be matched to the situation. The object is to change the size and/or state of the cloud particles. Precipitation from warm clouds can be increased if the small droplets can be turned into big droplets.

Hygroscopic materials should be effective in warm clouds. They are, in fact, being used experimentally, though it has proved difficult both to get the material ground to a small enough size to stay in the cloud long enough to be effective and to keep the particles dry until they are released to the atmosphere. Once a few droplets large enough to begin to fall are formed, coalescence should keep the process going until precipitation falls out of the cloud.

Hygroscopic materials should also be effective in cold clouds, but materials that initiate a phase change are more efficient. Some cold-cloud agents, such as dry ice, simply cool the air and the vapor and liquid in it to a temperature at which tiny ice crystals form spontaneously. This process is effective at air temperatures a few degrees below freezing

Figure VI-4 — TEMPERATURE DEPENDENCE OF NUCLEATING AGENTS

Substance	Effective Temperature °C
Carbon Dioxide	0
AgI	−4
PbI$_2$	−6
CuO	−7
Loam-Rugby, N.D.	−8
NH$_4$F	−9
V$_2$O$_5$	−10
Loess-Hanford, Wash.	−11
CdI$_2$	−12
Soil-Baggs, Wyo.	−13
I$_2$	−14
Ash-Crater Lake, Ore.	−17
Dust-Phoenix, Ariz.	−18
Kaolin-Ga.	−23
Diatoms	−31
Spores	−36

The table lists some of the more prominent substances that are used as nucleating agents and the temperature at which they become effective as nuclei.

or lower. Other materials, such as silver iodide, are known to be effective, but *why* they work is not clearly understood. The crystal structure of AgI is quite similar to that of ice, and this was thought to be the reason for its effectiveness. Recent studies suggest that pure AgI is a rather poor nucleating material, and that it must be contaminated with some other material to be useful in weather modification.

Different methods are needed to deliver the various materials to the cloud. Dry ice is dropped into clouds, usually from an airplane. The size of the dry-ice pellets depends on the vertical thickness of the cloud. Silver iodide can be released from the air or from the ground. Ground releases rely on the horizontal and vertical airflow to carry the material to the cloud.

One major problem is to confine the effects of treatment to a designated target area. The point on the ground where the effects will be felt is determined by the point of release of the material, the concentration of the material at the release point, the diffusion of the material (a function of the three-dimensional wind field), the time required for the material to become effective once it is in the cloud, and the time required for the altered cloud characteristics to show up on the ground. The usual procedure involves assumptions about mean values and average times, with reliance on the skill of the operator to integrate the various factors subjectively. Several mathematical models have been developed that predict the area of effect; as these models, and the data they use, improve, targeting procedures should also improve.

Despite the uncertainties in how the material works, how much is needed, and where and how it should be released, present capabilities are sufficient to warrant a certain number of operational precipitation-modification programs. In these cases, the areas to be affected are relatively small and the objectives sufficiently narrow so that the uncertainties can be taken into account in the program designs.

Evaluation — The final phase of a functioning weather-modification system is evaluation of the results. Evaluation techniques include the standard statistical approaches: target vs. control; treat vs. no treat; randomized crossover, and so on. Both parametric and nonparametric statistics are used. A few new variations have been considered but are not being used except experimentally. Given a suitable experimental design, existing statistical evaluation procedures are acceptable for programs that go on for several years and in which the evaluation can wait until the end of the program.

Full evaluation includes not only the amount of precipitation produced but also the economic consequences of the activity and the effects on the social and biological environment.

Current Scientific Status

Large quantities of data at or near the earth's surface have been gathered from experimental areas. Upper-air data are generally insufficient in terms and frequency and density. Because most weather-modification activities are rather small and independent of one another, data gathering is not standardized with respect to time of observation, duration, precision, or reliability. Some of the data from commercial programs are not readily available. Perhaps the greatest limitation of the present data base is the scarcity of measurements of some of the important factors in precipitation augmentation, such as natural nuclei counts. Lack of suitable instruments is, in part, responsible for this situation.

Extra-Area Effects — While scientists have not had the quality data they would have liked, significant advances have occurred in the past few years. One interesting phenomenon was recently recognized: In major field programs for increasing rain, changes in the precipitation pattern well outside the designated target areas have been noted. The changes were patterns of negative and positive anomalies, but the increases were more substantial than the decreases. This suggests that some sort of dynamic effect is caused by cloud seeding, resulting in an average precipitation *increase* over a very large area. These effects are sometimes felt upwind and laterally as well as downwind of the target area. In at least one experiment, the precipitation of an entire area was increased, with target-area precipitation significantly greater even when compared with the precipitation-increased controls. How universal these effects are and under what conditions they occur are not clearly understood. The importance of this phenomenon in evaluation is obvious.

The Significance of Cloud-Top Temperature — One of the most important discoveries of the 1960's was identification of the importance of cloud-top temperature on the effectiveness of cloud seeding. Stratification of data by temperature indicates large precipitation increases from seeded winter orographic clouds when the temperature at or near the cloud top is between about $-15°$ and $-20°$ centigrade. When the temperature is $-25°$ or colder, precipitation decreases from the same kind of clouds are observed. This suggests that sufficient natural nuclei have a negative influence on the precipitation process. Figure VI-5 summarizes some of the above data.

Technological Improvements — Important advances have been made in finding seeding materials other than silver iodide and dry ice. Many organic and inorganic materials have been studied in the field and in the laboratory. Several of the organics have been found superior to silver iodide in many respects, including cost, and work is progressing on

Figure VI-5 — OPTIMUM SEEDING CONDITIONS

Figure VI-5(1)

Stratification	Stat. Meth.	Scale Change			Sample Size		
		Climax I	Climax II	Wolf Creek	Climax I	Climax II	Wolf Creek
−35 thru −26	NP1	−31	−46	−15	S32, N34	S18, N17	S43, N61
	NP2	−22	−25	−22			
−25 thru −21	NP1	− 1	+ 6	+22	S53, N56	S23, N32	S57, N63
	NP2	− 5	− 1	+23			
−20 thru −11	NP1	+100	>+200	>+200	S35, N41	S20, N17	S64, N69
	NP2	>+200	>+200	>+200			

Figure VI-5(2)

Stratification	Stat. Meth.	Scale Change			Sample Size		
		Climax I	Climax II	Wolf Creek	Climax I	Climax II	Wolf Creek
0 to <0.7	NP1	<−50	<−50	−20	S24, N21	S15, N12	S33, N33
	NP2	<−50	<−50	−24			
0.7 to <1.3	NP1	+11	+ 5	−14	S76, N86	S36, N42	S58, N81
	NP2	+ 8	+16	−15			
1.3 to <2.0	NP1	+53	>+200	>+200	S20, N24	S10, N12	S73, N79
	NP2	+100	>+200	>+200			

Figure VI-5(3)

Stratification	Stat. Meth.	Scale Change		Sample Size	
		Climax I	Climax II	Climax I	Climax II
0 thru 11	NP1	+16	− 2	S25, N27	S15, N17
	NP2	0	+ 4		
12 thru 16	NP1	+49	+ 9	S27, N21	S16, N13
	NP2	+20	+53		
17 thru 21	NP1	<−50	<−50	S28, N28	S9, N12
	NP2	−38	−20		
22 thru 27	NP1	>+200	>+200	S26, N25	S12, N13
	NP2	>+200	>+200		
28 thru 43	NP1	−40	−32	S14, N30	S9, N11
	NP2	−39	−32		

The table presents stratified data from three sets of experiments in an effort to show what factors are important in seeding in Colorado during the winter. The optimum conditions are summarized as follows: (1) the 500 mb temperature should be between −11° and −20°C; (2) the computed vertical gradient of potential condensate in the 700-500 mb layer should be 1.3 to 2.0 g/kg/100 mb; and (3) the 500 mb windspeed should be between 22 and 27 mps. The probability of each of these events has been computed, but is not presented here.

making them suitable for operational use.

Closely connected with new seeding materials are advances in delivery systems. Increased understanding of diffusion processes now puts positioning of generators, either airborne or ground, on a more objective basis. New devices for producing nuclei permit more efficient use of nuclei material. Advances in radar techniques, coupled with improved understanding of cloud characteristics and dispersion properties, permit safer and more effective use of aircraft in seeding operations. The use of rocket-launched, pyrotechnic seeding devices is receiving considerable attention.

Modeling — Mathematical models play an increasingly important role in both research and operational precipitation-augmentation programs. They are used operationally in recognizing treatable situations, in choosing particular clouds to seed, in specifying the position of mobile generators so that the effect will be felt in the target area, and in specifying the area of effect from fixed generators. These models, developed from the basic laws of physics, are usually relatively simple, and can be run on moderate-size computers in near real-time.

More sophisticated models have been used only for research programs, in part because present-generation computers are not capable of handling them in the time-scale needed for operational use. The value of these models lies in suggesting effects to look for in the field and in suggesting factors to be studied in more detail. Three types (scales) of models are currently available: (a) microphysics models, which consider the formation and growth of water droplets and ice crystals; (b) dynamic models, which consider motions and processes within the cloud (see Figure VI-6); and (c) airflow models, which consider cloud-forming processes. None of these models alone is adequate to describe the complexities of precipitation augmentation; several attempts are being made, therefore, at combining or chaining them.

Implications for Society

Precipitation augmentation is becoming an active partner with the other components of the water-resources system. In many parts of the nation, it may prove to be the most economical and socially acceptable method to increase usable water supplies.

Figure VI-6 — SIMULATED EFFECT OF CLOUD SEEDING

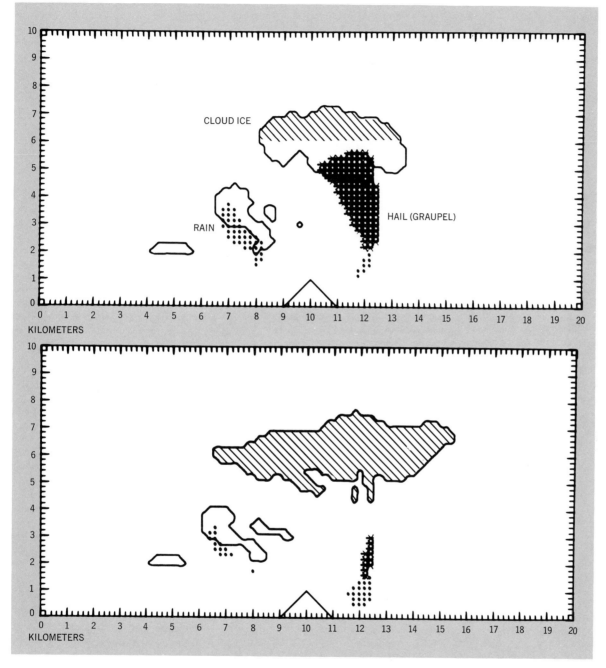

The two diagrams demonstrate a silver iodide seeding experiment done on computer-generated clouds. The numerical model simulates the growth of cumulus-type clouds forming over a mountain ridge in a domain 20 km wide and 10 km high. The general environmental airflow is from left to right. Clouds have formed to the left in the model and grown to form an anvil present at 7 km. The upper diagram shows the non-seeded case; the bottom, the seeded case. Seeding is simulated by changing all cloud liquid to cloud ice and the rain to precipitating ice at −10°C instead of −25°C in the natural (non-seeded) case. The hail (or graupel) shown is in concentrations greater than 1 gm of hail per kg of air. Rain is in concentrations greater than 1 gm per kg. These results demonstrate the effects of overseeding — less rain and less hail come from the seeded cloud since the large amounts of cloud ice that form are carried aloft and downwind in the anvil.

Furthermore, precipitation augmentation affects other natural resources besides water. For example, an increase in precipitation will have an effect on the natural plant and animal communities in and around the target area. Extra water on the soil may bring additional lands into grazing capability, but it may also hasten the leaching of nutrients. The availability of additional water may cause changes in man's use of the land. He may change the kinds of crops he grows. He may reap greater harvests from smaller acreage. None of these effects, however, is expected to be large.

Potential Benefits — The interactions between man, his institutions, and precipitation augmentation are important. The direct benefit of additional precipitation is that it helps to assure an adequate supply of water for municipal, industrial, and agricultural uses. Secondary benefits include the generation of low-cost electricity and assistance in abating air and water pollution. Relatively small operational projects for water supply and power generation have existed for years. What is needed is an integrated program in which many benefits can be realized from one activity.

Potential Liabilities — Precipitation augmentation does have associated liabilities. A few people object to any deliberate tampering with nature, some on moral or religious grounds, others simply on aesthetic grounds. Some of those who live or work in the target areas of augmentation operations could suffer financial loss, especially where the economic benefits are derived some distance away from the target area. Increased precipitation in the form of snow could decrease the growing season and the tourist season. Erosion could increase slightly — although, alternatively, increased vegetation from the additional moisture could cause erosion to decrease. Undesirable plant life may increase in certain areas. Increased

snow could raise snow-removal costs (although an estimate made for the Colorado Rockies indicates no such effect for a 10 to 20 percent snow increase). Potential liabilities exist, at least in theory, in the possible extinction of a few species of flora or fauna and in the modification of river channels. The net value of precipitation augmentation must include determinations of the relative importance of man, nature, and their interaction.

Legal Issues — Precipitation management raises a variety of legal issues. Who owns the water in the atmosphere? How should losses related to precipitation augmentation be compensated? How should operations be regulated? How should the money to pay for operations be acquired (taxation by water district, state tax, federal funds, etc.)? Should research projects be treated differently from operational projects with respect to liability? When water needs in one state can be helped by precipitation augmentation in another, who makes the decisions?

Normative Issues — There are some reputable scientists who believe that, while seeding does affect certain cloud characteristics, there are too many conflicting results from cloud-seeding experiments to say that observed precipitation increases from seeded clouds were caused by the seeding. But the majority of scientists who question precipitation augmentation ask not "Does it work?" but "Should we use it?" In other words, precipitation augmentation, while far from perfected, is considered by such scientists to be an operational reality. Precipitation augmentation today is thus in a position similar to that of nuclear power plants several years ago. Discussions center largely on the risks to people and the environment and on economic feasibility rather than on scientific capability. Answers to these questions await interdisciplinary studies of real and hypothetical situations.

Requirements for Scientific Activity

The practical objective of current precipitation-augmentation research is the development of a precipitation-management system. The system includes more than the ability to analyze water needs, recognize opportunities, treat opportunities, and evaluate results. A fully developed system includes the ability to specify the results of treatment in advance with a high degree of confidence. It includes the ability to specify the areas that will be affected by the treatment, as well as the ability to assess beforehand the environmental consequences. Such systems need to be developed and thoroughly tested.

To provide solid answers to the many unanswered questions of precipitation augmentation, some improved instrumentation must be acquired. Some sort of standard nuclei counter is needed. Radar systems specifically designed for weather modification are needed to replace the surplus military equipment now being used. A variety of airborne and surface remote-sensing devices would be useful. Especially needed are devices for determining the moisture distribution in the air from the surface to about 18,000 feet. Cloud-particle samplers are needed for cloud physics measurements. Several versions are available, but none provides the scientist with all he needs to know.

Accurate recognition of treatable situations is not yet a purely objective procedure. Better definition of the essential weather conditions is needed. Factors such as moisture flux are not easily measured on the scales needed for precipitation-augmentation projects. Mathematical models and the computers to run them should be an integral part of the recognition system. Improved instrumentation will be needed to acquire the data for the system.

The search for more effective treatment techniques must go forward.

Figure VI-7 — CONCENTRATION OF ICE NUCLEI IN A CITY

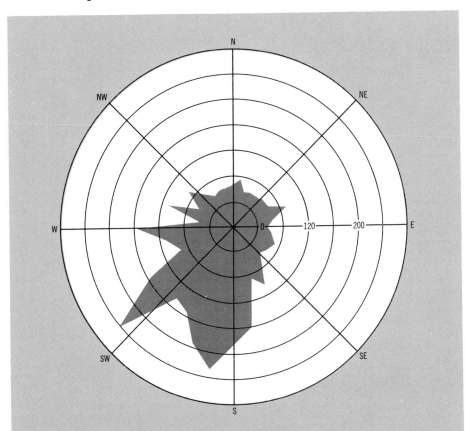

The diagram shows the concentration of ice nuclei observed in Seattle, Washington, from 1 July to 3 November 1968. The scale gives the numbers of ice nuclei per 300 liters of air active at −21°C. The concentrations measured in the city were six times greater than the concentrations of nuclei measured at two unpolluted non-urban sites. From the plot of the concentrations on the wind rose, it is possible to deduce that there are sources of nuclei SW and SSW of the sampling site, which was in the northeastern part of the city. Analyses show that man-made sources of ice nuclei dominate over natural ones. Just what effect these nuclei have on the microstructure of clouds, and the development of precipitation, is not known, although studies in a growing number of cities seem to show that precipitation increases downwind of industrial areas.

Less expensive and more readily available materials are needed. Seeding materials that have beneficial side effects (such as fertilizing characteristics) or no side effects are desirable. More precise delivery techniques are needed so that the results of the treatment can be properly targeted and so that the optimum effect can be achieved.

Better specification of the extra-area effects recently discovered is necessary for both targeting and evaluation. The causes of the extra-area effects need to be understood so that the recognition and treatment systems can take the effects into consideration. Inadvertent modification of clouds by atmospheric pollutants is another vital but little understood issue. (See Figure VI-7) In some situations, inadvertent modification can be controlled. In others, it cannot be controlled but can be considered as a factor in the precipitation-aug-

mentation system. Similarly important are the interactions between two or more neighboring augmentation projects.

Advanced studies of both the positive and negative interactions of precipitation augmentation with other systems need to be carried out. Factors in the natural environment will be affected by changes in precipitation. Short- and long-term consequences must be assessed from scientific, economic, and cultural viewpoints. The studies should not be limited to just the more obvious issues, such as ecological effects. The studies should consider the entire environmental system, which includes man.

Increasing interest in the environment by both the scientific community and concerned citizens' groups argues for a more deliberate study of the environment as a system. Much literature has been circulated recently suggesting our impending doom if the quality of the environment continues to deteriorate. Other studies have shown that severe water shortages will be widespread by the year 2000. While some of these statements may not be rigorously based on fact, they do suggest the importance of early development of a technology that can play a role in enhancing both the quality and quantity of the water portion of the environment.

How rapidly the fully developed precipitation-augmentation system described above can be made available is in part a function of the level of effort. The first such system could be operational by 1975. This system will be effective for winter orographic storm situations in sparsely populated, high-elevation areas. Shortly thereafter, a similar system for convective clouds could be operational. Through evolutionary processes, systems for other cloud situations, and improved versions of the first, could be available by the 1980's.

3. FOG

Modification of Warm and Cold Fog

The principal impetus for the development of methods for modifying fog has come from civil and military aviation. Despite improvements in instrument-landing techniques, dense fog over an airport severely restricts or prevents aircraft landings and takeoffs. Such occasions, even if they last only a few hours, impose substantial financial penalties on the airlines, cause inconvenience and loss to the traveling public, and delay or abort military missions. Dense fog is also a serious hazard for marine and surface transportation. (See Figure VI-8) On the other hand, fog is beneficial in certain forested regions in which the fog-drip from the trees supplies significant moisture.

The time- and space-scales of fog and its frequency of occurrence are all small enough that no large-scale changes of climate appear likely even

if all fogs were to be dissipated. However, the climate of certain local areas with a high incidence of fog would certainly be changed if the fog were eliminated.

Cold Fog

Modification of supercooled, or "cold," fogs by seeding them with ice nucleants has developed to the point of operational use at a number of airports where such fogs are relatively frequent. The scientific basis for modifying supercooled fogs is well established; the remaining problems involve the engineering of reliable and economical operational equipment and procedures.

Nucleants — Cold fogs are seldom supercooled by more than a few degrees centigrade and, therefore, the

ice nucleants must have the highest possible threshold-activation temperature. Dry-ice pellets and liquefied propane, carbon dioxide, and freon have typically been chosen to meet this condition. Silver iodide is not expected to be effective above $-5°$ centigrade. Consideration should be given to the use of certain organic nucleants such as urea and phloroglucinal, which have been reported to have relatively high activation temperatures.

Dispensing Methods — To be effective, the nucleants must be distributed fairly uniformly through the volume of fog to be modified. The earliest, and still the most effective, procedure is to distribute dry-ice pellets from aircraft flying above the fog; vertical distribution is assured by the rapid fall of the pellets through the fog. Nucleants in the form of fine particles or liquefied gases must be introduced directly into the fog, which may involve hazardous flight levels. The costs of aircraft seeding and the limited storage life of dry ice have led to the development of ground-based dispensers. Liquefied refrigerant gases are commonly used, often with fans or blowers to distribute the resulting ice crystals through the fog.

Fog is almost always accompanied by a wind drift, and the location and timing of the seeding operation must be selected so that the clearing moves over the airport at the desired time. This requires timely wind observations, precise navigation for airborne seeding, or extensive arrays of fixed seeding dispensers. A wind shift during the operation may cause the clearing to miss the airport.

Cost Considerations — Operational successes in the clearing of cold fog

Figure VI–8 — A DRIVING HAZARD

The photograph shows a section of an interstate highway running through the valleys of central Pennsylvania. The valley in the foreground is clear, with excellent driving conditions. Once the driver enters the gap between the valleys, however, visibility begins to decrease until it reaches near zero. Although a local phenomenon, this condition causes many accidents each year.

have been reported by the U.S. Air Force in West Germany and Alaska, by Orly Airport in Paris, and at several commercial airports in north-western United States. Cold fog at most American airports is so infrequent, however, that the standby cost of a cold-fog modification system probably cannot be justified. (It should be noted that the ice fogs that form in cold regions such as Alaska cannot be modified by seeding with ice nucleants.)

Warm Fog

Warm fog is much more common than cold fog. Many methods have been proposed over the years for modifying warm fog, but those that have shown significant success all involve the evaporation of the fog drops. The evaporation may be achieved by heating the air, by distributing hygroscopic particles in the fog, or by forcibly mixing the fog with the drier and/or warmer air above the fog layer.

Heating was employed at military airfields in England during World War II with considerable operational success. This so-called FIDO (Fog Investigation and Dispersal Operation) method was further developed at Arcata, California, after the war, and an operational system was installed at Los Angeles Airport. Moderate success was claimed, but the method was abandoned because of the large amounts of fuel required and the psychological and safety hazards of operating aircraft between two lines of flames.

The fundamental unsolved problem of thermal-fog modification is the uniform distribution of heating throughout the fog. In a typical fog, heating sufficient to raise the air temperature by about 1° centigrade will cause the fog to evaporate in a short time. Arrays of point heat sources, particularly linear arrays, can be expected to lead to convection,

non-uniform heating, escape of heated air aloft, and horizontal convergence of fog near the surface. The U.S. Air Force has had some success using jet aircraft on either side of a runway as heat sources. Further engineering developments aimed at providing reasonably uniform heating by means of blower-heaters specifically designed for the task may be worthwhile in view of the basic attractiveness of thermal-fog modification.

Hygroscopic particles introduced into fog grow by condensation, thereby reducing the relative humidity and leading to the evaporation of the fog drops. This transfer of the liquid water to a small number of larger solution droplets leads to an improvement in visibility in the fog. More complete clearing occurs as the solution droplets fall out under the action of gravity. Hygroscopic particles act something like ice crystals in a cold fog, with the important difference that the equilibrium vapor-pressure over the solution droplets rises rapidly as the droplet is diluted, approaching that of pure water.

To minimize the total quantity of hygroscopic material required to modify a fog, the hygroscopic particles should be as small as possible, consistent with the requirements that they be large compared to the fog drops and that they fall out of the fog in a reasonable time. Since the solution droplets become diluted as they fall, the deeper the fog the larger must be the initial size of the hygroscopic particles. When the depth of the fog is more than a few hundred meters, accretion of the fog drops by the solution becomes an important mechanism in the lower portion of the fog.

Mathematical models of the modification of warm fog by hygroscopic particles have been devised and used to guide field experiments. The theory of the growth of hygroscopic particles and the evaporation of fog drops is well established. Reasonably

adequate information is available on the drop-size spectra and liquid water content of natural fogs. Turbulent diffusion is arbitrarily introduced on the basis of a few estimates of the eddy-diffusion coefficient in fogs. However, these mathematical models are static in that they do not model the natural processes that form and dissipate fog. Dynamical models must be developed that incorporate these processes. Among other advantages, such models should yield the characteristic time of the fog-formation process. It seems evident that any artificial modification must be accomplished in a time that is short compared to this characteristic time of fog formation. This is of the utmost importance in the design of fog-modification experiments.

In field experiments, hygroscopic particles have been released from aircraft flying above the fog. The usual assumption that the trailing vortices uniformly distribute the particles in the horizontal is highly questionable. Failure to achieve uniform distribution of the seeding particles is probably one of the principal causes of unsatisfactory modification experiments. A non-uniform distribution can be countered only by increasing the total amount released to insure that there is an adequate concentration everywhere. A closely related problem is the marked tendency of the carefully sized hygroscopic particles to emerge in clumps. Imaginative engineering design is needed to solve these problems, and nothing is more important at the present time.

Air Mixing—Mechanical mixing of the warmer and/or drier air above a relatively thin fog layer will usually cause the fog to evaporate. The U.S. Air Force has produced cleared lanes by utilizing the strong downwash from helicopters; this technique is effective only in shallow fogs, however. The cost/effectiveness ratio is probably large, but it may be justified for certain military purposes when the helicopters are available.

Summary

In summary, the modification of cold fogs with ice nucleants is an operational success, and further engineering improvements are to be expected; but there are only a few regions where the frequency of cold fogs is sufficiently high to justify the expense of a permanent installation. Warm-fog modification by heat or by seeding with hygroscopic particles is achievable in the relatively near future. The requirements for success are more adequate numerical models of fog and, most importantly, imaginative engineering design so that the assumptions made in the experimental design can be realized in practice. However, it remains true today, as thirty years ago, that the total cost of warm-fog modification will be high enough to discourage its extensive application. Some recent benefit/cost figures are shown in Figure VI-9.

Figure VI-9 — RESULTS OF FOG-SEEDING PROGRAMS

Station	Air Delays Avoided	Cancellations Avoided	Diversions Avoided	Cost	Benefit	Benefit ÷ Cost
Los Angeles*	60 Hrs.	22	60	$63,000.	$129,790.	2.1
Seattle*	50	21	50	34,500.	96,481.	2.8
Salt Lake City	50	50	27	5,800.	63,650.	11.0
Spokane	25	73	25	4,000.	28,141.	7.0
Medford	7.5	35	15	1,200.	14,970.	12.5
Boise	1	—	2	2,600.	2,157.	0.8
Omaha	6	1	—	2,300.	2,988.	1.3
Des Moines	3.5	2	—	300.	1,793.	6.0
Total	203 Hrs.	204	179	$118,300.	$339,970.	2.9

*Cold fog; all other stations are warm fog cases.

The table lists the operational benefits versus costs experienced by United Airlines during the winter of 1969-70. Benefits have been calculated as monies that would have been spent were fog dispersal not available or unsuccessful. Cost of delays were computed from crew salaries, aircraft maintenance, and fuel and oil costs. Diversion costs included alternate ground transportation, meal and hotel costs, and overtime charges for ground personnel. Not included were intangibles or incomputables such as maintenance dislocation, ferrying equipment, need for reserve aircraft, and mispositioning of flight crews when flights were diverted. Also not included is the cost of customer inconvenience when fog disrupts operations. It is of interest to note that benefits were twice the costs of the program at Los Angeles even though fog was successfully dispersed in only 32% of the cases.

Fog Dispersal Techniques

To assess the present state of fog-dispersal techniques and define the work to be done, it is necessary to consider three types of fog.

Ice Fog

This type of fog is an increasing problem for aviation and other forms of transportation in a few high-altitude localities. Comparatively little research has been done to develop economical methods of combating ice fog. The only technique available at present is the brute-force method of applying heat to evaporate it. Further research is required to assist in the development of more efficient means of thinning or dispersing this type of fog.

Supercooled (Cold) Fog

In the contiguous United States, approximately 5 percent of the dense fogs that close airports to operations are of the cold type. In more northerly latitudes, the percentage is higher during the winter. Other forms of transportation are equally affected when visibility drops below one-half mile, but the economic impact is probably not as great as it is on aviation.

Dry-Ice Dispersing Techniques — Dispersal of cold fog by seeding crushed dry ice from light aircraft is an operational reality at approximately a dozen airports in the United States. Some of these programs have been established each winter since 1962. The physical changes that occur are well understood, stemming from the research of Schaefer, Langmuir, and Vonnegut in 1946. Although the dry-ice technique is theoretically effective in converting supercooled water to ice crystals only at temperatures colder than $-4°$ centigrade, operational experience has demonstrated unequivocally that this technique is effective up to $0°$ centigrade through proper sizing of the dry-ice pellets and proper control of the seeding rates for the conditions prevailing.

This method of dispersing cold fog is about 80 percent effective. The failures that do occur are primarily related to operational problems such as miscalculating wind drift, which results in the cleared area moving off target. Occasionally, too, the technique is stretched beyond the capability of the physical reactions to take place, typically in supercooled fog decks whose upper layers are several degrees warmer than $0°$ centigrade.

Ground Dispensing Methods — Because of such operational problems and the complex logistics that are required in dispersing an airport fog by means of aircraft, a ground dispensing system, which employs essentially the same physical principles, is more desirable. Liquid propane has been used effectively as the seeding agent; it has reached a degree of sophistication in France, where control of supercooled fogs at Orly Airport is completely automated through the use of seventy fixed dispenser heads deployed around the target area. Liquid propane has been used operationally to combat cold fogs in the United States, but, primarily for economic reasons, the technology has never been developed beyond the use of a few portable dispensing units.

Researchers have suggested that liquid propane and other cryogenics, in addition to providing the cooling mechanism, also alter the fog droplets through a clathration process. Since this latter process may increase the effectiveness of liquid propane

in fog temperatures several degrees warmer than $0°$ centigrade, further investigation is warranted. Many airports are subjected to dense winter fogs with characteristic temperatures slightly warmer than freezing. Development of this clathration process would pay off in benefits at many airports that cannot support the more expensive warm-fog dispersal programs.

Warm Fog

Since all but about 5 percent of the dense fog that closes airports and cripples other forms of transportation in the populated latitudes is of the warm type, it would be expected that there has been some preoccupation with measures to alleviate the warm-fog problem. Formal research into fog physics and development of laboratory techniques for dispersing fog have, however, been under way less than forty years. Out of desperation, some brute-force methods for evaporating fog have been undertaken where economics was not a factor.

Houghton's work at the Massachusetts Institute of Technology in the 1930's was the first formal research aimed at fog dispersal. A number of other studies on warm fog were subsequently undertaken by federal military and civilian agencies, but until the 1960's none of the fog-modification concepts was applied to routine commercial or military activities. Economics, problems of logistics, or deleterious effects on the environment were the deterrents.

Modern Techniques — At least one installation of a refined thermal system for evaporating fog at a busy airport is planned for 1972. Other thermal methods that utilize energy more efficiently are under development. All of these systems are expensive and will probably be limited to application at major airports or other sites where the economic pressure of fog paralysis is high.

For two years, warm fog has been regularly dispersed at a few U.S. airports through chemical seeding techniques that had been partially confirmed by fog physics research and laboratory testing. This approach is feasible, and is producing economic benefits exceeding costs of the programs by a factor of about 3 to 1; but it is considered in the developmental stage because aircraft dispensing is required. For full reliability and optimum benefit/cost ratios, a ground dispensing system must be developed that will use the most effective materials. A number of promising concepts have been conceived and some have been laboratory tested. Further development work is required, but success will depend on better basic knowledge of fog makeup than we have today.

Basic Warm-Fog Physics — Sufficient knowledge of fog physics exists to disperse warm fog with heat. The more attractive and economically feasible approaches to warm-fog dispersal, which do not employ heat, require more basic physical knowledge in order to develop the most efficient system.

Recent research involving the use of hygroscopic materials as seeding agents has provided some much-needed knowledge about fog, but there are still some baffling blind spots. This new knowledge came fifteen years after successful feasibility tests were conducted, using the same principle, but which were not continued because of logistic problems. It is hoped that another long delay will not develop before we can explain, for example, why polymers, surfactants, and other substances, when diffused properly, produce positive results, apparently through a strong ionization process. Supersaturated solutions of nontoxic materials with endothermic properties, and the electrogas-dynamic principle, are promising dispersal materials and techniques which require further development, as does research on the physics of fog.

4. TROPICAL WEATHER

Monsoon Variations and Climate and Weather Forecasting

The monsoon area extends from western Africa to northeastern Australia, being bounded to the north by the great mountain ranges of southern Asia. In the southern hemisphere it encompasses southeastern Africa and northern Australia but does not extend beyond the equator over the central Indian Ocean. (See Figure VI-10) Its peculiarity, distinguishing the area from all others, is the marked difference in prevailing surface wind directions between winter and summer. Winds blow predominantly from continent to sea in winter and from sea to continent in summer.

Thus, in general, since moist air covers the continents in summer and dry air in winter, the summers are usually wet and the winters dry. Over the northern hemisphere this pattern is significantly distorted by the huge, elevated mass of Himalaya-Tibet which, through its thermo-mechanical effect on the atmospheric circulation, supports the vast permanent deserts east of 70° E. longitude, insures that India, Burma, and Thailand experience arid winters and very wet summers, and keeps China relatively cloudy and moist throughout the year.

Except for destructive winds associated with relatively rare tropical cyclones in the China Seas and Bay of Bengal, the attention of meteorologists in the monsoon area is focused on only one phenomenon — rain. Accurate long-range forecasts for agricultural planning, or short-range forecasts for irrigation or of floods would be invaluable to the economy of every country in the area. But rainfall variability on every time- and space-scale — from inter-annual to diurnal and from intercontinental to mountain/valley — render climatology of limited use in providing the necessary planning information.

Status of Tropical Meteorology

Long-Range Forecasting — Most existing work was done in India and Indonesia before World War II. Multiple-regression equations based on lag correlations were first used in the 1920's to forecast seasonal rainfall. Unfortunately, performance was disappointing — droughts and floods were never anticipated and predictor/predictand correlations proved to be most unstable. Apart from a modest continuing search in India for new correlations, little effort is now being made.

Unless the deterministic forecast methods to be tested in the Global Atmospheric Research Program (GARP) perform much better than even their most optimistic proponent expects, there is little chance of useful developments in forecasting seasonal rainfall extremes.

Short-Range Forecasting — For the past fifty years the practice of tropical meteorology has been distorted (usually unfavorably) by uncritical grafting of hypotheses and techniques developed in middle latitudes. As one scientist has observed:

We have again and again observed very reputable and highly specialized meteorologists from higher latitudes who were determined to solve the problems of tropical meteorology in a very short time by application of modern scientific methods and use of new scientific resources such as

Figure VI–10 — MONSOONAL AREAS

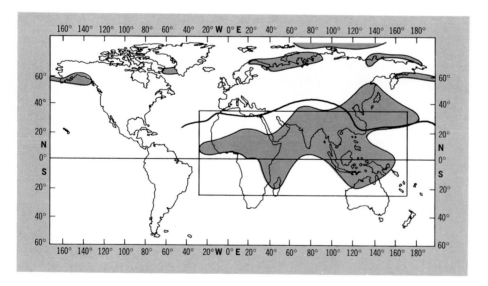

The map delineates the regions of the world that are monsoonal—i.e., where the prevailing wind direction shifts at least 120 degrees between January and July. By sharpening the definition according to principles developed by Ramage, it is possible to define the true monsoon area as that included in the rectangle shown covering large parts of Asia and Africa.

computerization. Then, after a few years, they find out that the thing doesn't quite work this way and the tropics cannot be approached by the methods used to solve problems in higher latitudes.

Training of Tropical Meteorologists — Almost every professional meteorologist in Burma and Thailand holds an advanced degree in meteorology from a foreign university, and yet their contributions to knowledge of even their own country's meteorology has been miniscule. In part, this is because many monsoon-area meteorologists have received intensive training in other countries, especially in the United States and the United Kingdom, but almost never by teachers with any experience in, or appreciation of, monsoon meteorology. In this country, even the *tropical* meteorologists who instructed them, confidently and quite unjustifiably, would extrapolate their tropical *oceanic* experience to the continents.

Numerical forecasting is the latest invader from the higher latitudes. Since some of the training received in other countries is at last beginning to seem relevant, everyone with access to a computer is trying out the models. Despite the fact that none of the models has demonstrated any *weather* forecasting skill over the Caribbean and around Hawaii, and despite the fact that problems of grid-mesh size are even more critical over the continents than over the oceans, resources which can ill be spared are being squandered on the latest fad — on the unsupported and unjustified assumption that numerical forecast techniques have already significantly improved on subjective analysis and forecasting in the tropics. The machine churns out reams of charts — while professional meteorologist positions remain unfilled.

In the monsoon area, the best aid to local forecasting is the cloud picture from an Automatic Picture Transmission (APT) satellite. But the only way to use this information

intelligently is through hard, *subjective* evaluation, and this is so unfashionable that a computer is often considered more desirable than an APT read-out station. A monsoon-area meteorologist, after intelligently and deliberately studying a detailed climatology and a sequence of carefully analyzed synoptic and auxiliary charts (including APT pictures), can forecast consistently better than chance and significantly better than a numerical model. A statistical prediction should always be available to him. He should modify that prediction only when he discovers a significant change trend in the charts. When in doubt, stay with statistics. This may seem obvious, but such down-to-earth advice is rarely given during academic instruction.

Training Facilities in the Tropics — If training in middle-latitude institutions is so inadequate, what about indigenous programs?

In Asia, the Royal Observatory, Hong Kong, is a good but small center of research, emphasizing urban pollution and hydrological planning. Useful, practical, and theoretical studies are being pursued in the People's Republic of China. The Institute of Tropical Meteorology in Poona, India, is conducting good climatological studies but is also uncritically applying numerical forecast models developed in Washington, D.C., and Honolulu. The program in the University of the Philippines, launched with some fanfare three years ago, has apparently made no progress — an expensive faculty waits for enrollments but is ignored by meteorological services in the region. The Department of Geography in the National University, Taipei (Taiwan), has done good work, particularly on the effects of typhoons, while the Department of Oceanography in the University of Malaya (Kuala Lumpur) has made a promising beginning with useful climatological and synoptic studies.

Apart from a small department of meteorology in the University of

Nairobi, in Kenya (which has turned out at least one promising scientist), and, possibly, some activity at the University of Ibadan, in Nigeria, nothing much seems to be happening in Africa. Australia largely neglects monsoon meteorology except for a small in-house effort in the Regional Meteorological Center, Darwin.

Over-all, the U.S. military interest in southeast Asia has contributed more to meteorological research and to improvement in meteorological training in the monsoon area over the past five years than any other factor. Research conferences sponsored by defense agencies have produced significantly more than just military benefits. One spin-off was the World Meteorological Organization training seminar conducted in December 1970, in Singapore.

Summing up, short-range monsoon weather forecasting can be improved, but there is little chance of improvement stemming from the BOMEX experiment in the Atlantic (see Figure VI-11) or from continued training of monsoon-area meteorologists in institutions with little understanding of, or interest in, the *peculiar* problems of monsoon weather. More can probably be done by supporting the efforts in Taipei, Hong Kong, Kuala Lumpur, and Nairobi, particularly in the direction of temporarily assigning outside experts (perhaps on sabbatical leaves) to these places. The experts might even learn something from the experience!

Scientific Communication — One other serious problem is that research into monsoon meteorology is provincial. Investigators have seldom been aware that in other monsoon regions similar problems have been under study or even solved. Insufficient scientific communication partly accounts for this. The only widely distributed journals are published in middle latitudes. Regional journals or research reports are often well distributed beyond the monsoon area but poorly distributed within it.

Figure VI–11 — ARRAY FOR BARBADOS OCEANOGRAPHIC
AND METEOROLOGICAL EXPERIMENT (BOMEX)

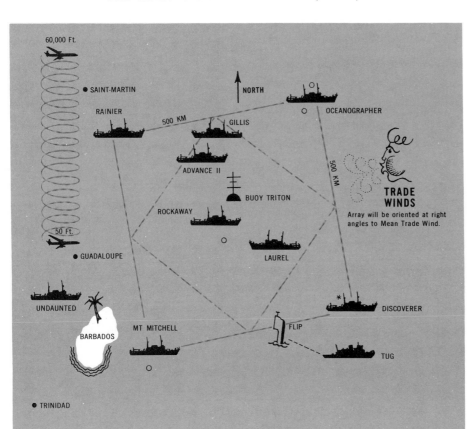

● Land Based Station   ○ Current Stations   ∗ Thermistor Array Moorings

The deployment of instrument platforms for BOMEX is shown in the diagram. This figure represents the consequence of designing a group of experiments of sufficient scope and precision to test hypotheses and obtain useful new data from an intermediate-scale system. The event is unique in human history. This experiment was participated in by the Departments of Commerce, Defense, Interior, State, and Transportation, the National Aeronautics and Space Administration, Atomic Energy Commission, the National Science Foundation, National Center for Atmospheric Research, and more than 10 universities.

Basic Concepts

The general character of the monsoons and their inter-regional variations reflect the juxtaposition of continents and oceans and the presence or absence of upwelling. However, without the great mechanical and thermal distortions produced by the Himalayas and the Tibetan Plateau, the vast northern-hemisphere deserts would be less desert-like, central China would be much drier and no colder in winter than India, while even over the Coral Sea winter cloud and rain would be uncommon.

Within the monsoon area, annual variations are seldom spatially or temporally in phase. Even if these variations were understood and their phases successfully forecast, accurate day-to-day weather prediction would not necessarily be achieved, for the climatological cycles merely determine *necessary* conditions for certain weather regimes; synoptic changes then control where and when the rain will fall, and how heavily, and whether winds will be destructive.

Synoptic-Scale Changes — Although not new, a most important concept is that of wide-ranging, nearly simultaneous accelerations or decelerations within a major vertical circulation. Causes are elusive, although the changes generally appear to be triggered by prior changes in the heat-sink regions of the vertical circulation. This is a field of truly enormous potential for numerical modeling, on a time-scale between synoptic and seasonal, in which fluctuations in radiation and in air-surface energy exchange might produce profound effects.

The concept both explains previous difficulty in maintaining continuity of synoptic analysis and demands that notions of day-to-day weather changes be examined and probably modified. Even during winter, fronts seldom remain material boundaries for long and air-mass analysis confuses more often than not.

That synoptic-scale disturbances often appear to develop and to weaken in response to changes in the major vertical circulations might explain why many of the disturbances are quasi-stationary. In turn, synoptic-scale vertical motion determines the character of convection and the efficiency with which energy is transported upward from the heat source.

Synoptic-scale lifting, by spreading moisture deeply through the troposphere, reduces the lapse rate and increases the heat content in mid-troposphere. Thus, though it diminishes the intensity of small-scale convection and the frequency of thunderstorms, it increases rainfall and upward heat transport. Conversely, synoptic-scale *sinking*, by drying the mid-troposphere, creates a heat minimum there, hinders upward transport of heat, and diminishes rainfall. However, the increased lapse rate favors scattered, intense small-scale convection and thunderstorms.

In the monsoon area, the character of the weather, on the scale of individual clouds, seems to be determined by changes occurring successively on the macro- and synoptic scales. *Rains* set in — not when cumulonimbus gradually merge but when a synoptic disturbance develops, perhaps in response to change in a major vertical circulation. *Showers*, too, are part of the synoptic cycle. Individually intense, but collectively less wet, they succeed or precede rains as general upward motion diminishes.

When synoptic-scale lifting is combined with very efficient upper-tropospheric heat disposal, the lapse rate may be steep enough to support intense convection. Then, a vast, "continuous" thunderstorm gives prolonged torrential rain. Many times this takes place within the common upward branch of two major vertical circulations.

Needed Scientific Activity

Many tropical meteorologists have striven to make their work appear as quantitative and objective as possible. This commendable aim has led to important *climatological* insights. However, in synoptic studies their quantitative results have usually been belied by nature's quantities. A numerical model which determines that air is massively rising over the deserts of Arabia has limited validity no matter how quantitative and objective it might be. Energy-budget computations in which precipitation and evaporation are residuals, or must be estimated, have also had their day.

Forecasting and research should be inseparable. The very few monsoon-area weather services that enable their forecast meteorologists to spend at least one-third of their time on research have thereby greatly enhanced staff morale and their scientific reputations, to say nothing of improved forecast accuracy. Combined forecast-research programs could well be successfully directed to solving problems and to increasing the number of recognizable models of synoptic circulations.

The area covered by synoptic analyses should be sufficiently broad for the major vertical circulations to be monitored. Then interaction with synoptic disturbances and consequent effects on rainfall could be detected and possibly anticipated.

Mesoscale gradients within synoptic systems and their diurnal variations might be better understood were studies to combine information from weather radars and weather satellites. Ceraunograms could help bridge the gap between meso- and synoptic scales. Aerial probing of continuous thunderstorms would likely illuminate the shadowy picture we now have of energy transformations.

We should view the future of monsoon meteorology with optimistic discontent. Regional progress in understanding and forecasting weather has been disappointingly slow. However, attacks are being vigorously pressed on problems of concern to the entire monsoon area. What is needed is the *intra-area* exchange of people and ideas.

Tropical Meteorology, with Special Reference to Equatorial Dry Zones

The outlook for meteorological observations in the tropics, as now programmed, is excellent for many purposes and far superior to the past. Much can be done with existing and prospective observations in the way of field experimentation and synoptic-statistical modeling. Ambitious projects like special or worldwide networks or expeditions, however, should be undertaken only if the necessary data base is really assured. Furthermore, meteorology, as a discipline, is still far too self-contained; special efforts are needed to promote interdisciplinary research.

Four problems are particularly in need of concentrated research in tropical meteorology during the 1970's:

Water Supply — This age-old problem is becoming aggravated by population increases in tropical countries, as elsewhere. The need is to find ways to assure an adequate water supply over the middle and long term — i.e., on a seasonal or annual basis. Several avenues of scientific development could be promising: First, it has become more than ever urgent to improve weather-prediction methods. Second, experiments for increasing precipitation artificially need to be broadened to see whether (a) such increases are possible at all on tropical land areas; and (b) enough water can be produced by man to make a significant difference. While not directly a part of meteorology, desalination of sea water and diver-sion of large rivers (e.g., part of the Amazonas in northeast Brazil) also offer possibilities for enhancing tropical water supplies.

Tropical Storms — Again, the problem has both predictive and modification aspects. Prediction beyond 12 to 24 hours remains a large problem in the areas affected by tropical storms and hurricanes. The German Atlantic Expedition of 1969 has again raised the question of whether tropical storms can be "modified" and, indeed, whether or not it would be wise to do so. It should not be overlooked that tropical storms in many situations and many areas bring great economic benefits, even though news releases usually cite only the damage they cause.

Role of the Tropics in the General Circulation — The role of the tropics in hemispheric or global circulation is known to be important. The long-term (five days or more) prediction models now being developed require a tropical data input that is not yet adequate. In particular, studies are needed of (a) how constant the tropics are as a source of energy and momentum, and (b) the appropriate way to include in the models the energy infusions into the atmosphere from more or less point sources — i.e., from small-area cumulonimbus cloud systems. In addition, ways must be found to represent surface interface processes, not only evaporation and sensible heat transport, but also momentum exchange, especially on the equator itself.

Hemispheric Interchange — Any interconnection between the extratropical regions of both hemispheres must take place via the tropics. From the spread of various tracers or aerosols, over a scale of weeks or months, we know that an exchange of air does take place. An understanding of these exchanges is particularly relevant to problems of air pollution. Actual pollution problems in the tropics are not likely to become severe because of the unstable stratification, although tropical countries are, of course, exposed to sedimentation or washout of pollutants by precipitation. In the longer view, however, the ability of the air to transport pollutants across the equator requires serious study of the air exchange — its mobility, the magnitude of the exchange, preferred paths, and the like, with a view to eventual control of such transports.

Needed scientific activity under each of these major categories is discussed in the sections that follow.

Tropical Water Supply

Some parts of the tropics are subject to recurrent, severe droughts.

Those of northeast Brazil, which have led to large out-migrations of population and great economic and political instability in all of Brazil, are an example. These droughts, superimposed on an average rainfall that is itself marginal for a tropical economy, have lasted from two to as long as nine consecutive years. The longer droughts have occurred in the more recent part of the climatological records, suggesting a secular drying out — a most unfavorable circumstance.

Many scientific questions remain before such tropical droughts can be understood, much less controlled. The droughts (as well as the intermittent heavy rainfall years) must be related somehow to the anomalies of the northern- and southern-hemisphere general circulations and possibly to some oceanic temperature distributions that do not follow directly from anomalous surface trade-wind speeds and directions, as well as to associated surface divergences or convergences. But the controls that govern these relationships are completely unknown at present. Lack of data over the tropics, the southern oceans, and even the North Atlantic at lower latitudes has prevented any definitive study. Little adequate use has been made of such information as is available — surface temperature, pressure, and precipitation anomalies over wide areas, as well as recent findings on wind anomalies over the equatorial Atlantic.

Data Base — New data are accumulating very fast for all parts of the tropics, eliminating the old excuse that lack of observations prevents progress. Data have been accumulating from the rapidly growing number of commercial flights over tropical areas. Programmed new satellite data are adding even more rapidly to the pile. An energetic attack on the discovery of the controls of equatorial dry zones and variable rainy seasons should be possible in the 1970's as a result of these new data. Once the controls are known, it will be possible to see whether prediction of the con-

trol functions can be achieved with synoptic-statistical modeling techniques, although direct deterministic prediction does not appear in the picture for the foreseeable future.

Cloud Modification — The question of cloud-modification potential in the tropics remains unresolved. Nonprecipitating cumulus congestus may be a preferred cloud form over many semi-arid tropical areas. But past efforts to study the possibilities of modifying such clouds have been rather sporadic. Early interest in Australia has lagged. A few serious cumulonimbus studies have been made in the Caribbean, but these relate to the atmosphere over open sea; since surface heat sources are much stronger over land, these oceanic experiments cannot be applied directly to the tropics, although they may be useful indirectly if they are successful in making cumulonimbus grow.

Quite apart from modification experiments, it would be of value merely to learn the cloud composition at different locations in order to assess what might be termed the "stimulation potential." Even in this respect, knowledge has remained deficient. There exists on this subject a great need not only for scientists but also for adequate instrumentation (notably radar) and good technicians. Good radar technicians actually available for meteorology are rare, and in tropical countries they tend to be either nonexistent or insufficiently skilled. The World Meteorological Organization has a large technician-training program, which merits support.

Tropical Storms

Tropical storms are notoriously variable in frequency from year to year and region to region. (See Figure VI-12) Sometimes the connection with the general circulation is obvious, but not always. The role of hurricanes in the general circulation is not yet fully determined, and general-circulation research, with a focus on general cir-

Figure VI–12 — FREQUENCY OF TROPICAL CYCLONES

North Atlantic Ocean	73
North Pacific—off west coast of Mexico	57
North Pacific Ocean, west of 170°E	211
North Indian Ocean, Bay of Bengal	60
North Indian Ocean, Arabian Sea	15
South Indian Ocean, west of 90°E	61
South Indian Ocean, northwestern Australia	9

The table shows the frequency of tropical storms per 10 years. The numbers are only estimates of the number of tropical cyclones to be expected, since, until recently, there have been no reliable statistics except for the Atlantic, where ship traffic has been heavy and island stations numerous for many years. Surveillance by satellites will provide worldwide coverage of tropical cyclones.

culations favorable or unfavorable to tropical storms, is definitely needed. Clearly, such storms are not mere nuisances. A single hurricane can replace the function of the equatorial trough zone in the Atlantic for vertical transport of heat and moisture and their transmission to higher latitudes.

Altogether, the true value of such storms — when, where, and under what circumstances ——needs to be stressed and measured. Coastal damage and associated flooding from hurricanes in areas such as southeastern United States usually receive the widest publicity. It is forgotten that, as these storms move slowly inland and turn into unspectacular inland rains, they have on occasion saved the cotton crop and even relieved water shortages of cities such as Atlanta. Lowered water tables over southern Florida and other areas, with their danger of salt-water intrusion into the water supplies of cities like Miami, can also be counteracted by hurricane precipitation. In terms of dollars, then, hurricanes can often bring benefits that are comparable to the damage they cause.

Impact of the Tropics on World Weather

Long-Period Trends — As the energy and momentum source for the general circulation, the tropics are most likely to have an important impact over long time-scales (from months to years). The excess of energy acquired and held by the tropical oceans may undergo slow variations of possibly great importance for long-period circulation anomalies. Bjerknes, for example, has speculated on the equatorial Pacific and its influence over large areas beyond the tropics.

Expanded observational networks at sea and, again, satellite data now appear sufficient for empirical researches to begin on such aspects of general circulation. Theoretical modeling would also be useful to indicate how much variation in the tropics is needed to produce an eventual circulation upheaval elsewhere. From models that have been run so far, it appears that the heat accumulations or deficits need not be very large.

The intensity of the mean meridional circulation is also a matter for serious study. Data are marginally sufficient to calculate this circulation on a monthly, if not weekly, basis. Variations in the cell have hardly been considered at all; yet they would profoundly affect, among other things, the energy and momentum balance picture, subtropical jet streams, stress in higher latitudes on the

ground, and relations to the intensity of the Siberian winter high.

Short-Period Fluctuations — Variable exchanges with the tropics may be responsible for the "index cycle" of the general circulation in the westerlies on a two- or three-week scale. Prediction experiments now planned in connection with the Global Atmospheric Research Program (GARP) may or may not lead to an understanding of such influences. Separate studies — using diagnostic data from the National Maritime Commission and other hemisphere analyses and data storages — would also be of considerable value. Such studies could also investigate whether the exchanges are forced from higher latitudes, and in this way learn more about the mechanisms for the variability of the atmospheric machine.

For prediction equations, much emphasis has been given to parameterization of cumulonimbus convection, since a few thousand cumulonimbus cover roughly 0.1 percent of the tropics at any one time. Much research on this subject is under way, although some dispute remains as to the form the research should take. GARP takes the view that a master tropical experiment must be conducted for final clarification. While a series of smaller projects might be inadequate for the problems to be solved, the master experiment may not succeed either, since experimental difficulty increases nonlinearly with the size of an experiment. Furthermore, there is a deplorable tendency to ignore the results of past expeditions in writing the prospectus for new ones; in present planning, for example, such large undertakings as the German Atlantic Expedition and its results have been generally overlooked.

Emphasis should not be placed exclusively on oceanic observations. Obviously, the oceans hold much of the key to world weather; but predictive models should eventually be geared mostly for continental areas, where predictions are most needed. Continental models will necessarily differ from oceanic ones. Continents do not have surface-heat storage in the sense of the oceans, and frictional stresses as well as nuclei spectra for condensation and freezing are different. Oceanic research could thus usefully be supplemented by research over land. Collaboration with existing continental experiments, such as that of northeastern Brazil, could bring large technical rewards.

Interhemispheric Communication

In many ways, it appears that the center of the equatorial convergence zone separates the hemispheres meteorologically as well as physically. Each has a self-contained energy and momentum budget, for example. If this picture were true for all time-scales, then the two hemispheres could be treated as independent of each other for all practical meteorological purposes.

No one really believes this, however, although there is much doubt as to the time-scale on which interhemispheric mechanisms are important. Preliminary calculations based on data dating from the International Geophysical Year (IGY), in the 1950's, have not revealed any important connections; but then, the tropical network of IGY was so deficient that it is impossible to treat these data as definitive. Here we see the danger of inadequate observational efforts. Better data are likely to emerge from superpressure balloons, World Weather Watch stations and satellites, and the buoys and other installations of the GARP network. If these networks and data sources are kept up and expanded, a good start could be made during the 1970's on resolving the questions relevant to the importance of interhemispheric communication for long-range weather changes.

Irrespective of long-period weather control, an understanding of mass exchanges across the equator is important to the prospects for worldwide pollution control. We know that mass exchanges across the equator occur, but we need to determine whether the drift of pollutants across the equator occurs with indifferent distribution in troposphere and stratosphere. If that is the case, nothing can be done to protect one hemisphere from the other, but there may be point-, or small-area, injections in preferred and stationary locations. If that is so, trajectory calculations toward these areas and measurements along them would at least permit warning of impending transports of particular pollutants at a high level.

5. DUST

African Dust and its Transport into the Western Hemisphere

Meteorologists have recently discovered that enormous quantities of dust are raised over arid and semi-arid regions of North Africa and injected into the trade winds over the North Atlantic. Outbreaks of dust from the Sahara take about one week to reach the Caribbean. The amounts of dust are highly variable in space and time, both from day to day and season to season, but the period of maximum dust transport across the Atlantic (June to early September) coincides with the Atlantic hurricane season. Dust outbreaks from Africa often appear on meteorological satellite photographs as a semi-transparent or transparent whiteness that resembles thin cirrus clouds. (See Figure VI-13) In such outbreaks, surface visibility can be moderately reduced as far west as the Caribbean.

African dust outbreaks and the hurricanes that also have their origin over Africa may be interrelated in some ways. While it is highly unlikely that African dust can cause wind disturbances to form into hurricanes or hurricanes to dissipate, there is enough observational and theoretical evidence to suggest that the two phenomena might affect each other indirectly or directly in a secondary role. The dust's ability to directly influence hurricanes lies in its ability to affect the thermodynamics of cloud growth through its role as an ice or condensation nucleator. More indirectly, the dust can affect the energy balance of the tropics by its ability to block incoming radiation from the sun or outgoing infrared radiation from the earth's surface.

Dust can also serve as a tracer of atmospheric air motion. There is some evidence that an enhanced dust transport accompanies the movement of wind disturbances off the west coast of Africa. The dust content of the air can be modified in the disturbance either by being washed out in rain or by being evacuated to very high altitudes in the updrafts that accompany giant cumulus clouds. When it is transported to levels well above the 3- to 4-kilometer depth over which it is normally found, the dust can more readily affect the energy balance and particulate concentrations in other parts of the globe.

Characteristics of Dust Transport

Since 1965, quantitative measurements of windborne dust transport have been made on a year-round basis at a tower on the island of Barbados, in the lower Antilles. (Recently, two more such stations have been set up to measure dust in Bermuda and Miami.) These measurements, made by scientists from the University of Miami, show that the airborne dust loading is highly variable from day to day, season to season, and even year to year. Like hurricanes, the primary activity is in summer when the dust transport averages 10 to 50 times more than in winter, with the daily amounts varying from about 1 to 40 micrograms per cubic meter.

Variability — Air-trajectory analysis shows that the summer dust originates over arid to semi-arid regions in the northwestern corner of the African continent, and is swept southward and toward the Caribbean by the strong northeasterly winds that exist in that sector during summer. The width of the dust-carrying airstream is only 300 to 500 miles wide as it leaves the coast of Africa, and the depth of the dust layer is about 12,000 feet as determined by the depth of mixing over Africa. Although this flow of dust is more or

Figure VI-13 — DUST OVER THE TROPICAL ATLANTIC

This satellite photograph was taken by the ATS-3 satellite on the afternoon of August 11, 1970. It shows a great cloud of African dust between 30° and 60° W. longitude just north of the Tropic of Cancer.

less continuous, the variations in dust content of the air are often quite abrupt.

Locally, the variation in dustiness can be due simply to a shift in the dust-laden airstream. In many instances, large increases in dust loading in the Caribbean can be tied to specific outbreaks of dust-storm activity over parts of North Africa. At other times, the increases in dust loading of the trade winds are attributable to the venting of the normally dusty air over the African continent by a favorable wind regime which brings air from deep in the interior of the Sahara into the Atlantic trade winds. In many cases, however, it is impossible to assign a cause to the dust outbreak or even to detect the variation of dust loading downwind from Africa without direct measurements.

Visibility — The presence of African dust in the Caribbean can be seen as thick haze, with visibility reduced from 20 to 30 miles, in the case of no haze, to only between 6 and 15 miles. In exceptionally hazy areas of the Caribbean, the horizon resembles that on a dry day of the American Midwest or on a muggy day in a large city of the Northeast. Indeed, the dust loadings over the Caribbean are probably comparable to or greater than those that would be found over much of continental United States.

Source — There is an abrupt change in the general source region of the dust between winter and summer. After October and until May (with some rare deviations), the dust is ash-gray to black and is thought to originate over the sub-Sahara from the Cameroons through central Nigeria and the Ivory Coast. In the summer, however, the flow of dust is primed by the strong northeasterly winds associated with the intense pressure gradient that exists between the low pressure of the central Sahara and the relatively high pressure along the western coast. Then,

the dust is a reddish-brown color with a tinge of yellow.

Particle Size — A surprising aspect of the size spectra of the dust reaching the Caribbean is the relatively large fraction of the dust (5 to 20 percent) with particle sizes in excess of 10 microns. In general, the higher the dust loading the higher is the fraction of dust in the larger size ranges. According to Stokes, settling-velocity particles in excess of 10 microns would settle out of the air before reaching the Caribbean unless they were raised to heights well in excess of 20,000 feet. Since the visible dust top is rather distinct at about 10,000-15,000 feet over the Caribbean, and is directly related to the top of the turbulent mixing layer over the Sahara, which is at about the same altitude, one can assume that virtually all the dust falls from below 10,000-15,000 feet. Although a substantial fraction of the dust undoubtedly settles out before reaching the Caribbean, a certain fraction of all size ranges is prevented from being lost by the recycling of air (turbulent mixing) in the dust layer over Africa and in the trade winds.

Vertical Distribution — Recent observations of the vertical distribution of the dust show that the dust concentration in the air downwind from the Sahara is greatest in the layer between the dust top and the top of the cumulus layer (say, 4,000 to 8,000 feet). In the lower layers, the trade-wind air may be air of non-Saharan (or partially Saharan) origin that flows southward to undercut the original dust airstream, being thereby enriched by mixing and by fallout from above.

Possible Relation of African Dust to Tropical Disturbances

A great deal of indirect theoretical and observational evidence exists to suggest that African dust may play some secondary role in the growth or suppression of tropical disturb-

ances and the entire energetics of the tropical atmosphere. Conversely, some observations indicate that African disturbances have some effect on the movement of dust into the Caribbean and that the behavior of the dust is at least superficially affected by the presence of these wave perturbations.

Dust as a Nucleator — It is well known that the size spectra and numbers of condensation nuclei have a profound effect on the population of water droplets in clouds and the ability of the cloud to precipitate. These condensation nuclei are derived from various types of atmospheric aerosols — salt particles, dust, pollution, and the like. Much research has been done both in the laboratory and in the field, to determine the nucleating properties of various substances and their relative importance in cloud growth.

Similarly, the formation of ice crystals from supercooled water in clouds depends on the presence of foreign freezing nuclei and on the distribution of existing ice crystals. Almost any substance will nucleate ice at some temperature, but only a relatively few types of substances are efficient in this capacity — i.e., are able to promote freezing at temperatures warmer than about −20° centigrade. The best-known and most efficient type of nuclei air crystals is silver iodide, which has been used in cloud-seeding experiments. But silver iodide is not found naturally in the air in significant quantities. The most efficient *natural* ice nuclei are the clay minerals—notably kaolinite, illite, and montmorillite. These three minerals are abundant in the soils of North Africa and have been found to be a prominent constituent in the African dust. Since the haze top is near the freezing level, the dust could only be effective in freezing if it were entrained into large cumulus which protrude to heights well above the haze top.

Until very recently the Atlantic trade winds were thought of in terms of a maritime environment in which aerosol distribution was made up of sea-salt particles which provide the clouds with giant hygroscopic nuclei for condensation and with possible sites for freezing. The Barbados measurements, however, show that the bulk dust density in the air is greater than the expected concentration of sea-salt particles, even near the surface. Additional measurements made recently from aircraft near Barbados show that the ice nuclei were as high as 10^3 to 10^4 per cubic meter in visibly dusty areas, values that are comparable to those found over the continents. At other times, the ice-nuclei concentrations were found to be negligible in areas of dense haze. These measurements suggest that the ice nuclei are deactivated under certain conditions, possibly by surface contamination with Aitken nuclei, water droplets, or some form of pollution.

Such ambiguities in the physics of ice nuclei and the lack of aerosol measurements in the tropics preclude even an educated guess as to the effect of African dust on the growth of disturbances. At present, arguments can be made for either suppression or enhancement of cloud growth given an abundant supply of aerosols.

Much more evidence is required to form a quantitative picture of how much dust is entering the convective clouds associated with the disturbances and what the distributions are of ice and condensation nuclei in the cloud environment and the population of ice crystals and water drops in the clouds. Additional aerosol and dust measurements need to be made along the African coast and by aircraft flying in the vicinity of African disturbances. A more detailed knowledge of the vertical distribution of dust and other aerosols should be sought in these flights. If efforts are going to be made to seed disturbances, it would be important to know exactly what the background seeding capacity of the environment is during

a period of exceptionally high dust content in order to estimate the seedability of the clouds in these hazy areas. Aerosol measurements of any sort made over Africa itself would be most useful.

Dust as a Tracer of Air Motion — Besides being an active participant in the condensation and energetics of cumulus clouds, the dust is useful as a tracer of air motions in the trade winds, thereby leading to an understanding of the dynamics of air motion at low altitudes. Some tentative evidence exists showing that the dust transport off the African coast is much enhanced by the passage of an African disturbance south of the dust-producing area. Intensely hazy areas, visible on satellite photos, were concentrated immediately to the rear (east) of an African disturbance on two or three occasions in the summer of 1969. In these particular dust outbreaks, the leading edge of the dust mass remained close to the axis of the easterly wave disturbance as it crossed the ocean and passed the island of Barbados. Statistics for the past three years show that the passage of African disturbances by Barbados is accompanied by a significant diminution in dust loading just prior to its arrival and a marked increase, leading to maximum dust loading, immediately after passage of the wave axis by Barbados. It is not clear whether the disturbance actually prevents the dust from passing the wave.

Examination of radiosonde data shows that the temperature, stability, and water-vapor content of the air is singularly different in the dusty area. In general, air of high dust content is accompanied by a minimum of cloudiness. This is probably due to a more rapid subsidence of the strong northeasterly trades that are especially susceptible to the raising of dust over the continent and to the increased stability at low levels found in the dusty air, rather than to an interaction of the dust with the clouds.

Chemical, mineralogical, and color analysis of the dust is another possible method for determining the origin, composition, and seeding possibilities of the dust. This has been done on a number of selected occasions using the Barbados dust samples. The results so far are inconclusive, but they do show significant variations in quartz, calcite, iron, and other substances between winter and summer dust. In addition, the lead and zinc content of the summer dust is anomalously high, especially in comparison to the very low amounts of these elements in the winter dust. These two elements owe their abundance to industrial contamination, notably fossil fuels. Therefore, the air that carried the dust from the northwestern corner of the Sahara was likely to have been over industrial Europe immediately before its arrival over Africa; conversely, the winter dust is carried in an airstream of long-standing duration in the tropics.

Measurement Techniques and Their Implications

Radon-222 — Some indirect measurements of dust content can be made using radon-222 as a tracer of Saharan dust. Radon-222 is liberated from soils in large quantities and is mixed throughout the lower layers of the atmosphere in much the same way as water vapor and dust are mixed from their sources at the earth's surface. Unlike dust, however, radon gas is not washed out by rain. This property (insolubility) can provide a means of studying the washout of dust and the later movement of Saharan air after it has passed through a cycle of cumulus convection.

Thus, radon-222 measured in the high troposphere may be useful in tracing the outflow of dusty air from the tops of cumulonimbus and can lead to a substantiation of the theory that the high concentrations of ice nuclei and dust particles sometimes found in the upper atmosphere are of terrestrial origin. Radon measurements in the southern hemisphere south of the North Atlantic trade winds can provide valuable information on cross-equatorial flow and the flow of air across the Intertropic Convergence Zone.

In one aircraft expedition made by a U.S. research team flying between Miami and Dakar, a high correlation was found between haze and radon activity. This relationship between dust and radon activity was substantiated in further aircraft flights made near Barbados in 1969 and by some measurements made on board the USS *Discoverer* the same year. Radon was also measured south of the equator on the flight. More such flights and expeditions are needed to expand our fragmented knowledge of dust transport.

LIDAR — Another indirect method for estimating the vertical distribution of dust is with LIDAR, which measures the back-scatter from a laser beam. However, back-scatter measurements are highly dependent on particle size and are extremely difficult to interpret in terms of dust distribution without supporting data to accompany them.

Turbidity Measurement — More useful than LIDAR in the study of dust is the measurement of turbidity from photometric measurements of skylight distribution and spectral attenuation of solar radiation. These turbidity measurements can also be compared with atmospheric back-scatter and albedo as determined from satellites. Atmospheric dust over the tropical Atlantic can have an important effect on the energy balance of the tropics and, consequently, on the global circulation. Since the atmospheric turbidity is a function of the aerosol content of the air, the total incoming and outgoing radiation and the changes in absorptivity and emissivity on the vertical can affect the heating and the convective instability of the trade winds. There is some evidence that the growing pollution over the earth during the past few decades has resulted in an increase in atmospheric turbidity and a slight decline in worldwide temperature. An increase in turbidity at low latitudes can effect a decrease in worldwide temperature and a slowing down of the general circulation of the whole earth. At present there is some question as to the cause of the turbidity increase over the years. It may actually be due to natural causes such as volcanic eruptions or changes in dust content of the air rather than to industrial pollution. Since significant changes in dust loading from year to year do occur in the Atlantic trade winds (the amount of dust reaching Barbados in the summer of 1969 was double that in the previous four years of record), it would therefore be useful to measure turbidity in the Atlantic trade-wind area on a yearly basis in order to determine the natural fluctuation in the components of the radiation balance there.

African dust may thus influence tropical storm development indirectly, by means of its capacity to alter the long-term thermodynamics of the tropical environment.

PART VII

WATER RESOURCES, FORESTRY, AND AGRICULTURE

---

1. WATER RESOURCES

Estimating Future Water Supply and Usage

Most estimates of water supply and usage have been couched in terms of average annual water supply and projected usage at some future date. For small areas within the scope of a single project or a system of projects, water supply is sometimes stated as the mean flow available during the most critical dry period in the record. Such assessments have the virtue of simplicity and are reasonably well understood by the layman.

At the national level, a statement of mean water supply and mean usage is probably entirely adequate because water-supply problems are never solved at that level. At the regional and local level, however, use of the mean supply available and a projected future usage deprives the planner of the opportunity for strategic evaluation of alternatives. The planner is concerned with supplying water for a specific period of years into the future. It is virtually certain that the actual streamflows during this future period will not duplicate those of the historic past and that water usage at the end of the period will not precisely equal the forecast. Faced with such uncertainty, the planner would be wise to treat both variables in terms of probability. Only through a probabilistic treatment can he evaluate the risk of expanding water-supply facilities too fast, with consequent excessive costs and risk of losing future technological advantages, or of developing a system so slowly as to threaten a serious water shortage at some future date.

Estimates of Water Supply

The data base for estimates of water supply consist of approximately 10,000 gauging stations operated mostly by the U.S. Geological

Survey; in addition, many thousands of wells provide information on groundwater levels. There may be specific local deficiencies in this data base, but on the whole it must be judged reasonably adequate. It is fortunate that this base exists, because only time can remedy deficiencies — from 30 to 100 years of record are required to describe statistically the characteristics of water supply.

Qualifying Factors—Interpretation of existing data on streamflow and groundwater is complicated by the fact that few stations record virgin conditions. Regulation by reservoirs, diversion from streams, pumpage from groundwater, alteration of stream channels, vegetation-management practices, urbanization, and many other factors render available data series inhomogeneous over time. In some cases, the effect of man's activity is rather accurately known and appropriate corrections can be made. In most instances, however, only the sign of the change can be stated with accuracy.

Synthetic Streamflow Records — The last decade has seen the development of hydrologic simulation using both digital and analogue computers. Simulation is capable of transforming precipitation data into synthetic streamflow records. Simulation brings many thousands of precipitation stations operated by the National Weather Service into the data base and makes it possible to make streamflow estimates at sites where no gauging station exists. Because precipitation records are generally longer than streamflow records, simulation permits the extension of flow records at currently gauged sites.

Similar development has taken place with respect to simulation of

groundwater basins primarily through the use of analogue models. Although these models cannot perfectly reproduce historic streamflow or groundwater basin performance because of errors in the data inputs and deficiencies in the models themselves, errors in model outputs are generally random and pose no serious problem in probabilistic estimates of water supply. Simulation models also permit adjustment of observed flows or groundwater levels to virgin or natural conditions. It may be concluded, therefore, that we are now able to combine observed and synthesized data into a data base covering a sufficient period of time to define the mean and variance of water supplies with reasonable accuracy.

Problems of Data Projection — The historic data base, observed or simulated, does not fully satisfy the need for projections of future water supply, however. The water-supply planner is concerned with possible events over a specific period ranging from 20 to 100 years in the future. He is particularly concerned with the sequences of annual flows, because a series of consecutive dry years will impose a much greater burden on his reservoir (surface or subsurface) than the same number of dry years dispersed over his planning horizon. To meet this problem, the field of stochastic hydrology has developed during the 1960's.

Stochastic Hydrology — In stochastic hydrology, generating functions derived from the estimated statistical characteristics of the historic record are used in conjunction with random numbers to generate many possible flow sequences. Thus, a thousand years of stochastic streamflow can be broken into ten 100-year periods, from which the planner can estimate the probability that a proposed reservoir will be adequate against any of these ten alternative futures.

Streamflow is inherently more variable than precipitation and it is fair to assume that we know the statistical parameters of precipitation with greater accuracy than those for streamflow. It follows that the stochastic generation of precipitation data should be a more certain process than stochastic generation of streamflow data. Stochastically generated precipitation data can be converted to streamflow by deterministic simulation models, although the process would be substantially more expensive than direct stochastic generation of flow data, since deterministic simulation is inherently more complex and time-consuming. Preliminary work on stochastic generation of rainfall has recently begun, but further research should be encouraged.

The Relevance of Climate — In addition to the stochastic properties of future streamflow, a number of other issues arise before the planner can be content with his projections of future water supply. The first of these is the question of long-term climatic trends. An abundance of data demonstrates the existence of such trends in terms of geologic time and in terms of periods as short as a few hundred years. However, no sound basis exists for predicting the existence of a trend and its consequences over the next century. Climatic trends could alter the water-supply outlook in arid and semi-arid regions, since the hydrologic balance is sensitive to small changes in precipitation input or evapotranspiration outgo. Techniques that could identify causes and project trends, even in an approximate fashion, would be extremely valuable to the water-resource planner.

The Relevance of Human Activity — In addition to natural climatic trends, future water supplies may be affected by man-induced changes, both intentional and inadvertent.

Intentional changes include those brought about by land-management practices, vegetation management, desalinating of brackish or saline waters, or effective reclamation of waste water. The question that confronts the planner is "Will any of these become practically useful and if so when?" The issue is the evaluation of probable rates of technological advance. It will be seen that similar questions arise in the discussion of water usage.

Inadvertent changes in water supply may be brought about by urbanization, which increases surface runoff and decreases infiltration to groundwater. If one can make reasonable projections of future urban growth, deterministic hydrologic models can project the alterations in streamflow and accretion to groundwater. More subtle are the effects of air pollution, urbanization, and changes in land use and vegetative cover as they may affect climate. These possibilities underline the importance of research on climatic change.

Estimates of Water Use

The problem of predicting future water use is far more complex than that of predicting water supply, if only because of the much larger number of components that must enter the forecast. It is convenient to divide the discussion of water use into the requirements for the several purposes to which water is most commonly applied. Before each of these purposes is discussed, however, two general topics should be noted.

General Considerations — First, the distinction between diversion and consumption should be underlined. For many purposes, large quantities of water are diverted for use but only a small fraction of the diverted water is consumed; the rest is returned to the environment — sometimes degraded in quality. (See Figure VII–1) An outstanding example is the use of

water for cooling in industry and power generation, which actually consumes very little water; most of the water used is returned to a stream or to the groundwater substantially warmer than when originally diverted.

Because of the re-use aspects, discussion of diversion requirements is confusing. Here we will consider only consumptive use. Consumptive use is defined as that portion of the water which is evaporated or combined in the product so that it is no longer available for re-use in the original source system.

A second topic which deserves consideration on a general basis is that of population forecasting. For nearly all water uses, estimates of population and its geographic distribution are fundamental. If probability estimates of future water use are to be derived, they must begin with estimates of probable future population. Research has been done on the variance of population estimates as indicated by statistical evaluation of historic predictions. A more fundamental study might explore the uncertainties in each of the factors involved in population forecasting.

The most difficult problem is the forecasting of local population by county or city units. Factors that do not enter national population forecasting are involved in predictions of the distribution of population. Not the least of the factors that may affect future distributions is government policy concerning desirable population distribution. Some research on the optimal size of population concentrations may be useful. Is there a city size at which the unit cost of infrastructure is minimized? What are the advantages of population dispersal against increased growth of major metropolitan centers?

Domestic Water Use — The question of domestic water requirements depends largely on two issues. One

Figure VII–1 — DISPOSITION OF WATER DIVERTED FOR IRRIGATION

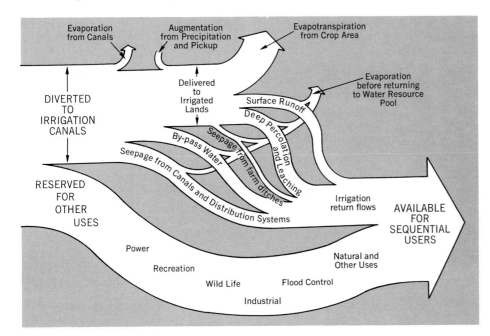

The diagram shows schematically what becomes of water diverted for irrigation purposes in the U.S. The width of the stream represents the relative quantity of water moving in that path. Water is consumed by evaporation from various sources and evapotranspiration from irrigated areas. This reduces the water supply available for sequential uses. The non-consumptive paths such as seepage, runoff, and percolation return water to the resource pool, leaving it available for subsequent uses. This return water may improve or degrade the water quality depending on the initial quality of the water, the uses to which it has been put, and the particular characteristics desired by the sequential users.

is the technology of water use. Planners have generally assumed a slow increase in per capita water requirements. It should not, however, be exceptionally difficult to redesign conventional plumbing fixtures and water-using appliances so that water-use rates are reduced without sacrificing the amenities of present users.

The second factor that might significantly affect domestic consumption would be changes in life styles. A shift from dispersed single-family residences to multi-family residences would be the most significant change. Savings in water would be achieved through reduction in lawn and garden water requirements. Changes of this kind are probably closely related to technology through construction costs, transportation techniques, disposition of leisure time, and public policy with respect to taxation. Sub-

jects for research on the impact of technology on society in this area are abundant.

Industrial Water Use — The average values of industrial water use per unit of product produced are extremely large in many industries. There are, however, many opportunities for reducing water use by recycling, recovery of by-products, and other techniques. Estimates of future industrial use are dependent on estimates of future industrial production and the extent to which water-conservation techniques are applied.

Water in Agriculture — The largest water-using sector in the United States today is irrigated agriculture. In states like California, over 90 percent of the water use is for irrigation. Future agricultural water requirements are therefore extraordi-

narily important. Unfortunately, they are difficult to assess. What are the future needs for food and fiber production? How much food and fiber will the United States produce for export? How much can food and fiber production in the humid eastern states be expanded? How can water-use efficiency in agriculture be improved? What is the possibility of breeding crop types requiring less water or capable of using brackish water instead of fresh water? To what extent will it be possible to raise crops in arid regions in controlled environment chambers? Will extensive, low-cost greenhouses in which water use can be carefully controlled become technically feasible? These questions all involve issues of technical feasibility, extent to which efficiency of production can be improved, and time-rate at which these developments can be expected.

Energy Production — The consumptive water requirements for the production of electric energy are relatively small. A hydroelectric power plant actually consumes only small amounts of water evaporated from the reservoir surface. A thermal plant consumes the water evaporated in cooling the condensers. If predictions that power demands will continue to double every decade (thousand-fold increase in 100 years) prove accurate, however, the current relatively small use will grow rapidly into a major source of water consumption.

Again, the projection of water requirements for power production raises mainly technological issues. What are the prospects for new types of thermal power producers for which cooling-water requirements are less? Are there possibilities of cooling methods that are less demanding on the water resource? Use of heated condenser water for irrigation shows promise of minimizing the "thermal pollution" of streams and improving the efficiency of irrigation. Not all thermal power plants can be situated close to potential irrigated areas, however. What other uses of waste heat may be feasible? Is it conceivable that per capita power requirements may be reduced by reducing power requirements in the home and industry? Can climate control be achieved? Will future urban centers require less energy and water for airconditioning?

Navigation — Navigation is not an extremely heavy user. Evaporation losses from reservoirs from which water is released to maintain navigable depths downstream constitute the primary consumptive use. The quantity is probably so small that it deserves little consideration as compared with other demands on our water resource. However, it is appropriate to ask what future transportation technology may be expected. Will relatively slow, bulk transport by water continue to be a favored procedure? Will high-speed surface or air transport encroach on the market for bulk transport to the point where future expansion of navigation facilities may stop?

Recreation — Like navigation, recreation is not presently a heavy con-

sumer of water. Primary water use by recreation is evaporation from reservoirs constructed solely for water recreation or from an increased water surface area in reservoirs because of projected recreation. It is unlikely that reservoirs will be built solely for recreational purposes in water-short areas. Recreation does not appear to be a factor of great uncertainty with respect to future water use. However, it may be appropriate to mention here the possibility of evaporation suppression from water surfaces by the use of film-forming chemicals or covers. If successful techniques for evaporation suppression could be achieved, requirements for many of the uses discussed above could be reduced.

Fish and Wildlife — It is currently accepted that the maintenance of fish and wildlife requires that a continued flow be maintained. A substantial part of this flow is eventually discharged into the oceans where it can no longer be used. Water requirements for this purpose are surely not well known. The mechanisms by which a reduction in dis-

charge into estuaries may affect marine life need to be established. This need derives from two competing aspects. We need to know how much water must be permitted to flow to the oceans in order to maintain fisheries for both economic and sports purposes, and the extent to which this fresh-water flow influences other estuarine and oceanic resources. We also need to know the consequences of excessive flood flows through estuaries. Are such flows beneficial or detrimental? In addition to the consequences for fisheries and wildlife, what are the effects of regulating streamflows to the ocean on sediment deposits in estuaries and harbors and on nourishment of beaches?

In summary, probability estimates of water supply are limited only by hydrologic understanding, and solutions appear to be close at hand. Projections of water usage are heavily dependent on projections of new technology. Little effort has been devoted to this latter problem and, therefore, current projections of use are quite uncertain.

Water Movement and Storage in Plants and Soils

Since only five feet of soil can generally store fully ten inches of precipitation and since evaporation from soil and foliage returns to the air about 70 percent of our precipitation, these two factors represent a significant portion of the hydrologic cycle and a determinant of our water resources. (See Figure VII–2) Further, and less often noted, the relations of precipitation, evaporation, and storage will determine the escape of soluble substances such as nitrate from the region of roots and into groundwater and streams.

Because the plant roots are intertwined among the soil particles and water flows readily from one to the other, plant and soil — and, for that matter, the atmosphere as well —

must be analyzed as a continuous system. Then the components can be examined in order of their impact on the system, and the results used to improve our understanding and ability to predict the functioning of the entire system outdoors. Fortunately, our ability to cope with the entire system has been advanced materially in recent years.

Total Evaporation

Essentially, the soil-plant-water problem is to measure the extraction from the soil, conduction to the leaves, and then evaporation from the leaves. Some water may short-circuit this path and be evaporated from the soil or leach beyond the

roots, but a lot — often most — takes the route of soil to plant to air.

Evaporation from the Canopy — Recently, research has greatly improved our understanding of how water gets from the canopy of foliage to the atmosphere above. When evaporation from the canopy strata is viewed as a factor in an energy budget and evaporation and convection are set proportional to temperature and humidity differences, the evaporation (and the temperature and humidity of the air within the canopy microclimate) can be calculated from the weather above and below the canopy, the profiles of radiation and ventilation, the distribution of foliage area, and the boundary layer and stomatal resistance of the foliage. In

Figure VII–2 — THE HYDROLOGIC CYCLE

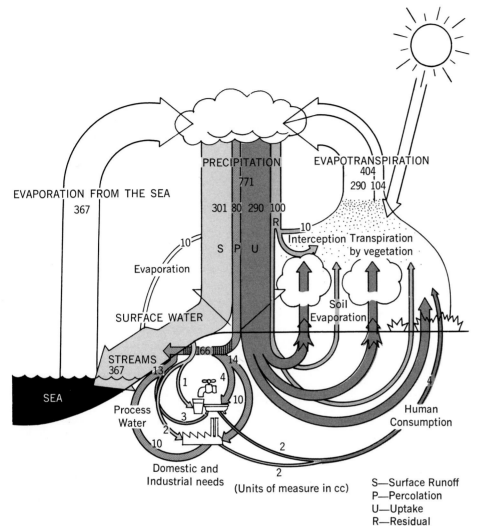

This is an idealized version of the water cycle. The numbers attached to the various processes are relative units of measure. Note that the truly important parts of the cycle are evaporation from the sea, precipitation, and evapotranspiration.

area and porosity as well as weather and evaporation. Fortunately, since the invention of a simple, portable porometer by Wallihan in 1964 and the subsequent calibration of several modifications, porosity can easily be measured.

Earlier hydrologic observations suggested that different vegetation consumed different amounts of water in evaporation. The simulators mentioned above, along with experiments with sprays that shrink stomata, have now established that evaporation can be changed by modest changes in the canopy. During the coming years, therefore, one can expect a variety of experiments seeking the most effective and least injurious ways of conserving water in the soil through treating or modifying the vegetation.

Microclimatic Measurements

Turning to the *distribution* of evaporation, temperature, and humidity within the canopy — in contrast to the sum of evaporation discussed above — one finds that a greater number of parameters can be effective. The changes in temperature and humidity along the path conducting water and sensible heat out of the canopy depend on the boundary layer around the leaf and the turbulence of the bulk air within the canopy. These two factors generally are of smaller magnitude than the stomatal resistance and hence are relatively ineffective, we believe, in changing the sum of evaporation. However, when we turn to the distribution of temperature and humidity within the canopy — the microclimatic question — these parameters are influential. Scientists do not yet know how to measure them, however.

Boundary-Layer Resistance — Formerly, this was estimated from a conventional fluid mechanics equation, employing the square root of leaf dimension divided by wind speed. Recently, however, Hunt and

1956, Penman showed how evaporation from abundant foliage sufficiently wet to have wide stomata could be calculated from the net all-wave radiation available above the canopy. The recent advance is, therefore, in understanding how foliage condition can decrease evaporation below Penman's potential and how the evaporation and consequent temperature and humidity within the canopy are changed. The total evaporation from the canopy, according to our new understanding, is affected profoundly

by the leaf area and, more subtly, but still considerably, by the stomatal conductivity or porosity of the foliage for water.

Future Observations and Experiments — This understanding has been arrived at by means of mathematical simulation. To make a substantial improvement in our understanding — or even to test our present understanding — future measurements of evaporation from crops and trees must include observations of leaf

others have claimed that this estimate is greater than the true resistance within a canopy. Presumably, this question can be resolved by fluid mechanics, energy budgets, and the new porometers.

Diffusivity Within the Canopy — This is harder to measure. At present it is estimated by measurements of radiation absorption and temperature and humidity gradients. The method is susceptible to error, produces estimates at variance with the wind speed and employs the very temperatures and humidities that one would like to predict. A new method of estimating diffusivities within the canopy is required but none has yet appeared.

Microclimatic observation will undoubtedly continue in the future. If the observations are to be most useful in testing and improving our understanding, they should include the vertical variation in leaf area and porosity as well as radiation, temperature, humidity, and ventilation. Since this makes a formidable list of equipment and tasks before a complete, and hence worthwhile, set of observations can be made, microclimatic and evaporation studies seem ideally suited as testing grounds for cooperative or integrated teams of scientists.

Horizontal Heterogeneities — The final remark concerning the aerial portion of the problem must concern horizontal heterogeneity and advection. Chimneys and sun flecks among the foliage clearly render our ideal, stratified models unrealistic. Therefore, efforts to incorporate these heterogeneities into the analysis are welcomed, even if they only prove that the ideal, homogeneous model

gives the same average evaporation and microclimate as the realistic model.

The larger heterogeneities connoted by "advection" are known to be important, justifying the term "oasis effect." Advection of carbon dioxide has already been treated simply in a photosynthesis model, and incorporating large-scale advection into the existing evaporation models seems manageable and worthwhile.

Water Storage in Soil

The transport of water to foliage from soil has not yet been mentioned. Relatively less can be said about it in a systematic way. As a complement to the simulation of evaporation from foliage, we need a comprehensive simulator of this portion of the path of the water that will tell us how much water gets to the leaves and, more important, how stomatal resistance is modified. The simulator concerning soil and plant is more lacking in foundation than one concerning plant and air. Nevertheless, beginnings have been made by Cowan and Raschke.

Gaps in Scientific Understanding — These primitive simulators reveal serious deficiencies in our understanding of (a) the relation between water potential in the leaves and stomatal resistance; (b) the conductivity of different root regions; and (c) the conductivity between soil and roots. This last matter includes the difficult problem of root distribution through the soil profile. The actual storage capacity of the soil and relation between potential and content seem fairly well established. The effect of changes of temperature in

time and depth is yet to be coped with.

New instruments usable in the field should help. The new porometers have been mentioned already, and the Scholander pressure chamber promises to reveal water potentials, even in roots. We are still left, however, to search for root distributions. In the case of temperature differences, on the other hand, the problem is to improve our logic rather than our observations.

The next problem is the escape of water from soil storage via a moist surface or by leaching rather than through vegetation. These two escapes greatly affect the loss from the root zone of salts and nutrients that pollute the water below. Evaporation and land leaching from the soil have been measured carefully in bare soil, but the present challenge is to understand the parameters sufficiently well to estimate them when a canopy of foliage is also removing water. This is a fundamental problem of the movement and loss of water from a heterogeneous porous medium with a variable and heterogeneous temperature. The research of the past has not brought us a lucid understanding of the system; at present, progress seems most likely to come from devising a better logical framework on which to hang our measurements.

A Final Word

The reader may have noticed that time has not been mentioned. That is, analyses or simulators of an instant only have been described. Intellectual satisfaction and eventual utility requires that our understanding and predictors be extended through time, with the storage of plant and soil as parameters.

A Note on Subsidence and the Exhaustion of Water-Bearing and Oil-Bearing Formations

Virtually all rocks near the earth's surface are to some degree porous, and if water is available it fills the pores. In some rocks the pores are large enough and well enough interconnected so that water can readily flow from volumes of higher pressure to volumes of lower; such rocks are called aquifers — water bearers. Other rocks have pores so fine and so poorly interconnected that water passes through them only slowly, even under high pressure-gradients; these are aquitards — water-retarders. Among the common rocks, sandstones, conglomerates, cavernous limestone, and scoriaceous lavas are the chief aquifers; shales are the principal aquitards.

Subsidence

Where water has access to an interbedded series of aquitards and aquifers both are commonly saturated, but the aquitards are sufficiently impermeable as to permit considerable pressure differences to exist between the several aquifers. When a well is drilled to any particular confined aquifer and water is withdrawn from it, the water pressure in the aquifer is decreased and the aquifer shrinks in thickness. The weight of the rocks overlying the aquifer, which had formerly been in part sustained by the pressure of the contained water on the base of the overlying aquitard, has become effectively greater because of the decrease in hydrostatic pressure; under the effectively greater load, the aquifer yields elastically and the volume of its pores diminishes.

Though Young's modulus for most sandstones is between 140,000 and 500,000 pounds per square inch, a significant pressure reduction in an aquifer several hundred feet thick can readily cause a subsidence of several feet at the surface of the

ground. Such a subsidence may create serious problems in drainage, sewage disposal, and utility maintenance. More important than simple elastic compression of the aquifers, however, is the fact that the lowered pressure in the aquifers permits slow drainage into them from adjoining or interbedded aquitards. This permits the aquitards also to be compressed by shrinking their pore spaces.

Thus, at the Wilmington oil field, in California, the loss of pressure in the oil sands after 1936, when production on a large scale began, led to a surface subsidence of more than 32 feet (see Figure VII–3) before recharging of the oil sands with sea water under pressure finally stabilized the surface. Of this subsidence, only about 10 feet could be attributed to

elastic compression of the oil sands; the remaining 22 feet was almost certainly due to de-watering of the associated shales. The cost of this subsidence was many millions of dollars, since the railroad terminals, docks, shipyards, drydocks, and power plants had all to be rebuilt, together with the streets, water, and sewer systems of a large part of the city of Wilmington.

Similar subsidence caused by withdrawal of fluids under pressure has been noted at many other seaside localities: Lake Maracaibo, Venezuela; Goose Creek, Texas; Huntington Beach, California; Redondo Beach, California. None caused as great a loss as that at Wilmington.

It is possible for similar subsidence to pass unnoticed at areas inland be-

Figure VII–3 — SUBSIDENCE IN LONG BEACH, CALIFORNIA

(Illustration: Courtesy of the Geological Society of America.)

Superimposed on the photograph of the port area of Long Beach, California are contours of equal subsidence in feet as they existed in 1962. The subsidence in the upper right resulted from withdrawal of fluid from the Signal Hill oil field between 1928 and 1962. The major subsidence in the foreground was due to withdrawal from the Wilmington oil field.

cause a definite reference surface is not obvious. Nevertheless, the failure of the Baldwin Hills Dam in western Los Angeles, with the loss of many lives and millions in property damage, was probably due to withdrawal of fluids from the underlying oil field. The subsidence of many feet beneath the city of Mexico was caused by withdrawal of water from the lake sediments on which the city was built; considerable expenditures have been needed to take care of drainage disposal.

Two other areas in California have suffered large losses through withdrawal of water from beneath. In the Santa Clara Valley, pumping of water from a confined aquifer at depth has led to subsidence as great as 9 feet between 1934 and 1959 in the city of San Jose; subsidence has also been considerable farther north in the valley, including such important industrial areas as Sunnyvale.

On the west side of the San Joaquin Valley, dewatering of surficial sediments had caused the surface to subside as much as 23 feet by 1963 and forced alterations in the plans for the new irrigation system now under construction.

Exhaustion of Groundwater

Most of the agricultural production of the High Plains of Texas and eastern New Mexico tributary to the cities of Lubbock, Amarillo, and Portales depends on water pumped from the Ogallala Formation, of Pliocene age. The Ogallala is composed of gravel and sand that was deposited as a piedmont fan from the Rocky Mountains to the northwest. Erosion since its deposition has cut deeply enough to sever the connection with the mountain streams whose sediments led to the formation. The result is that water pumped from the formation is not being recharged from the mountains; the small amount of recharge that feeds into the underground reservoir is simply seepage from the overlying arid surface. Estimates by the Texas Agricultural Experiment Station were that recharge amounts to only about 104,000 to 346,000 acre feet of water for the Texas portion of the High Plains, whereas pumpage averaged 5 million acre feet during the period from 1954 to 1961. Obviously, the water table is sinking at a tremendous rate, ranging from 1.34 to as much as 3.72 feet per year, and the cost of pumping is rising accordingly. The water is being mined, just as

literally as is coal from a coal seam, and a drastic change in the economics of the region is unavoidable.

The Texas study projects the decline in irrigated acreage from 3.5 million acres in 1966 to 125,000 acres in 2015. Cotton production is expected to decline from about a million bales in 1966 to 355,000 bales in 2015, of which 70 percent will be grown on dry land. At 1966 prices, the aggregate annual value of agricultural production is projected to decline 70 percent in fifty years. Drastic economic change is clearly in sight, not only for the farm operators but for suppliers of farm machinery, automobiles, and other inputs into agriculture. Urban decline is also inevitable.

Water is being mined at many other places west of the 100th meridian — notably in the Mojave Desert of California and many of the intermontane valleys of the Basin and Range Province in Arizona, California, Nevada, Utah, and Oregon. In each of these, results comparable to the inevitable decline of the High Plains are foreseeable, though the rate of decline will vary from area to area.

2. FORESTRY

Water Quality in Forests

Lands classified as forest, approximately three-quarters of them in private ownership (see Figure VII–4) make up almost exactly one-third of the total land area of the United States. A large portion of this is well supplied with precipitation, and the excess over that lost by evapotranspiration is the source of much of the water reaching streams, lakes, and ground waters.

Water issuing from essentially undisturbed forests, even those on steep terrain or with thin or erosive soils, is ordinarily of high quality — low in dissolved and suspended matter except during major floods, high in oxygen content, relatively low in temperature, and substantially free of microbial pollutants. These qualities are desirable and highly visible to recreational users of these lands, and some are absolutely essential to fish such as trout and salmon. They are also highly important to downstream users, whether agricultural, urban, or industrial. In addition to any legal rights these users may have acquired to water volume, they often have built-in dependencies — aesthetic, technical, or economic — on quality features; they are commonly prepared to resist any real or prospective impairment, regardless of the interests of the owners of the lands from which the water comes or other social claims on its use.

Nevertheless, these water-yielding lands are required for a variety of other goods and social purposes — timber, recreation in many forms, grazing and wildlife production. A very large proportion of public and private land is held especially for such uses, whereas only rarely is there any direct recompense to the landholder for the outflowing waters. Despite contrary advocacy, it will seldom be defensible to propose water

quality as the exclusive goal of forest land management over large areas.

Now, all uses, all manipulation of soil and vegetation, pose some potential risk to water quality — sometimes major, sometimes trivial. Even wilderness camping, construction of roads essential for adequate fire protection, or forest cutting or herbicide treatments to reduce transpiration and so increase water yield conceivably could affect water quality adversely. Accordingly, conflict between absolutely unaltered water quality and other land uses will likely be inevitable at times, and may have to be resolved on economic or political grounds. Moreover, conflicts between competing land uses — as forage *versus*

timber, large game *versus* domestic animal grazing, industrial raw materials *versus* scenic impact — may be resolved on grounds other than water quality.

But there is abundant evidence — chiefly from U.S. Forest Service experimental watersheds — to demonstrate that other uses of watershed lands either already are or can be made compatible with essentially unimpaired water quality. A variety of techniques and constraints will be needed, such as where and how roads are built, the nature and timing of silvicultural or harvesting practices, how recreationists travel and camp. Many of these are known already; others are under investigation; still

Figure VII–4 — OWNERSHIP OF U.S. FOREST LANDS

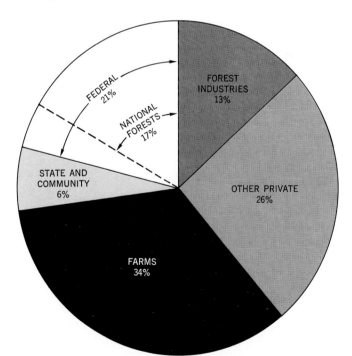

The diagram shows the forest ownership pattern in the U.S. in 1952. Federal, state, and local governments owned only 27 percent of the forest land. An additional 13 percent was under the control of forest industries. Such a situation makes forest management difficult because many private owners lack the incentive, knowledge, or interest to use approved forestry practices on their lands.

others must be devised. In a few fragile landscapes only limited access and use may be allowable.

There can be no simple, universal prescriptions for reconciling conflicting uses with each other or with water quality. The land classified as forest comprises an enormous number of combinations of vegetation types, soil and bedrock characteristics, landforms and slopes, and climatic regimes. The latter include variation in total precipitation, its distribution and intensity on the watersheds, and features such as snowpack accumulation. This great number of combinations prevents easy generalization of studies on one watershed to others with different soil, slope, or precipitation features. It also emphasizes the need for much better characterization data — climate, geology, hydrology, and soils — for many important watershed regions, for investigation of predictive models, and for expansion of on-the-ground "adaptive research" aimed at converting principles discovered thus far into locally feasible guides for day-to-day operation.

Factors Affecting Water Quality

To a considerable degree, water quality has always figured in a larger concern with the protective function of forest cover upon stream flow — that is, flood control, water yield, and watershed maintenance or improvement. The same natural or man-induced features that make for low infiltration rates, rapid surface runoff, and reduced storage in the soil mantle also lead variously to higher flood peaks but reduced flows in low water periods, to surface erosion and channel cutting, to sedimentation of downstream channels and empoundments, and to high turbidities and sometimes high contents of material swept from the soil surface. Thus, turbidity and sediment content are valuable indices of impairment or improvement of the protective function of watershed, in addition

to being direct measures of water quality.

Water "quality" is a nebulous feature until described in terms of specific attributes such as turbidity, organic content, temperature, nitrate, phosphate, pesticide or other chemical content, and bacteriological quality. These are sometimes discussed as considerations of equal probability, hazard, and rank, but in fact, turn out to be far from equivalent in any respect.

Temperature and Oxygen — Removal of trees or brush greatly increases direct radiation to small streams and materially raises maximum temperatures in the warm seasons — up to 7° to 8° centigrade higher, according to some studies. Such increases may be unfavorable or lethal to desirable fish, especially to salmon and trout species which spawn in small headwater streams, and they also contribute to higher average temperatures of downstream waters. The physical basis of this effect is fairly straightforward, of course, and the temperature increase of small streams has been predicted quite accurately through use of an energy-balance technique.

Experimental observations are limited and there can be no generalization about the importance of this effect to quite different climate and ecological regions. Within the Pacific Northwest, however, knowledge of temperature increase and oxygen decrease following removal of cover is sufficient to call for protection of spawning waters.

A highly effective management remedy is to leave narrow strips of live vegetation for shade; such strips are also important safeguards against stream or bank disturbance by logging operations. Such remedies may entail substantial sacrifice of timber values, as well as higher costs for harvesting and regeneration, and application may well hinge on benefit/cost analyses. Further, one can fore-

see occasional instances of conflict between retention of shade and decreased water temperature on the one hand, and efforts to increase low water flow through reducing vegetation in the riparian zone on the other.

Pesticides — A number of plant-protection or plant-control chemicals have been applied to forest vegetation, and the need for such agents will certainly continue even though particular classes of compounds, such as chlorinated hydrocarbons, are banned. Reduction of losses during major insect outbreaks, control of competing vegetation, and protection of new plantations or regeneration areas are three common situations in which use of chemicals might be essential to timber, recreation, or watershed values.

In principle, any such materials might enter streams either by direct application from aircraft or sprayers, or after washing over or through the soil, or through gross spills and carelessness. The first of these is sometimes thought to be the major concern, although the latter is likely to be the most difficult to predict and control.

For the most part, the compounds applied to forests will be similar to those used elsewhere in properties such as persistence, toxicity, mode of decomposition, and fixation or accumulation by soil, and will be subject to similar precautions. In some instances, however, there may be special problems of forest use arising from difficulties of precise application on rough terrain, or to coarse or rocky soils, or to the possibility of rapid, short-distance transport into streams — as, for example, after treatment of riparian areas. Furthermore, the quality standards applied to headwater streams may well be more stringent than tolerated elsewhere.

But in all this it should not be forgotten that by far the largest fraction of forested land is entirely untreated with pesticides of any sort, and the greatest part of the remainder would be treated only at intervals of several to many years. For example, a single application of 2,4,5-T to control overtopping brush on regeneration areas probably would not be repeated within the life of the new stand.

Numerous monitoring studies with insecticides such as DDT and its successor materials during the past two decades have demonstrated the magnitude of direct and secondary input into streams to be expected from broadcast aerial applications. These also indicate both the hazards of applying highly toxic or persistent materials in this way and the measures required to avoid or minimize direct contamination of waters. Again, fewer though significant studies with ground and aerial applications of herbicides demonstrate that careful regulation of mode, rate, and season of application allows use even in streamside areas with no or minimal contamination. Since phenoxy and amitrole herbicides degrade fairly rapidly in the forest floor, confining application to places and seasons where overland flow will not occur within a month or two avoids possible runoff.

But, plainly, continued systematic experiments with pesticides or other easily detected markers under a large variety of field conditions is needed to insure a high degree of predictability. Moreover, the increasing constraint on the use of some materials is likely to place a high emphasis on development of nontoxic or easily decomposed materials, and on alternative strategies of pest control.

The Effects of Fire — Concentrations of dissolved solids in forest streams are normally low, and increases of any magnitude are usually associated with major disturbances or additions. From time to time concern has been expressed over the effects of fire, clearcutting or other

destruction of cover, increased area of nitrogen-fixing vegetation, and forest fertilization. Unfortunately, attention is sometimes directed solely to maximum concentrations in the waters from the affected areas. When the aggregate of small watersheds forming a single forested drainage basin is viewed as a system over time, however, events affecting small areas and at long intervals, such as clearcutting in a sustained-yield forest, necessarily have only minor influences on the quality of large-volume streams issuing from the entire basin. In contrast, drastic large-area events such as a major wildfire or insect pandemic could increase outflow concentrations for a relatively brief period.

Plant ash remaining after severe fires can temporarily raise the base content and alkalinity of streams from affected areas. Accelerated decomposition of organic matter in and on the mineral surface after fire may increase nutrient outflow, though this has not been demonstrated. These several changes are probably trivial, however, in comparison with more serious and long-lasting effects on water temperature, turbidity, and flow characteristics, especially if reestablishment of cover is long delayed.

But fires are of many kinds, and forest landscapes vary enormously in susceptibility to post-fire erosion. Turbid streams, floods, and disastrous mudflows are well-known consequences of fire in the steep brushlands of southern California. (See Figure VII–5) There are many such landscapes with highly combustible vegetation where uncontrolled fire is a major hazard to watershed values, including water quality. Well-documented case histories, as well as small-scale experiments, thoroughly demonstrate the flood peaks, gulleying, sediment transport, and channel filling, as well as long-term impairment of water quality following severe wildfires on sensitive soils and slopes. Hence, research on fire be-

havior and control, fuel reduction by prescribed fire, and wildfire detection and suppression are essential to maintenance of water quality. This point is too often overlooked, and efforts at economic analyses or "total social costs" fail to weigh the probability — and overwhelming damage — of major wildfires against the costs and minor damages of roads or other measures that facilitate fire control.

Disastrous effects on water quality from wildfire are far from universal, however. In some places, wildfire may be followed by significant surface washing or mass movement but part or all of the sediment comes to rest and is stabilized before reaching the streams. Furthermore, there are large areas of stable soils and slopes that resist detachment and maintain adequate hydrologic capabilities even after severe fires.

Much remains to be learned about soil and water behavior following fire, and especially about mass movement on steep or unstable slopes, about the possibilities of adverse precipitation events in the interval before revegetation of newly burned surfaces, and about seeding or other measures to hasten such revegetation. The sheer magnitude and obviousness of the immediate post-fire consequences, the costs and complexities of long-term studies on large burns, and concern with newer threats to water quality tend to divert attention from quantitative studies of recovery processes.

Nevertheless, present knowledge allows arraying likelihood and possible extent of wildfire influences on a scale from none to very great, according to landscapes, fuel type, and fire characteristics. Such knowledge also allows use of prescribed fire, at times of low hazard, for a variety of purposes — preparation for regeneration, improvement of wildlife habitat, and, notably, reduction of accumulated fire fuels that would otherwise vastly increase wildfire hazards. In most of the southern

Figure VII–5 — EFFECTS OF FOREST FIRES

The upper photograph shows an orchard near Santa Barbara, California. The single open storm drain was normally adequate to handle storm runoff. In 1941, however, the region enclosed by the dotted line was burned out in a brush fire. The lower photograph shows the debris deposited by the runoff of a single light rain after the fire.

pine forests prescribed fire is actually a legacy from annual burning by Indian populations, and several studies fail to show any deleterious consequences of its repeated use. Known or probable exceptions, however, are some areas of new forests planted on severely eroded lands, and some steep and sensitive soils. Again, some studies of "slash burning" for reduction of logging debris in the Douglas fir region reveal that the soil cover is totally removed from only a small percentage of the burned area so that infiltration remains high and sedimentation negligible. But greater fire severity, or slopes on which mass movement occurs, increases the likelihood of soil movement into stream channels. Generally feasible alternatives to fire have not yet been found, but several interests — including smoke abatement, possible value of logging wastes, and fish manage-

ment, as well as water quality *per se* — have encouraged such research.

In some regions the predominance of alder and some other nitrogen-fixing shrub species can be increased by fires, disturbance, or silvicultural treatment. Stands of alders fix significant quantities of atmospheric nitrogen, and some fraction of this addition enters streams. The extent of such contributions and their eventual effect on stream concentrations are unknown, except by order-of-magnitude estimates. However, these indicate that fixation per unit area over a period of some years must often exceed the nitrogen additions considered in forest fertilization proposals. Hence, consequences of these natural additions are of very considerable interest.

Reduction of the forest cover by fire, wind, insects, and clearcutting causes an abrupt increase in surface temperatures and in mineralization of the organic matter. The resulting nutrient release may be followed by increased leaching of nitrates and associated cations into streams. These effects are highly dependent on climate and the quantity of surface organic matter, and on the rapidity with which a new cover of vegetation appears. The well-known studies at Hubbard Brook (New Hampshire), although artificial in some degree, served to focus attention on the maximum quantities of nutrients that may thus enter streams. Several other studies in regions of lesser organic accumulation and where natural revegetation is allowed, show only minor increases. A considerable number of experimental treatments and monitoring to study this effect further are now under way.

Virtually no attention has been given to other forest management treatments which probably act in the same direction although at lower intensity. These are drainage of forested wetlands, broadcast burning, and site preparation by destroying vegetation and disturbing the soil.

The exact magnitude will be highly variable, depending on soil and climate. The effects of all such treatments on nutrient release, like those of clearcutting, are temporary, self-limiting, and not subject to recurrence on the same area within the foreseeable future. Though these nutrient changes may be consequential for vegetation on the treated area, estimates suggest that any influence on water quality must be slight.

The Effects of Fertilizers and Other Nutrient Sources — In recent years there has been a sharp increase in the number of experiments and operational trials using artificial fertilizers to increase timber growth and wildlife food supplies, and to develop protective vegetation on disturbed or eroded soils. Large-scale applications of nitrogen on timberlands, notably in the Pacific Northwest, have provoked concern that the added fertilizer would enter streams and lakes, increasing eutrophication and perhaps reducing quality of urban water supplies.

Several lines of evidence, including lysimeter studies on fertilized areas as well as the "clean-up" of sewage and other waste waters applied to forest soils, demonstrate that forest ecosystems are highly efficient collectors and "sinks" for added nutrients. The capacity of such sinks appears great due to the large biomass low in nutrient content, wide carbon-nitrogen ratios of forest organic matter, and the high phosphorus-fixing capabilities of most mineral soils; but the details are poorly known. Again, the possibility of increased nutrient content in soil and vegetation resulting from fertilization has raised the possibility of greater release following timber harvest. Such questions point to the need for far more precise characterizations of the "compartments" and "fluxes" of ecosystem models before these can have any predictive value.

Present knowledge of the fate of nutrients entering the soil indicates that the more serious source of water contamination would be direct entry of the applied fertilizers into streams and lakes. This might occur either through the distribution into such waters during aerial application, or in consequence of surface washing at some periods of the year. The latter chiefly concerns the borders of streams and the associated system of "temporary" streams where overland flow mass occurs briefly at periods when the underlying soil is saturated. The extent of such channel expansion and its role in transport of dissolved or fine suspended matter has been generally overlooked.

Thus far, however, the forest land managers involved have been highly sensitive to water-quality considerations and have withheld application of nitrogen fertilizers in the vicinity of lakes or streams. In consequence, the tolerable upper limits of rate and distribution are as yet unknown. But several studies of fertilized watersheds and monitoring of streams from fertilized areas are already under way and will warrant continued attention.

Another important localized source of nutrient enrichment comes about through the high concentrations of recreational users at major campgrounds, ski developments, and the like. Treatment of the human waste generated at such areas may or may not render the effluent waters "microbiologically safe," but the nitrogen and often the phosphorus contents usually enter the streams. The resulting nutrient load is susceptible to reasonably accurate determination, but the effects on the biology of headwater streams and the magnitude of such enrichment in comparison with other sources mentioned above certainly require study. This problem is only marginally a concern of "forest management," but in the face of steadily increasing recreational demands the solutions are likely to be difficult or expensive. Among the options will be prohibition of such use, elaborate treatment plants or new technologies of waste disposal, or acceptance of altered water quality. In any case, both the projection of recreational expansion and hydrological data on the streams should be adequate for prediction of consequences when such recreational uses are being considered.

Bacteriological Quality — Increasing recreational use is also a major threat to bacteriological quality of water from forested areas. Small numbers of hikers and workers, like small stock and wildlife populations, can use a large area without making much impact. But in forest areas heavily used by campers, hikers, or workers human waste treatment is commonly inadequate, primitive, or nonexistent, posing possible hazards to downstream users of untreated waters from such areas. Routine treatment offsets any such threats in urban distribution systems but the problem of reconciling health, aesthetics, and recreational use remains.

Sediment, the Pre-eminent Factor — Concern with the varied aspects of water quality, though necessary, sometimes deflects attention from sediment load, which is the major, most costly, and almost ubiquitous cause of impaired quality. Fine suspended matter, mineral or organic, as "silt" or "turbidity," imposes high treatment costs for urban and some industrial uses. It also clogs irrigation ditches, destroys spawning grounds and bottom vegetation, and reduces recreational and scenic values. Coarse materials fill channels and divert streams in flood, and often destroy the usefulness of flooded lands.

Sediment movement into streams, together with flow rate and land-treatment effects, have been the main thrust of watershed research. As a result, the sources of fine and coarse sediments in forest watersheds are reasonably well known, as are the general relationships between sediment production on the one hand, and

Figure VII–6 — RELATION OF SEDIMENT PARTICLE-
SIZE TO FLOW RATE

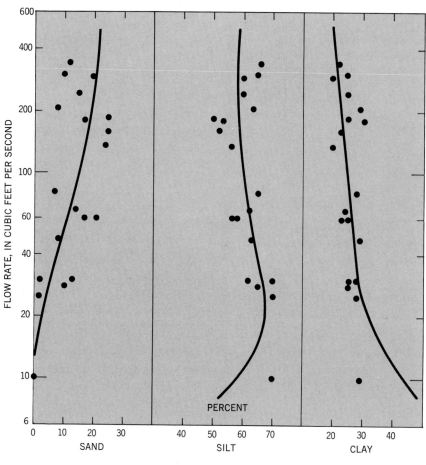

The graph shows lines of best fit for measurements of sediment particle-size distribution made from 1961 to 1964 in the Scott Run basin, Fairfax County, Virginia. There appears to be no change in particle-size distribution with time. The low-flow regimes show high concentrations of silt and clay. As the flow decreases and the speed slows, the silt particles—being heavier—drop to the stream bed, leaving the fine clay particles to become the greater portion of the load. As the flow increases, there is an increasing concentration of the larger, sandy particles.

hydrological behavior and disturbance of vegetation on the other. (See Figure VII–6)

On the majority of forest watersheds, the principal cause of erosion and stream turbidity outside of flood periods is exposure or disturbance of the mineral soil surface. This may come about through any of a number of causes — excessive grazing, trampling by livestock or humans in large numbers, roads and skid-trail construction, and, as mentioned, sometimes after severe fire.

Current overgrazing and the legacy from even more severe overgrazing

in the past poses severe problems in some low-rainfall forest areas of western United States. Reducing further damage by livestock, and occasionally by big game, is more of a political-economic problem than one of technical know-how. Repair of past damage, however, is handicapped by the large area and low values of affected lands, the slow pace of natural recovery, and limited funds for both research and application of known principles.

Increasing recreational uses — including human traffic on trails and campgrounds, development of roads,

ski runs, facilities, and now the large numbers of off-the-road vehicles — create an array of new problems for forest land management. Obviously, hazard to water quality is only one of these, though often significant. Less obviously, new kinds of use conflicts are being generated, and research in behavior and values is likely to be as important in addressing these as is that in economics and watershed management.

Contrary to popular belief, the mere cutting of trees, even completely and over large areas, seldom leads to any surface erosion, especially if regrowth occurs promptly. The critical factor determining whether logging operations will or will not influence stream turbidity is how the felling, skidding, and hauling are conducted. There is now a substantial body of research and experience in several forest regions demonstrating that the mechanical operations and necessary road construction can be carried on with minor or no impact on watershed values and stream turbidity.

Several essential principles of road design, construction, and maintenance, as well as for protection of stream channels, have emerged that minimize soil exposure and arrest sediment transport. These principles are readily translated into practice in many landscapes, though the operational details and controls are known for only a few. In some steep mountains or slide-prone areas, however, geological structure and topography impose unforeseen hazards and extremely high costs. Greater availability of soil and geotechnical information might reduce both, though the resources for providing information to large wildland areas are meager. In any case, cost factors as well as watershed considerations have dictated new attention to harvesting and transport systems, including the long-used aerial cable methods and feasibility tests with balloon and helicopter logging.

Hence, with the exception of fragile or very steep lands, our present levels of knowledge and technology are generally adequate to minimize these sources of disturbance or reduce their consequences. This is true even though many elements — including lack of exact prescriptions, increased costs, momentum of existing systems, and unawareness of long-run damages — may cause actual practice to lag well behind the prospects demonstrated by research.

Needed Scientific Activity

As the foregoing indicates, a substantial body of knowledge and application has been accumulated through "watershed" or "watershed management" research on forest areas. Extension of research results and at least qualitative predictions to similar landscapes can be made with some confidence. Greater certainty, exactness, and extent of predictions are possible simply through increased funding of existing research installations. Predictive models and simulation relating streamflow to physical variables and precipitation are being explored by hydrologists. Success would bring extension to forest watersheds for which numerous data are available, and might call for new modes of examining factors controlling surface soil loss, bank erosion, or other sources of turbidity.

Nevertheless, even within current concepts, there are enormous gaps in our knowledge of watersheds. Many large areas are poorly known in terms of exact climatic data, soil units, and the hydrologic behavior or response of watersheds to treatment. In some instances, the simple conceptual models derived from study of soil in the laboratory or agricultural field bear little resemblance to the behavior of wildland soils, especially those on very steep slopes. Much greater efforts at watershed characterization and in study of the actual functioning of small soil-

geomorphic "systems" under field conditions are badly needed. Such work is not entirely lacking (see Figure VII–7), but the investigators so employed are few and the number of mixed-discipline investigative teams far fewer, especially in the light of the large areas involved.

Three examples illustrate such needs:

1. Only within the last decade has it been recognized that fire on the steep California brushlands not only destroys the protective cover of vegetation and litter but also imparts a non-wettable quality to the soil itself, apparently through condensation of heat-volatilized substances from the litter. The result is reduced entry of rainfall, increased surface flow, and erosion. This complexity has

required new research approaches, and calls for revision of existing notions of infiltration in both burned and protected soils.

2. Hewlett's variable source area concept of water outflow, alluded to earlier, is still novel and its consequences for water quality are only now being explored. In certain landscapes it seems to provide a mechanism for direct overland transport of surface materials to streams without passing through the soil filter, a possibility usually overlooked.

3. Again, assessments of landscape stability, normal sediment loads, and tolerance of man-made disturbance are commonly based on short time periods and assumptions of

Figure VII–7 — EFFECT OF LAND USE ON SEDIMENT YIELD AND CHANNEL STABILITY

Land use	Sediment yield	Channel stability
A. Natural forest or grassland.	Low	Relatively stable with some bank erosion.
B. Heavily grazed areas.	Low to moderate	Somewhat less stable than A.
C. Cropping	Moderate to heavy	Some aggradation and increased bank erosion.
D. Retirement of land from cropping.	Low to moderate	Increasing stability.
E. Urban construction.	Very heavy	Rapid aggradation and some bank erosion.
F. Stabilization	Moderate	Degradation and severe bank erosion.
G. Stable urban	Low to moderate	Relatively stable.

The table shows various land uses and their effect on the relative sediment yield from the surrounding landscape as well as on the stability of stream channels. The most severe sediment problems occur during urban construction, when covering vegetation is removed and the flow regime in channels is changed by realignments, increases or decreases in the flow, or obstructions placed in or alongside the natural flowway.

gradualness. But the geologic processes that shape the steep lands are often violent and erratic. Landslides, avalanches, massive floods, and abrupt changes in stream cutting and deposit are normal incidents in the down-wearing of steep mountain slopes. Since hazard is often unsuspected and frequency is on a larger scale than laymen reckon with, such events often appear as "ac-

cidents" or are attributed to the wrong causes.

It is clear that man's activities in some susceptible landscapes decades and centuries ago have increased the frequency or severity of such events and triggered self-accelerating erosion of unstable slopes. Now, landslides and slips associated with road construction are a continuing problem as roads are extended into steep remote areas. Hence, there is need

for much better understanding of soil and geomorphic processes on vulnerable steep lands with a view to characterizing hazards and devising measures of avoidance or control. Such research concerns not only forest management operations but equally highway construction, ski-slope developments, powerline clearance, mining, and all other activities that change stream courses, slope loading, or the stabilizing effects of vegetation.

Factors Relating Forest Management to Water Quality

Water derived from forested watersheds is generally the highest-quality water found under natural conditions although, contrary to popular opinion, water from pristine forest streams is frequently unsafe for human consumption. Under natural conditions, water quality is a function of:

Geology and Geochemistry — Parent materials and the products of their weathering influence mineral content.

Topography — Elevation, exposure, and steepness influence the form of precipitation, time and mode of delivery, evaporation rates, water temperature, infiltration opportunity.

Climate — Climate influences or determines the amount and form of precipitation input and the time and mode of delivery of water; indirectly, it influences sediment and organic content, rate of weathering, soil development, and vegetative cover.

Soils — Type and depth of soil mantle are significant factors in water quality determination, especially in surface water. They influence the rate and amount of infiltration and percolation and, consequently, quality and amount of groundwater recharge, the rate and amount of erosion, and, thus, the sediment and chemical content of surface water. Soil influences

biological activity and nutrient cycling processes and is a determining factor in type and density of vegetative cover.

Biota — Includes animal and plant forms. Animals, from soil bacteria and microorganisms to large wildlife forms, play a significant role in determining water quality. Similarly, vegetative forms from lowly mosses through forests exert an influence on water quality. These combined influences include bacteria, nutrients, organic matter, and sediment or turbidity content, hydrogen ion activity, suspended solids, and water temperature.

Natural Disturbances — Natural catastrophes including forest fires, insect and disease depradation, earthquakes, volcanic eruptions, landslides, avalanches, hurricanes, and tornadoes all influence water quality, often in a major way.

The Role of Forests

Forest vegetation influences and in turn is influenced by climate, soil development, geologic weathering, other biota, and natural disturbances. Examples of some forest influences which directly or indirectly affect water quality include:

1. An ameliorating influence on local climate leading to lower

water temperatures and lower evaporation rates and also, usually, to greater transpiration rates and higher production of atmospheric oxygen.

2. A favorable influence in reducing flooding levels, erosion, and consequent sedimentation production and turbidity in streams.

3. A favorable influence in the area of nutrient cycling; more nutrients are held in and on forest land.

4. High production of organic matter may produce short-term discoloration, and sometimes odors, in surface water. At the same time, this organic material has a very favorable influence on biotic activity in and on soil.

5. Forest vegetation, particularly deep-rooted types, tend to provide optimum natural protection against avalanching and landslides.

6. Forests generally consume more water than other vegetation; thus, less total water may be available downstream for dilution.

7. Forests tend to buffer highs and lows of streamflow volume and the quality of this water.

Impacts of Forest Management on Water Quality

Other than changes brought about by the (usually rare, except for forest fires) catastrophic natural disturbances over which we have little or no control, the major changes wrought in water quality from forested watersheds are those resulting from man's activities. Major disturbances and and activities due to forest management and man's activities include: fire, forest clearing or removal, timber harvest, road and right-of-way construction, cultural operations, insect and disease control, solid waste disposal, and recreational activities and developments.

Forest Fires — Whether natural, deliberate, accidental, or incendiary, forest fires are generally conceded to have a deleterious effect on water quality. The degree of influence depends on the type and intensity of the fire, the time of year, and topographic and soil conditions. Ground fires occurring on stable soils may produce only minimal deterioration in water quality, while intense fires on sensitive soils and on steep slopes may occasion serious damage. Effects on water quality may be due to increased water temperatures, increased ash, mineral, and organic content, as well as higher sediment and turbidity loads due to increased runoff and erosion. The effects may be restricted to a single season or year or they may last up to several decades.

Fire used as a management tool — e.g., to effect deliberate ecological change, to control insects and disease, or for slash disposal — is ordinarily planned in areas and at seasons when damage to water quality would be minimal.

Forest Clearing — Removal of forest for agricultural land use, for urban or industrial development, or for vegetative-type conversion (e.g., forest to grass) may completely alter the water-quality regime. Changes will be greatest during the period of maximum disturbance. Following recovery, the water-quality regime will take on the characteristics of the new land-use pattern. In some cases — e.g., the conversion of pinyon juniper or chapparal forest types to grass — there may be an improvement in water quality from the sediment-turbidity standpoint.

Timber Harvest — The effects of timber harvesting on water quality will depend on the intensity and type of harvest operation and on the manner of product removal. Light selection cuts will normally have minimal or no effect, while clear cuts that open up large areas will tend to increase water temperatures and increase the potential for subsequent erosion and sedimentation. Contrary to popular belief, the removal of the forest crop itself ordinarily does not occasion serious damage except on very steep slopes or on unusually sensitive soils. The major damage is usually due to harvesting and removal methods — i.e., skid trails, log landings, heavy-equipment disturbance, and, especially, road construction and inadequate maintenance. On occasion, yarding areas or equipment servicing areas may provide a source of contamination as a result of oil, gasoline, or chemical spills.

Road Construction — Road and right-of-way construction in forests is a major problem insofar as water quality is concerned. During and following clearing and construction, substantial areas of raw roadbed and cut-and-fill slopes are exposed to erosion; frequently, large amounts of erosional materials are washed into stream channels. Damage can be substantially reduced through road location, carefully supervised construction methods, immediate rehabilitation of exposed areas, and good maintenance practices. The same holds true for the construction of rights-of-way for power lines, pipelines, and waterways (surface or underground).

Cultural Operations — In addition to the harvesting process, intensive forest management may involve one or more cultural operations such as forest thinnings and cleanings. When such operations are done mechanically, little or no impairment of water quality should result. However, when chemicals such as sodium arsenate or 2,4,5-T are applied, caution must be exercised to keep such materials away from streams.

Insect and Disease Control — To protect commercial and noncommercial forests, wilderness, and recreation areas as well as forest parks from periodic disease and insect epidemics, control operations are essential. The most effective and most economic control methods have involved chemicals such as DDT. The environmental dangers inherent in chemical control methods, including water-quality deterioration, have become increasingly apparent and controls have recently been imposed. In some cases, controlled light ground fires in forest areas have been applied to destroy vectors. Such operations have little influence on water quality if applied carefully under controlled conditions. Ecologic controls also have little or no impact upon water quality.

Solid Waste Disposal — In harvesting timber crops as well as in the primary conversion (sawmilling), relatively large volumes of solid waste in the form of slash, slabs, and sawdust need disposal. To accelerate new forest development, to destroy breeding areas and food for forest insects and disease pests, and to enhance the forest environment it has been a common practice to burn the forest slash. While such practices have only minimal effect on water quality, they are being halted in many forest areas due to air-pollution considerations. Similarly, at primary conversion plants there are major problems in the disposal of sawdust, slabs, and edgings. Again, fire has been used as a primary method of disposal but is now being drastically reduced due to air pollution. Some of this waste material is being used to produce secondary products such as compressed-sawdust fireplace logs.

Recreation Activity and Development — Outdoor recreation activity and developments in forest areas are increasing many-fold each year and are contributing to water-quality problems. Some of the forest wilderness areas are now badly overused, and lack of sanitation facilities and overuse by horse pack trains as well as human trampling are locally lowering water quality. A major problem in many forest areas results from increasing use by four-wheel-drive vehicles and trail motorcycles which increase erosion and add to sediment problems in streams. Recreation developments in the forest ranging from camp and picnic grounds and summer homes to large ski areas are frequently poorly designed or poorly maintained from the standpoint of sanitation; they, too, are contributing to water-quality degradation.

Other Forest Uses — Special uses of forest land — such as grazing by domestic livestock, mining operations, and summer colonies or communes of people living on forest areas — may contribute special problems in water quality. In general, grazing by domestic livestock is decreasing on forest lands; consequently, from this standpoint an improvement in water quality can be expected. In mining operations involving large-scale land, subsurface disturbance, and road construction,

water-quality problems increase, sometimes markedly, both from the standpoint of erosion and attendant sediment production and in mineral content of both surface and ground water.

Steps Needed to Improve Water Quality

While the quality of water derived from forest lands is in general superior to that from other types of landscapes or land uses, there is degradation in many areas. Action is needed to protect water quality where it is good and to improve that which is being downgraded.

Water-Quality Standards — By federal legislation each state has had to set water-quality standards. Unfortunately, in many areas the standards set for some streams are higher than natural, or "pristine," water. For various reasons, many states lack background data on natural water quality. If realistic standards are to be set and observed, some additional monitoring of forested water-source areas is needed.

Application of Available Knowledge — In many instances, degradation of water quality is due to lack of application of principles already known to us. More rigid requirements can be written into timber sale and road construction and maintenance contracts and then enforced.

Where sanitation facilities are inadequate around recreation sites or summer homes, forced improvement or closure can improve water quality. Closure or zoning of forest areas to specialized uses such as four-wheel-drive vehicles can be helpful. Reduced use of sensitive wilderness areas or elimination of horse traffic in such areas is likewise an available tool.

New Research — In many instances, remedial measures will be conditioned by the availability of new research information. Examples include: What is the human carrying capacity in parks and forest recreation areas with respect to water quality? What type of chemicals, and in what concentrations, can be used to control insects, diseases, and weed species without impairment of water quality? What type and pattern of forest harvesting can be safely applied? At what seasons of the year should we restrict forest use to protect water quality? What type of mineral extraction activity is permissible and what kinds of safeguards are necessary? How can forest areas be used safely and beneficially in solid waste disposal — wastes from the forest itself (slash) and from industries and municipalities? What is the impact of watershed management activity to increase water yields on the water-quality regime? What are the relationships between wildlife use and domestic grazing and water quality?

3. AGRICULTURE

Global Food Production Potentials

By the development and application of technology in food production the world can be well fed generally, even with its prospective doubling of population by the year 2000. The physical, chemical, biological, and engineering sciences must be used to develop production systems that will effectively utilize arable land, water, solar energy, energy from fossil fuel or other source required for mechanization of agriculture, improved seeds, livestock, fertilizers, pesticide chemicals and other pest-protection means, genetics, ecology, disease and parasite control in man and animals, social science relevant to industrialization of agriculture and urbanization of the world generally, and the building and use of scientific and technological capability in every country to meet its needs.

A great deal of science basic to agriculture has happened because men wanted to find out why — why tillage was useful — why fallow was useful — why ashes stimulated new plant growth. Man learned by experience; he knew even in ancient times that good seed, in good soil, well watered under a friendly sun produced a good harvest. The major plant nutrients required have been known for more than a hundred years. Commercial manufacture of superphosphates began about 1850, although nitrogen did not become available in Germany until World War I and in the United States until 1925. Mined potash and sulfur supplement natural reserves.

Current Scientific Understanding

The theoretical scientific basis of plant nutrition is an essential and major portion of the science basic to agriculture and world food production. Soils of the world vary widely in their reserves of major and minor plant nutrients. Some of them contain toxic amounts of such minerals as molybdenum or selenium. Others are very deficient. Amendment depends not alone on mineral analysis but also on the physical nature of the soil and its ion exchange capacity. The ability of the soil to produce crops must be assessed locally, often repetitively.

It has been estimated that there are potentially arable lands in the world equal in area to those now under cultivation — i.e., around 1.5 billion hectares. (See Figure VII–8) One of the recommendations of the President's Science Advisory Committee on *The World Food Problem* was: "The agricultural potential of vast areas of uncultivated lands, particularly in the tropical areas of Latin America and Africa, should be thoroughly evaluated."

Water is a major factor in all food production. The science of hydrology, the technology of water management are basic to agriculture. Irrigation — with its concomitant problems of waterlogging or drainage, salinity

Figure VII–8 — POTENTIALLY ARABLE LAND
IN RELATION TO WORLD POPULATION

| Continent | Population in 1965 (millions of persons) | Area in billions of acres | | | Acres of cultivated land per person | Ratio of cultivated to potentially arable land (percent) |
		Total	Potentially arable	Cultivated		
Africa	310	7.46	1.81	0.39	1.3	22
Asia	1,855	6.76	1.55	1.28	.7	83
Australia and New Zealand	14	2.03	.38	.04	2.9	2
Europe	445	1.18	.43	.38	.9	88
North America	255	5.21	1.15	.59	2.3	51
South America	197	4.33	1.68	.19	1.0	11
U.S.S.R.	234	5.52	.88	.56	2.4	64
Total	3,310	32.49	7.88	3.43	1.0	44

The table shows the total area of the continents of the world, the part that is potentially arable, and that which is presently being cultivated. The cultivated areas include land under crops, temporary fallow, temporary meadows, lands for mowing or pasture, market and kitchen gardens, fruit trees, vines, shrubs, and rubber plantations. The land actually harvested in any given year is about one-half to two-thirds of the total cultivated land. Of the potentially arable land, about 11 percent of the total requires irrigation for even one crop. It is important to note that Africa, Australia and New Zealand, and South America cultivate significantly less than half of their potentially arable land. The continents where most of the land is being used are those where the population density is greatest.

or leaching — poses added problems for hydrologists and engineers. But these areas of science and technology are useless unless they are used in adequate systems of agronomy, involving knowledge of soil chemistry, soil physics, plant physiology, plant genetics, and soil-plant-water relationships in every microclimate where crop plants are grown.

Science basic to optimal use of solar energy and science basic to effective use of fossil fuel or other energy source in crop production, transportation, and storage and processing of food crops is essential. In many countries, fossil fuel must be imported while human labor is in oversupply. Since a man is equivalent only to about one-eighth horsepower, it is difficult, if not impossible, to use enough human labor at the precise time when planting, harvesting, or cultivation is required.

Crop-Plant Genetics and Breeding — Genetic capacity of crop plants and livestock species for the produc-

tion of food useful and acceptable to man is a first requirement. Comes then the question of whether native plants and animals developed in and adapted to the many niches of a local ecosystem are better suited to serve man's needs there than those introduced from other places?

The answer is that, for subsistence agriculture, the native varieties have many advantages. Natural selection over many generations has enabled them to survive the pests and competing organisms of their area of origin. But often this adaptation enables them to survive with only a meager excess for man's use.

When man brings a new seed from a far place, it often fails in the new location; but not always. If it happens to be adapted to the new location it may thrive there in the absences of the diseases and pests it has left behind. Thus, sunflowers thrive in Hungary and the Ukraine while they are little exploited in their native Kansas, where they are weeds

beset with many enemies. So, too, soybeans thrive in Illinois — far from their native China. Figure VII-9 shows two other transplanted species.

Selection, sometimes rather simple phenotypic selection, has developed crop plant variants used in various parts of the world that are often preferred for organoleptic quality though inferior in productivity. "Baking quality" in bread wheat is not useful in macaroni wheats, for example. Phenotypic selection continues to be an important crop-breeding tool.

Science basic to plant breeding has contributed (a) controlled methods of hybridization that have added yield to some crop plants, especially maize; (b) dwarfism, which has made possible dramatic yield increases through response to heavy fertilizer and water applications without lodging, especially in rice, wheat, and sorghum; (c) genetic disease resistance, especially resistance in wheat to rust; and (d) selective breeding for photoperiod

Figure VII-9 — TRANSPLANTED SPECIES

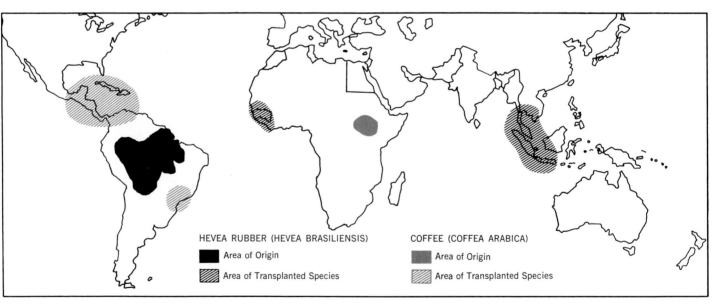

The map shows the area of origin of coffee *(Coffea arabica)* and hevea rubber *(Hevea brasiliensis)* and the areas where, having been transplanted, they are now principally cultivated. In its place of origin, coffee is subject to native red rust *(Hemilaea vastatrix)*, whereas in the New World, no native diseases exist. Hevea rubber is found in the New World only in the wild. In the Old World, where major production takes place today, there are no native pests.

response suited to latitude, especially important in such crops as soybeans, maize, and wheat.

Each country must have capability for continued breeding improvement of the crop plants it produces. Plant pathogens, for example, often develop new strains virulent to plants genetically resistant to old pathogens within a new crop plant generation.

Animal Science — Aside from the relatively few true vegetarians in the world, who abstain from milk and eggs as well as from flesh, animal protein foods are status foods. Elasticity of demand for animal protein foods in the developing countries, in terms of consumer income, is very high. As income permits, these people will demand and obtain larger amounts of animal protein foods.

While this demand may divert some cereals from human to animal food, most animal protein foods in the developing countries are and will continue to be produced from forage and milling offals and other products, including garbage, rejected as human food. There is, therefore, a very real need for the development of research and technological capability based on the animal sciences in all countries of the world.

Among the principal problems requiring attention is research and technology for the control and eradication of animal diseases, parasites, and the arthropod and other vectors of some of the major diseases of animals and man. An abbreviated list of the principal diseases would include foot-and-mouth disease, rinderpest, bovine pleuro-pneumonia, East Coast fever, African horse sickness, encephalitides, African swine fever, malaria, trypanosomiasis, and schistosomiasis. Schistosomiasis is a major restraint on the full realization of the benefits of irrigation in tropical countries. The snail intermediate host of this parasite thrives in irrigation ditches. Two hundred million people are afflicted.

Research is developing, or has developed, control methods for all the diseases listed. Immunization, isolation, and vector control are all important for one or more of them.

Large game herbivores seem to be genetically resistant to, or tolerant of, some of these diseases. Research on propagation and management of such species may give new sources of animal food.

Fisheries as Food Sources — There is a very wide area of fisheries biology, culture, and engineering essential to the scientific basis for world food production. Quantitatively, fisheries constitute and have potential for only a minor portion of the world's food needs. However, in many nations they represent a qualitatively excellent and preferred source of protein and concomitant minor nutrients essential to human health and well-being. Methods of harvest, preservation, and processing of marine and estuarine fish and shellfish and methods of culture and propagation of estuarine, coastal, and anadromous species can protect and increase these sources of high-quality human food.

In many countries, including our own, pond culture of carp, trout, catfish, crayfish, frogs, and other edible fresh-water species have a substantial potential for increasing supplies of preferred, high-quality protein foods.

Beneficial eutrophication — utilizing animal wastes as nutrients in controlled aquatic ecosystems — offers substantial potential for increasing food production, recycling wastes, and enhancing the quality of the environment. Knowledge of fish and shellfish nutritive requirements, their reproductive requirements, their diseases and parasites, toxins and contaminants, both chemical and biological are areas needing research and technological, institutional, and personnel capability in many countries.

Arctic and antarctic food production might be increased by national and international management of the harvest of food species and regulation of numbers of competing non-food species.

Food Protection — Achievement of the important objective that our food supply shall be safe and wholesome requires a basis in many sciences and a highly varied set of technological capabilities that must be available in every country.

Among the principal problems are: material toxicants (alkaloid and others); mycotoxins, resulting from certain strains of mold, potent in parts per billion, carcinogenic in test animals; botulinus toxin — food-poisoning organisms such as Salmonella; insect infestations; and spoilage organisms.

Protection by controlled environments, chemicals, cold, and sterilization requires intimate knowledge of the physical and chemical nature of food products and the effect of methods of protection on nutritive and functional value and on safety and wholesomeness.

In India, the National Council of Economic Advisers has estimated that insects take 15 percent of the standing crop and another 10 percent after it is harvested and stored. Losses from rats are also severe both in fields and storage bins. Use of plant-protection chemicals increased from six million acres in 1955 to a current 200 million acres.

New Directions for Science

The world is principally dependent for its food supply on a very small number of crop and livestock species. Wheat, rice, rye, barley, oats, sorghum, maize and millet, sugarcane, sugar beets; potatoes, taco, cassava, sweet potatoes; soybeans, cowpeas, beans, and peas; vitamins, in variety, a little protein of fair quality from cole crops and other green and yellow vegetables, from fruits and nuts, cattle, buffalo, sheep, goats, pigs; chickens, turkeys, ducks, and geese.

Research is heavily concentrated on crops of commercial importance. Research on such crops and their commercial production does not help the subsistence farmer who must trade his small surplus for the necessities of life — salt, needles, cloth — that he is unable to produce. We need social science to guide us to the assimilation of the subsistence farmer into commercial agriculture or to urban industry. Until recently, applied research in most developing countries was poorly financed and completely lacking in relevance to the problems of local farmers. Even where research was directed at producing practical results, it was generally concentrated on cash crops for export rather than on basic food staples.

It is not enough to produce high yields of nutritious grain. In India, prices for fine-grain rice from old,

low-yielding native varieties are virtually unrestricted while prices of the coarser high-yielding varieties are controlled. Total production is reduced by diversion of acres from high-yielding to low-yielding varieties. The affluent pay for what they want; the poorer consumers become dependent on rationed supplies of low-quality grain.

The Institutions — Industrialized nations of the world have — in institutions widely varying in structure — produced, taught, and applied the scientific information that is the basis of agricultural technology. In the United States, federal-state cooperation among the U.S. Department of Agriculture (USDA) and state agricultural experiment stations in each of the states provides a useful means of coordinating research, teaching, and service. Agricultural research has had the objective of producing results useful in improving the productive capacity of the land, the efficiency of crop, livestock, and forest production, the use of agricultural products, and the welfare of rural people.

This system, while close-knit, is not closed. Inputs from all the science of the world and important contributions to it are commonplace. Shull at Princeton, East at Harvard, and Jones at the Connecticut Agricultural Experiment Station at New Haven all contributed to the scientific basis on which hybrid corn was developed. But so, too, did a hundred others in USDA and the state agricultural experiment stations who painstakingly identified and modified the genetic stocks and the ways in which they could be used effectively in producing commercial seed for every latitude in which corn is grown.

Developing nations must have their own institutions for agricultural teaching, research, and service. They emulate the model on which our Land Grant College system was conceived. They may find other organizations better suited to their needs. In any case, they must have institutions of their own to produce, teach, and apply the science and resultant technology basic to efficient agriculture in a coordinated manner.

The Hazard of Drought

In most of the world, where men till the soil or graze animals, drought is a recurrent phenomenon. Given the preponderance of agriculture as a source of livelihood in the world, drought emerges as the major natural hazard of geophysical origin for man in terms of areal extent and numbers of population affected, if not in the intensity of harmful effects. Because it is a recurrent phenomenon, human adaptation or adjustment becomes possible. Indeed, most agricultural systems involve some adaptation.

This statement takes as its starting point a human ecological context for the discussion of drought adaptation, illustrates the process of adjustment with two examples from widely differing societies, and concludes with

suggestions for the development of certain lines of scientific endeavor that promise to broaden the range of drought adjustment available to agriculturists.

What is Drought?

In this ecological context, drought is defined as a shortage of water harmful to man's agricultural activities. It occurs as an interaction between an agricultural system and natural events which reduce the water available for plants and animals. The burden of drought is twofold, comprising the actual losses of plant and animal production and the efforts expended to anticipate drought, and

to prevent, reduce, or mitigate its effects.

Several important concepts follow from this definition of drought. First, for the purpose of this statement, only agricultural drought is being examined; plant-water relationships that affect, for example, watershed yield are not considered. Second, drought is a joint product of man and nature and is not to be equated with natural variation in moisture availability. Natural variation is intrinsic to natural process and only has meaning for man in the context of human interaction. Third, the measurement of successful adaptation is in the long-term reduction of the social burden of drought, not simply in the increase in agricultural yield. The scientific effort required to improve human adaptation to drought must meet the same standards of efficacy, technical feasibility, favorable cost, and social acceptance that should govern any adaptive behavior.

Farmer Adaptation to Drought

In at least three parts of the world, the problem of human adaptation to drought is under continuing, intensive study. Saarinen has studied farmers' perceptions of the drought hazard on the semi-arid Great Plains of the United States; Heathcote has studied pastoral and agricultural farming in Australia; and Kates and Berry have carried out pilot studies of farmer perception among smallholders in Tanzania. By way of illustration, the work of Saarinen and Kates can be compared directly, using farmer interviews from comparatively dry areas of the respective countries. The focus in Figure VII–10 is on actions, on alternative adjustment strategies to reduce drought losses.

The two studies were carried out quite independently; therefore, it is of considerable interest that the data from differently phrased questions are comparable. The available, perceived strategies for mechanized U.S. grain farmers are not intrinsically different from those of hoe-cultivator Tanzanians. The mix of perceived adjustments differs, however — more actions in total being proffered by the U.S. farmers, more of these related to farm practices, and more of these requiring high-level technological inputs. Tanzanian farmers seem more inclined to pursue adjustments not directly related to agricultural practices, and thus are more prepared to change their livelihood pattern than to alter their specific cropping behavior. Thus, the major contrast that emerges is between a flexible life pattern with an unchanging agricultural practice as opposed to a more rigid life pattern with an adaptive agricultural practice. These behavioral patterns are suggestive of either alternative perceptions of nature itself or of opportunity for mobility. The Tanzanian farmer seems willing to move with an uncertain nature; his American counterpart appears ready to battle it out from a fixed site.

Broadening the Range of Available Adaptive Behavior

A farmer or rancher faces the recurrent, often perennial choice of plant or grazing location, of the timing of plant and cultivation, of the appropriate crops or stock, and of methods of cultivation and grazing. In seeking to broaden the agriculturist's range of choice of drought adjustment, the scientist offers his usual and somewhat paradoxical knowledge: We know more about plant-water relationships than seems evident from the application of our knowledge; but we know less about these relationships than we need to know in order to apply the knowledge widely.

Data Base — We could *now* provide for many parts of the world much improved information on which

Figure VII–10 — COMPARATIVE PERCEPTIONS OF
FEASIBLE ADJUSTMENTS TO DROUGHT

TANZANIA FARMERS

If the rains fail, what can a man do?

ADJUSTMENTS	No. of Replies	Percent of Total
Do nothing, wait.	17	12.14
Rainmaking, prayer.	15	10.71
Move to seek land, work, food.	51	36.43
Use stored food, saved money, sell cattle.	16	11.43
Change crops.	9	6.43
Irrigation.	15	10.71
Change plot location.	4	2.86
Change time of planting.	—	0.00
Change cultivation methods.	1	0.71
Others.	12	8.57
		99.99

Adjustments per farmer = 1.07

U.S. FARMERS

If a meeting were held and you were asked to give suggestions for reducing drought losses, what would you say?

ADJUSTMENTS	No. of Replies	Percent of Total
No suggestions	16	8.25
Rainmaking, prayer.	2	1.03
Quit farming.	1	0.52
Insurance, reserves, reduce expenditures, cattle.	16	8.25
Adapted crops.	2	1.03
Irrigation.	46	23.71
Change land characteristics by dams, ponds, trees, terraces.	26	13.40
Optimum seeding date.	—	0.00
Cultivation: stubble mulch, summer fallow, minimum tillage, cover crops.	78	40.21
Others.	7	3.61
		100.01

Adjustments per farmer = 2.02

The table shows the replies received from farmers in Tanzania and the United States when questioned about what they were willing to do in case of drought. Some 131 farmers in Tanzania and 96 in the U.S. were queried. In Tanzania, farmers mentioned an average of only one possible adjustment whereas U.S. farmers could think of an average of more than two to overcome the drought problem.

to base these decisions. To do so we would need to bring together the scattered record of climate, the fragmentary knowledge of soil, the dispersed experience with varieties and breeds, and the complex measurements of the impact of cultivation or grazing practice on available soil moisture. Within a framework of water-balance accounting, simulated traces of climatic data can provide probabilities of moisture availability directly related to specific varietal needs or stocking patterns. If these probabilities are used as appropriate weights in programming models, crop yields may be balanced against drought risk, desirable planting times determined, or the role of labor- or capital-intensive moisture-conserving practices assessed.

A special role for the use of such data is for the planned agricultural settlement. Wherever men are induced to move to new, often strange environments, greater drought risks are often incurred as a function of their ignorance. The dust bowls of the American West, the Virgin Lands of the Soviet Union, and the Groundnuts Scheme of colonial Tanganyika provide tragic evidence of the universal cost of learning about new environments even with, or perhaps because of, the application of considerable technology. Thus, much might be done for both the indigenous and pioneer agriculturalist through the assemblage of the available data base, through the identification of missing information by systems analysis, through the filling of critical gaps by experiment and field research, and through the distillation of the final product in such form as to provide meaningful answers to the perennial questions of farmers, ranchers, and planners be they peasant or agro-industrial producers.

Water-Saving Cultivation — A number of the critical gaps in our knowledge have already been identified. For example, data on water-yield relationships in less than optimal conditions are difficult to obtain.

We know for most plants how much water they need to survive and how much water they can use if water is readily available, but we know little about the trade-off between these two points. The breeding of new varieties has, to date, seemed to require more rather than less water for the high-yielding varieties; there seems little widespread exploration in breeding of the balance between yield and water need.

Though some water-saving cultivation methods are widely practiced, the actual effects of some measures are disputed, partly because these effects seem to vary greatly with soil, slope, rainfall, and cultivation practice. For example, tie-ridging, a water-conserving practice in semi-arid tropical areas has a very mixed effect depending on the crop, soil, slope, and pattern of rainfall encountered. The proper timing of planting or grazing requires much more analysis. The probability of below-average rainfalls that might lead to drought is calculated in certain standard ways, usually involving the assumptions that rainfall events are independent and that the relative frequency or some mathematical isomorphism of historic events provides useful probabilities of future expectation. But neither of these approaches adequately forecasts the persistence of below-normal rainfall characteristic of drought conditions in temperate areas or the monsoonal delays associated with drought in tropical areas. Forecasts of persistence require knowledge of the climatic mechanisms associated with the phenomenon and forecasts of monsoonal delay require understanding of the associated weather systems.

Irrigation — For a considerable part of the world, irrigation represents a crucial drought adaptation. But irrigation efficiency is notoriously low; the amount of water wasted prior to field application from conveyance, seepage, phreatophytes, or in misapplication is very high. For all of these sources of water loss, the po-

tential contribution from applied research is great.

Nevertheless, in many parts of the world, water availability is far in advance of water utilization because farmers are slow to adopt the new system. It is with irrigation, as with the adoption of new hybrids or in the choice of any new adjustment, that the social sciences have a special role in bridging the technical isolation that characterizes much research and development and in placing such efforts into the ecological matrix of farmers' life styles, agricultural systems, and socio-institutional settings. For many farmers, acceptance of irrigation literally means the acceptance of a new way of life. Thus, the question is still wide open as to which farmers make the best settlers for the great new irrigation projects now on the drawing boards of many developing countries. Or consider the achievements of the Green Revolution. We are told that the rapid adoption of high-yielding rice and wheat, particularly in South Asia, will give needed breathing space in the critical Malthusian struggle for survival. But we are warned that such adoption comes at a cost of further stratifying rural society and intensifying existing trends that create classes of prosperous landowners and landless rural workers. An even more complex social interaction is found among farmers on the shores of Lake Victoria who seem to be shifting from drought-resistant millet to bird-resistant maize because their children, who formerly stayed in the fields at harvest time to protect the crops from bird pests, are now in school!

All of the foregoing, the propensity to adopt innovations, rural class stratification, even bird pests, are factors capable of analysis, if not solution, within a framework of human ecological systems analysis. But just as plant breeders have had to develop strategies of genetic change and varietal development capable of providing new strains quickly, so must social scientists begin to develop analytic frameworks capable of accepting varied data and providing better, if not the best, answers.

Priorities for Scientific Effort

Priorities for scientific effort designed to broaden the range of choice available to those who are subject to recurrent drought can be listed as follows:

1. The assemblage and analysis of existing data in a systems context and its preparation for use in such form as to help answer the agriculturists' perennial questions: where, what, how, and when to plant or graze?

2. A review of the relationship between the development of high-yielding varieties and their moisture requirements, with a view to developing cereal grains combining drought-resistance and higher-yielding qualities.

3. A search for simplified forms of systems analysis or critical-path analysis capable of identifying crucial obstacles, needs, niches, and interactions in agricultural systems related to broadening the range of drought adjustment.

4. Improvement in the efficiency of irrigation water use.

5. Review and analysis of existing dry-land cultivation methods with a view to improvement and wider dissemination of moisture-conserving techniques.

6. Research on climatic and weather systems is designed to provide better forecasts of persistence in temperate areas and monsoonal delay in tropical areas.

The thrust of these suggestions is in application, to make more use of what is already known through synthesis and systems analysis or simply scientific review, to seek a marked advance through social science technique in the adoption of what we already know, and to seek selected new knowledge where the gaps in existing knowledge are great or the opportunities seem particularly rewarding.

PART VIII

AQUATIC ECOSYSTEMS

1. COMPONENT RELATIONSHIPS

Trophic Dynamics, with Special Reference to the Great Lakes

Trophic dynamics is that kind of ecology which concerns itself with energy flow through the component organisms of an ecosystem. The ultimate source of energy for any living system is, of course, the sun. Green plants, converting the sun's radiant energy into chemical energy, are said by ecologists to constitute the first trophic level within an ecosystem. All photosynthetic plants, regardless of systematic affinity, are thus grouped together by ecologists because they all perform this same basic function.

Animals that subsist largely by eating green plants constitute the second trophic level, be they aphid or elephant. Their energy source is once-removed from the initial fixation of radiant energy. Although animals of this trophic level are referred to by ecologists as "primary consumers," the lay term "herbivore" is often useful. Carnivores that prey largely upon herbivores of any sort constitute the third trophic level.

There are usually no more than five trophic levels in an ecosystem because the inevitable loss of energy in the shift from one trophic level to the next higher means that the total energy contained in the bodies of organisms on the fifth trophic level is small relative to the first. This relatively small amount of energy at the top level is disposed into a small number of large and usually widely dispersed bodies, since there is a tendency for the predators at the top levels to be larger than their prey. (See Figure VIII–1)

While the fifth level is often reached in marine ecosystems, in the Great Lakes it is not. Large lake trout feeding upon fish would be the top predators in the open-water com-munity. They operate on the fourth trophic level. Smaller lake trout often subsist largely on small crustacean herbivores; they would be assigned to the third level. Roughly speaking, about half of the living material in a large lake at any one time resides in the tiny cells of the numerous photosynthetic algae — the first level.

In lakes as large and deep as the Great Lakes, the overwhelming preponderance of life is found in the open waters — away from the shore and bottom. Yet it is still desirable to refer to this assemblage of life in the open waters as a "community," not an "ecosystem," because the open waters lack full representation of still a different trophic category — "reducers." Reducers is the term ecologists apply to the variety of bacteria and fungi that derive their energy from the complex molecules in the dead bodies and feces of other organisms of the system. Energeti-

Figure VIII–1 — TROPHIC LEVELS

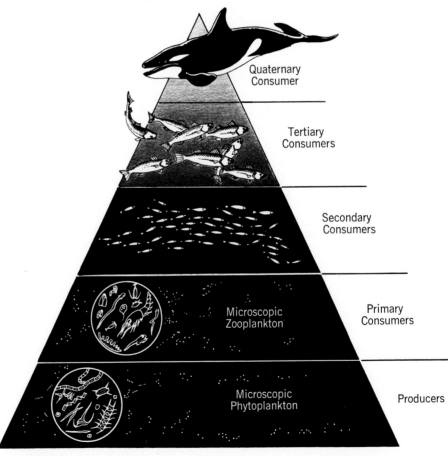

Quaternary Consumer

Tertiary Consumers

Secondary Consumers

Microscopic Zooplankton — Primary Consumers

Microscopic Phytoplankton — Producers

The figure illustrates an ecological pyramid showing various trophic levels. The higher the step in the pyramid, the fewer the number of individuals and the larger their size. In some environments, large animals circumvent some of the levels in the food chain. For example, man takes from all levels below himself, including that of the producers.

cally speaking, this biological reduction is excessively wasteful, but the small molecules that result from this degradation can be utilized by the photosynthetic plants, and thus reenter the trophic levels discussed above. It must be stressed, however, that a not inconsiderable amount of reduction of dead algae and the abundant feces of the animal plankton occurs as these sink slowly through the depth of the water. There is thus a recycling of biologically active elements within the water body itself, not dependent upon the seasonal recurrence of full vertical circulation and the cool-season reintroduction of the accumulation of the products of reduction on the bottom back into the open-water system of temperate lakes.

Contrasting Trophic Dynamics in Terrestrial Systems — Comparison of some of the basic attributes of the open water of a great lake, or of the ocean itself, with those of a well-developed terrestrial system such as a forest reveals some basic dissimilarities. The general features of trophic dynamics sketched at the outset apply, of course, with equal validity to terrestrial and aquatic systems. The dissimilarities arise from the differences in the structure of the dominant green plants.

Individual producers of the forest attain great size, each striving to spread its photosynthetic apparatus so that it may be fully exposed to the sun, unshaded by its neighbors. The trunk and branches by which each forest tree maintains its leaves in the sun provide, in the aggregate, a rigid three-dimensional framework in relation to which the other organisms of the system dispose themselves. The leaves are the food source for aphid and caterpillar, sloth and deer, tapir and gorilla. The permanent woody plexus has made it possible for this variety of sizes of herbivores to evolve, each achieving a different way of exploiting the same food resource but each small in

size compared with the green plant, some part of which each consumes.

How differently the photosynthetic apparatus is disposed in the Great Lakes! Here the individual plants are tiny — microscopic solitary algal cells or clumps and colonies just visible to the unaided eye (or, when dead or moribund, evident to both eye and nose as floating scum). The principal herbivores in the open waters are small crustaceans, large compared to the individual algal cells that constitute their major food, but often too small to cope with large clumps of algal cells.

To photosynthesize, the algae must be in the upper, lighted water layers. Under ice, algae are often concentrated at the very top of the water, but in warm seasons they are swept around in the Langmuir spirals induced by the wind moving over the water's surface. When wind is strong and temperature low, the spiral currents may carry the algae too deep for adequate light to penetrate. But during the warmer half of the year the myriad cells of the phytoplankton are slowly spiralled through the well-lighted, warmer layer of lake water. Quite unlike the forest situation, the green plants of the open water display no semi-permanent, three-dimensional pattern of structure in relation to which animals can orient themselves and evolve special behavior patterns. The open waters provide no place to hide!

One reason to stress the differences between these two kinds of communities is that man, the observer, is primatively a member of a forest or grassland community, and some ecologists have too much betrayed their experience of the forest in their interpretation of the dynamics of open-water systems. A part of this difficulty of interpretation has been the tendency to expect, in essentially structureless open-water systems, the same kind of fine-grained adjustments of organism to environment

that have evolved in the substratum-dominated terrestrial systems.

Man-Induced Disturbances — The nature of the dynamic model of relationships within the open-water community of the Great Lakes is of more than academic concern. Man has seriously disturbed the biotic properties of these lakes by his multifarious activities. If the quality of these lakes is to be improved and continuously maintained at an improved level, a correct and complete understanding of the ecological interrelationship is required.

The overgrowth of the algae in Lake Erie is probably the most obvious manifestation of the disturbances that the biological communities of all the lakes have sustained to varying degrees. An algal overgrowth, or, in ecologists' terms, an increased standing crop of the phytoplankton, is a characteristic recent manifestation of lakes in Europe and North America on the shores of which large concentrations of human populations reside.

The biological waste produced by the people of cities is biologically reduced, to varying degrees, into small molecules of biologically active elements such as nitrogen and phosphorus. When these are flushed into lakes directly, or into their tributaries, they augment the natural supply of plant nutrients.

This "cultural enrichment" of lakes is cumulative. Once the simple compounds of nitrogen and phosphorus enter the lake in solution, they are quickly and effectively taken up by the green plants — the phytoplankton as well as the rooted water plants along the shore. Henceforth, these elements will reside in the complex molecules of organisms. They spend but little time in solution in the lake water; the amount of nitrogen and phosphorus that will escape through a lake's outlet, dissolved in the water, is remarkably small compared to that leaving the lake in the tissues of emerging insects or organisms otherwise removed from the lake.

Approaches to Quality Management

Management of lakes to maintain quality seeks two goals, both of which involve maximizing the rate at which the energy-rich compounds of nitrogen and phosphorus fixed in algae are passed to higher trophic levels. One goal is to reduce the standing crop of phytoplankton, thereby making the water more transparent; the second is to find an economical way to remove nitrogen and phosphorus from the lakes.

The third trophic level in the open-water community is the lowest at which nitrogen and phosphorus are concentrated into packets of a size that man can manipulate and use. These "packets" are the bodies of the fish that eat the animal plankton; they can be fished from the lake and used directly as human food (as lake whitefish once were in large amounts) or they can be used as a protein source for animal nutrition (as alewives can be).

We began this discussion of man-generated changes in lakes by suggesting that our conception of trophic dynamics within the open water is crucial to attempts to redress some of these biological imbalances. There are two alternate concepts of these relationships (to be sketched below). They differ in their relevance to achieving the two management goals set out above. The more recent formulations stress the role of predation by plankton-eating fish in controlling the species composition of the plant and animal plankton. This concept offers hope that the two goals are not only compatible but might be achieved by the same manipulations of the system. On the other hand, the older concept — which stresses competition within a trophic level as the prime determinant of

plankton composition — presents no simple dynamic model of relationships among the first three trophic levels. Attempts at management of disturbed lakes will, therefore, not only hope to achieve practical goals but also to test and extend the conceptual models.

The Scientific Data Base

In general, the data base for evaluating and extending knowledge of the trophic dynamic systems of the Great Lakes is inadequate. This dynamic approach demands knowledge of the interrelationships of the elements of the lake ecosystem, while all that is now available are unrelated segments of data concerning various aspects of the ecosystem. Data on the seasonal changes in the physical and chemical parameters for more than a few stations at a time in any one lake have become available only within the past decades. Attempts to relate these physico-chemical to biological changes have only been sporadic. Of the biological data, that on changes in the composition of the fish stock is probably most nearly adequate. That on the plant and animal plankton, which comprise the bulk of the biomass, is spotty and inadequate. A recently published bibliography of the Great Lakes plankton studies lists over 400 papers, but, as the bibliographer added,

The biology and ecology of the plankton remains poorly known. Most papers are descriptive and concentrate heavily on taxonomy and distribution of certain organisms. Experimental work on the dynamics of Great Lakes plankton is urgently needed in light of rapidly changing environmental conditions and fluctuating fish stocks.

The last sentence makes the essential point: Significant studies of the trophic dynamics involve simultaneous studies of physico-chemical parameters, the phytoplankton, the zoo-

plankton, the planktivorous fish, and the piscivores.

Various bits of work done recently in Lake Michigan can be put together to provide some insight into the trophic dynamics of that lake. This has provided the reassuring information that changes in the composition of the animal plankton following changes in stocks of planktivorous fish (establishment of alewives, to be specific) have been precisely what would be predicted from knowledge of the dynamics of much smaller lakes. Furthermore, the time required for the changes to be manifest in the animal plankton of Lake Michigan is not inordinately greater than the time required in smaller lakes. This is not surprising, because the total size of the system should be less significant than the mean ratio of planktivore/zooplankter.

Theoretical Formulations: Control from Above

A recent theoretical formulation states that the composition of the first trophic levels in the open-water communities of large lakes is determined in large measure by the selective feeding habits of the planktivorous fish. The prey selections by the schools of zooplankton-eating fish directly determine the species composition of the animal plankton. This indirectly affects the quantitative and qualitative composition of the phytoplankton (algae, bacteria) because species of animal plankton differ in the effectiveness with which their populations can collect algae and other small particles from the lake water.

Large crustacean zooplankters of the genus *Daphnia* play a crucial role in the indirect control of the first trophic level resulting from the selective feeding of the third level. The large *Daphnia* are both the favorite food of freshwater planktivores and the most effective collectors of small particles (1-50 microns) from the medium. When planktivore stocks are sufficiently high, the populations of large *Daphnia* are reduced to insignificant numbers. Since the smaller crustacean competitors that replace them (see Figure VIII–2) are less effective in collecting small algae, the algal populations will tend to increase, making the lake water less transparent.

This theory, in essence, states that the composition of the open-water community is determined by the trophic actions of the highest (third and fourth) trophic levels. The formulation suggests a management concept for controlling the effects of the continued enrichment pollution of the Great Lakes. In essence, the plan would be to reduce planktivore pressure in such a way as to maximize the populations of *Daphnia* which are most effective in removing algae from suspension. The plankton-eating fish could be removed by man through fishing. Removing the fish would remove some "packets" of nitrogen and phosphorus in the lake ecosystem at the same time as it permitted the proliferation of *Daphnia*. The fish themselves, depending on their species, could be variously used as human food, animal food, or as a source of oils and other material for chemical manipulation.

The stocks of planktivores could also be kept in check by introducing and manipulating stocks of piscivorous fish. For example, the introduction of coho salmon into Lake Michigan is an attempt at controlling the burgeoning population of the alewife (*Alosa pseudoharengus* — originally a marine planktivore that, despite its abundance in many freshwater lakes, is still imperfectly adapted to the peculiarities of a freshwater existence). While this method of controlling planktivores has the advantage of permitting the nitrogen and phosphorus to be removed in large packets that tend to find greater acceptance as human food, the total amount of these elements that could be extracted from the fourth trophic

level of the lake is at most one-seventh of that which could be removed via the third. It is thus less satisfactory as a means of decreasing the total amount of nitrogen and phosphorus from a lake than is removal of fish from the third (planktivore) level.

The entire matter of the use of the fish removed from the Great Lakes as food for man or beast has been complicated by the fact that various stable and toxic chlorine-containing compounds such as DDT, DDD, DDE, and PCB's are concentrated in the oil and body fat of the fish of both trophic levels.

Theoretical Formulations: Control from Below

In contrast to the concept of control of the composition of the open-water community indicated above, the alternate concept — widely held a decade ago — still has adherents.

The control-from-below theory envisions the composition of the community as being primarily determined by competition within each trophic level. In this view, the composition of the first level — phytoplankton — is determined by the particular configuration of physico-chemical conditions at the season in question. The species composition of the second level — zooplankton — is determined primarily by competition among populations of the various species of crustaceans and rotifers that could occur within the lake for the kinds of phytoplankton thriving at that moment. Each species is most effective in collecting only a portion of the total range of sizes and kinds of algae available. The planktivores feed on whichever species of zooplankter is available at the time.

It can be appreciated, therefore, that changing the intensity of planktivore predation upon the zooplankton would be expected, by the control-from-below hypothesis, to alter the total quantity of zooplank-

ton — but not necessarily its specific composition. Since this concept does not consider that planktivore predation has any pronounced effect on the species composition of the zooplankton, there is no theoretical basis for attempting to modify the composition and standing crop of the algae by manipulating the stock of planktivorous fish.

Requirements for Scientific Activity

Examination of the simultaneous changes in the abundance of all the various species that comprise each trophic level is necessary to evaluate the alternative concepts of trophic dynamics outlined above. This is an enormous task, even in the Great Lakes where the variety of species on all levels is very much less than it would be in an equal volume of the ocean.

The greatest difficulties of enumeration and categorization are presented by the extremely numerous small organisms of the plankton. Automatic methods of counting the plankton and categorizing them according to size must be developed. The Coulter method of counting and sizing particles by the drop in electrical potential that each generates while passing through a small aperture through which an electric current passes is not entirely satisfactory. This data must be stored electronically so as to be immediately available for use with data on physico-chemical conditions, on the one hand, and data on the characteristics of the fish populations, on the other.

In addition to methods of automatic data collecting, it will be necessary to make provision for the proper taxonomic assignment of species of the plant and animal plankton. This information, gathered from aliquots, must be applied to the automatically acquired data on size categories. At present this is an operation that is tedious at best and nearly impossible at worst.

Figure VIII–2 — EFFECT OF ALEWIVES ON ZOOPLANKTON

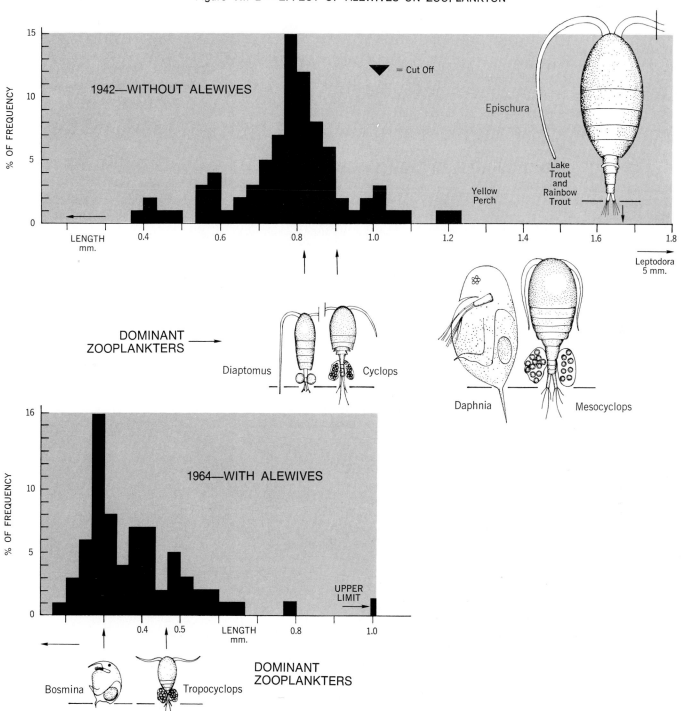

The histograms show the distribution and composition of crustacean zooplankton (as well as one predatory noncrustacean) before and after a population of *Alosa pseudoharengus* (alewives) became well established. The arrows indicate the size and the position in the distribution of the smallest mature instar of each dominant species. Such larger zooplankton as *Daphnia* were present, but they represented less than one percent of the total sample count. The triangles denote the lower limit or cut-off point of the zooplankton consumed by the several species of fish indicated. Note that with the advent of the alewives, the size distribution of the zooplankton was depressed significantly to smaller species.

Seasonal changes as well as natural and man-induced changes in the fish stocks continually perturb the lake ecosystem. Continuous analysis of the perturbations of the plant and animal plankton should make it possible to evaluate the concepts of trophic dynamics, leading to the development of techniques and concepts

necessary for managing the Great Lakes so as to maximize both water quality and fish yield.

The primary requirement is the assembly of a scientific staff together with the equipment and instrumentation (ships and collecting gear) necessary for collecting extensive sam-

ples. The samples should be converted into data as automatically as possible. Taxonomic identification services should be established. Methods for data storage and rapid retrieval should be developed. Much could be done within five years toward the development of effective management concepts if a concerted effort were made along these lines.

Effects of Artificial Disturbances on the Marine Environment

The capability of predicting the specific consequence of a general disturbance of a natural community is basic to planning and evaluating environmental controls. Large sums of money and considerable effort could be saved if we could foresee the effects of a particular human activity.

History has taught us what to expect from the destruction of forests and prairies. But we cannot now predict, with any confidence, more subtle disturbances or the long-term cosmopolitan consequences of drastic change. This circumstance is rapidly changing. Recent theoretical developments have directed our attention to new ways of looking at the problem. There is reason to believe that it will soon be possible to predict change, at least in relatively simple ecosystems such as exist in the sea.

Ecological Generalities

Few long-term studies have been made on the changes that occur in natural communities. We must therefore rely more on theory than experience. It is now recognized that there is a fundamental relationship between the number of species, the number of individuals of any species, and the stability of the environment. For example, there are fewer species with relatively larger numbers of individuals in severe or unstable environments than in environments whose fluctuations are predictable. If the environment becomes more

stable in time, the number of species increases. If the environment is disturbed in any way, the number of species decreases.

Succession and Regression — Around the turn of this century ecologists recognized that, wherever a land surface was laid bare, it was colonized by species in a regular order. It was possible to predict, on the basis of previous observations, which species of animals and plants would appear first and which would later replace the earliest immigrants. This process of succession of one natural community by another continues until a stable climax community is reached. However, succession is a reversible process. Any disturbance will drive the climax community down to a lower level of succession. The disappearance of species is also in a more or less regular order.

If we had data on the changes in all natural communities, we could predict the consequences of a general disturbance using the principle of succession. In the absence of such studies, there may be another way of obtaining relevant data: There is evidence that natural communities are continually responding to local variations in the stability of the environment. Small-scale disturbances drive down part of the system without appreciably affecting other areas. If this is the case, a community can be viewed as a temporal mosaic, portions of which are at different levels of succession. In this circumstance, the variations in species composition

observed in space could be similar to those observed in time. If samples taken throughout a natural community at one time are placed in order of diversity, the array should simulate the order of species appearance or disappearance in succession or regression.

The Impact of Pollutants

At least some of the changes associated with pollution resemble those observed in natural sequences. For example, the order in which marine species disappear as a sewage outfall is approached is often the reverse of the order in succession. Using this principle, we can take samples throughout an area, arrange them in order of diversity, and predict the changes that would occur in the vicinity of a proposed outfall.

Some pollutants and other types of disturbances are probably specific in their effects upon communities, affecting some species more than others. Prediction in these cases will require knowledge of the physiological responses of particular species to the particular compound or disturbance. However, where the disturbance is general, as in pollution from domestic sewage or dredging, we should be able to predict the effects upon the community using the kinds of observations and samples now taken by ecologists.

Prediction in Shallow-Water Communities — Simple communities, low in diversity, are strongly influenced by stresses imposed by the physical environment. Complex communities, high in diversity, tend to be more stable and integrated. It should be easier to predict change in the simpler, physically controlled communities than in the complex, biologically controlled associations.

Marine communities in shallow water appear to be simpler than those in deep-sea and terrestrial environments. Therefore, the planktonic and benthic marine communities in shallow water offer the greatest opportunities to test hypotheses concerning succession and the relationship between environmental stability and diversity. This is fortunate, since these communities are of great economic importance and yet suffer the greatest exposure to artificial disturbances. If we can perfect methods of prediction in shallow-water communities in the next several years, there will still be time to develop the economic and political institutions needed to prevent the wholesale degradation of these important ecosystems.

Needed Scientific Activity

In the next several years we will need to perform field and laboratory experiments explicitly designed to test the growing body of ecological theory. For the purpose of developing our prediction capability, we should perform such experiments in areas that are undergoing or about to undergo artificial stress.

Ecological surveys are now commonly made in connection with proposed reactor installations or sewage outfalls. While such studies vary tremendously in quality, most are worthless. Most are poorly designed without any regard to previous experience or theory. It is not possible to generalize from the data obtained from most of these surveys because of the great differences in the methods of sampling and analysis used. One of the most pressing needs in applied marine ecology is the development of high and uniform standards for the performance of routine ecological surveys.

Monitoring — At the state and national level, it would be highly desirable to develop programs to monitor environmental events. We could maximize the use of data obtained from the study of artificial disasters if such studies were performed by highly trained teams of observers. High school and college biology teachers might be enlisted in this effort. It would not be difficult to cover the coastlines of highly populated areas such as California. Centers for environmental control could be established to train teams of observers, to develop standards of performance, and to collate and analyze data. Such data would be of immeasurable value in designing basic research programs and in developing environmental controls.

Research and Training — On a long-term basis, we must continue to support basic research in population dynamics. In shallow-water communities there is a particular need to place more emphasis on larval recruitment. Our understanding of the temporal changes in benthic marine communities is severely limited by our lack of knowledge of larval ecology.

It is essential to expand research and training in systematic biology. Systematics remains as the foundation of nearly all ecological research. Yet our attempts to attract talent and support in these areas are feeble. The major museums of this country should be the focal points of this effort, but they are suffering decay and neglect.

Scientific Preserves — In the long term, it is important to establish large scientific preserves to serve as standards of environmental quality, as natural laboratories, and as sources of larvae for the maintenance of species elsewhere. We must begin this program as soon as possible, for few areas remain suitable for these purposes along our coasts.

In conclusion, there is reason to believe that we will have a limited capability of predicting changes in natural communities within the coming decade. This capability will be greatly expanded by the rapid development of ecological theory and the performance of critical experiments in natural communities. To achieve these goals, we should increase basic research in systematic biology and population dynamics, establish scientific preserves, and develop programs to monitor environmental events. If we begin now, we may be able to halt the degradation of the marine environment as early as 1990. If we do not begin now, we will reduce the natural communities along our coasts to a level where their contribution to our economy and general welfare will be trivial.

Marine Flora and Fauna in the Antarctic

The environment of the antarctic seas is less variable than that of temperate latitudes with respect to temperature and salinity, but the quality of light throughout the year may be quite different because of the long periods of light and dark and the winter ice cover. In many parts of the antarctic, especially near the continental margin, the temperature of the ocean water is near 0° centigrade or below, and nowhere in the regions known as "antarctic" — that is, south of the Antarctic Convergence — are surface waters warmer than 1.0° centigrade. In deeper water the temperature is almost constantly around −1.8° centigrade. As the Canadian biologist Dunbar has pointed out, a cold constant temperature is not a limiting factor for the development of life, and the antarctic seas are rich and immensely productive, at least near the surface and at shallow depths.

Marine Life of Special Interest to Man

Oxygen and nutrients are high in these cold waters, as might be expected from the abundance of life in them. Two centuries ago man drew heavily on the stocks of seals of the sub-antarctic islands; more recently, he has reduced the stocks of blue whales to such low levels that it is no longer economical to pursue them.

Recently there have been discussions of utilizing the vast populations of the krill, *Euphausia superba*, which are the principal food of the blue whales, the Adelie penguins, and several kinds of fishes. It is estimated that the total populations of krill are equal to all the rest of the fisheries of the world, at least in gross tonnage, or about 60 million metric tons. However, the krill occurs in patches and the small size of the individuals poses difficult processing problems. Also, the animals are "tender" — that is, they must be processed immediately. For these reasons, immediate extensive use of this resource appears unlikely. Among other significantly abundant fishes are representatives of the family Nototheniidae; these are currently being fished on an experimental basis by the Soviet Union.

There seems to be less fisheries potential in the shallow-water or sea-bottom life, which is often abundant and varied but lacks the extensive beds of large bivalves found in arctic waters. Large seaweeds are abundant around the sub-antarctic islands and near the shores of the Antarctic Peninsula, and invertebrate populations are large in the vicinity of McMurdo Sound and the Soviet base in the Davis Sea. Most of the assemblage consists of such organisms as sponges, bryozoa, and echino-

derms, of little potential commercial value. The bottom fauna is of considerable theoretical interest because of its apparently stable or slowly changing composition, at the same time combined with a diversity of components comparable to that of the Indo-Pacific coral reef environment.

The rates of turnover or replacement of the antarctic fauna have yet to be worked out in the detail necessary for rational harvest of the fisheries stocks, but the unfortunate history of the blue whale suggests that our relations to the fishery resources of the antarctic will be governed primarily by socio-economic rather than ecological considerations. That is, we will simply fish until stocks are so reduced that it becomes unprofitable to expend the effort and funds necessary to keep the catch up.

Examples of Adaptation

The adaptations and peculiarities of the flora and fauna of the shallow waters near the antarctic continent are of great scientific and theoretical interest. Two of the most interesting concern the adaptation of fishes to water that is below freezing by the production of a sort of natural anti-freeze substance (according to one researcher) or to a higher concentration of salt in the blood (according to another); other fish adapt to the low temperature and high oxygen by developing the ability to function without hemoglobin. The disagreement between deVries, who finds that certain fishes may resist freezing because of a protein containing carbohydrate in their blood, as contrasted with Smith's observation that this is effected by increased salt, should stimulate more intensive and critical work on the blood of antarctic fishes.

The adaptations of the Weddell seal, the southernmost mammal, are of particular interest. This animal is capable of diving for periods of more than 40 minutes to depths of 400

meters (about 1,200 feet), can swim under water for at least two miles, and has excellent sense of direction under water. A thorough understanding of the physiology of this mammal will help us to understand the problems of diving, which is an increasingly significant activity in man's expanding use of the sea.

Status of Scientific Activity

At the present time there is considerable interest in the nature and significance of diversity in the sea — that is, whether a high ratio of differences to total numbers of all kinds or abundances is related to a situation that may be in equilibrium or indicative of a long-established condition, or whether, conversely, a low proportion of different kinds of species indicates recent, temporary, or changing conditions. Many pollution programs are predicated on the idea that diversity may be associated with stable and presumably favorable or optimum conditions. As yet we lack adequate data to ascertain whether or not diversity exists and what it may signify, especially for situations at the bottom of the sea.

The benthic environment of the antarctic should provide us with useful information on this controversial problem because it appears to be a comparatively unchanging environment with a rich variety of species. The problem will require a more intensified level of field ecological work on a year-round basis than is being done at present, at least by U.S. researchers. It is in this area that theoretical formulation and mathematical modeling (already being attempted for situations in other regions) would be most appropriate, but we still lack the data base. For example, we are still unable to evaluate data concerning diversity in different regions of the antarctic.

Physiological aspects seem to be much better in hand; a concerted attack on some of these problems is under way by a group on board the R. V. *Alpha Helix.*

Instrumentation — We are reasonably well equipped, especially in physiology, to undertake antarctic studies, although details of apparatus can always be refined. One problem that seems to plague divers in particular is the vulnerability of photographic equipment in the cold antarctic waters; various kinds of seals continue to break down and put cameras out of commission. We need some functioning under-water photomonitoring systems for the dangerous antarctic waters in order to obtain information under winter conditions near the bases.

Manpower — Our principal requirement is interested manpower in order to expand field ecology programs in the next five years to produce data relevant to theoretical ideas in ecology at a scale to keep up with such work elsewhere. Obviously, there is need for some sort of ecological monitoring to help us check on the worldwide deterioration of our environment. In the antarctic, this activity would also provide data of basic and theoretical importance.

Systems Approaches to Understanding the Oceans and Marine Productivity

The ability of man to affect the biological character of the near shore regions is universally recognized; polluted harbors and lagoons turn blue water to green from enhanced production of algae. Man's ability to add potentially significant quantities of manufactured materials, some of which are biologically active, has been acquired only recently, and recognition of this ability has been startling to scientists and laymen alike. Nevertheless, this unpleasant news is true, with DDT providing the most spectacular and potentially harmful example recognized so far. However, large quantities of an industrially useful class of chemical compounds, polychlorinated biphenyls (PCB), are also being added to the sea.

The DDT experience suggests that the marine ecosystem is highly vulnerable in two areas: (a) the microscopic plants or phytoplankton that form the basis for the biological productivity of the sea, and (b) the reproductive stages of marine animals, beginning with those grazing on the phytoplankton and extending as far as the birds.

The phytoplankton, as the green plants of the sea, are intimately involved not only with the production of food organisms in the sea but with atmospheric processes as well — for example, the production of oxygen and the absorption of carbon dioxide. The optical qualities of the sea surface also are strongly influenced by the amount of phytoplankton present. Preliminary experiments and observations suggest that the range of sensitivity of marine phytoplankton extends to concentrations as low as one part per billion, coinciding nicely with man's current capacity to add exotic materials to the sea. Figure VIII–3 illustrates this sensitivity.

The role of the ocean as a source of food, especially of protein, and as a means of livelihood for fishermen needs no elaboration. Large-scale changes in the level of production of phytoplankton or in species composition are certain to be reflected rapidly in the populations of fish. Other economic and health considerations arise in connection with the pollution of the sea near bathing beaches.

The Status of Simulation Modeling

From the foregoing discussion, the marine ecosystem appears as a complex biological system interacting with its immediate physical environment and with the atmosphere. The use of high-speed digital computers in conjunction with simulation models of oceanic productivity and of subunits such as coastal regions and upwelling areas is now possible; it offers the only real hope of obtaining predictive capacity for this important ecosystem.

Although the many observations of plant productivity made in the past twenty years have yielded reliable general patterns, the dynamics of marine production is poorly understood. The simulation model approach has been discovered by biological oceanographers relatively recently, largely as a result of the U.S. effort in the International Biological Program. One interdisciplinary group involving meteorologists, physical oceanographers, biological oceanographers, and fisheries experts is engaged in the construction of a series of simulation models of upwelling regions, where a disproportionately large share of the world's fisheries resources are located. This group appears to be the only one engaged in a serious program of this nature.

The relatively strong field of theoretical physical oceanography has provided a mathematical basis sufficiently sound to enable at least one computer simulation model of the Pacific oceanic circulation to be built, with the result that all known currents appear with approximately the correct transport rates. Such models can provide the necessary hydrodynamic base for ocean ecosystem models. However, a large part of the theoretical formulation necessary for biological modeling has never been developed to a satisfactory degree.

Recently, a considerable amount of productive research has been carried out in which the sea is examined from the viewpoint of continuous culture theory, the latter studied intensively for industrial and sewage

Figure VIII-3 — SENSITIVITY OF PHYTOPLANKTON TO INSECTICIDES

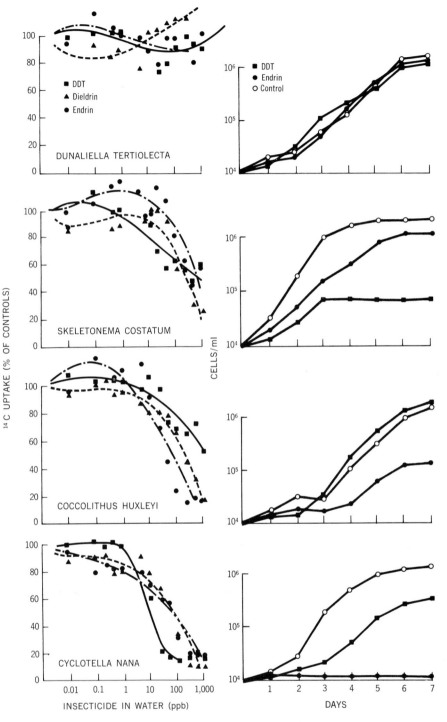

The left-hand charts show the uptake of ^{14}C by phytoplankton as a function of the concentration of several insecticides. At concentrations greater than one part per billion (ppb) in three of the four species studied, the reaction in uptake is great. The right-hand charts show the effect of adding 100 ppb of DDT and endrin to water containing several types of phytoplankton. The insecticides were added each day for 7 days and solvent was added in equal volume to the controls. The insecticides significantly reduced production in three of the four species under investigation.

treatment applications. Through this line of research, some of the results of the intensive activity in biochemistry and molecular biology are being incorporated into biological oceanography, and satisfactory calculation models for the absorption of nutrients by phytoplankton are being developed rapidly. Since phytoplankton production is limited in most regions of the sea by the rate at which nutrient-rich waters from below are brought to the surface by hydrological processes, the equations linking phytoplankton production and basic hydrological parameters of the ocean circulation are virtually at hand.

From this point on up the food chain, the situation deteriorates. Little useful information exists on rates of grazing by the zooplankton, the small animals intermediate between most fish and phytoplankton. At this level, animal behavior must be taken into consideration and reproduction patterns become important. Although general patterns are known, the details remain to be filled in and are largely lacking for modeling purposes. The structure and behavior of some fish populations is better known as a result of the pressure of economic value, and simulation models have been developed that are useful in the management of specific fisheries. These models, however, are not linked in their present form to the food chain supporting the fishery. Efforts are currently under way to form this link, using the Peru anchovy fisheries as a basis. In some of the advanced simulation models, the response of fishermen to various regulation regimes is taken into consideration.

Future Requirements

A library of simulation models of oceanic productivity is needed to deal with the problems posed by man's intervention. Some models should be designed to give large-scale coverage without great detail— for example, models of each of the major oceans. Others are required for specific coastal regions and, finally, for specific estuaries. Within a geographic class, models will be needed for specific purposes in addition to at least one base model primarily describing plant-environment effects. The addition of such models to the tools presently available to managerial personnel and policy-makers at the international, national, and local levels could be one of the most important steps to be taken in the near future.

Although it is difficult to predict the amount of time required to build these models, some of them should be operational within the next five years. Obviously, the potential dangers inherent in an inaccurate or incorrect model are great, and it is absolutely essential that careful consideration be given to validation, a step that is almost certainly more difficult than building the model.

If the models are to be useful, provisions must be made for collecting the required input data. Although it is not usually possible to specify these requirements with accuracy un-

til the models are built and running, intelligent guesses can nevertheless be made; and if serious modeling efforts emerge, they should be made available to the various environmental monitoring programs such as GNEM (Global Network for Environmental Monitoring) at an early date. The potential of the simulation models for the detection of anomalous conditions should not be overlooked; perhaps it is not too early to propose the use of simulation models for monitoring to GNEM and other planning groups. Monitoring possibilities are especially attractive at the local level. For example, the deviation of the pattern of the phytoplankton plume produced by a marine sewage outfall from that predicted by a validated model might be used to indicate that a toxic compound of a certain class had been introducd into the collection system; the approximate quantity might be indicated as well.

The resources for carrying out the necessary research and computer programming are severely limited at present. However, the progress in simulation modeling made by mete-

orologists, especially at NCAR (National Center for Atmospheric Research), is immediately useful, and the interests of young oceanographers and graduate students are highly compatible with such a program. Given an environment amenable to interdisciplinary research, computer facilities, laboratory facilities, ship time, access to aircraft, etc., the work could be carried out with a good probability of success. Provision for training of students should, of course, be implicit in any such effort, since the intelligent use of any successful models will depend on the availability of qualified scientists of very high caliber.

The highest priority should probably be given to the development of ocean-wide models in view of the potential dangers inherent in the present situation, the virtual impossibility of applying any positive corrective action, and the long recovery time implied by the nature of the ocean circulation. However, the rapidly increasing rates of coastal and estuarine pollution call for strong efforts in modeling of these systems, too.

2. OCEANIC PRODUCTION

Primary Plant and Animal Life in the World Ocean

Aquatic Plants

In the sea as well as on land, the primary producers of organic matter are plants. It is estimated that roughly 20 billion metric tons of carbon is fixed by photosynthesis in the sea each year. This amount of carbon fixed annually should not be confused with the total amount of plants, in terms of carbon weight, existing at any one time. Since the process of organic production takes place at a rapid rate in the sea, the average standing crop of plants is a small fraction of the annual production. This makes a sharp contrast to the plant production on land. The total quantity of terrestrial plants present at any one time is, on the average, much greater than the annual production.

Potential Use by Man — Another striking difference between oceanic plants and terrestrial plants is in their size and distribution. The vast majority of plants in the sea are microscopic single-cell algae (see Figure VIII-4) in contrast to the grass, crops, shrubs, and trees that form the bulk of terrestrial vegetation. These small organisms, collectively called phytoplankton, are diffused over vast areas of the ocean. Even the greatest concentrations of phytoplankton, which occur in productive areas at certain times, are nothing compared with the density of plants in green land areas. The enormous expense of collecting these diffused, single-cell organisms from sea water makes harvesting of marine plants for man's use completely uneconomical. Furthermore, many of the dominant species of phytoplankton have hard siliceous or calcareous skeletons that make them unpalatable to man. For these and many other reasons, the use of phytoplankton as an important source of food appears quite out of the question.

There are various seaweeds and other large aquatic plants, some of which are used for food or for manufacturing industrial products. Most of them, however, are attached to the bottom and therefore confined to shallow inshore waters. The total yield (in wet weight) of these plants for all purposes from the world ocean is about 900,000 metric tons a year, or approximately 1.5 percent of the total landings of marine fisheries. More than half of this amount is harvested in Japan. Harvesting of large aquatic plants could be increased greatly, but its contribution to the supply of plant food as a whole would be insignificant.

The Role of Phytoplankton — The infeasibility of using phytoplankton for food or other purposes does not, of course, affect their basic role in the economy of the sea. Animals cannot manufacture living substance from inorganic materials. They derive it directly by grazing on plants or indirectly by eating other animals that have eaten plants. Thus, the amount of carbon fixed by plants (measured by ^{14}C methods) is widely used for evaluating the basic productive capacity of the sea. On a global scale, it may be used for roughly estimating the potential harvest of the sea. Starting with the total fixation of organic carbon and using various assumptions on the efficiency of energy transfer, one can theoretically arrive at estimated harvestable outputs at different levels of the food chain. Estimates obtained by this method vary widely, depending on the assumptions used. Nevertheless, they indicate a general range within which the potential harvest of the sea should fall, as well as the sources of inaccuracy inherent in this method.

It has been demonstrated that, among the areas where intensive exploitation of living resources has been taking place, areas of high primary productivities generally coincide with those of high yields from fisheries. Such primary productivity data by area are useful in a variety of ways. Used in combination with catch statistics in heavily exploited areas, they provide means to test the validity of various assumptions on the efficiency of energy transfer, particularly when data on secondary production (i.e., zooplankton) are also available. They also indicate some of the areas that are grossly underexploited but in which abundant potential resources are likely to occur, as is the case with certain parts of the Indian Ocean, the tropical Pacific, and the South Pacific. When such information is combined with data on the forms of animals likely to be abundant in the respective areas, it will provide a substantial scientific basis for planning the exploration and exploitation of such areas in order to extract greater amounts of animal protein material from the sea. Also, the differences in primary productivity between areas are such (1:50) that there are many areas in the world ocean that could be written off, based on productivity data alone, as potential fishing grounds for large-scale industrial operations.

Numerous measurements of primary production have been made, but they are largely in the limited areas of the world ocean, and data are quite scarce for most other parts. It would be desirable to incorporate primary production measurements in

Figure VIII–4 — SOME PHYTOPLANKTON

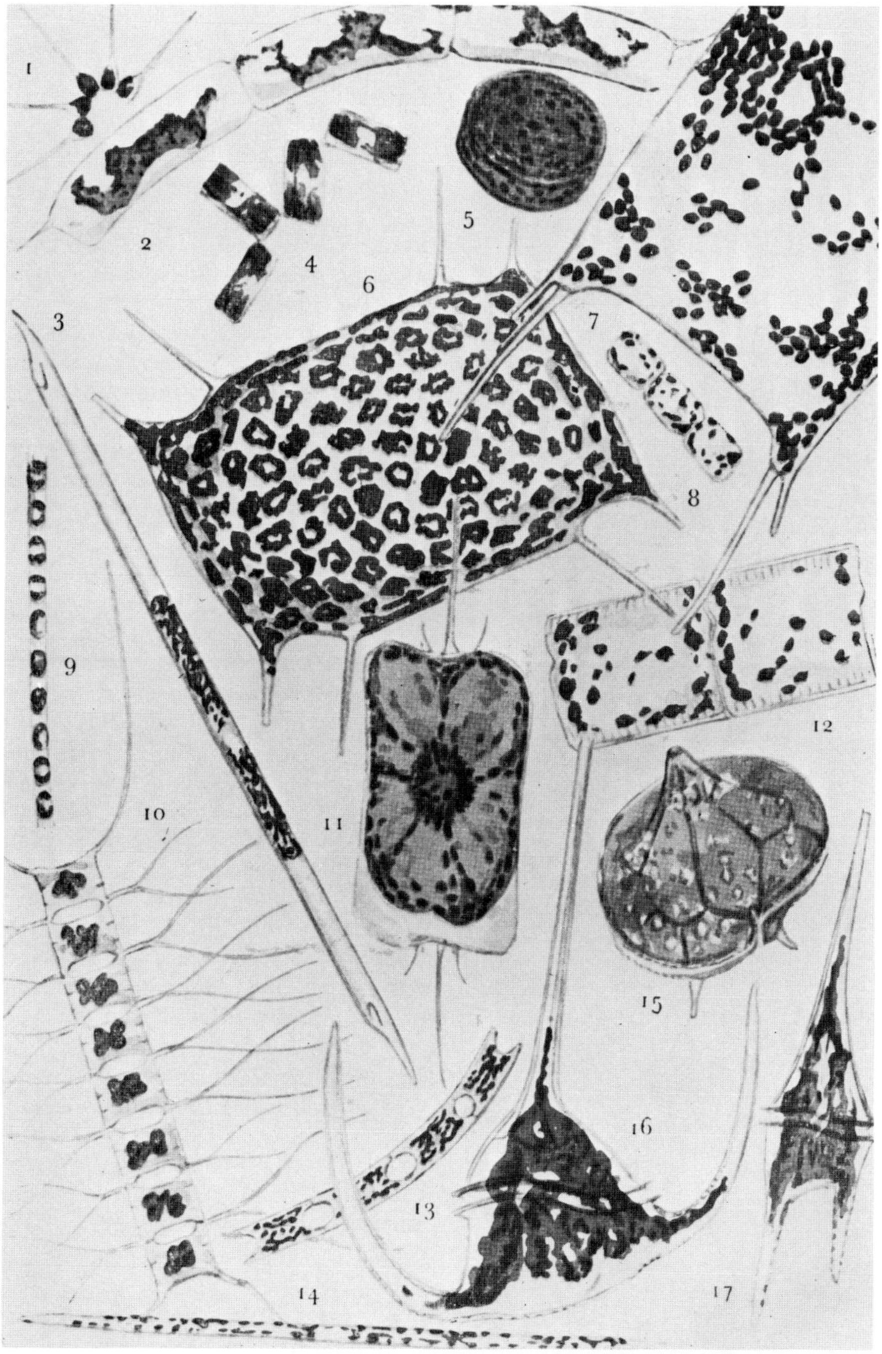

The illustration shows drawings of some phytoplankton, enlarged about 400 times.
Diatoms:

1. Asterionella japonica
2. Rhizosolenia stolterfothii
3. Rhizosolenia alata
4. Grammatophora serpentina
5. Coscinodiscus excentricus
6. Biddulphia regia
7. Biddulphia sinensis
8. Lauderia borealis
9. Skeletonema costatum
10. Chaetoceros decipiens
11. Ditylium brightwellii
12. Guinardia flaccida
13. Eucampia zoodiacus
14. Thalassiothrix longissima

Dinoflagellates:

15. Peridinium depressum
16. Ceratium tripos
17. Ceratium furca

as many oceanographic programs as possible, with particular attention paid to the usefulness of such data as a basis for evaluating the relative potentials of food production in different parts of the world ocean.

Zooplankton

Since most oceanic plants are extremely small, the typical forms of marine herbivores are also very small and planktonic, again making a sharp contrast to grazing animals on land. An enormous variety of small crustaceans and other invertebrates, mixed with the young of larger animals including fish, form a community of herbivores and little carnivores collectively called the zooplankton. Although some species of larger animals, such as bivalves, anchovies, and sardines, also utilize phytoplankton to varying degrees, the herbivores of the zooplankton, particularly such crustaceans as copepods and euphausids, play an overwhelmingly important role in converting plant material into animal material. The size of planktonic herbivores in adult stages ranges from less than one millimeter to over five centimeters. They have efficient filtering apparatus to collect phytoplankton. Figure VIII–5 illustrates some of the zooplankton.

Potential Use by Man — Aside from their ecological role as the main grazers in the sea, plankton animals give some promise of being harvested directly by man. Before going into the detail of this aspect, we must explain why man should want to take the trouble of harvesting these little animals. As organic matter is transferred from plants to herbivores, from herbivores to first-stage carnivores, and from first-stage carnivores to those of higher stages, there are large losses of energy or materials from respiration and decomposition. The food web in the sea is so complex that we have no simple methods of estimating an average loss at each stage of transfer. For the sake of simplified discussions, the efficiency of transfer from

Figure VIII–5 — SOME ZOOPLANKTON

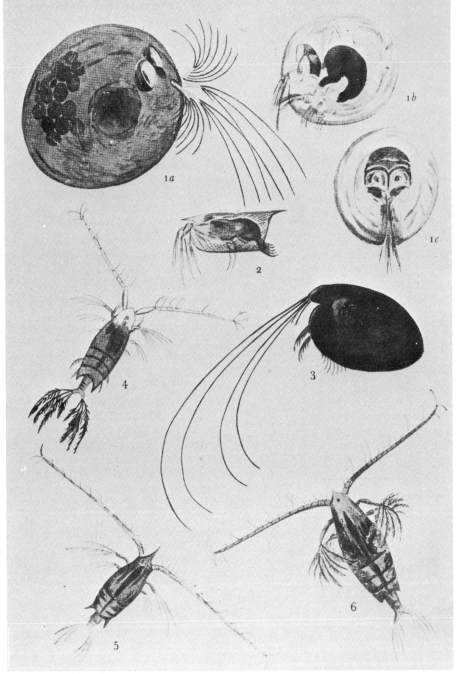

(Copyright 1965, Houghton Mifflin Company, Boston, Mass.)

The illustration shows drawings of some zooplankton, enlarged about five times.
Ostracods:
1. Gigantocypris mulleri: (a) adult with eggs, (b) and (c) two views of young and more transparent specimen
2. Conchoecia ametra
3. Cypridina (Macrocypridina) castanea
Copepods:
4. Arietellus insignis, female
5. Gaetanus pileatus, female
6. Euchirella maxima, female

one trophic level to the next higher level might be considered to be on the order of 10 percent, the loss being 90 percent. This means that the total production (hence potential yield) of zooplankton is much greater than that of small fishes feeding on zooplankton, and the latter in turn far exceeds that of larger fishes preying on small fishes. Such small fishes as anchovies, sardines, and herring actually make up the bulk of the world's total catch of fish. As the exploitation of living ocean resources becomes more and more intensive, man will sooner or later look into the possibility of utilizing small planktonic animals, the abundance of which is enormous.

On a very limited scale, zooplankton has been used for many years in some countries of Asia. In Japan, for example, brackish or inshore species of mysids (*Anisomysis*, *Acanthomysis*, and *Neomysis*) have been used as materials for a traditional food called "tsukudani" and also as feeds for aquaculture. A deep-sea pelagic species of sergestid shrimp (*Sergestes lucens*), which grows to 40-50 millimeters, has long been processed into dried shrimp. In Southeast Asia (Malaysia, Thailand, Indonesia, and Singapore), shrimp paste manufactured from inshore species of sergestid shrimps, mysids, and other small crustaceans has been a popular food consumed in substantial quantities. The total amount of zooplankton now utilized, however, is negligible compared with the amount available in any part of the ocean.

For large-scale harvesting of zooplankton, certain conditions would have to be met. It would not be economically feasible to harvest zooplankton indiscriminately. Harvesting must be done in areas where dense concentrations of larger forms of zooplankton occur, and special plankton fisheries must be developed for this purpose. Such concentrations of larger forms are found in many areas at certain times.

The Antarctic Krill — There is general agreement, among scientists, that one of the most realistic targets would be the exploitation of the enormous resources of antarctic euphausids (krills), particularly *Euphausia superba*. The species occurs only in the antarctic (i.e., south of the Antarctic Convergence), and is particularly abundant in waters off South Georgia and around Antarctica near the edge of the pack-ice. Vertically, it occurs to a depth of several hundred meters at larval stages, but adults are often found in dense concentrations in the surface layer, forming patches of various sizes and shapes. Sexual maturity is reached in about two years, with an average size of 50 millimeters.

The krill is the most important food of whalebone whales migrating into the antarctic in the summer; it very often constitutes the entire stomach contents of whalebone whales caught there. Many other animals, including seals, birds, and fishes, also depend on the krill for subsistence. (See Figure VIII–6)

Although no reliable measurements are available, the total annual production of *Euphausia superba* might be as much as one-half of the total production at the level of herbivores. Based on the estimated amount of the krill eaten by whalebone whales in the antarctic when the whale stocks were large (they have been reduced greatly by overexploitation), the potential yield of *Euphausia superba*, when fully exploited, might be as high as 50 to 100 million metric tons, or roughly equal to the present total fishery yield from the entire world ocean.

For some years, the Russians have been conducting experiments in the antarctic to develop methods of catching and processing the krill. They have used large surface trawls and pumps to collect the krill, which have then been processed into meal or paste, and oil. The krill meal has a reasonably high protein concentra-

Figure VIII–6 — AN ANTARCTIC FOOD CHAIN

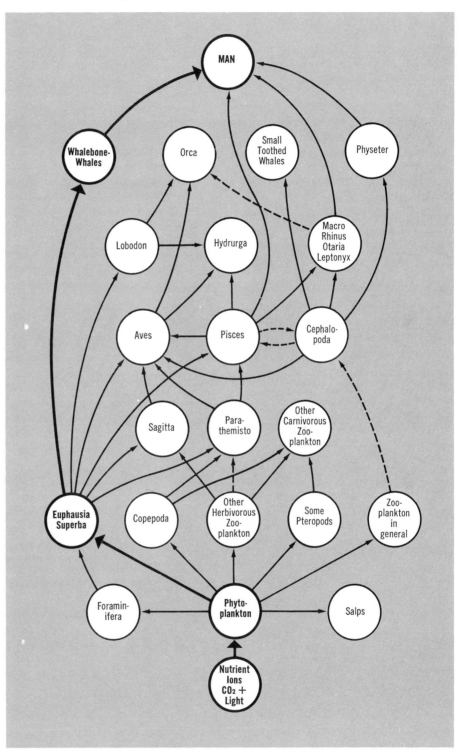

The diagram shows some of the major food chains found in the antarctic. Note that the chain to the whalebone whales is relatively direct; the organic material synthesized by the phytoplankton passes through only one intermediate animal, the krill *(Euphausia superba)*, before becoming transformed into whale flesh. This direct change of plankton is extraordinary and a notable exception to the normally low efficiency of the conversion of organic material from the sea.

tion and the oil is rich in vitamins. The high proportion of unusable chitin (in the shell of the krill) and the rapid spoilage rate present technological problems. But these problems will be solved sooner or later, and the commercial exploitation of the antarctic krill might become a realistic proposition in the future. The Japanese have also shown some interest; research into the exploitation of the krill is now part of their national oceanographic program, although they have not done very much so far.

There are many other areas in the world ocean where large concentrations of euphausids (of sizes smaller than *Euphausia superba*) are found, but the possibility of exploiting them appears even more remote than in the case of the antarctic krill.

The California Red Crab — Another form of zooplankton that has attracted much attention is the Cali-

fornia red crab, *Pleuroncodes planipes*. The animal has a pelagic phase as well as a demersal (bottom-living) phase. The relationships between the two are not well understood, although the pelagic phase appears to consist of relatively younger individuals. It is possible that the younger individuals can alternate between the two phases.

In their pelagic phase, the crabs are capable of grazing on phytoplankton, particularly larger diatoms. They appear in vast surface concentrations in waters off Baja California and become an important item in the diet of a variety of predators — birds, tunas, and whales, among others. The red crab in the demersal phase also occurs in dense concentrations.

Two species similar to the California red crab are commercially utilized in Chile, but their concentrations are found only on the bot-

tom. The exploitation of the California red crab for manufacturing meal for animal feeds has been suggested by many scientists. No experiments have been conducted, however, to test the commercial feasibility of catching and processing the crabs for this purpose.

In summary, the potential of zooplankton as a source of animal protein material is great, and man will go into this phase of exploitation of living ocean resources sooner or later. It is obvious that fisheries for zooplankton would have to be developed for specific forms of animals in specific areas. However, even for the species that appear most promising, such as the antarctic krill or the California red crab, much more work is needed both in developing the technology of catching and processing and in understanding the ecology of the species involved, before their commercial exploitation becomes a reality.

The Southern Oceans in the Production of Protein

The antarctic oceans can be defined for the purposes of this discussion as the region between 60° and 65° S. latitude in the three months of summer: January, February, and March. Such an area subtends 3 million nautical square miles of surface water. During the other nine months of the year, the weather and the extension of sea-ice obliterate this area as exploitable for proteins by man. Inclusion of sub-antarctic waters would triple this area and extend its time of usability at least two months longer: December through April.

This discussion involves only animal proteins. There are no sources of plant proteins, unless some may be obtainable from the giant kelp *Macrocystis*.

Protein Sources in the Antarctic

Historically, this 3 to 9 million square nautical miles of surface water, and the water-column under the surface, have been rich in biomass of animal proteins. The waters in summer have teemed with invertebrates, particularly the relatively small pelagic shrimp *Euphausia* and related genera. There have been many nesting birds, particularly on the sub-antarctic islands. Seals have been abundant from the ice-pack north to the sub-antarctic islands and elephant-seals on the sub-antarctic islands. Whales have been, in the past, the most conspicuous form of animal life, and in their abundance have supplied the whaling industry with the bulk of its raw materials, mostly

oil, for fifty years, 1910-1960. The supply of whales is practically gone now, however. Fish have been found sporadically in immense shoals, but with such irregularity as to time and place that no fishing industry has grown up in antarctic and sub-antarctic waters.

Species of Current Interest — With the demise of the whaling industry — which *can* return, but only after many years, and which never utilized the animal proteins to the fullest extent — and with the end, in the nineteenth century of the fur-sealing and elephant-sealing industry — which could have supplied proteins, but never did, only fur or oil — attention is now being directed toward harvesting euphausid shrimp and fish. As yet, however, no one is able to predict the success or failure of attempts to exploit these supplies of protein food in southern waters. There have also been some exploratory harvests of shrimp-seals ("crab-eater seal"), in order to obtain oil and hides and, possibly, meat.

The dominant and incredibly abundant species of euphausid is the two-inch *Euphausia superba*, also known as krill. This species often concentrates in such numbers that it colors the surface reddish and washes up on the decks of ships in heavy seas. It should be possible to harvest great quantities in slow hauls of fine-meshed nets — but what to do with them then?

The amount of shell in relation to meat may prevent utilization for human consumption, but the shrimp could be ground into a meal for poultry. As the shell is "soft," such a ground, dried meal might make a highly satisfactory protein additive to human food. The Soviets are the only group to have made exploratory harvests of *Euphausia superba*; what success they had or what they did with the shrimp is not clear.

Among other invertebrates, there are considerable numbers of giant barnacles, mussels, and stone-crabs in sub-antarctic waters; harvest of these can be increased if transportation to markets improves. None of them is important, however.

Seals, particularly the ice-floe seal, or shrimp-seal, *Lobodon carcinophaga* and the elephant-seal *Mirounga leonina* are potential protein foods for animal consumption if the entire carcass, except for hide and fat, is ground and frozen in bags of 25 to 50 pounds. Such fresh meat-meal would then include all meat, bones, and entrails, and be nourishing as an additive in poultry food, and as a staple for fur-bearing animals.

Populations of the southern fur-seals on sub-antarctic islands are growing steadily, to the point where limited harvest will be possible in a few years without damage to the stock. Here again, after hide and fat are removed and utilized, the entire carcass can be ground and frozen in bags and used as fresh meat-meal for poultry and fur animals. Such controlled exploitation could also include the large southern sea-lion *Otaria byroni*.

Exploitation by Man

The Norwegians have already conducted postwar sealing in the antarctic, principally on the shrimp-seal. Fishing is under exploratory investigation now by the United States, by Germany in cooperation with Argentina, and probably by the Japanese and Russians. Also, some Chilean fishing boats are now operating out of Punta Arenas in the Strait of Magellan.

The results of these investigations seem to have been negative in large yields per unit of effort. But marketable fish have appeared off South Georgia Island in numbers in the past, and these concentrations formerly gave a good yield to local whalers fishing for their own needs. More exploration might reveal some pattern of availability by species, locality, oceanographic conditions, and season.

Whaling has been the only industry in antarctic waters, indeed in the entire antarctic area, land or sea, except for the nineteenth-century fur- and elephant-sealing, which was conducted largely on sub-antarctic islands.

Whaling started in 1904 at South Georgia Island. From then until the worldwide depression of the early 1930's it grew in volume and geographic coverage to a very high point — too high, as was evident even then, for maintenance of a sufficient stock for continued high yield. In the late 1930's, whaling again increased greatly. It shut down during World War II, but increased again from 1946 to 1960, and it was obvious to most concerned people — all except the whaling companies — that the end was not far off. This end almost came in the late 1960's, and now the yield of whales is so low that whaling is conducted by two countries only, the U.S.S.R. and Japan, who harvest mainly the sei-whale, formerly an undesirable species because of its relatively small size (to 55 feet) and its relatively low yield of oil and meat. Some finbacks are taken, but the few remaining blue and humpback whales are completely protected.

There has been some effort by the whaling industry in the past and present, especially by Japan, to save some of the proteins from whales, either in the form of refrigerated fresh meat, meat extract, or meat-meal. But the main product has been oil.

The prognosis for whaling in the future is unclear. The industry may continue on a low scale, but surely it cannot grow as long as the populations of fin- and sei-whales are held to low levels. Humpbacks may increase to visible and perhaps harvestable numbers in five to ten years, but whaling from shore stations in lower latitudes on the winter-reproducing herds — same stocks — may then be undertaken.

Estimates of the time it will take for the blue whale to recover run as long as fifty years. All whaling should cease for a while to allow even the fin- and sei-whales to recover. They could then yield a fair harvest while the humpback and blue whales also recover. And emphasis should be on meat as well as oil.

Signs of Pollution — Contamination of the antarctic waters is not now pronounced, although DDT has been found in the fat of some penguins and, perhaps, seals. The prognosis for the future is not good, however, as is also the case with water and land environments for the entire world.

In summary, we have the following potential sources of animal proteins in antarctic and sub-antarctic waters:

1. Whales — large source originally, but much depleted by impact of man.

2. Seals — some depleted by im-pact of man, but others not; uncertain source.

3. Fish — not depleted, but uncertain as a source.

4. Euphausid shrimp — not depleted, and perhaps more abundant than before slaughter of whales, but uncertain as a source.

5. Other invertebrates — not de-pleted, but uncertain as a source.

Geographic considerations point to utilization of animal proteins from antarctic and sub-antarctic waters by nations of the southern hemisphere — Australia, Chile and Argentina, and South Africa. Perhaps more of South America and Africa can also benefit. Hitherto, most of the oil and other by-products from whales of antarctic waters have gone to the mass of humanity in the northern hemispheres. But this need not continue.

Scientific Aspects of North Pacific Fisheries

The fisheries of the North Pacific have expanded dramatically, particularly in the past decade. This expansion was the result of increased utilization of the variety of living resources available and exploitation of new grounds (both in a geographic and bathymetric sense). There has been, particularly in the northeastern Pacific, a dramatic increase in yields as a result of Soviet and Japanese fishing operations in the Bering Sea and through the arc of the Gulf of Alaska southward to central California. Figure VIII–7 shows a map of the world's fisheries.

The growth pattern of fisheries in this area, as with many areas of the world, has changed during the past fifteen years. Fisheries may grow to maturity, exceed the productive capacity of the stocks, and collapse in a matter of a few years. Hence, man's utilization of the ocean's biological potential suffers from an inability to cope with "pulse-type" fishing activities, lack of an effective organizational structure to implement management systems, and a rather shabby concept of the impact that selective fishing may have on the resource community. In addition, potential interaction of fisheries with other demands on the ocean and its seabed (mineral exploitation, petroleum, etc.) is not predictable.

In summary, the existing problems as they relate to North Pacific fisheries are: (a) how to optimize yields or dollars from what we are now using; (b) how to minimize multiple-use conflicts; (c) how to maintain the productivity of the system (avoiding degradation and product contamination); and (d) how to extract the rather extensive under-utilized biological material that inhabits this part of the ocean.

Status of Scientific Knowledge

Data Base — There is now a fair body of scientific information characterizing the fish and shellfish in the North Pacific Ocean. We have a relatively good understanding of the geographic and bathymetric distribution patterns of the demersal forms, and we are beginning to have a fairly good grasp of the general magnitude of these resources. The North Pacific pelagic overshelf species are also relatively well known, as are their distribution and behavior features. Our understanding of the distribution features and magnitude of the pelagic oceanic species is far less good. Knowledge of the types, distribution, and abundance of benthic invertebrates, although far from perfect, is probably adequate to get some gross concept of their potential contribution as food for man. By contrast, our knowledge of pelagic invertebrates, even in the shallower waters, is quite poor; and we have only a rudimentary understanding of the community, their distribution, abundance, and the quantities that might be available as a food supply for mankind.

We have fair information on seasonal and bathymetric migratory patterns for two dozen or more species of fishes in the northeastern Pacific, and perhaps no better in the western Pacific. However, from these data we cannot formulate a general model of the seasonal distribution patterns of biological matter. The specifics of such movement and migration on many species are absent. Our knowledge of the factors that influence behavior and gross distributional patterns of adults is also rudimentary, and we know even less concerning hydrological parameters that are critical in determining survival of the young.

The underlying processes for determining year-class strength, cyclic

Figure VIII-7 — DISTRIBUTION OF THE WORLD'S FISHERIES

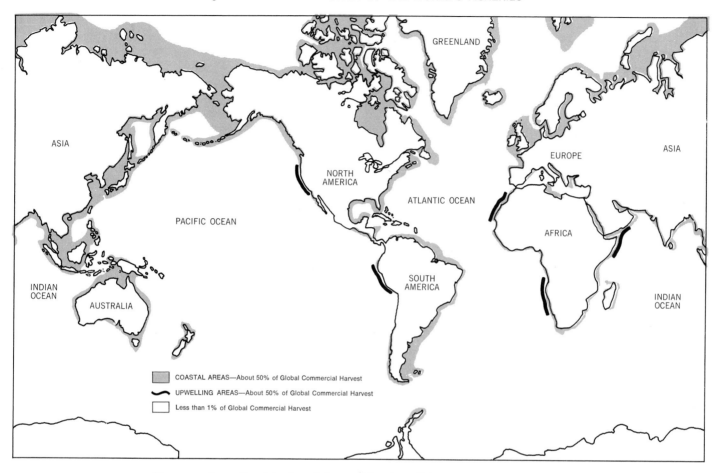

COASTAL AREAS—About 50% of Global Commercial Harvest

UPWELLING AREAS—About 50% of Global Commercial Harvest

Less than 1% of Global Commercial Harvest

The map shows the fisheries of the world today. Fish production in the future will depend on the responses of this system to exploitation and on the opportunities that may derive from a better understanding of the system. One critical factor is the total fish production of the oceans, which has recently been estimated to be only four times greater than the 1968 catch, for corresponding species. Another is the vital role played in estuaries and along coastlines, where pollution threatens the nurseries of many commercial species. A third is the role of upwelling. Weather is important to the success of fishing, and further improvements in local weather forecasting await a better understanding of larger-scale meteorological phenomena. Altogether, the systems of air, water, and life are intimately interwoven in the production of fishery yields.

dominance, and succession in the ocean communities are the subject of considerable rhetoric, most of which is rather fanciful. Hence, we have not been able to get a firm grasp of the relationship between parental stock and subsequent recruitment, nor have we been able to interpret the implications of environmental contamination (degradation) on early life-history phases of marine fauna.

Knowledge of the environment that various groups of commercially exploited fish and shellfish inhabit has improved considerably in the past decade, although it is descriptive in character. We can probably state that we now have a fairly firm estimate of mortality coefficients (mortality, growth rates, etc.) for representative species that are subject to commercial fishing. It is possible that

we can generalize and make fairly good estimates for species for which these coefficients have not been established. Similarly, we are starting to get a fix on the response of single-species fisheries to the mortality resulting from man's exploitation.

Limitations — By contrast, however, the existing models are inadequate to cope with multi-species or

243

community exploitation. The concept of optimizing yields from single species, although argumentative, is established in principle. But models are not yet available on which to base an aggregate species-management rationale, and we haven't the foggiest idea of the possibilities of exploiting marine fishes on a range-management concept. Finally, although there is a good body of information relating to feeding patterns of fish, the trophodynamics, or energetics, of food-chain systems are still poorly understood and are, to a degree, rooted in mythology.

Recent Additions to Scientific Knowledge — Considerable new information on the distribution, magnitudes, and community aspects of demersal and benthic fishery resources has been compiled, particularly during the past decade for certain areas of the North Pacific.

Important among these are the recent Soviet works (four volumes) which provide life-history data and information on the dynamic aspects of the fish and shellfish resources of the Bering Sea and Gulf of Alaska. These volumes also include new contributions as related to benthic communities, some new descriptive oceanography, and an attempt to establish environmental-resource relationships. In addition, the recent contribution to the understanding of the Kuroshio Current should provide a basis on which to examine its influence on the adjacent fishery resources.

The contribution of oceanography to fisheries in the past decade lies largely in describing the environment. This contribution must be tempered, however, by the fact that the descriptive features to date are too gross to deal effectively with some problems, particularly those relating to survival of eggs, larvae, and young of species that are commercially utilized. Furthermore, the availability of theoretical formulation, including mathematical modeling, exceeds our empirical capacity to evaluate modeling forecasts.

Needed Scientific Advances

The major scientific controversies concerning the North Pacific fisheries relate to (a) the total possible contributions of its elements to the food stream, (b) the importance of mariculture vis-à-vis developing more efficient systems to utilize wild stocks, and (c) the character of relationships between adult populations and recruitment.

Fisheries Management — Among the priorities for scientific advance is the need to develop management concepts and techniques for timely implementation of management. Fisheries management has been and continues to be largely remedial in character. We need to cope with the problem of pulse-fishing activities, examine it as a theoretical basis for utilizing ocean resources, and find mechanisms that will allow us to forecast trends sufficiently in advance of their manifestation to implement effective management. The concept must cope with managing aggregates as well as single species.

The most critical scientific needs as regards management and use of North Pacific fisheries relate to deriving the nature of the stock recruitment relationship, the reaction of multi-species fisheries, the prediction of environmental factors that bring about year-class fluctuations or otherwise influence stock recruitment relationships, and a clear, fundamental understanding of the potential impact of persistent pesticides and other foreign substances on the productivity of the total ocean food chain, as well as the potential contamination of the food sources.

A number of fishery resources in the North Pacific appear to have been overexploited, resulting in loss of food potentials. This seems to have been the product of failure to find an effective means of implementing management decisions and the inability of existing monitoring systems to detect important changes in sufficient time to react in a responsive manner.

Resource Assessment — In addition to the problems of managing exploited resources, there is a real need to evolve the fishing strategy that will allow us to use the full potential in the ocean. This may require considerable information on the behavior patterns of species (a) in the natural state, (b) in response to existing fishing gears, and (c) in response to physical or chemical stimuli that might be used for herding or aggregating marine life.

One of the shortcomings is technological instrumentation to carry out resource-assessment activities. Most of the classical methods are not really effective for the task. One of the real weaknesses of the data is that they do not provide contemporary information. The greatest success is likely to come from the development of sonar assessment techniques. Integration of returned echoes, in conjunction with a means of identifying the target, could provide a reliable method for obtaining stock data over wide areas within reasonable costs. Acoustic holography offers some promise of fish identification detected at relatively close ranges.

Impact of Pollution — Perhaps the greatest urgency relates to the area of the multiple demands on the ocean's environment. The hazards of pollution in the North Pacific and the potential contamination of the food resources therein are major questions that must be answered in the next decade. We are only beginning to consider the possible implication of man's multi-purpose needs on the ocean's environment. The whole field of pollution — ranging from persistent pesticides and other industrial chemicals to oil pollution and the like — obviously represents a danger which is not adequately understood.

These dangers must include potential alteration of the environment as the result of the heat added as a by-product of generating electricity by nuclear means. The whole concept of the ocean's capacity to produce food for man and the technological capacity to use it is a subject of current discussion. The impact of loss of these resources or inability to develop their potential must be considered in evaluating future food sources.

We cannot assume that pollution problems will be resolved in time to maintain present biological production. Indeed, man's multi-purpose needs to use the water environment for transport, to exploit its mineral potential, to develop it for real estate and industrial purposes, and to use it to dispense his waste products increase the likelihood that we may ultimately degrade the general productivity of the sea. In this respect, the criterion of sublethal level of tolerance is irrelevant if the accretion of pollutants continues. Time, in this instance, does not possess the infinite quality usually ascribed to it.

Some Scientific Problems Associated With Aquatic Mammals

The following list of problems associated with aquatic mammals is made up mostly of broad, general problems. There are also many specialized problems, such as diving physiology or the ecology of specific parasites.

Pollution Hazards

Effect of Pesticides, Petroleum, and Other Pollutants on Marine Mammals — The flow of pesticides and other chemical pollutants into the ocean is concentrated in marine mammals since they are at the top of the food chain. (See Figure VIII–8) It is known that chlorinated hydrocarbons are in the tissues of marine mammals in every part of the world. The effect of the chemicals is not at all known. A possibility exists that the apparent high rate of premature births in California sea-lions is related to pollutants. Little is known about the effect of petroleum on marine mammals except that it reduces the insulating capability of fur. This is lethal for sea otters and fur seals in the marine environment and for the furred fresh-water mammals such as otter, mink, muskrat, and beaver.

Pollution of the types mentioned is continually increasing. Unless the hazards are understood, marine mammal populations can be reduced or lost before the potential effects of the hazard are realized. A variety of sampling experiments and tests with captive animals can be devised to show the effects of the pollutants.

Conservation and Management of Stocks

Management of World Whale Stocks to Preserve the Species and Restore a Resource — Short-term economic gain has been the overriding consideration in the exploitation of the large species of whales. Pursuit of this end has resulted in depletion

Figure VIII–8 — THE FATE AND DISTRIBUTION OF MARINE POLLUTANTS

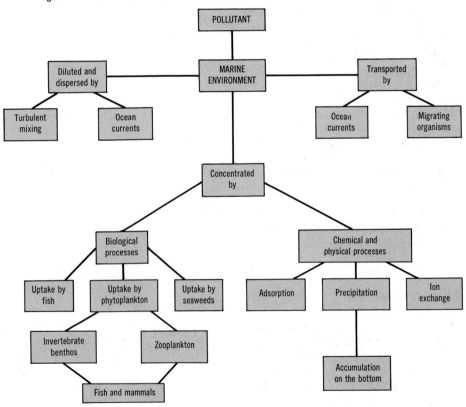

The diagram shows the various processes that determine the fate and distribution of pollutants in the marine environment. Under favorable conditions, the pollutants are diluted, dispersed, and transported by turbulent mixing, ocean currents, and migrating organisms. Unfortunately, the oceans are not mixed thoroughly and high concentrations of pollutants exist in local areas. In addition, there are biological, chemical, and physical processes taking place that concentrate pollutants and lead the pollution back to man.

of all of the large whales with the possible exception of sperm whales. Sufficient biological and statistical knowledge is now available to put a rational management system into effect. In part, this may have been done. Continued studies are needed, however, to make certain that the quotas already in effect can be supported by the whale stocks (to date, populations of large whales have been measured principally by catch effort) and to help in the establishment of new quotas and regulations. This will require a combination of biological, statistical, and diplomatic effort.

International Study and Conservation Agreements on the Ice-Seals of the Bering and Chukchi Seas — The expansion of commercial killing of ice-seals (ribbon-, bearded-, and harbor-seals — ringed-seals are little hunted) by the Soviet Union has resulted in depletion of the ribbon-seal population and has put an added strain on the subsistence living of the Alaska Eskimo. There is a need, agreed to in principle by the United States and the U.S.S.R., for rational harvesting of the ice-seals, arranged by an international agreement. Cooperation between countries increases the effectiveness of data collecting and reduces the effort required of each party.

The knowledge needed to manage ice-seal populations is difficult to collect. Harvest quotas set on a trial-and-error basis may be used temporarily until more data are available.

An International Policy on Exploiting the Seals of the Antarctic — World whaling and the harp-seal hunting in the North Atlantic yield less and less. As a result, nations such as the U.S.S.R. and Norway have begun to look at the seals of Antarctica as a source of leather and oil. An international policy covering quotas that can be killed, by species and area, is still incompletely formulated. Some effort has been devoted toward developing an international plan. This work should be continued even though the basic data for quotas

is difficult to assemble and provisional quotas will need to be established at first.

The main protection for antarctic seals is the hostile environment. An opportunity thus exists to exploit marine mammal populations in a rational way.

The Conservation of Dolphins that are Killed in the Yellow-Fin Tuna Industry — The fishermen catching yellow-fin tuna off Central America with purse seines use schools of dolphins as indicators of tuna. The tuna, for unknown reasons, are under the porpoise schools and follow along with them. The purse seine is set around the dolphins and catches both dolphins and tuna. (See Figure VIII–9) Observers estimate that five dolphins are killed for each ton of tuna caught. Fishermen would like to release the dolphins to use again in finding tuna but no effective way of releasing them has been devised. A solution to the problem will require further study of dolphin behavior and experiments in net design.

Factors Affecting Distribution

Mechanisms Used by Marine Mammals to Guide Migration — Some marine mammals make extensive annual migrations. A variety of speculative suggestions have been made on how the mammals are able to navigate regardless of weather conditions and daylight or darkness. In fact, however, little is known about the mechanisms used to guide migration. The process appears to be more sophisticated than some of the theories might suggest. Discovery of these mechanisms would be of great biological significance and also important in human navigation and communication.

The methods of investigation that will explain how accurate navigation over thousands of miles is accomplished are not well worked out. A combination of approaches will probably be necessary.

Relation of Oceanographic Conditions to the Distribution of

Figure VIII–9 — A PURSE SEINE

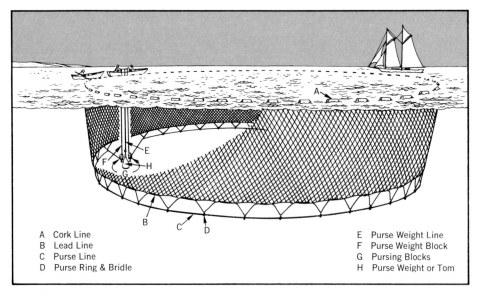

A	Cork Line	E	Purse Weight Line
B	Lead Line	F	Purse Weight Block
C	Purse Line	G	Pursing Blocks
D	Purse Ring & Bridle	H	Purse Weight or Tom

The sketch shows a purse seine being set. The net is placed in the water. The upper edge is kept afloat with buoys, while the lower edge sinks due to weight. The net is drawn around a large volume of water. It is possible to close off the bottom by pulling the net together, thus enclosing any fish within the volume. The entire seine — and all its contents — can then be picked out of the water.

Marine Mammals — Oceanographic conditions apparently have a strong influence on the survival of marine mammals, particularly during their first year. However, satisfactory correlations have not yet been demonstrated. Analysis of the accumulating data on ocean conditions can give a much better understanding of the ecology of marine mammals than now exists. Unless this can be done an impasse may have been reached in population studies on mammals such as the northern fur seal that spends many months at sea. Reasons for the great variation in survival of year classes cannot be found in the land environment.

3. ESTUARIES AND COASTAL ZONES

The Relationship of Fisheries to Estuaries, With Special Reference to Puget Sound

The total estuarine system of Puget Sound has historically provided food, recreation, and great aesthetic value to increasing numbers of people. Other major uses include shipping and waste disposal. Potential uses may involve oil exploration and drilling, utilization of other under-water nonrenewable resources, provision of more land and living space by modification of shallow water areas, and, of course, a great increase in food production through development of various types of aquaculture or even through enlightened manipulation and control of the larger man-made variables. It is the purpose of the following statement to point out the necessity for identifying existing and future goals and problems related to the fisheries of Puget Sound.

There is at present no scientific basis for deciding how to optimize the fisheries of Puget Sound while giving, at the same time, full attention to the other existing and potential uses of the estuary. Interaction among the multiple uses of Puget Sound can be expected to be either detrimental or beneficial to the fisheries, but as yet the places and extent of interaction are poorly known, the future significance of interaction is unpredictable, and therefore the opportunities for planned control are severely limited.

Types of Information Needed

To achieve a scientific basis for action there must first be an acceptable definition of the goal or goals being sought. That is, what benefits does man expect to realize from an estuarine system: food, recreation, tourism, industry, . . . ? For the purpose of this statement it is presumed that viable sport and commercial fisheries (both fish and shellfish) are accepted goals and that they are so strongly desired that any factor which significantly affects them should be identified as fully as possible.

Biological—The species of fish comprising the commercial and sport fisheries of Puget Sound are well known, and relatively good catch statistics are available for most of them. We have developed, and are continuing to develop, the capabilities to observe and record changes in fishery populations. Relationships between various species of fish populations, their environment, and the ultimate causes of change, however, are not well understood at present. For example, what effect does exploitation at one trophic level (e.g., herring) have on the abundance of fish at a higher level (e.g., salmon)? Predictions of changes in fish populations are still in their infancy and in most cases will remain so until these causes for change are better understood. Important questions need answers in this area. For example, how does progress in serving industrial and residential development needs affect the nursery areas and food-chain organisms that support the desired fish and shellfish species intended for commercial and recreational harvest?

Environmental — These are the environmental problems currently affecting the fish and shellfish species and their fisheries in Puget Sound:

1. Physical degradation.

   (a) Marinas, breakwaters, docks, landfills (residential and industrial), log booming, and sawmills.

   (b) Dredging, rechannelling of river mouths and estuarine areas.

   (c) Altered river discharge patterns due to man's activities.

   (d) Thermal power sites.

      1) Heat discharge.

      2) Screening of intake.

      3) Use of biocides.

      4) Radioactive uptake in food chain.

   (e) Litter pollution (disposal of garbage and other solid waste).

   (f) Bio-fouling (which has sometimes made gill nets in Puget Sound totally ineffective).

2. Organic and inorganic degradation.

   (a) Pulp-mill discharge.

   (b) Sewage discharge (including detergents and other household wastes).

   (c) Chemical pollutants (aluminum refineries, smelters, metal-plating).

   (d) Petroleum-product pollution (oil refineries and petrochemical plants).

   (e) Toxicants from plastics manufacturing.

   (f) Agricultural wastes; organic and inorganic fertilizers.

   (g) Siltation and debris from logging activities.

3. Possibilities for beneficial effects from man's activities.

   (a) Planned addition and dispersion of nutrients.

   (b) Selective warming by use of water discharged from power plants.

   (c) Control of unwanted species by manipulation of appropriate variables.

Political, Social, and Economic — How are diverse value measurements equated for the several benefits that may be derived from an estuary? What is the biological value of clean water? The aesthetic value? What is the value of a recreational fishery?

Gaps in Existing Knowledge

If the fisheries constitute only one of the values to be realized from an estuary, then satisfactory management of the entire system cannot be achieved unless there is a means of judging the other values and of expressing the possible interactions to be expected as the renewable and nonrenewable resources are harvested. Relative values cannot be judged unless there is comprehensive knowledge available about the estuary.

Descriptive Information —There is an immediate need for more descriptive information about Puget Sound. Patterns of water circulation need particular study, including the amount of fresh water in the system, amount and location of runoff, tides, winds, and density differences. Such information will be indispensable if the fisheries are to be protected from planned and unplanned disposal of waste in Puget Sound. It is entirely possible that the judicious addition of nutrients from domestic and agricultural sources might be accomplished in a manner to enhance the productivity of the fisheries. The extent of nonrenewable resources (oil, sand, aggregate) within Puget Sound should be more fully known. Directly or indirectly, their extraction could have a significant effect on the fisheries.

Baseline Studies — To fill another large gap in existing knowledge of Puget Sound, comprehensive baseline studies of present conditions—chemical, physical, and biological—are needed. Man-caused changes can hardly be evaluated unless a norm is known against which the deviations may be judged. Time-series studies of physical and chemical factors are required, as well as determination of the amounts and kinds of organisms and appropriate information on their condition. These basic studies would necessarily deal with each phase of an organism's life cycle in order to uncover, for particular species (e.g., English sole), the requirements while on the spawning grounds, in the planktonic phase, in nursery areas, and as a growing juvenile and adult. It is also vital to learn how much deviation in habitat conditions a fish or shellfish can tolerate and to know the optimum preferred level of each important environmental parameter. The lower trophic levels would also require detailed attention, inasmuch as they are indispensable to the continued harvest of fish and shellfish.

Economic Values — Until better economic measures are developed for evaluating the fishery resource, fish and shellfish species more frequently than not will continue to receive relatively low priority when compared to other competitive and detrimental uses of the Puget Sound estuary. Figure VIII–10 presents data for a similar situation in Corpus Christi Bay.

Modeling Studies — After suitable data are at hand, a modeling study should be conducted. By this means the organic-matter budget of Puget Sound could be simulated. The probable role of organisms as indicators of a changing environment could be studied. Furthermore, a theoretical treatment could be expected to aid in establishing an effective long-term sampling plan and in implementing a reasonably good predictive ability concerning changes in fish populations. Economic values and sociopolitical considerations must also be used in such a model if all areas of consideration for decisionmakers are to be included.

Figure VIII–10 — VALUE OF ECONOMIC ACTIVITIES IN CORPUS CHRISTI BAY

Economic activity	Dollars per acre per year
Biological-aesthetic uses	
Tourist and local resident expenditure	152
Commercial fishing	15
Total biological-aesthetic uses	167
Industrial uses	
Oil, gas, and shell	130
Cooling water	10
Transportation savings in shipping	64
Effluent disposal savings	1
Total industrial uses	205
Total dollar yield	372

The chart gives an estimate of the dollar value of major activities in Corpus Christi Bay during 1958. No one user was predominant, so no claim could be made for predominant right to use of the bay on economic grounds. Note the small dollar value of commercial fishing and the large value of aesthetic and mining uses.

Acquisition of Needed Information

Existing federal, state, and private agencies are fully capable of gathering and interpreting all the technical data that may be pertinent to an understanding of fisheries problems as related to the estuarine features of Puget Sound. The accumulation of certain types of basic data can proceed at once; for example, water circulation, life history and ecological studies of selected fish and shellfish, and tolerance of estuarine organisms (including ones at any level of the food chain) to induced environmental changes. But the full range of needed information cannot be anticipated until at least a broad definition of the desired goals has been achieved. Public participation in the selection of goals that are practical for the present and future management of the Puget Sound estuary will necessitate clarification of the alternative uses of the estuary that are available and their resulting effect on the commercial and recreational fisheries in Puget Sound. Identification of alternative uses of the Puget Sound estuary becomes, therefore, an immediate and pressing need.

Once the needed information for achieving desired goals is at hand, the implementation of recommended actions might well involve federal, state, local, private, and industrial groups. Communication between the involved agencies and groups is indispensable. Concerted action or unified jurisdictional authority must be established in order to assure appropriate execution of an adopted plan. A variety of formal and informal schemes are presently used to achieve at least partial coordination between agencies with overlapping authority and responsibilities relating to Puget Sound. A mechanism to guarantee consultation between agencies is needed, as well as a method to provide for regulatory actions that are consistent with respect to accepted objectives.

Prospects for Aquaculture

As a result of the rapid increase of interest in aquaculture, aquatic biologists and fishery biologists who are familiar with the inshore areas of the oceans have been besieged with questions from industrialists. These questions most often concern the costs of farming and the profit to be realized.

Major Considerations

There are no simple answers, for the factors involved are more complex than they might at first appear to be. A fishery biologist would need to possess the knowledge and skills of a variety of specialists to provide adequate answers. For instance, fishery biologists are rarely marketing specialists. They have traditionally been trained to manage populations of fish and shellfish from the standpoint of providing a maximum sustainable yield in terms of numbers of fish or weight of fish from a particular exploited stock. Only in recent years have fishery economists pointed out that a vital aspect of managing fisheries is the economic yield. Considering costs to harvest and market value, fishery economists ask at what level of fishing can the maximum economic yield to the fishery be realized.

To minimize costs it is often necessary to limit fishing effort, since harvesting is carried out by inefficient means because of restrictions on efficient gear or requirements of more vessels and men than are needed to harvest the crop. Information necessary to determine the optimum economic level of harvesting stocks from many fisheries is still unavailable.

The biologist is generally ill-prepared to present the type of information that industry is requesting for aquaculture. Unfortunately, the answer is very complicated, involving a host of variables.

Species Selection — There are questions the biologist is well qualified to answer, however, such as the feasibility of farming a certain few species. If he is asked about shrimp, for example, he can point out the extent of the available biological knowledge on this species and where difficulties may arise that will be costly to the investors. If asked about other species (for example, spiny lobster or the common pompano), he must reply that no one has reared these animals from eggs to adults and that a lot of basic research must be done before that species will be suitable for farming from a biological standpoint, which is, in turn, many steps and years away from farming at any economically profitable level. Suppose, for example, that larval life of the spiny lobster turns out to last five or six months; then the cost of rearing the lobster through these stages can be so high as to be unprofitable.

Furthermore, biological research, like everything else today, is extremely expensive. To obtain what might seem to be answers to simple, straightforward biological questions can be very costly, and even then the answers obtained may pertain only to a certain set of conditions tested in the experiments; under another set of circumstances, the biologist might find quite different results from his research.

Location — In addition to the selection of a farmable species, potential profit also depends upon the choice of a suitable geographic area. It is becoming increasingly difficult to find large estuarine areas and water supplies that are unpolluted and that provide the necessary requirements for aquaculture. Any hope of estuarine sea farming in many areas, especially those close to large cities, must be abandoned immediately because suitable areas cannot be found, or, if they are available, are priced prohibitively. Areas away from large cities offer greater hope for aquaculture, but the cost of just the land investment can be substantial, especially in sea farming.

Feed — Aside from finding suitable locations, a number of other important aspects can greatly affect fish-farm production and, hence, profits. Feeding, of course, is high on the list. What feeds are required for the farmed species as young and adults is important in the profit equation. Do these feeds provide rapid growth and high survival? Research into nutrition requirements has resulted in foods designed specially for trout and channel catfish in freshwater. But for many of the animals considered for sea farming, biologists are unsure of what foods they consume in nature, let alone what is the most desirable food for these species in captivity. This important quantity in the formula must be solved before costs and potential profit from mariculture can be estimated.

Manpower and Technology — What sort of personnel are available to operate a sea farm in a particular area bears on the potential profit. Some species require only rather menial tasks; others require skilled personnel or trainable persons. For example, mass rearing of microorganisms is a necessity. Again, until answers to these questions can be provided, the amount of profit possible is only speculation. In many areas of aquaculture today technology is moving rapidly, thereby making speculation based on today's techniques of little value tomorrow.

Market Information — Many reports in the past five years or so have produced abundant information on how many fish can be obtained from a certain amount of water in a particular time period. There is little freshwater farming and even less sea farming in the United States at the present time; therefore these figures have been obtained in other areas of the world. Since they give some guidelines as to productivity they are valuable in themselves, but they must be examined carefully. What sort of market exists for the species? In some areas of the world very small fish are an important market item. In the United States this is not the case. Also, we might ask whether this high production is the result of some unusually fortunate combination of circumstances? For example, when we consider the extremely high production of rafted mussels in the Bay of Vigo (Spain), where three-dimensional water use is practiced, we find that plankton is unusually rich. In some areas of Asia where human and farm sewage is used as fertilizer, production is extraordinary. At this time, in many of the developed countries, there would seem to be little hope of using fertilizers of this kind. It should be added that the time is probably approaching when we will have to utilize these wastes fully, but in a more sophisticated way, and fish farms are one logical place for doing so.

The entire present and potential market for any particular species must be examined with care before the question of potential profit can be answered. This is obviously within the expertise of the market specialists, not the biologists. The species considered now in the developed countries are those with high market demand and high price. However, if the species can be raised in large quantities, this picture can be altered greatly: they can become a popular consumer item and be available to a larger segment of the consumer population. Also, a number of other species are profitable to raise, but a lot of money would have to be spent on market promotion before the housewife would consider purchasing them.

Conservation Laws — The status of conservation laws can greatly affect profit from aquaculture. These must be relaxed to give the farmer complete freedom to market any size of fish any time of the year. Put another way, the farmer must not have to try to fit his operation into a scheme of laws supposedly designed to conserve stocks of wild fish. Two sets of laws concerning the same species should be in effect — one for the fishermen and one for the farmers. Conservation groups place restrictions on certain times of the year for extended periods. It is during these times that a substantial profit can be realized by sea farmers, who can control their production so that they can harvest at times of peak demand. This is common procedure in the Philippines, where milkfish are harvested during the monsoon season when fishermen cannot fish. In Japan, Fuginaga takes advantage of the great demand for live shrimp during their holiday season in order to obtain a premium price for his product.

Technology — There are many other important considerations which prevent anyone trained in a particular discipline from being in a position to provide answers to questions concerning costs and profits in fish farming. Engineering aspects of building ponds, sealing, and providing the necessary water flow are important facts needed for profitable aquaculture. Some corporation research and development personnel are visiting biologists as a means of keeping up on the trends in research and the feasibility of profitable aquaculture. They find that there is only a little commercial fish farming in the United States and that those operations that do exist are on a small scale. Even without the very formidable roadblock of the reluctance of private business to disclose costs and profits to would-be competitors, there is no long history of aquaculture in this country to permit estimates of average cost or average profit.

Current Research Activity

The larger, more progressive corporations are doing more than asking questions of the biologists. They are paying for research on the biological and marketing aspects of aquaculture in order to judge whether their corporations should enter into these ventures.

Despite the lack of economic data to justify large-scale aquaculture in developed countries, many facts and principles gained from biological research and from common sense serve as guidelines for anyone interested in fish farming. The developed countries have the technology to farm their waters efficiently, but they lack the decades of experience that is available in Asia, for example. Aquaculture in the developed countries must be a profit-making venture, and since markets for many of the species suggested for this are already present, or can be developed with little promotion, it would seem that it could indeed be profitable. In the developed countries, too, there has been a boom in oceanic research. A considerable share of the results of this scientific research is applicable to mariculture. It is quite obvious that the greatest potential exists for those species that feed low on the food chain, such as some of the crustaceans and mollusks. Figure VIII–11 shows one such scheme.

Biologists who are trying to evaluate the status and near future potential of aquaculture recognize that its maximum effort will be in the near shore waters where there is substantial evidence of extremely high fertility. Of course, the matter of ownership and operating costs becomes more complicated and costly as the distance from shore increases. In at least one United States oyster-farming operation, radar has been

used to detect trespassers into leased or owned bottoms who may be helping themselves to the ingredients for a stew, from private stock. In Spain, Japan, and the State of Washington, scientists and sea farmers have clearly demonstrated that high oyster production is possible by using hanging cultures, thereby utilizing all three dimensions of the water. There is no doubt that more use can be made of effluents from electrical power

plants, especially at the cooler latitudes where ponds or tanks using the warm-water effluent from generating stations can greatly lengthen the growing period of fish and shellfish.

A number of research projects on mariculture are providing much-needed research results. At the Florida Power and Light Company's new power plant, about forty miles south

Figure VIII–11 — SCHEME FOR USING SEWAGE IN AQUACULTURE

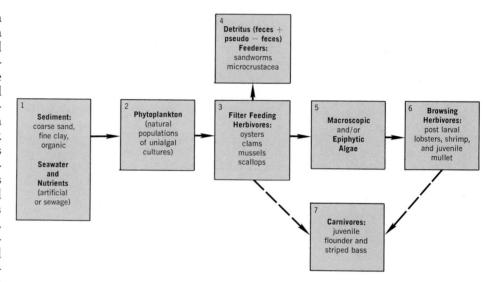

The diagram summarizes a continuous-flow food chain that may be operated in various permutations and combinations depending on the desired result. The system consists of the following components:

(1) Diluted (about 10%) sewage effluent as a growth medium for (2) a continuous culture of natural, mixed phytoplankton, which is harvested at the rate of 50% of the culture per day and passed through (3) suspended cultures (strings or racks) of filter-feeding bivalve mollusks (oysters, clams, mussels, or scallops), the phytoplankton diluted with filtered running seawater and so presented to a sufficient number of mollusks that almost all of the suspended algal cells are removed from the water by the animals. (4) Feces and pseudo-feces produced by the mollusks are deposited on the surface of the sand substrate of the animal culture tanks where this material is fed upon by sandworms, bloodworms, and/or other deposit feeders.

(5) Water flowing through the mollusk compartment containing inorganic and organic nutrients regenerated by the animals is passed into an additional chamber containing macroscopic algae and/or epiphytic, filamentous algae which utilize the regenerated nutrients. (6) The epiphytic algae and associated microbiota serve as food for browsing animals such as juvenile lobsters, shrimp, mullet, or other suitable animals.

(7) Although not part of a continuous-flow system, when steady-state equilibrium conditions are reached, animals from any of the above compartments may be fed to carnivores (juvenile striped bass, flounder, and lobsters are examples of readily available species) on a daily-ration basis, the success of this stage being dependent upon the operation of a large enough system to provide a constant supply of food over a sufficiently long period of time to the carnivores.

of the University of Miami's Institute of Marine Sciences, researchers are developing techniques to rear pink shrimp. There are seven ponds, which range from one-quarter acre to one acre, and a hatchery building wherein the stock is raised from egg to adult through the difficult larval stages. The questions that researchers are asking is whether it is possible to mass-produce pink shrimp with high survival and rapid growth rates on an economic basis, what is the best food for these shrimp, and what are the costs for food and labor. This research began a year or two ago, and progress has been gratifying. Large numbers of young, estimated at about 10,000, have been reared from the egg.

Shrimp are also being raised to market size in ponds and fenced-off portions of a bay by a newly formed company, near Panama City, Florida. In this operation, between 10 and 20 million brown shrimp have been reared from the egg to post-larval stages.

In a number of National Marine Fisheries Service Laboratories (St. Petersburg Beach, Fla.; Oxford, Md.; Milford, Conn.; Panama City, Fla.; and Galveston, Tex.), research on mariculture beneficial to industry is being carried out. At state universities on the Gulf of Mexico and up the east coast of the United States, research is also being conducted on desirable species to provide industry with baseline information to allow them to carry out commercial operations in sea farming.

At the University of Miami's Institute of Marine Sciences, a graduate student has succeeded in rearing thirteen species of marine fish up to their juvenile stages from eggs caught drifting in the sea. Sea trout and flounder are included in the list and should attract the attention of sea farmers.

There is high hope for increased study of aquaculture, but much more research and investment will be necessary before the important answers are available for making decisions on the economic advisability of entering aquaculture on a large scale.

4. DYNAMICS OF LAKES

Lake Circulation Patterns

Lakes are large bodies of water which would be mostly stagnant except for the "stirring" influence of wind on their upper surface. In rare cases, lakes are part of a river system and the flow of water through them drives a pattern of circulation, while small heated ponds can have their own thermally induced circulations. In most other lakes, however, including the North American Great Lakes, wind stress is the prime mover of any "circulation" (i.e., more or less organized motions) and "mixing" (i.e., random motions leading to the dispersal of an admixture).

Man uses lakes for several purposes. Most important, perhaps, is the "aesthetic" use (building a house on a lakeshore), closely coupled to a "recreational" use (swimming, boating, etc.); lakes are also used as a source of food (fisheries), of fresh water supply, as a sink for waste materials (sewage), and for waste heat (power generation). Some lakes also serve as waterways. These uses conflict to some degree, and optimizing the use of, say, the Great Lakes is not a simple problem. For example, in many places around the Great Lakes, the only present alternative to using the lakes as a waste-heat sink for power generation is to build cooling towers, which would increase the costs of power generation quite appreciably. At the same time, it is not certain whether or how far the discharge of large quantities of warm water into the Great Lakes would have undesirable consequences for some other use of these lakes.

Conflicts between different lake uses are alleviated by lake "circulation" and "mixing." For example, none of the Great Lakes is in any sense "polluted" as a whole at present, although the water near the shores certainly is in many places. The difficulty is that the pollution is usually concentrated in an "influence zone" near an effluent source, which is usually located at the shore. If all waste matter and waste heat discharged into a lake were mixed with its entire body of water, there would be far less interference with other lake uses—although there are clearly limits to the advantage to be obtained in this manner.

The main cause of circulation and mixing in most lakes is the stress that the wind exerts at the air-water interface. The actual patterns of circulation are also determined by the shapes of the basins, the thermal (density) structure of the water, and, for large lakes, the rotation of the earth. The problem is basically one of physical oceanography (or physical "limnology," to be precise, although the behavior of lakes is usually discussed in the oceanographic literature). However, heat by solar radiation, evaporation heat loss (both affecting density structure), and wind stress are inputs the knowledge of which comes from meteorology.

Evaluation of Current Knowledge

Generally speaking, problems of a meteorological nature are better explored than those of the oceanographic kind. Most existing knowledge on physical limnology was developed in connection with biological studies, witness the highly authoritative *Treatise on Limnology* by Hutchinson. Indeed, several eminent workers in physical limnology started their careers as biological limnologists. Inevitably, then, the character of existing knowledge reflects a certain bias toward problems of biological importance. For ex-

ample, the annual cycle of temperature distribution in lakes (which has a direct bearing on life processes) is well explored, while the dynamics of medium- and large-scale motions is poorly understood. "Meteorological inputs" are also better known. While it would be a gross exaggeration to say that the problem of predicting wind stress over a water surface is solved, we can make a much closer estimate of this stress than of the speed of the current produced by it.

Wind Mixing — In greater detail, the "wind mixing" of the top layers of lakes, their yearly cycle of "overturn," and similar "local" phenomena are fairly well documented, even if the basic mechanics of these processes (e.g., the formation of steep "steps" in the thermocline) are only now beginning to be investigated. Inspiring fundamental work in this area has recently been reported from the Mediterranean and the Great Lakes and from laboratory simulation. These studies have been complemented by results obtained through computer modeling in connection with the numerical forecasting of ocean circulation. The small-scale structure of turbulence, of internal waves, their "breaking" and interaction with turbulence (leading to vertical mixing, particularly across the thermocline) are highly relevant to the mixing problem and are under investigation in a few places.

Wave-Like Motions — Among the large-scale motions in lakes, the best understood are the "seiches," or regular surface oscillations, usually started by bursts of wind. Perhaps the most prominent example is provided by the seiches in Lake Erie, which acquire economic importance due to their effect on the output of the Niagara power plant.

Internal waves and seiches of large scale often play an important role in the circulation of moderate to large lakes. In the Great Lakes, it has recently been demonstrated that internal waves dominate the flow regime during summer in the central portions of the lakes — i.e., away from the shore zones. It is generally assumed that the energy of these large internal waves is degraded into smaller-scale motions that produce mixing. But there is a complete absence of information on how this degradation takes place; as a result, we don't know on what days to expect or not to expect "good" vertical or horizontal mixing.

Another completely obscure aspect of internal waves is the *mass transport* they cause. Individual particles execute back-and-forth motions in waves, often over a period close to 17 hours, but there is also a residual or "transport" motion on top of the wave-induced movements. The latter determines the bulk motion of any admixture to the lake, and next to nothing is known about it (in contrast to actual, instantaneous current velocities, which have been measured frequently and in many places). Indeed, lack of information on mass transport in a flow regime dominated by wave-line motions (particularly internal waves) may be said to be the greatest single "gap" in knowledge concerning circulation problems in lakes, particularly in the Great Lakes.

Currents — Persistent currents are usually weak in lakes, including the Great Lakes, with the possible exception of Lake Ontario, wherein the Niagara River plume may perhaps be classed a "current." Apart from this, the possibility exists that long, slow internal waves of the "Kelvin" type produce fairly concentrated currents with a lifetime of at least several days.

Recent work has indicated the existence of such quasi-permanent currents near the shores of some of the Great Lakes, but the evidence is far from conclusive. Observed currents at moored stations in the shore zone of the Great Lakes show a greater degree of persistence than in the central portions of the lakes, but the spatial and temporal current structure is too complex to allow reliable generalizations at present. Indeed, one of the main conclusions one may draw from recent work on coastal currents is that the details are too complex, and an experimental technique aimed at the determination of bulk mass transport in the shore zones (some appropriate tracer technique, for example) should provide more useful information than further direct current measurements, requiring the deployment of a large number of meters. Another important point is that current structure around the shores of the Great Lakes is different from place to place as well as from season to season — yet we know little about current or mass transport "climatology" even though this is most important in connection with the use of the lakes by man.

Some turbulent diffusion experiments have been carried out in the Great Lakes recently, simulating sewage outfall and warm effluent discharges. The data are mainly relevant to an initial phase of dilution (just after leaving the discharge), and even in this connection it is not certain that the diffusive properties determined would be similar to those in other locations, where the current structure may be radically different. On *large-scale mixing*, data are quite scant, but what information there is appears to show that any effluents discharged in the shore zone tend to remain there for several days (a phenomenon termed "coastal entrapment"). Indeed, it is not at all clear what the physical mechanisms are by which coastal waters mix with the main body of the lake.

There is little or no direct information on the connection between certain conspicuous thermal features of the lakes (upwellings, the "thermal bar" during the warm-up period) and any current structures that may be associated with them. However, theory suggests that some strong currents may accompany marked thermal features of this kind. It is also obvious that a sudden appearance or disappearance of upwelling along a shore has an influence on the water exchange between the shore zone and main lake mass. (See Figure VIII–12) Similarly, the fate of heated effluent may be very different from that of effluent with no thermal effects, because warmer and lighter water may "slide out" over the rest of the lake and assume a flat lens-like shape. Such phenomena are known to occur in rivers and estuaries but no detailed observations in lakes seem to be available.

Modeling and Instrumentation

Mathematical modeling of circulation and mixing in lakes (specifically the Great Lakes, or at any rate lakes large enough for the rotation of the earth to be important in their dynamics) is in its infancy, but some good first steps have been taken in the past twenty years or so. Numerical modeling on the lines suggested by atmospheric work should be comparatively easy (a two- or a three-layer model should be adequate), the main problem being to display the multitude of results in an intelligible form. It should be added, however, that no mathematical modeling has so far even been suggested for the main variable of practical interest, the total mass transport in the shore zone (due to currents *and* wave-like motions).

The instrumentation available for experimental work in physical limnology has not kept pace with modern developments in other fields of science. One agency reported that it had a 40 percent useful return rate from its own moored current meters during the 1969 summer season — a completely unacceptable situation which is nevertheless quite universal. Available current meters are not sufficiently sensitive at low speeds; they

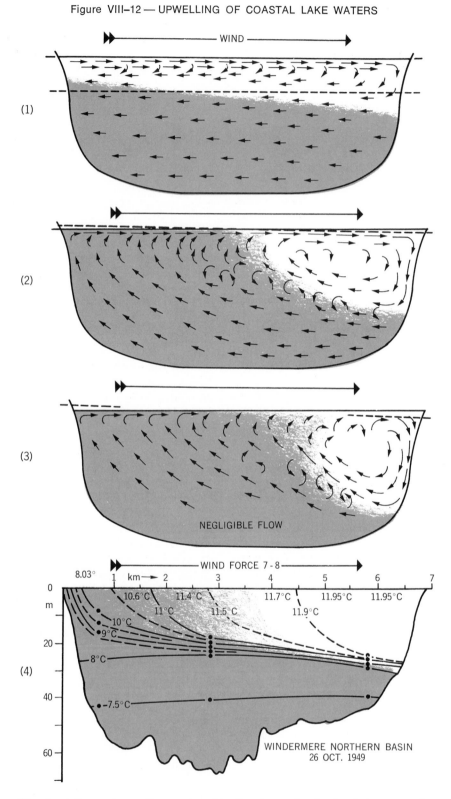

Figure VIII–12 — UPWELLING OF COASTAL LAKE WATERS

The circulation and upwelling produced by the stress of a steady wind on a small lake is shown hypothetically in sketches (1) to (3). In diagram (4) the actual thermal distribution is shown after 12 hours of wind stress. At the upwind end of the basin, the thermocline intersects the water surface.

are not at all accurate in a wave zone. An important recent addition to instrumentation has been the airborne infrared thermometer, which should be exploited more systematically in the future. Apart from this instrument and the fluorometer used in diffusion studies, we are still relying on crude, ancient devices quite unworthy of the Space Age.

Scientific Recommendations

A most encouraging recent development is that many fluid dynamicists previously in aerospace research are turning their attention to lake dynamics. This should be encouraged to the fullest possible extent. The full understanding of the basic *dynamics of lake motions* (where direct effects of turbulence are unimportant) should be well within the reach of fluid dynamicists today, and should also provide important insight into the somewhat less manageable problem of ocean dynamics. Further, studies of *internal waves and turbulence* (including their interaction) also promise to be fruitful for the understanding of mixing processes, particularly mixing through stable layers. At the same time, knowledge so gained is also relevant to certain atmospheric problems, notably to the understanding of clear air turbulence. Experimental studies of internal waves and turbulence are more easily done in a lake than 30,000 feet up in the atmosphere.

From a practical point of view, the greatest urgency attaches to coastal-zone studies of mass transport, currents, and diffusion. Present knowledge in this field is quite inadequate for even the crudest engineering decisions. For example, the cooling-water system for a large power plant next to one of the Great Lakes was designed on the basis of an underestimate of "typical" current speeds by an order of magnitude; as a result, the cooling water in that plant now frequently recirculates from outlet to intake, raising the cooling-water temperature, with deleterious effects on efficiency. Immediate and systematic work is required on the climatology of coastal currents at various locations and in various seasons. Also, it is necessary to conduct a long series of large-scale diffusion experiments to define the likely *"influence zones"* of potential effluent outlets, again as a function of location around lakes, particularly the Great Lakes.

Given the present dearth of knowledge, it would take perhaps ten years of concentrated effort to achieve some sort of consensus on the most urgent topics (climatology of currents and influence zones) that affect the most important of our lakes, the Great Lakes. It may take 25 years to build up a solid enough base of fundamental knowledge (dynamics of currents, mass transport, internal waves, turbulence, and mixing) for the construction of more detailed prediction models for long-term planning and "resource management."

The Effects of Thermal Input on Lake Michigan

Our concern for the environmental quality of the Great Lakes arises from their relatively closed condition. The lakes serve as channels for internal navigation, as highways to the world's oceans, as sources of water for cities and industries, including electric power, as recreational resources — and as sinks for the water-borne wastes from urban and agricultural land. As the multiple uses increase, problems appear. In spite of its large volume and generally good water quality, some parts of Lake Michigan — for example, southern Green Bay and some harbors near Chicago — are becoming grossly polluted; this is a development that the public is not prepared to tolerate any longer. The threat to environmental quality is a direct consequence of the multiple uses to which the lakes are put and of the rapid rise of population over the last century, particularly in the southern half of the region.

With present agricultural practice and systems of waste disposal, the Great Lakes — whether we like it or not — are the receptacles of waste products of all kinds, some of them long-lived. They are becoming overloaded beyond their natural capacity, in some places intolerably so. Is this an inevitable consequence of a large, highly industrialized civilization with a high standard of living? It need not be so, if we are willing to pay the price in regulatory planning and in dollars to maintain reasonable stand-ards of water quality and to work with nature rather than against it. It should be noted that water quality remains high in the northern part of Lake Michigan and in Lake Superior. This represents a national treasure that must be conserved and wisely managed for posterity.

Heat Dissipation Projected to 1990

One form of waste is waste heat. This particular use of Lake Michigan's waters is expected to grow rapidly with growing power demands by industry and by home-owners and institutions seeking to improve their interior environments (e.g., through airconditioning). The question is whether the price we pay for this must include biological deterioration of the lake.

It is perhaps not generally realized that some of the largest generating plants in the country already use Lake Michigan for cooling. The 1970 column in Figure VIII–13 indicates that the equivalent of 16,000 megawatts is added to the lake in the form of heat at present. According to a forecast by the Argonne National Laboratory, this figure is expected to be nearly doubled by 1975, when further large units (many of them nuclear generating stations) now under construction or being planned come into operation. Beyond that, projections of the increase are largely guesswork, but must presumably bear some relation to the projected rise in national demand, forecast as doubling every ten years up to 1990. If this demand is to be met, it will be done with larger units, mainly nuclear, and these need large heat sinks to operate at maximum efficiency. There are only three heat sinks with sufficient capacity: the ocean, the atmosphere, or (for the Midwest) the Great Lakes. The interest of power companies in Lake Michigan is, therefore, not surprising.

Effect on the Lake

Even allowing for improvements in thermal efficiency, heat dissipations from Lake Michigan for 1970, 1980, and 1990 are likely to increase at a rate that slightly more than doubles every ten years. (See Figure VIII–13) If these estimates are accepted as reasonable, we may calculate the orders of magnitude of the effect on the lake. This has been done in three ways in Figure VIII–13. A typical daily total of heat input from the sun in early summer is 300 of the units used in the figures (gram-calories per square centimeter of lake surface). The daily total heat output from power stations in 1990 is less than one percent of this, *if spread over the whole lake surface*. But this is, of course, unrealistic, bearing in mind that all the heat is injected near shore.

Figure VIII–13 — THERMAL INFLUENCE OF
ELECTRIC POWER GENERATION ON LAKE MICHIGAN

	1970	1975	1980	1990
Power to be dissipated, in units of 1000 megawatts, as heat	16	28	37	75
Equivalent daily heat input, g-calories per cm² of:				
(i) whole lake surface	0.57	1.0	1.3	2.6
(ii) inshore strip (depth less than 10 m = 33 ft.)	7	12.5	16	33*
Equivalent temperature rise °C, assuming a 10-day storage and complete mixing into:				
(i) whole lake volume	0.0007	0.0012	0.0016	0.0032
(ii) inshore strip (depth less than 10 m = 33 ft.)	0.14	0.25	0.33	0.66
Equivalent evaporation increase as decrease in lake level (cm per annum), assuming all heat lost through evaporation	0.34	0.62	0.81	1.63‡

* 5-10% of a summer day's natural heat input into the inshore strip.
‡ equals 1/20 ft., about 2% of natural evaporation, i.e., less than the annual variability.

The table shows estimates of the effect of heat input into Lake Michigan due to waste heat from the generation of electric power. These effects are indicated in terms of an increase in lake temperature and an increase in evaporation.

If we consider only the inshore strip of water (of depth less than 10 meters, or 33 feet), which covers 8 percent of the lake area, the picture looks different. In that case, the daily total input of heat from power stations for every day of the year by 1990 would be about 10 percent of the sun's input on a summer day.

Temperature Rise — Another way of looking at the matter is to consider the temperature rise of the whole or part of the lake attributable to power-station inputs. This is a much more complicated and uncertain calculation, because of lack of knowledge of the rate of dispersion and of how long the heat stays in the lake before it is lost to the atmosphere, or to space by back-radiation, or to increased evaporation. This retention time is a statistical estimate

in any case; it is certainly greater than one day and probably less than 30, so a guess at 10 days seems not unreasonable. With that guess we find, again, that the effect on the whole volume of the lake is negligible but that the effect on an inshore water strip is appreciable. For example, the temperature rise of the inshore strip, based on these assumptions (10-day storage and complete mixing into this inshore volume), would amount to 0.7° centigrade — i.e., a little over 1° Farenheit by 1990. These estimates do not, of course, take into account any major engineering changes or advances in design leading to better thermal efficiency.

The significant conclusion from this is that, because the heat input takes place at a number of point

sources, there will be measurable temperature rises locally but the average effect on the whole lake will not be substantial. It is with local effects, then, that we must be concerned.

Natural Phenomena — The natural temperature regime of the coastal water is complex. In summer, there is sporadic upwelling of cold bottom water, depending on the stress of the wind over the whole lake, coupled with the effects of the earth's rotation. The temperature at near shore intakes (for example municipal water plants) can sometimes change by many degrees in an hour.

Another phenomenon that adds to the complexity of coastal circulation, and which is not this time dependent on changes in the wind, is the so-called *thermal bar*. This is most marked in spring, when the shallow water near shore is warming up to temperatures above that of maximum density (4°C), while the offshore waters remain at their winter temperature below 4° centigrade. Where the warmer inshore and colder offshore waters mix, a water mass is formed close to the temperature of maximum density. This mixture is heavier than the original inshore and offshore water masses from which it was formed, and it therefore sinks. This continually sinking water mass (a convergence) forms a temporary barrier to *horizontal* mixing between inshore and offshore waters. At the same time, the convergence is a rather efficient way of carrying water (and, therefore, heat) from the surface into the deeper regions of the lake.

As the spring heating continues, the thermal bar migrates further and further offshore until, usually some time in June, the summer thermal stratification is established right across the lake. At times when the thermal bar is strongly established, water may be trapped inshore for several days or weeks. The effect of thermal discharges into that trapped water mass is a matter for conjecture. But it seems likely that situations could arise, at least on particular days in the year, when the thermal plume from an electric power station would travel along the shore for a long distance with relatively little dilution, rather as a plume from a smokestack is visible for miles when there is a temperature inversion in the atmosphere.

Evaporation — Although we have emphasized the local, near shore effects and minimized those offshore, there is one whole-lake consequence of larger thermal additions. This emerges when we consider the final fate of the added heat. A large part of it will be used in increasing evaporation above the natural level, although some will, of course, be lost by back-radiation and heat exchange with the atmosphere.

If we make the worst assumption, from the point of view of water conservation, that all the heat is lost through increased evaporation, the estimated power dissipation in Figure VIII–13 can be translated directly into water loss. Tabulated as centimeters of water lost from the whole lake surface per year, the loss rises to 1.63 centimeters, or about 1/20th of a foot, in 1990. Integrated over the whole lake surface, this is an impressive volume and, in fact, represents about 2 percent of the mean outflow of Lake Michigan, which is 46,000 cubic feet per second, and about 2 percent of the estimated annual natural evaporation. Some of this will, of course, be returned to the lake by later precipitation. It should be noted that the proportion of heat (and therefore water) lost through evaporation would be greater if cooling towers were used.

Needed Research

We need to be able to predict the local thermal effects with more precision and, in particular, to study the way in which the hot plume disperses, paying particular attention to *rates of diffusion*. In Lake Michigan this should be much more than an engineering study through physical or numerical models. It should also include an in-lake hydrographic study, because the current regime and consequent diffusion in the lake itself varies greatly. And we need to examine not only the average long-term circulation patterns, but also the fluctuating circulation patterns associated with such temporary phenomena as upwelling, internal waves, and thermal bars. There are a number of mechanisms that sometimes tend to keep water near shore for days or weeks. This is not to say that the lake is not well mixed at other times; indeed, at least once a year, in January, it is probably very thoroughly stirred. But we must also consider the consequences of rare types of circulation with minimal diffusion — for example, under extreme thermal-bar conditions — which may develop perhaps once every ten years.

And then, of course, there are possible *biological effects*. We clearly need surveys to identify biologically sensitive areas. We could learn much by carrying out some of these surveys near existing large fossil-fueled stations. These have been operating for years, but no one seems to have reported major deleterious effects on Lake Michigan. We should certainly look and see if there are any; we should also try to differentiate between true thermal effects and those arising from material wastes, looking also for interactions, harmful or beneficial, between thermal discharges and more conventional pollution.

At the same time, there should be a thorough search of the literature. There is a large body of published material, including that from Atomic Energy Commission (AEC) laboratories or AEC-supported work, on the effect of radioactive materials and thermal discharges on organisms. The public is clearly thirsting for knowledge on this subject, and annotated bibliographies would be most useful. We hear a great deal of loose talk about the harmful effects of radioactive and thermal discharges, so we should at least know what has been done before we decide which research gaps need filling.

Special studies should be made in the biological field. These should be concerned with concentration effects, already mentioned, and with the influences to which aquatic organisms are subjected in a fluid in which, while the levels of radioactivity may be very low, they spend the whole of their lives.

Engineers and others should be encouraged to collaborate in pilot studies leading to the *beneficial use of waste heat*. A number of exploratory projects are already under way: irrigation of fruit orchards to avoid frost damage; fish culture; raising the efficiency of other waste-disposal systems.

Finally, we come to *planning* and to the value judgments that planning entails. There is a great need for over-all regional planning, for example to decide on the siting of new nuclear power stations. They must avoid biologically sensitive areas (e.g., fish breeding grounds), they should not be grouped to aggravate the thermal effects, and if possible they should be placed where they could be useful. If, for example, waste heat could be used to keep the St. Lawrence Seaway open for a few more weeks in winter, that would permit overseas shipping lines to make one more run per year to the Great Lakes—a tangible benefit.

With competent and imaginative research and planning and with intelligent siting of power stations, it should be possible to enjoy the benefits of nuclear power without threat to other users or to our enjoyment of the Great Lakes. The research should include not only the study of near shore water circulation and the ecological consequences of the temperature rise, but also advanced engineering leading to beneficial uses of the waste heat. Design and planning must seek a high rate of heat dispersal by turbulence, avoid biologically lethal high temperatures, prohibit construction in biologically sensitive areas (to be identified), and preserve landscape amenities. The last point has perhaps not been sufficiently stressed. Power stations will have a permanence and remain a safety responsibility far beyond the short design life of the reactors. They will be monuments to our present generation. In view of the tendency to build larger and larger stations away from population centers, it can be argued that the threat to the landscape is greater than the threat to the lake.

5. LAKE EUTROPHICATION AND PRODUCTIVITY

Fishery Deterioration in the Great Lakes

Before human settlement, the waters of the Great Lakes abounded in fish characteristic of large lakes with cold, clear water. But the fish populations and the environment of the Great Lakes have undergone progressive deterioration for more than a century. Degradation has accelerated at an alarming rate in recent years. Valuable fish such as Atlantic salmon, lake trout, whitefish, blue pike, and walleye comprised 80 to 90 percent of the production of the early fishery; but in recent years these species have contributed less than 5 percent of the catch from the lakes in which they are still present. (See Figure VIII–14)

The Great Lakes, 64 percent of which lie within U.S. boundaries, cover 95,000 square miles and are the largest and most valuable freshwater resource in the world. The fish populations constitute the greatest and most valuable renewable resource of the lakes. Peak U.S. fishery production occurred around 1900, when 100 to 120 million pounds of mostly high-value species were taken annually. The catch subsequently declined. In 1963, it reached a low of less than 53 million pounds — composed primarily of medium- and low-value species (alewives, carp, chubs, perch, sheepshead, smelt, and suckers).

Causative Factors

Until recently, the causative factors of this drastic change have been a subject of great controversy. It is now known that modifications of the drainage by agriculture, urbanization, and industrialization, and intensive, selective fishing for the most valuable species have caused major changes that led to invasions of new species and deterioration of water quality.

The exact ways in which these influences have affected individual species or groups of species are not yet completely understood. Careful review of the entire sequence of events within the Great Lakes and their drainage, however, is providing information essential to the formulation of environmental criteria and elaboration of management plans that can be implemented to reverse undesirable trends and restore much of the value of the Great Lakes and their fisheries.

Settlement of the Lake Ontario basin and the construction of the Erie and Welland canals were the events that initiated a chain reaction that has now upset the ecological

balance of fish populations throughout the Great Lakes. As noted, Lake Ontario and the St. Lawrence River were once inhabited by an abundance of cold-water species dominated by the Atlantic salmon. Early accounts describe how the cutting of the forests and agricultural development increased water temperatures and lowered flows of streams in which Atlantic salmon spawned. Mill dams blocked spawning streams. Disposal of mill wastes in streams, as well as intensive fishing, also contributed to a sharp decline of Atlantic salmon during the mid-1800's.

The salmon were scarce by 1880 and extinct by 1900. Repeated attempts to re-establish them have

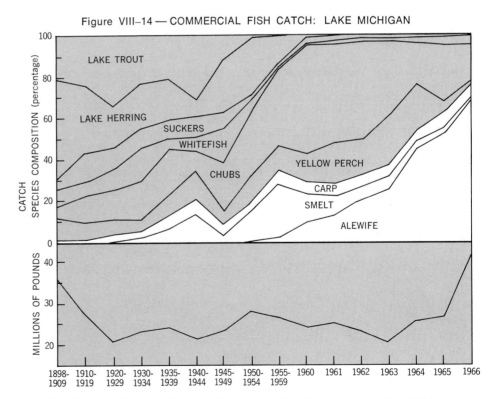

Figure VIII–14 — COMMERCIAL FISH CATCH: LAKE MICHIGAN

The diagram shows statistics of the commercial fish catch on Lake Michigan from 1898 to 1966. The degradation of the fish population is clearly evident; although the total catch returned to turn-of-the-century levels in 1966, almost all of it consisted of alewives and other low-value species.

failed. Even though a salmon fishery no longer existed and the problems of mill dams and pollution had been eliminated in most streams, the lower flows and warmer waters continued, indicating that removal of timber and agricultural development within the drainage had created conditions that made the region unsuitable for survival of the Atlantic salmon.

Effects of Marine Invaders — Elimination of the Atlantic salmon, which was the major fish predator of Lake Ontario, created conditions favorable for the entrance of the alewife, which was the first and most destructive marine invader. As the salmon were declining, the alewife was entering the Lake Ontario drainage via the Hudson River and the Erie Canal. By 1868, alewives had become abundant in the Canal and in the Finger Lakes, which drain into Lake Ontario. Large schools of small alewives were reported in Lake Ontario in 1873 — by which time the Atlantic salmon had been reduced greatly. The lake trout was another major fish predator in Lake Ontario, but it, too, was declining during this period, possibly due to heavy exploitation.

More recent experience in the other Great Lakes has shown that the small, landlocked alewives are unable to thrive when any of the Great Lakes is densely populated by larger fish predators. Without predators, however, the alewife in Lake Ontario was able to increase rapidly; it had become the most abundant fish by 1880. Furthermore, by 1900, the alewife had greatly reduced or virtually eliminated all of the previously abundant small species of Lake Ontario that depended on plankton during at least part of their lives; as past studies have shown, the alewife has a strong competitive advantage over native freshwater fish that also feed on zooplankton.

The alewife used the lake much less efficiently than native species, causing a reduction in the total amount of fish in the lake. The previously abundant native species had occupied all zones of the lake during the entire year. In contrast, the alewife ranged throughout the lake in dense schools but occupied different portions of the lake in various seasons; under its dominance, the vast deep-water region representing 70 to 80 percent of the area of the lake was unoccupied by other species during most of the year.

The parasitic sea lamprey was the second marine invader of the Great Lakes. It had free access to Lake Ontario via the St. Lawrence River but it did not become established in Lake Ontario until the 1880's. Conditions that made the lake unfavorable for the Atlantic salmon apparently made it suitable for the sea lamprey. The inland ranges of the two species do not overlap — the Atlantic salmon favors drainages that have durable, cool streams suitable for its fall spawning, while the spring-spawning sea lamprey favors streams that become warm following the spring runoff.

Once the Atlantic salmon, which fed on small fish, was eliminated, the sea lamprey, which feeds on large fish, became the dominant predator; once established in Lake Ontario, it prevented any sustained resurgence of lake trout, whitefish, or larger species of deep-water ciscoes (commonly called chubs by fishermen of the Great Lakes). Thus, the combined effect of the invasions of the alewife and the sea lamprey was to reduce drastically the fishery productivity of Lake Ontario.

If it were not for the Welland Canal, which provides a waterway that bypasses Niagara Falls and allows access to the upper lakes, the destructiveness of these marine invaders would have been limited to Lake Ontario. Both the sea lamprey and the alewife were able to negotiate the Welland Canal, however. The sea lamprey reached Lake Erie by 1921, was established in Lake

Huron in 1932, Lake Michigan in 1936, and Lake Superior in 1946. The alewife first appeared in Lake Erie in 1931, Lake Huron in 1933, Lake Michigan in 1949, and Lake Superior in 1954.

Neither the sea lamprey nor the alewife became a severe problem in Lake Erie, which had few suitable spawning streams for the lamprey and had substantial populations of predators to keep alewife abundance low.

Conditions in Lakes Huron, Michigan, and Superior favored the lamprey and alewives, however, and these lakes were to suffer fates similar to that of Lake Ontario. The influences of the lamprey and alewife occurred in the reverse order. As the lamprey became established in each of the upper lakes, it destroyed the lake trout that was the major fish predator of the upper Great Lakes. Loss of the lake trout was followed by establishment and rapid increase of the alewife population. In Lakes Michigan and Huron, the destruction of large fish by the sea lamprey and small fish by the alewife became as severe as in Lake Ontario.

Development of a chemical method of sea-lamprey control was first applied in Lake Superior and prevented the complete collapse of the lake-trout population that had occurred in Lakes Michigan and Huron. Although present control methods have not been sufficient to permit restoration of significant spawning stocks of lake trout in Lake Superior, sustained introductions of hatchery-reared trout have held the alewife in check.

The status of Lake Superior remains uncertain, however, as sea lampreys are thriving; the sparser populations resulting from the control measures have enabled the lamprey to reproduce more prolifically than ever. The remnant lamprey populations pose a serious threat to rehabilitation of a reproducing population of lake trout and to the abundance of other large native species — whitefish, lake herring, and larger deep-water ciscoes — as well as to the recently introduced coho and chinook salmon.

In summary, the invasion of marine species made possible by ecological disruption during settlement of the Lake Ontario basin in the 1800's has been a major contributing factor to substantial reduction of the fishery productivity of Lakes Ontario, Huron, and Michigan, and the ultimate effects on Lake Superior are still uncertain.

Effects of Deteriorating Water Quality — The most serious threat to the biological stability and fishery productivity of the Great Lakes has been a progressive deterioration of water quality. During early settlement within the Great Lakes drainage, organic pollution characteristic of nonindustrialized society fouled tributaries of the Great Lakes; it had virtually eliminated populations of river-run lake trout, whitefish, lake herring, walleye, yellow perch, and sturgeon by the late 1800's and early 1900's. These populations made up a major segment of the total fish stocks in the lakes and they have never recovered.

More recently, there has been increasing evidence that a much more ominous type of pollution has accompanied advanced industrialization. This "new" pollution consists of discharges of complex chemical and physical wastes from advanced industrial, agricultural, and urban activities, and from massive releases of heated waste water from industries and power-generating plants.

The combined effects of the "conventional" and "new" environmental contaminants cannot be described or their influences on aquatic life explained by existing criteria or methods. The mechanisms of their influence on aquatic life are unknown, but the fact that they have had major detrimental effects on aquatic life is beyond question.

Southern Green Bay, Saginaw Bay, Lake St. Clair, the Detroit River, and all of Lakes Erie and Ontario are polluted to the extent that they have lost virtually all of the "clean water" species that were once abundant in them. The sequence in which fish declined or disappeared and water quality deteriorated has been the same in all areas. The lake trout declined first, followed by lake herring, whitefish, sauger, blue pike, walleye, and yellow perch. The deep-water ciscoes are very sensitive to environmental degradation, but they decline late in the sequence because the deep waters are influenced later than shallow areas by contamination.

Lakes Erie and Ontario have been the most seriously affected by pollution. These were the two most productive Great Lakes. The species of fish characteristic of large northern lakes were once extremely abundant in both lakes, but *all* are now greatly reduced, rare, or extinct.

Since Lake Erie was not influenced greatly by the invasions of the alewife and sea lamprey, the loss of its valuable species can be attributed primarily to the complex, yet poorly understood, effects on aquatic life of massive introductions of biological, chemical, and physical wastes of an advanced industrialized society. Lake Erie still has large populations of fish. Sheepshead, carp, and goldfish, which have little present value or use, abound in the lake and its bays. Present biological information shows, however, that populations of the more valuable walleye, yellow perch, and smelt appear to be in imminent danger of collapse. Fishery productivity of the large central basin of Lake Erie has been reduced greatly in recent years by oxygen depletion in the bottom waters, which has made a major portion of the lake uninhabitable by fish or fish-food organisms.

The fish populations of Lake Ontario have been affected more seriously than any other lake. Early reductions of fish stocks due to influences of the alewife and sea lamprey have been compounded in recent years by additional reductions caused by the extreme deterioration of water quality in Lake Ontario, which is the ultimate recipient of all wastes entering both Lakes Erie and Ontario. The vast deep-water region of Lake Ontario is devoid of any valuable and abundant species of fish. The native species that supported the most productive and prosperous fisheries of the Great Lakes during the early and mid-1800's have all become greatly reduced or rare; many are extinct.

The native species lost in Lake Ontario due to water-quality degradation — lake trout, whitefish, lake herring, deep-water ciscoes, deep-water sculpin — are the only kinds of fish that thrive in any of the large, deep lakes of the world. If the water quality of Lake Ontario cannot be restored so that it is again favorable for these species, the lake's fishery potential will be lost forever. If the water quality of the other deep lakes — Michigan, Huron, and Superior — continues to deteriorate, their vast deep-water regions will also become fishery deserts.

Status of the Environmental Science

Development of an understanding of the precise causes of the biological degradation of the Great Lakes is in the formative stages, and is advancing slowly in a few scattered problem areas. Existing techniques and general knowledge of present and potential problems seem adequate to formulate a systems approach that could, when sufficient monitoring and research information become available, describe and predict the biological interactions in the Great Lakes environment and relate biological responses to activities of man in the lake basins.

A few cause-effect relations of environmental degradation are understood — e.g., the cause of oxygen depletion in Lake Erie and its relation to the disappearance of blue pike and the diminution of other fish and fish-food organisms in the region of the lake affected. The relation between excessive phosphorus and obnoxious algae blooms in Lakes Erie, Ontario, and other scattered locations has been established. Lake Ontario is no longer suitable for lake trout because the clean, rocky spawning areas essential for its reproduction are covered by a fibrous mat.

Studies of the effects of chemical and physical factors on biological productivity and stability are in preliminary stages for a few species. Some information is being obtained on the physical requirements for successful incubation and hatching of the alewife, the sea lamprey, and some species of the whitefish family. Thermal stresses and physiological responses that influence alewife die-off and abundance are under study.

Problems of species interaction are incompletely understood and only a few are subject to adequate study at present. Information on selective feeding of the alewife and the resultant effects on changes in the composition of fish-food organisms gives clues to possible competitive advantages of the alewife that may explain the decline of various species when the alewife becomes dominant. There is some evidence that more complex feeding interactions and competition during certain life stages of smelt, deep-water ciscoes, and lake herring may have contributed to the sharp reduction of lake herring in certain areas of Lake Superior in the absence of alewives. The ability of the unchecked sea-lamprey populations to destroy a lake-trout population by eliminating all mature trout has been documented by detailed studies in Lake Michigan, but the relation between lamprey-attack mortality of lake trout and other large native species is not known. Thus, the degree of lamprey reduction that will be required to restore substantial stocks of large species, as a step toward restoration of a favorable balance of all fish species, is still uncertain.

Also unknown or uncertain are the relations of physical, chemical, and biological change to the declines of native species throughout the Great Lakes. These are the species or kinds of species that must be rehabilitated to restore the fishery productivity of the Great Lakes. To prevent deterioration of the lakes from progressing to the point where biological and fishery restoration may be extremely difficult or impossible, control of environmental degradation and undesirable species must be undertaken before research on cause-effect relations of the various factors of degradation can be completed. Nevertheless, the research must be initiated expeditiously and pursued vigorously.

The Need for Monitoring — A basic requirement for research to gain a full understanding of the fishery environmental deterioration of the Great Lakes is a comprehensive monitoring program to measure all aspects of the chemical, physical, and biological environment. The present data base and existing instrumentation and techniques are adequate to start development of a suitable monitoring system. Data from monitoring are needed to provide measures of the long-term trends and the frequency, intensity, and duration of short-term fluctuations in environmental factors. Particular attention should be given to physical and chemical contaminants, and the measurement of changes in the composition and biomass of biological components of the environment. Meaningful monitoring will require a full understanding of the sources and identity of all physical, chemical, and biological contaminants entering the lake.

Research Questions — Environmental monitoring and the sources and identity of contaminants will provide the data that are needed to give clues for cause-effect relations that can be investigated by specific field and laboratory studies. What factors contribute to failure of hatching or early survival of the previously abundant native species that must be restored? Precisely how might certain chemicals, such as pesticides and heavy metals, influence the physiology, behavior, reproductive process, or survival of various species of fish? What effects would massive releases of thermal wastes in various locations and by various methods have on eggs, fry, young, and adult fish, and fish-food organisms, in different seasons? These questions must be answered to provide suitable guidelines for maintaining the biological stability and productivity that might be achieved after the present environmental degradation has been halted and reversed in the most seriously affected lakes.

Even under very stringent protection, the Great Lakes will continue to be influenced by growing urbanization and industrialization within the drainage. These influences will undoubtedly cause some uncontrollable changes (physical and chemical contamination, directly or indirectly related to pollution or modification of the atmosphere) and accelerated enrichment. Change may continue to be too rapid for biological processes to accommodate to it. Thus, research will be required to determine the rate of change that can be tolerated and still maintain biological stability and fishery productivity in the Great Lakes. This information will be essential for possible future modification of the initial guidelines and standards that must be enforced immediately to "save" the Great Lakes.

Need for Increased Understanding and Action

It has been said that, for the aquatic ecologist, fish are the miner's canary. The reason why some species have disappeared is unknown, but deterioration of water quality that has an adverse influence on fish may signal a trend that could soon have detrimental effects on other life dependent on water, including humans. Restoration of the Great Lakes for fish should also restore their value for all other uses.

The essential measures that must be taken from the environmental standpoint to restore the lakes that have been severely damaged (Erie and Ontario) and reverse deterioration of the others (Michigan, Huron, and Superior) are clear. The attack must be basin-wide, must be initiated expeditiously, and pursued vigorously. The plan must include: (a) improvement of land uses within the drainages that have direct or indirect influences on the lakes and their tributaries; (b) elimination of sources of physical, chemical, or biological pollution entering the lakes directly or indirectly; and (c) restoration of favorable and productive fish populations within the lakes.

Restoration of Environmental Conditions — Improvements within the drainage basin of the Great Lakes will require extensive restoration of vegetation and forests that were destroyed by wasteful land practices of the past century. This will improve the water quality and increase the stability of the flow of tributaries entering the lakes. Land-use practices, both urban and domestic, must be modified and closely regulated to prevent toxic substances (pesticides and others) and fertilizers from entering the runoff of the drainages. (See Figure VIII–15) No practice should be allowed that would influence streams or rivers biologically, physically, or chemically in such a way that water conditions would become less favorable than those that might be expected from natural runoff.

The most crucial problem of lake restoration is the elimination of all sources and kinds of pollution that enter the lakes. Any treated effluents or domestic and industrial wastes that are permitted to enter the lakes must be of equal or better quality than

the waters in the lakes they enter. Effluent from waste treatment that cannot meet these standards should, after being treated to the highest degree possible, be diverted into drainages outside the Great Lakes basin. These effluents would be of higher quality than the water of rivers into which they would be diverted; thus, the practice of diverting them from the Great Lakes would have the dual benefit of preventing degradation of the Great Lakes and improving the water flow and quality in rivers of the north and central United States.

Costs of water treatment (particularly for industrial wastes) might be reduced greatly by the construction

of inland waterways wherever feasible to permit reuse of water and provide channels for the diversion of treated waste waters from the Great Lakes basin. A number of proposals for the construction of such channels in the Great Lakes and central U.S. regions have already been made. It may, in fact, be necessary to divert excess water from the Great Lakes region to irrigate the arid south-central sections of the United States before the end of this decade. Present collective drainage-disposal systems are a move in this direction; but, unfortunately, they are not being planned to fit a basin-wide system and will probably have to be modified or rebuilt at great cost before the century ends.

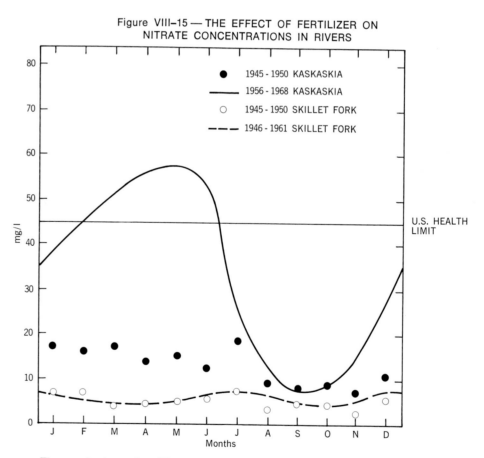

Figure VIII–15 — THE EFFECT OF FERTILIZER ON NITRATE CONCENTRATIONS IN RIVERS

● 1945 - 1950 KASKASKIA
— 1956 - 1968 KASKASKIA
○ 1945 - 1950 SKILLET FORK
- - - 1946 - 1961 SKILLET FORK

U.S. HEALTH LIMIT

mg/l

Months

The graph shows the difference in nitrate concentrations between two rivers in Illinois — the Kaskaskia River, which drains a heavily fertilized farming area, and the Skillet Fork River, which drains an area where little fertilizer is applied. The threefold increase in nitrate concentration for the Kaskaskia River between 1945-1950 and 1956-1968 follows the increased use of industrially fixed nitrogen fertilizers.

Release of heated waste water into the Great Lakes should not be permitted until studies have shown that the previously abundant native species will not be adversely affected. The only fish that can thrive in lakes the size of the Great Lakes are cold-water species, and all spend portions of their life cycle either near the shore or the surface of the lakes. Fish in the larval and juvenile life stages are the ones that usually live near shore or the surface and would be most sensitive to the influence of heat wastes in these regions. Their presence in these regions would be mostly during late winter to early summer, when thermal gradients would be the sharpest and possibilities of detrimental effects the greatest.

Restoration of Fish Stocks — Current with restoration of more favorable environmental conditions, steps must be taken to restore more favorable stocks. Sea-lamprey control now being conducted in Lakes Superior, Michigan, and Huron must be intensified and extended to Lakes Ontario and Erie. Measures to reduce alewives should be intensified by introduction of large predators such as lake trout and salmon and by exploitation where necessary. The most critical requirement, while reducing alewife populations, is a concurrent restoration of the small native forage species. This transition will require several decades and will require careful measurement and close regulation of the kinds and amounts of fish introduced or removed from the lakes.

Successful restoration of fish in Lakes Erie and Ontario will require sufficient improvement of water quality to permit establishment of previously abundant species. Control of sea lampreys and reduction of alewives in Lake Ontario should reverse deterioration of fish stocks as water quality is improved. Restoration of Lake Erie will require the development of some method to reduce the extreme abundance of

sheepshead in the open lake and carp in the shallow areas to create conditions favorable for return of more desirable species.

Present Urgency

The need for immediate action to restore the environmental quality, biological stability, and fisheries of the Great Lakes cannot be stressed too strongly. At present, Erie and Ontario are the only lakes that have been measurably affected by water-quality deterioration throughout the entire lakes. One of the largest rivers in the world — the St. Clair-Detroit River system — flows through these lakes, and the water entering this river system from Lake Huron is still of high quality. Erie and Ontario are the smallest of the Great Lakes and have flushing rates (ratio of lake volume to volume of annual inflow) of approximately 3 and 8 years, respectively. Thus, if *all* wastes are prevented from entering Lakes Erie and Ontario, there should be initial improvement of water quality within 5 to 10 years and significant improvement of water quality and aquatic life within 20 years.

The most urgent need, however, is to stop the environmental deterioration of Lake Michigan. Degradation of Lake Michigan has approached the point that biological processes are being adversely affected. Once disrupted, it may not be possible to restore the fishery productivity of Lake Michigan. Even with complete removal of all wastes from effluents entering the lake, or diversion of all effluents from the basin, the water from natural runoff into Lake Michigan would be richer than water within the lake. Consequently, Lake Michigan could not be flushed or "cleaned." (The only possibility for flushing Lake Michigan would be to divert a large quantity of water from Lake Superior and introduce it at the southern end of Lake Michigan.) The deterioration of Lake Michigan would hasten the deteriora-

tion of Lake Huron. If this should occur, the present source of "clean water" essential for the restoration (flushing) of Lakes Erie and Ontario would be eliminated.

Policy Requirements

The techniques and instrumentation are available and there is a cadre of scientific personnel knowledgeable about the broad biological problems and requirements for their solution on the Great Lakes. There is, however, no U.S. organization with the specific mission or clear responsibility to conduct the studies or establish the guidelines that are necessary to assure the biological stability or maintenance of the over-all fishery productivity of the Great Lakes, other fresh water, or estuarine waters of the United States. Also, the facilities are lacking for necessary further study. There is also no provision in the scattered existing monitoring systems for the comprehensive coverage of all physical and chemical parameters that would be required for biological studies, and biological and fishery monitoring are minimal in some areas and lacking in most areas.

The Great Lakes are a national and international resource and must be managed as a complete system. There is no federal agency or combination thereof that can assume full U.S. responsibility, nor are there international agreements that can guarantee full and effective joint international action. Of the several agencies and commissions with responsibilities concerning the Great Lakes, the Great Lakes Fishery Laboratory (U.S. Department of the Interior) and the Great Lakes Fishery Commission (U.S.-Canada compact) have the broadest experience and delegations of responsibility for studies and the greatest capacity to make recommendations concerning environmental quality — particularly concerning problems related to biological degradation and fishery resources.

The Great Lakes Fishery Laboratory has made evaluations of environmental quality and fishery responses to environmental change ever since it was established in 1927. Its present laboratory facility and four research vessels constitute the greatest U.S. capability to provide guidelines and criteria for Great Lakes fishery and environmental restoration. At present, however, its efforts are limited to partial studies on certain sections of Lakes Superior, Michigan, and Erie, with token attention to Lakes Huron and Ontario. Resto-

ration of the Great Lakes environment will require full attention to all lakes, and will need much more than the present effort by the Great Lakes Fishery Laboratory and the fragmentary efforts of other U.S. Federal water-related agencies that have smaller capability and less comprehensive Great Lakes responsibilities.

The Canadian government has recognized fully the urgency for action on the Great Lakes. It has started the construction of a federal labora-

tory on Lake Ontario which, when completed in 1972, will house 250-300 scientists and will be capable of surveillance of all water-quality, biological, and fishery aspects of the Canadian portion of the Great Lakes. An even more substantial facility would be required to meet the full U.S. commitment on the Great Lakes, since the United States has 64 percent of the Great Lakes within its boundary and contributes some 80 to 90 percent of the industrial, urban, and agricultural contamination entering the lakes.

Problems of Eutrophication in the Great Lakes

One of today's pressing problems is to formulate and execute a management program for the nation's freshwater resources. These resources are of tremendous value; they are used for water supply (domestic, industrial, agricultural), recreation, navigation, hydroelectric power, waste disposal, and food supply. Only a few of the nation's fresh waters are used for multiple purposes, and these few will be short-lived if present practices are followed. The underlying cause for this situation is the use of these waters for waste disposal, which results in chemical enrichment, or eutrophication, jeopardizing all other uses and producing a general deterioration of the human environment. Therefore, the overriding water-resource problem is not water scarcity but water management directed toward control of pollutants at the source and means of ameliorating the eutrophic effects of existing polluted waters.

Among the numerous water bodies in the United States and Canada, the Great Lakes are the largest in area and volume and rank as the most important single water resource in respect to economic, recreational, and aesthetic values. They constitute about 40 percent of the total surface waters of North America, possess a

drainage basin of 295,000 square miles in which live nearly 40 percent of this country's population. According to reliable projections, these lakes lie in the pathway of the most rapid industrial and urban development in the United States and Canada.

Despite their great value, there is an astonishing lack of fundamental knowledge about the Great Lakes. This stems from their great size, international and national political fragmentation of their drainage basin, need for an interdisciplinary approach to their complex problems, and need for meaningful, total system studies of this mesoscale aquatic system.

Furthermore, there has been little sense of urgency in establishing management procedures for these waters because of the misbelief that this vast quantity of water is capable of receiving almost unlimited quantities of pollutants without producing harmful effects. Inland communities use streams entering the Great Lakes to transport their waste without realizing that the lakes become the eventual receptors of this waste. Less is known about waste assimilation in lakes, especially large ones, than streams, but we do know that the residence time for pollutants is much greater in lakes. In streams residence time is on the order of days or weeks,

while in the Great Lakes it is decades or centuries. It is evident that the Great Lakes environment is dangerously susceptible to pollution because most avenues of waste disposal in the drainage basin terminate in these lakes.

Physically, the Great Lakes drainage basin is one system; but politically it exhibits a pattern of fragmentation. This physiographic unit is shared by eight states in the United States and two provinces in Canada. The heads of these political units can speak only for their respective units. There is no unified plan or approach for the management or utilization of their waters or the solution of common problems in the drainage basin. Within the United States, a dozen or more federal agencies are charged with Great Lakes missions, each carrying out its mission commendably but none concerned with the lakes as a complete system. Superimposed on this pattern are the efforts by each Great Lakes state to deal with these waters within the framework of its policies. Only the International Joint Commission attempts to represent the international interests of the United States and Canada; it, too, has a commendable record of accomplishments but its objectives are limited.

The Great Lakes Basin Commission, established in 1967, could provide a mechanism for initiating regional planning and management. But although the mechanisms, the technical and scientific knowledge, and the manpower and economic need exist for unified efforts in pollution abatement, water-resources management, and regional planning of the Great Lakes drainage basin, these efforts are lacking. This fact is of deep concern, because decisions are being made and priorities established in the absence of a unified or regional plan or an understanding of the Great Lakes as a total system.

Status of Great Lakes Eutrophication

Although eutrophication of the Great Lakes is a pressing national problem, it has received little attention until recently. Our understanding of the processes accounting for the lakes' aging and eutrophication (chemical enrichment) is based primarily on studies of small lakes, and much of this information is not directly transferable to the Great Lakes because of scale difference.

In general, aging processes begin at the time of lake origin and go on until the lake becomes extinct through filling, ecological succession, and eventual transformation into a terrestrial habitat. Nature or direction of aging is controlled by such natural forces as erosion and deposition, hydrological and meteorological processes, chemical enrichment, biological productivity, and ecological succession. The time-span of lake existence may vary from a few decades to many centuries depending on the rates of these controlling forces or processes.

These natural forces, operating in the absence of man, will produce a predictable direction and rate of change for a given ecosystem. But man, through his activities (cultural forces), modifies the natural trends

and rates. Therefore, man's major role in lake aging is that of determining the rates of change, especially through chemical enrichment, commonly referred to as eutrophication.

The activities of man that contribute significantly to the process of lake eutrophication are:

1. Discharge of domestic and industrial wastes into waterways.

2. Land-use practices that result in runoff carrying silt loads, fertilizers, farm-animal wastes, and pesticides.

3. Discharge of waste heat from nuclear and fossil-fuel power plants and industrial processes.

4. Discharge of pollutants into the air, which eventually enter waterways by precipitation and fallout.

Our limited knowledge of Great Lakes eutrophication has been derived from a large number of isolated studies over several decades. There has been no attempt at a unified, multidisciplinary study of one lake or of the total Great Lakes as a system. The general trends have been identified but the mechanisms and rates are known only qualitatively.

The general status of Great Lakes eutrophication may be summarized as follows: Each of the five Great Lakes has undergone measurable environmental changes in the past fifty years. The lakes are now characterized by:

1. An increase in chemical content of water and sediments (phosphorus, nitrogen, calcium, sulphate, potassium, and chlorine);

2. An increase in biological productivity;

3. A change in species composition of biota;

4. A decrease in concentration of dissolved oxygen;

5. A decrease in transparency;

6. Highly polluted conditions in inshore areas, harbors, and bays.

Lake Erie is the most advanced eutrophically because of its shallowness, its southernmost geographic location, and its large pollution input from urban, industrial, and agricultural sources. Lake Ontario ranks second as a result of its position furthest downstream in the interconnected system of five lakes and its large volume of deep water. It, too, has received heavy pollution inputs from cities, industries, and agricultural activities. Lake Michigan ranks third, with conditions in its southern one-third being similar to those of Lake Erie; the northern portion is of high quality, resembling conditions in Lakes Huron and Superior. The latter two lakes and the northern part of Lake Michigan comprise about 90 percent of the total volume of the Great Lakes; they represent the last large volume of good-quality water in the United States.

The data base for the Great Lakes is poor. It lacks uniformity of quality, and is sparse or lacking in certain areas. Much of the usable data have been collected at irregular times over a period of fifty years. There are serious data deficiencies in the following areas:

1. Lake circulation, both openlake and inshore;

2. Characteristics of thermal bars that form inshore and isolate the nutrient-rich river effluents for periods of several weeks;

3. Quantity, concentration, and form of chemical inputs from domestic, industrial, and land drainage sources;

4. Atmospheric input;

5. Role of lake sediments in the cycling and storage of chemical substances;

6. The precise residence time of water in each lake basin;

7. Utilization and cycling of nutrients by biota;

8. Population dynamics of various communities;

9. Energy budget;

10. Water budget.

Without more complete information in these areas, the eutrophication of the Great Lakes cannot be effectively controlled.

Importance of Scale in the Design of Great Lakes Studies

The matter of transferability of information and experiences derived from studies of small to large lakes requires careful evaluation before a Great Lakes eutrophication program is established. Although the fundamental processes of aquatic systems, whether large or small, are basically the same, the mechanisms controlling these processes and the rates may vary importantly with water-body size. In the size-series of water bodies from small lakes to oceans, the Great Lakes represent the mesoscale aquatic system. The lakes are subject to essentially the same physical, chemical, biological, meteorological, and geological conditions as the oceans and they possess both lacustrine and oceanic characteristics. Nevertheless, a direct transfer of information from small lakes to these large lakes is difficult for a number of reasons. Some characteristics that make the Great Lakes uniquely different from small lakes are:

1. Visible effects of Coriolis force on water circulation;

2. Distribution of upwelling and sinking according to relationship of current streamlines and the shore;

3. Discrete water masses which maintain distinct limnological characteristics;

4. Modifying effect on weather;

5. Large water volume in proportion to area of water surface and lake bottom;

6. Existence of a wide range of industrial and urban complexes, land uses, shore development, and water uses in the 295,000 square miles of drainage basin;

7. Each of the five lakes differs in size, morphometry, and limnological characteristics, but they are interconnected, resulting in a flow-through or downstream effect;

8. Residence time for water in a lake basin may exceed 100 years.

Scale, then, becomes an important factor in designing studies on the Great Lakes. Two ways to meet some of the inherent difficulties are: (a) extrapolation of experience from small to large lakes, including laboratory-type studies as well as studies from scale enclosures (plastic bags, cylinders, etc.) and the experience gained from intermediate-size lakes; and (b) development of appropriate mathematical models (black-box models, hydrodynamic models, productivity models, etc.). Transfer from physical models (small lakes) could be facilitated by developing some kinds of transfer coefficients, analogous to Reynold's numbers.

Plans for Action

It becomes apparent that water-resource problems of the Great Lakes are large, diverse, and urgent. There is general agreement among scientists, engineers, political scientists, and socio-economists that the most fruitful approach to the solution of these problems is a direct study of the lakes through use of systems-analysis techniques and a well-designed program of data collection and analysis. There is also basic agreement that an effective program to control Great Lakes eutrophication must place primary emphasis on controlling nutrients and pollutants at source of entry and secondary emphasis on measures to ameliorate the effects of these substances after entering the lakes.

Modeling Efforts — Several organizations and research teams are developing a set of linked systems-modeling studies that will use simulation as a research tool in conjunction with the study of the Great Lakes. The long-range objective of this effort is to construct a region-wide comprehensive model. Initial efforts are directed toward a water-quality model on a regional scale, a water-quality subsystem model for one or more subregions within the Great Lakes basin, and a regional economic-growth model. These efforts are too new to have produced tangible results, but this kind of thinking dominates present Great Lakes investigations. The organizations offering leadership in this approach are: the Great Lakes Basin Commission, with emphasis on regional models; the Council on Economic Growth, Technology and Public Policy of the Committee on Institutional Cooperation (CIC), with emphasis on water-quantity and water-quality models; the University of Michigan Sea Grant Program, with emphasis on comprehensive modeling of a subregion (Grand Traverse Bay); and the University of Wisconsin Sea Grant Program, with emphasis on modeling of Green Bay.

Data Collection and Systems Analysis — Two field-data collection programs and related systems-analysis efforts that are under serious consideration will serve as examples of current thinking on Great Lakes investigations. The first is a materials-balance study of one of the Great Lakes, preferably Lake Michigan because it lies entirely within U.S. boundaries, simplifying operational logistics and interdisciplinary study, or Lake Ontario, which is the object of the International Field Study on the Great Lakes of the International Hydrological Program. This would involve a study measuring the input from industrial and urban sources, land drainage, and the atmosphere. The output would include measurements of loss through outlets, retention by sediments, removal of biota, and loss to atmosphere. Other aspects of the study would be directed toward the dispersal of input materials in the lake by currents and general water circulation, and the interaction between input materials and the biota. The major problem to be solved by this study is the assimilation capacity of the lake water — that is, the amount of material it can receive without deterioration in quality. The object would be to prevent inputs above the assimilation capacity, as well as to determine the costs for maintaining a given water quality. This would require establishment of water-use priorities, a political decision yet to be made. Also, information on the kinds, quantities, and concentration of materials entering the lake would make it possible to evaluate the relative importance of a pollution source and to identify the sites where pollution-control measures would be most effective. Moreover, it would produce high-quality information essential for predictive capabilities (modeling) concerning the nature and rates of eutrophication, and it would serve as a model for studies of the other Great Lakes.

A large part of the required data for this materials balance is presently being collected by several federal and state agencies and regional universities conducting investigations on Lake Michigan and its drainage basin. Success of this study would require cooperation among these organizations. The organizational structures, personnel, and facilities are in existence; only a coordinated effort is needed. Such a study would not lessen the present need to deal with urgent local problems by federal and state agencies, but it would produce new and exciting possibilities for attacking pressing Great Lakes problems on the basis of a total system and long-term planning.

In the second example, the proposed study would focus on a major river system, such as the Grand River in the Lake Michigan basin, aimed at determining the impact of its discharge on the inshore lake waters receiving it, and alternative methods of reducing this impact. A materials balance of the river and the source of materials would be determined for the entire river. The accompanying systems analysis, among other things, would determine the benefit/cost implication of maintaining an acceptable water-quality standard and would pinpoint alternatives for solving the local water-resource problems. The impact of river discharge on the inshore area would involve studies of currents, thermal-bar phenomena, and biochemical interactions. The significance of such a study is evident when it is realized that approximately 90 percent of the pollutants entering the lakes do so through river systems. This would serve as a model for attacking the problems of other major rivers entering the lakes.

Expected Results — These suggested attacks on Great Lakes eutrophication would identify rather specifically: the need for new instrumentation such as automatic monitoring devices; the application of remote sensing methods to water-resource investigations; the prevailing socioeconomic and political problems; and the need for an interdisciplinary effort involving the cooperation of personnel from universities, industry, and government. It would also make possible reasonable estimates of costs involved in establishing a management program for the entire Great Lakes basin. The high rate of Great Lakes eutrophication argues for immediate action on the general problems presented in this discussion.

Pollution and Recovery in Lake Washington

The city of Seattle lies between Puget Sound and the west side of Lake Washington. Early in this century, the lake was used for disposal of raw sewage, and unsatisfactory conditions developed. In the early 1930's, most of the sewage was diverted to Puget Sound, and for a few years the pollution of the lake was considerably reduced. But Seattle was expanding and smaller towns around the lake were growing. In 1941, a two-stage biological sewage-treatment plant was established on the lake, and by 1954 ten such plants had been built. Another one was built on one of the inlets to the lake in 1959. In addition, some of the smaller streams were heavily contaminated with drainage from septic tanks. Studies of the lake in 1933, 1950, and 1952 showed increases in the content of algae and nutrients and decreases in the amount of oxygen in the deep water during summer.

In 1955, a conspicuous growth of the alga *Oscillatoria rubescens* developed. This event attracted attention because this species had occurred early in the process of deterioration of a number of European lakes. Thus, it seemed to be a distinct harbinger of pollutional deterioration.

Eutrophication — The problem is that sewage treated ("purified") by normal processes is relatively rich in nutrients, especially phosphate. As a result, when the effluent is put into a lake, it acts as a plant fertilizer and stimulates the growth of algae. While some increase in biological production may be favorable, overproduction of algae results in water of low transparency; large quantities of decaying algae also produce bad odor problems. In such lakes, dissolved oxygen may be exhausted from the deep water by decomposition, and this eliminates many desirable species of fish (whitefish, trout, salmon). These conditions interfere with most uses of a lake — recreational, water supply, and fisheries. As long as the sewage is well treated, human health problems are not dominant, but some individuals are sensitive to algae and develop skin rashes or nausea when they are in contact with the lake.

This effect of pollution, often called eutrophication, is common around the world. It is well documented by many studies. Lake Washington was thus exhibiting perfectly normal behavior when its increase in the abundance of algae began.

Public Action — Public concern over the sewerage situation had been growing in the entire Seattle metropolitan area. In 1955, the Mayor of Seattle appointed a Metropolitan Problems Advisory Committee to study sewerage conditions, among other things. The obvious beginning of deterioration of Lake Washington and the rather clear-cut predictions that could be made about its future condition gave focus to public concern. At the same time, it was recognized that unsatisfactory conditions also existed in Puget Sound and that a broadly based, coordinated program was necessary.

As a result of the Committee's action, a campaign was organized by public-minded citizens' groups to develop a governmental organization to handle the problem (Municipality of Metropolitan Seattle, or "Metro"). An active informational campaign was carried out, mostly using information about the actual deterioration of Lake Washington and predictions about its future.

After a certain amount of difficulty, Metro was passed on the second vote in 1958. A project of sewage diversion from the lake was started in 1963 and completed in 1968. The total cost of Metro to date is about $145 million, of which about $85 million is attributable to the Lake Washington part of the project.

Results of Diversion of Sewage — With the first diversion of about a third of the sewage, deterioration of Lake Washington slowed, and further diversions were promptly followed by more improvement as measured by increased transparency of the water and decreased amounts of phosphorus and algae. During late summer of 1969, the deep-water oxygen conditions were more favorable than in 1933, phosphate was nearly down to the concentrations seen in 1950, and summer transparency was two-and-a-half times as great as in 1963. (See Figure VIII–16)

It is important to realize that action was taken before the lake had deteriorated very far, relative to the well-known problem lakes in Europe and the Midwest of this country. The condition of the lake changed conspicuously enough that there was no doubt about its reality, but action was taken early in the process.

Generalizations from the Lake Washington Experience

It is clear that Lake Washington responded promptly and sensitively to both increases and decreases in nutrient input. Lake Washington should not be regarded as unusual; many lakes are similar enough in their chemical characteristics that

Figure VIII–16 — TRANSPARENCY MEASUREMENTS IN LAKE WASHINGTON

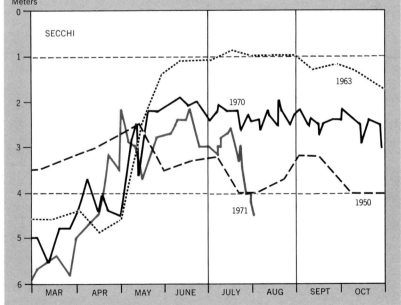

The graph shows observations of transparency made in Lake Washington from 1950 to 1971. The measurements are made with a Secchi disc, a 20-centimeter white disc that is lowered into the water until it disappears from view.

they would respond just as sensitively. These considerations are relevant to making predictions and to the development of plans for handling the pollution of the Great Lakes and others that are receiving effluent or are going to.

If one is going to make a complete statement about the processes that control the productivity and abundance of organisms in lakes, he has to refer to the whole set of environmental variables: nutrients including (in addition to nitrogen and phosphorus) carbon, such micronutrients as iron, copper, cobalt, and others. He has to discuss light penetration into lakes, the kinetics of photosynthesis, and a great many other things. But to take practical steps to improve the condition of a particular lake that has been polluted is another matter. It is not necessary to recapitulate the entire history of limnological investigation in that lake. We know a great deal already, and can make use of the general knowledge we have developed from pure limnological research.

A point of particular interest has to do with the relative importance of phosphorus (P) and nitrogen (N), a matter about which there has been some uncertainty. For practical control, the proposition very often would be to ask what the effect would be of removing most of the phosphorus from the effluent. That is, to simplify a little, what would be the effect of heavily enriching with nitrogen? The answer to this has to lie in the condition of the receiving water. If the natural waters, for geological reasons, are relatively rich in N, so that P is the primary limiting factor, phosphorus enrichment is likely to increase production.

The obvious thing to do is to find out which element is limiting in each particular case. A variety of techniques exist, ranging from bioassay with lake-water samples to which nutrients are added through analysis of lake water and plankton

for N and P. Some studies have shown that added P alone was enough or almost enough to account for the observed effect of sewage.

Another rather new approach to this problem of diagnosis shows that in Lake Washington, before pollution, nitrate was in excess in the sense that when phosphate approached zero during the spring growth of phytoplankton, there was a distinct excess of nitrogen. After pollution with phosphorus-rich sewage, P was in excess in 1962. In 1962, then, Lake Washington might well have responded to an increase in nitrogen which would have permitted the phosphorus to be used up.

This point is easy to get mixed up. One must keep clear whether one is talking about the effect of adding an element or removing it. One does the first when trying to explain why a given lake has gone into nuisance conditions; one does the latter when thinking about how to improve the situation by removing something. In June of 1962, adding phosphorus to Lake Washington would not have increased algae because there was an excess. Removing phosphorus would have decreased algae.

In the long run P is the more important element in much of the world. But there are places where phosphorus is relatively rich in the natural water supplies. Goldman has proposed, for instance, that Lake Tahoe would be susceptive to nitrogen enrichment. Also, there are some organisms that seem able to get along with much less phosphorus than others.

If all this is correct, then for each case we have to identify a key element, limitation of which would improve the lake. One could theoretically limit production by eliminating any essential element, but in fact there are very few elements that one can control. The single element that is most easily removed from effluents is phosphorus. So the question boils

down to asking whether limiting phosphorus, either by removal from sewage or by limiting detergents, will be enough to make an adequate difference. This means, too, that one must find out whether there is enough P from agricultural drainage into a given lake to make a difference.

In Lake Washington, phosphorus has decreased much more than nitrogen or carbon dioxide. (Sewage is relatively much richer in phosphorus than is the natural water supply to the lake.) The abundance of algae has decreased in very close relation to phosphorus, not in relation to nitrogen. (See Figure VIII–17) This suggests that, in similar lakes, any limitation on the amount of concentrated sources of phosphorus reaching the lake will be beneficial. That is, improvement should result in proportion to the removal of concentrated sources of phosphorus. Large changes could be made by reducing the phosphorus content of detergents. In some places it may be worthwhile to install treatment processes to remove phosphorus from effluent.

This discussion is focused on the eutrophication problem. Inflow of toxic wastes (lead, mercury, cyanide, herbicides, DDT, etc.) was not an important part of the Lake Washington problem, but it evidently is a part of the Lake Erie problem. In every case of lake deterioration, one should find out if toxic wastes are important. Nevertheless, Lake Erie would probably be measurably improved by limitation of sewage phosphorus. Characterizing Lake Erie as "dead" seems quite incorrect.

Unsolved Problems

Plenty of interesting problems remain in studying the natural mechanism of control of productivity and abundance of organisms in lakes. In particular, what is the relation between the rate of input of nutrients and the productivity of lakes? It is common to express the annual input

Figure VIII—17 — MEASUREMENTS OF ALGAE, PHOSPHORUS, AND NITROGEN IN LAKE WASHINGTON

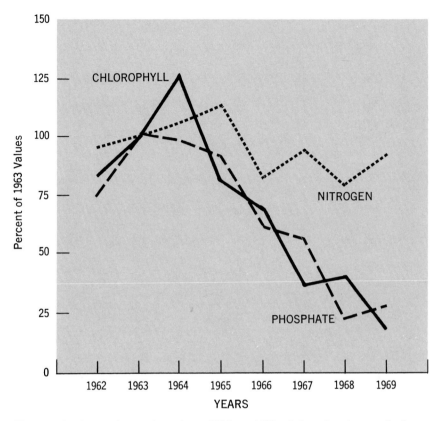

The graph shows observations from 1962 to 1969 of the abundance of algae, and the concentration of phosphates and nitrates. Yearly values are percentages of the 1963 values of the concentrations.

general viewpoint of basic "pure science" limnology, this would improve our understanding of the comparative limnology of productivity — why lake districts tend to have a certain uniformity and yet why individual lakes in one region differ in productivity.

Obviously, improvements in our understanding of these matters would be of tremendous practical importance. In few situations can there be a clean, clear-cut, total diversion of sewage as with Lake Washington. Often one will want to know what would be the effect of making some percentage reduction in the phosphorus content of sewage, or of diverting some fraction of the effluent. There is also the question of the effectiveness of agricultural drainage, which has probably been exaggerated. Nevertheless, we could find out whether it would be worthwhile trying to modify agricultural practices in a watershed.

Conversely, one might want to make a very precise adjustment of enrichment to maintain fish production at as high a level as possible without damaging the desired species or creating algal nuisances.

The problem, then, is to improve the predictability of limnological conditions, especially the productivity and abundance of organisms.

Demonstrably, Lake Washington has permitted a step forward in this direction, but we have a long way to go. Progress is more likely to be made by limnologists working with very broad questions than by anybody else working with very specific and limited questions on a purely practical basis. Progress will be faster and better if some more experiments can be carried out with real lakes. For example, Lake Erie might be regarded as a prime object for limnological experimentation.

on an areal basis as kilograms per hectare or pounds per acre. But this is an imperfect and even misleading calculation. Obviously, the effect of a given input will vary with the depth and volume of the lake. That is, a given input will affect a shallow lake more than a deep one.

Also, this calculation takes no account of the fact that some of the influents are much more concentrated than others. It seems evident that a very concentrated source relative to lake water will mix in and raise the nutrient content of the lake, while a source with the same concentration will merely displace an

equal volume and not make a net increase. This is why sewage effluent is so important relative to any normal ground drainage: it can be 1,000 times as concentrated in phosphorus as the natural water. One could double the nutrient input of a lake either by doubling the rate of inflow at the same concentration or by doubling the concentration in the same inflow. The effects are likely to be quite different.

Thus, we have to learn how to deal with the water budget as well as the nutrient budget, and to calculate the relative effect of influents of different concentration. From the

PART IX

TERRESTRIAL ECOSYSTEMS

1. COMPONENT RELATIONSHIPS

Environmental Design

All living organisms modify their environment and leave their imprint on it. This imprint leads to environmental change. The uniqueness of the human imprint is in its scale and tempo. Both by accident and by conscious intent, man has been and continues to be engaged in environmental modifications that are extensive, intensive, and rapid. His interventions in and manipulations of the processes of the planetary life-support system (ecosystem) have produced a set of complex problems — the problems of environmental design.

The entire planet has become man's niche. He is reshaping the world. The natural ecosystem is being transformed into a human ecosystem. Just as the development of a natural ecosystem can be characterized by a continuum of seral stages ranging from primitive to climax (see Figure IX–1) so can the transformation of natural ecosystem to human ecosystem. A continuum of anthroposeres comprises the stages of succession. The primitive stage includes a collection of shelters, a discrete cultural tradition, and hunting and gathering to support subsistence. The most recent stage consists of an interlocking web of subsystems each of which includes the city, its satellite towns and villages, a diversity of cultural traditions, a complex of communication links to areas of agricultural production, pools of wild plant and animal genes, natural resources, depots for wastes, and recreational sites. Increasingly, man is drawing on the resources of landscape and allocating them to the fulfillment of his own needs and requirements. Perhaps the climax stage will be the total transformation of the natural ecosystem to a human ecosystem. As the human population multiplies, this process of transformation accelerates. Man intervenes more and more in ecological

Figure IX–1 — SERAL STAGES OF A DECIDUOUS FOREST

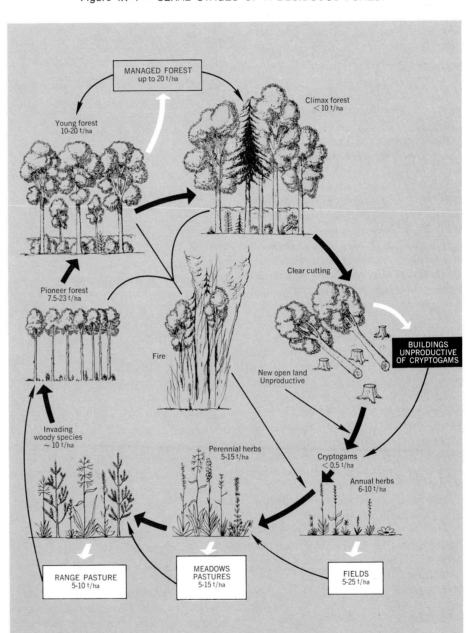

This figure is a schematic diagram of the successional sequence in a deciduous forest. The rectangular areas indicate where man has arrested the successional sequence to create other systems. The numbers indicate annual dry-matter production in metric tons per hectare (1t/ha = 100g/m²). Cryptogams are plants — ferns, mosses, algae, and the like — which reproduce by spores and do not produce flowers or seeds.

processes that he does not fully comprehend.

There are two reasons for the problems of environmental design. First, man cannot, with any certainty, now foretell the consequences of the transformations in which he is engaged. Second, he cannot yet design alternate processes for his own ecosystem that will assure his survival.

Some Specifics

In his design of the environment, man seems to have locked himself into a course that will bring him to the climax visualized before he has developed the knowledge and skills for managing such a human ecosystem. This is the essence of the problem. We shall examine briefly a few aspects in order to gain a perspective on the decisions about environmental design that man must make in the decades ahead.

Urban Growth — From the viewpoint of environmental design, the city may be conceptualized as an empirical allocation of the landscape to accommodate high population densities in functionally effective configurations of structures, spaces, institutions, and processes. Although the city gives the appearance of independent existence, it is inexorably bound to its surround, for the city is a specialized consumer of resources. It is entirely dependent on a continuing inflow of biological and physical-chemical resources for its very existence. These resources include foodstuffs, fuels, and a variety of raw materials. Its productivity can be measured in terms of diverse fabrications.

The city has become the scene of some intriguing shifts of population. There is at once an outward migration of people from the central city to the suburbs and an inward migration of people from the country to the city. To accommodate these flows, urban sprawl has developed; the central city, which began to deteriorate, is being rebuilt to house greater population densities; and vast transportation links have been constructed to carry workers between residence and place of work and to relate the city to its surround. The spread of the city has consumed large areas of productive agricultural land. The shift of population into high-density areas has sharpened the dependence of the city on the remaining agricultural lands and on the efficiency and effectiveness of the communication links with that managed landscape.

Monoculture and the Shrinking Gene Pool — For relatively fewer and fewer persons to support the growing dependent populations residing in high-density areas, the productivity of agricultural lands must be continually intensified. High productivity demands that an increasing amount of the landscape be transformed from low-producing climax associations of a diversity of plants and animals to high-producing monocultures of domesticated plants and animals bred to provide for human needs and requirements and for resistance to pathogens and adverse weather conditions, particularly cold and drought. To assure that these managed lands are maintained as monocultures, they are protected from invaders by a variety of biocides toxic to the invaders but not toxic to the domesticated organisms or the consumers of the produce. Because the nutrients extracted from the soil by the domesticates are not recycled but diverted to the human consumers, the nutrients must be restored as chemical fertilizers. To maintain the vigor and the resistance of the domesticates, they must be continually inbred with material from appropriate wild genes.

As the demands upon the landscape intensify, its transformation to managed agricultural systems spreads and the space that can be allocated to pools of wild plant and animal genes shrinks. As the stocks of wild genes diminish, the opportunity for invigorating the domesticates and for providing new domesticates is reduced. Because man's food base is already rather narrow, an important decision in environmental design will be how to provide adequate space for reservoirs of wild plant and animal genes.

Conservation and Recycling of Resources — Reservoirs of wild genes represent only one decision in environmental design to conserve natural resources essential for the human ecosystem. Because of their vital role in subsistence, steps must be taken to preserve the quality of lakes, rivers, estuaries, and zones of oceanic upwelling so that their biological productivity is maintained. Man also extracts other natural resources from the landscape. These resources provide fuel to support his activities and materials for his fabrications. Because the supply of these resources is finite, environmental designers must plan for their conservation, allocation among competing needs, and processes whereby essential materials may be recycled.

Managing feedback in the emerging human ecosystem is one of the most complex problems in environmental design. In the natural ecosystem, organic detritus is fed back into the environment and recycled into new organic forms. Relatively little detritus accumulates in the environment. Man adapted his methods of managing wastes to the processes of the natural ecosystem, but the scale and tempo of waste production have exceeded the capacity of natural feedbacks and the toxic nature of the human detritus has disrupted the orderly functioning of the organisms in the ecosystem. Man must now devise innovative processes to manage the rapidly accumulating detritus of the human ecosystem.

Because the resources of the landscape are limited, the decisions of environmental design for the allocation of these resources among competing demands must include the principle of multiple use. The most pressing demand that might best be handled by this principle stems from the time man has for leisure. A response to population growth is a shorter work period for each individual. As a consequence, there will be an increase not only in numbers of persons but also in the time available to each person for constructively filling leisure time. Among the ways of using leisure time is to engage in any one of a number of outdoor recreational activities. The demand for this type of leisure outlet is already mounting and the pressure will not diminish. Therefore, in designing the environment it will be necessary to allocate to recreation a variety of resources that can fill these specific needs as well as the more general needs of the human ecosystem.

Requirements for Scientific Activity

Science is on the threshold of realistically tackling these problems of environmental design. At the very least, the problems can be stated in broad perspective. That in itself is a start in the direction of formulating approaches to their solution.

A-disciplinarity — These problems are a-disciplinary. That is, they relate at once to no particular discipline yet involve many, perhaps all disciplines. The major problems of the sciences concerned with environment make meaningless the traditional boundaries that have separated man's compartmentalization of knowledge and methodology. That science is on the threshold of tackling a-disciplinary problems is evidenced by the increasing use of such phrases as interdisciplinary, multidisciplinary, pandisciplinary, and problem-oriented configurations of diverse specialists. Apparently, some scientists are ready to leave their feudal baronies and join in innovative configurations specifically focused on solving well-defined problems, however complex they may be.

Quantitative Analysis — The problems of environmental design are problems of ecosystems analysis. Largely through the initiative of scientists associated with the International Biological Program, a beginning has been made on the comprehensive and quantitative analysis of ecosystems. (See, for example, Figure IX–2) In order to be able to guide the transformation of natural ecosystems to human ecosystems, detailed quantitative knowledge must be available of the processes and regulations of the planetary life-support system. Techniques must be in hand for comprehensive surveillance and monitoring of appropriate physical, chemical, biological, and social indicators. Simulation models of ecosystems must be available to study and predict the outcomes of alternative strategies in environmental design. In large part, these expectations can be fulfilled through analysis of ecosystems.

Criteria for Environmental Quality — The quality of the environment is another facet of the problems of environmental design. As the transformation from natural to human ecosystem proceeds, it will be necessary to preserve environmental qualities essential to the continuing productivity and vitality of the biosphere and those adjunctive qualities that insure the habitability of the environment. At the same time it will be necessary to limit the accumulation of wastes in air, water, and soil and regulate the use of agricultural chemicals and food additives so as not to jeopardize the fitness of the ecosystem. The task of formulating criteria to serve as

Figure IX–2 — A SYSTEMS MODEL FOR A GRASSLAND ECOSYSTEM

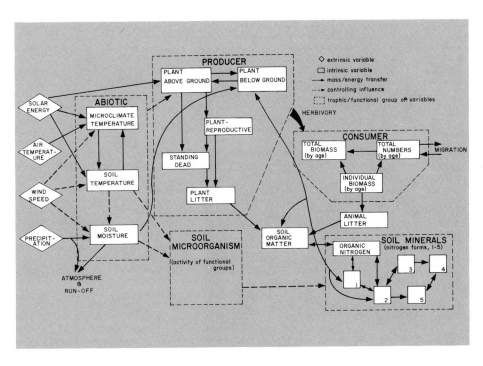

This diagram represents a significant step forward in the conceptual approach to the study of an ecosystem and has proved invaluable in the design of research, team organization, and analysis of data. Nonetheless, the level of sophistication shown here is well below that needed for application in practical problems. The complexities arising from the several hundred species and several thousand relationships are still overly simplified, as are the interactions of the system with human intervention. This figure is typical of the general level of modeling in all subfields of environmental science, and demonstrates the youth of the field.

guidelines for designing environmental quality has only just begun. In part, information on which to base these criteria will emerge from the analysis of ecosystems. However, more attention must be devoted to the biology of man, for he is the least systematically studied organism from the viewpoints of function and behavior.

Leisure Science — In terms of fulfilling man's needs and requirements, systematic studies must be undertaken of what has been called leisure science. The constructive and rewarding use of leisure time will be one of the central problems of environmental design and scientists have just begun to look at this problem area. The gamut of the problems of leisure includes the physiology, psychology, and sociology of leisure, recreational facilities and resources, and tourism.

Implementation

We have examined the problems of environmental design in broad perspective. We have noted that there is a readiness on the part of scientists to become involved in the comprehensive and complex tasks that must be undertaken for the solution of these problems. In particular, we have pointed to an emergence of such studies as ecosystems analysis, criteria of environmental quality, human biology, and leisure science. What might be done to implement the study of the problems of environmental design?

Because the problems of environmental design are adisciplinary, it will be necessary to develop institutions wherein problem-oriented configurations of scholars can be brought together to work effectively and efficiently in teaching and research. The administration of these institutions is most important, for being able to manage adisciplinary work is just as relevant as knowing how to tackle problem-oriented studies. It can be argued, for example, that present-day crises are just as much managerial crises as they are environmental ones.

These institutional formulations are being explored in the federal establishment, in state governments, and at colleges and universities. Progress has been slow because traditional values and alignments are difficult to overcome. Innovation creates insecurity among established feudal baronies. Allocation of limited financial resources between the old and the new strains both institutional formulations. Because there is a growing commitment to developing innovative problem-oriented institutions, it would seem most important that this commitment be realistically and responsibly encouraged.

Maintenance of the Biosphere, with Special Reference to Arid Lands

For centuries, man has been imposing unusual stresses on the ecosystems with which he comes into contact. Probably no other organism has so rapidly, and on such a worldwide scale, forced far-reaching changes on ecosystems previously in equilibrium. By removing particular species of plants, clearing land for crops, changing the balance between herbivores and their predators, altering the patterns of water movement, or spreading poisons through the landscape, man has imposed his will on nature.

But man's will has been shortsighted. Accustomed in most of the workaday world to see the results of his efforts in hours, days, or, at the most, in the interval from seedtime to harvest, he has not realized that ecosystems operate on a time-scale which, though short by evolutionary standards, is long by his own. It may take a generation or a century before the more far-reaching effects of his modification of ecosystems become fully apparent. In order to attain wisdom in his relations with natural ecosystems he must, consequently, develop long-sightedness — he must find means of predicting what the effect of his actions will be, not tomorrow, but next century.

The arid lands constitute a part of the biosphere that is more vulnerable than most. The desert areas of the Near and Middle East stand today as a lasting reminder of man's ability to modify — albeit unintentionally — this part of his environment. It is only by an attempt to regard ecosystems as wholes, and to develop an understanding of their dynamics, that such dangers can be averted and wise use of these delicately poised areas can be assured. To do so requires a reversal of what has for decades been the main current of scientific endeavor.

Analytical vs. Systems Approaches

When man looks at and considers his surroundings, he feels impelled to divide them into discrete units which he can classify and name. His mode of thought is based on verbalized categories and is not adapted to continuous variation and interrelation. Furthermore, just as giving something a name may tend to divert attention from the thing to the name one has given it, so categorization of one's surroundings diverts attention from the real whole to the categories into which it has been divided.

Science has long been concerned mainly with these discrete entities into which the environment has been divided — discrete in thought, though not in reality. And many of these entities have been so sundered as to be the subject of separate disciplines requiring quite different training. The meteorologist and the entomologist, the bryologist and the hydrologist are unlikely to come into contact, and unlikely to understand one another if they do. Yet weather and insects, mosses and streams are parts of a common over-all pattern within the landscape, and understanding of each considered in isolation is bound to be imperfect.

Even within a discipline it has been usual to narrow the focus, so that one is looking at a particular organism, a particular function, a particular organ or tissue — perhaps the role of stomata in controlling transpiration, the function of kidney tubules, the enzyme systems of glycolysis, or the mechanism of adsorption of ions on the surface of clay particles. This analytical approach in science — constantly subdividing one's categories, and getting to know more and more about less and less — has had great success. But there is no doubt that its practitioners have found it difficult to see the woods for the trees.

Over the past twenty years a realization has been growing that this fragmented attitude is inadequate to the subject matter of scientific study. Science is recognizing the need to try to fit the pieces together again and return to the complex whole that is reality. One form of this newly prominent synthetic effort is what has become known as systems analysis, involving the application of mathematical and computer techniques to the problem.

Systems Ecology — Systems analysis applied to ecology ("systems ecology") views the ecosystem as a whole and examines processes within it as they depend on all the other components of the ecosystem — meteoro-

logical factors, soil, plants, animals, and microorganisms. In the analytic approach, the photosynthetic rate of a leaf was viewed in isolation as dependent on the radiation impinging on it, and the temperature and humidity of the air around it. Perhaps the analytic approach delved even deeper, and the oxygen exchange of a chloroplast was viewed as a function of the radiation of different wavelengths absorbed by the pigments and the ionic balance of the protoplasm in which it was embedded. In systems ecology, in contrast, the focus is broader, and attention is directed to the gas exchange of the vegetation as a whole, or perhaps to each of the populations of different species of which it is composed; changes in rate of this process are considered, not in a simpler system actually or conceptually isolated, but in their whole real-world context — affected by the general meteorology of the area, by the soil which determines the supply of water and nutrients to the roots, by the animals exerting selective defoliation, pollinating, or transporting propagules.

In arriving at this overview, systems ecology may indeed make use of the results of analytic studies covering parts of the system. But the process of synthesis will demonstrate processes and effects in the ecosystem that would never have been recognized if the partial processes had been considered only in isolation.

Systems ecology does not avoid the need for simplification — ecosystems are indeed so complex that to think about them in their full complexity would be beyond human powers, even with any conceivable concentration of mechanical aids. But whereas the scientific approach of earlier decades has been by subdivision and isolation — what one might call a "vertical" simplification — systems analysis requires a "horizontal" simplification, in which all major components are considered but each is whittled down to the bare essentials.

Models and Submodels

Generally, the synthesis of partial processes into a representation of the ecosystem as a whole is conceived in terms of a model. The practical process of building and testing models is closely linked with the use of computers, both digital and analogue (or hybrid) — in fact, it is doubtful whether this activity would even have approached its present development without the availability of computers.

Once a model is built, a computer program representing it may be written, and repeated operation of the computer program then simulates the behavior of the ecosystem, as simplified in the model, under different sets of conditions. Empirical tests of this sort can then play a valuable part in improving the model, even where the analytical work involved in a direct approach would daunt a mathematician. The process of model development using computer simulation consequently has a large "boot-strapping" component.

Development of an ecosystem model is sometimes based on observations of the ecosystem as a whole — changes in quantities within it, or rate of processes such as the movement of material from one part of it to another. It may take the form of a set of differential equations with coefficients to be estimated, perhaps subject to constraints. Alternatively, the model may be divided into a number of submodels, each of which can be studied separately and its best mathematical representation (again in terms of differential or difference equations) determined. Figure IX–3 is an example of one such submodel. The submodels are then combined, and the performance of the model as a whole studied.

These two approaches may in fact arrive at a model of the same structure, but the estimates of constants will differ. If they are of the same structure, the fit *to the set of data used* will be better with the first ap-

Figure IX–3 — MOSQUITO SUBMODEL

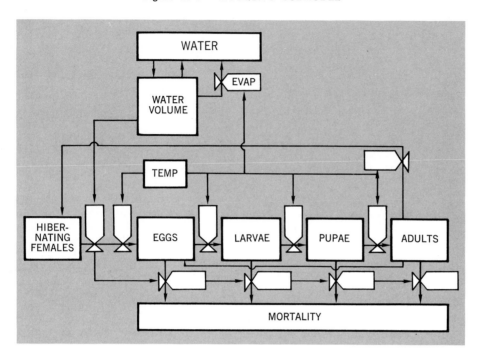

The figure is a submodel, or subsystem, of the larger desert ecosystem model. This particular submodel is designed to elucidate how water level and temperature affect the production of mosquitos in desert playas. Note that water volume is important initially to the female and the laying of the eggs whereas temperature is important throughout all stages in the mosquito's life; temperature is also important to the effectiveness of the water volume.

proach; but these data will themselves provide no validation of the model. In general, however, the development of separate submodels as a first step is likely to lead to a more sophisticated total model, with greater variety in its content, than is likely to be attained by using trial and error to modify a complete model without subdivisions. On the other hand, the possibility that important elements of interaction between submodels developed separately may affect their behavior when brought together is an ever present danger with this approach, and must be examined by validation comparisons of model behavior with that of the ecosystem as a whole.

Data Base — Both approaches to ecosystem modeling, and modifications of them, have been explored in recent years, and various simple mod-

els have been developed for aquatic and terrestrial systems. Only exceptionally, however, have the data been sufficient even for the construction of a model, let alone for testing it. The reason is that the data have usually been collected earlier, perhaps for a different purpose, and without reference to the particular type of model that was being built. Even where data were collected with modeling requirements in mind, the development of the model has often indicated the need for data additional to those already collected.

Standard Models — The problem of modeling does not need to be tackled afresh and independently for each new ecosystem that comes under scrutiny. There is a great deal in common in the general structure of relationships within different terrestrial ecosystems, even as diverse as

tundra and tropical forest, though none of the species are the same and the balance of the various life forms and processes is quite different. Even between aquatic and terrestrial systems, there are numerous analogies. Consequently, it may be expected that experience in modeling one type of ecosystem will greatly simplify the problems when a new type of ecosystem is considered, though all parameters may have to be estimated afresh.

Moreover, the value of model development is not limited by national frontiers. Where the same landforms and biota occur on both sides of a frontier the same models can be expected to represent the ecosystems there, so that a model for the Sonoran desert in Arizona should also apply to the Sonoran desert in Mexico. Even where different biota are involved in different countries, the general ecosystem structure as represented in the model will often be the same, and only the constants and data used may need to be changed in order that the same models should be applicable.

Terrestrial Systems — In general, the more successful models have been concerned with aquatic ecosystems; they are simpler, with fewer components, and limnologists are more accustomed to recording a wide range of data than are terrestrial ecologists. Few terrestrial models cover more than a limited selection of ecosystem components. In the arid lands, particularly, it is not possible to point to any complete ecosystem model based on well-authenticated data.

The paucity of models for complete terrestrial systems does not indicate a similar lack for subsystems. Certain parts of terrestrial systems have been the subject of considerable modeling activity. Some aspects of meteorology, for instance, are well served in this way, as is hydrology. There are models for soil nitrogen cycling, for photosynthesis and plant growth, and for predation. Many of these submodels, however, have only been claimed to apply in greatly simplified systems, and it remains to be seen whether they are also relevant in more complex natural systems.

Uses for Models

As for the use to which models can be put, it is easier to indicate possibilities than to point to examples of their actual use. We will leave aside uses at the intermediate stages of the model-building process, where an imperfect model can itself, by the development of internal inconsistencies over a long computer run, or by sensitivity analysis of various parameter estimates, point to ways in which it can be improved. The process of model building is indeed highly instructive, and aids greatly in the development of insights into the functioning of ecosystems. Once a model has been built and validated, though, it can be used for purposes extrinsic to its construction.

Experimentation — The model can, for instance, be used for experimentation on scales that are impracticable in real life, and many sources of error inescapable in the field can be eliminated. Questions can be asked and answered, for instance, on the effects of competition between species under different meteorological conditions. Such questions could be included in a field experiment only by extending it over different years or different locations, where extraneous and irrelevant sources of variation would be introduced.

Environmental Management — When the treatments postulated for the model are such as would be possible in practice, this use of the model leads directly to its potential value as a management tool. The effects of any proposed manipulation may be explored far more quickly and cheaply than would be possible in the field, and, either by trial and error or by a formal optimization procedure, a

choice can be made among a number of possible management strategies, once goals have been clearly defined.

In the arid lands, for example, the management goals that might be set for particular areas could include prevention of soil erosion by wind and water; increased runoff of groundwater recharge; increased (or maintained) grazing capacity for domestic livestock; increased numbers of wildlife (either for hunters or as an amenity); and even increased landscape values, insofar as they can be defined (good strands of flowering ephemerals following rain, or good growth of the more spectacular plants — Joshua tree, saguaro, palo verde — might fill this bill).

The practicable management treatments would certainly include different grazing practices (livestock type, density, and season, together with methods of stock control); shrub removal and/or seeding; wildlife control — by hunting permits, for example; introduction of exotics (plants and animals); and perhaps weather modification. The existence of a reliable model of the system, and a convenient computer implementation, would enable the effects of any of these proposed treatments to be evaluated in terms of the selected goals (appropriately weighted if multiple); the whole could then be subjected to benefit/cost analysis.

The arid lands of the United States are under heavy developmental pressure, which is likely to increase rather than decrease. The multiple-use concept often applied to them usually means multiple stresses. Yet management, except in limited fields, is perforce largely intuitive at present. Development of the management tools outlined in the previous paragraphs, accordingly, takes on the look of urgency where our arid lands are concerned.

Needed Scientific Activity

We should now examine what are likely to be the roadblocks restrict-

ing progress in this direction — where and what sort of scientific effort will need to be expended to make these possibilities into realities.

Monitoring — The range of ecosystems currently being monitored adequately to provide satisfactory tests of alternative models is far too small. It is of the greatest importance that the ecosystem models produced should be of high generality, even though of limited precision; it is far more valuable to be able to give tentative predictions over a hundred million acres than to predict accurately the course of events on a hundred acres. This means that observational areas against which model results can be checked must be spread widely enough, and be numerous enough, to cover the variation over which generalization is intended.

Moreover, the establishment of these monitored ecosystems for the purpose of validating models under development should be treated as a matter of some urgency. Their value largely depends on the period over which observations have been made, for long periods provide the most exacting test of models. There are a few sets of data already in existence — largely collected by the U.S. Forest Service — extending back for decades; these are of the greatest value, even though only a limited range of variables was monitored. Field studies for the specific purpose of validating ecosystem models are also currently being set up under the International Biological Program. (See Figure IX–4) Many more such sets of data will be needed for the modeling work that lies ahead, and in each of them a wide range of variables should be recorded as a routine.

Ecosystem Modeling — It would be premature to try to standardize approaches to ecosystem modeling. The subject is not yet ten years old, and it is far too early to try to put it into a straitjacket. Several methods of modeling are presently under test;

Figure IX–4 — A MODEL VALIDATION STUDY

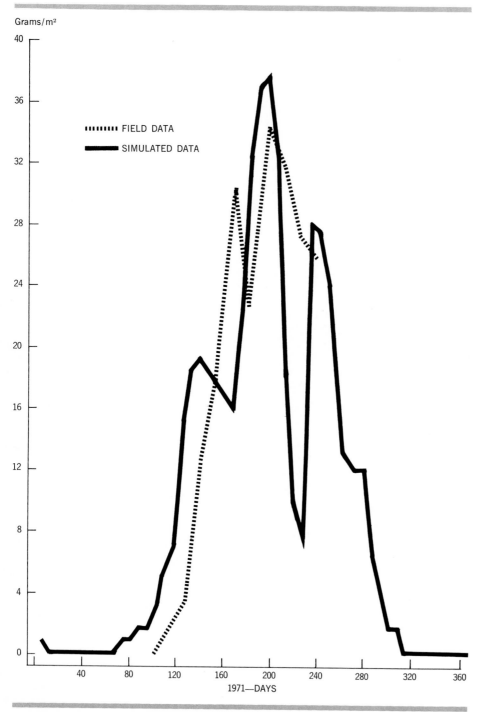

The graph shows the output of blue gramagrass biomass in g/m² as simulated by computer for the growing season of 1971. This simulation is one of the many outputs of the grasslands ecosystem model. Also plotted on the graph are actual field measurements of the blue grama production at the Pawnee site. Although there are differences in the curves, the over-all result indicates that the model *is* simulating the actual production. The differences can be explained, at least in part, by the fact that the abiotic variables that are input to the model are not measured at the same location as the sampling point for the blue grama biomass.

they should be given every encouragement to develop independently (though with plenty of opportunities for contact) for some years to come. In the meantime, some new approach, not yet conceived, may well show itself superior to any.

It is clear that modeling of abiotic parts of the ecosystem is considerably in advance of the development of submodels for the living components. More effort needs to be given to devising suitable forms for the latter submodels, and this will probably involve intensive experimental work on a variety of subjects.

A good deal more thought needs to be given to the process of validating models and comparing alternatives. Statistical considerations will clearly play an important part, but at present most statisticians avoid the subject.

Techniques To Incorporate Diversity — Simplification is essential in the modeling of ecosystems; but the methods of simplification at present in vogue (in terms of compartments, trophic levels, and such) are unlikely to be the most fruitful. There is little doubt that the diversity of an ecosystem is an important factor in its dynamics and stability, and means must be found to take this diversity into account in the model. The diversity or heterogeneity that is important may take various forms; first and foremost, the division of the biomass into species, each of which has distinctive responses to the environment and, consequently, distinctive niche requirements; second, variation within a species of genetic and acquired characteristics, including responses to external factors and the timing of vital processes such as seed germination, metamorphosis, and reproduction; third, spatial differentiation and patterning, partly dependent on the inanimate substrate, partly developed through the dynamics of the ecosystem itself.

Such heterogeneity has mainly been incorporated in models by multiplying the number of distinct compartments recognized; but this process cannot be carried very far. Until some more adequate technique is devised to deal with the various types of heterogeneity, the models developed will be but a pale reflection of reality.

Computers — Installations at the disposal of ecosystem modelers are often rather inadequate for the task. Modeling teams may be obliged to use rather slower machines, with limited storage, whereas ecosystem simulations are bound to be demanding both of space and time. Programming and model testing could be greatly facilitated by a shift from batch processing to interactive terminals,

which are now available at few centers.

Digital computers are, in principle, far from ideal for the simulation of continuous processes. One would consequently expect a large hybrid computer to be appropriate for ecosystem modeling; this may often call for an alternation of continuous and discontinuous operations, which could be performed, respectively, on the analogue and digital sections of a hybrid computer. Unfortunately, the programming of hybrid computers is at present far more difficult than that for digital computers, and facilities for remote-terminal programming do not exist. Hardware developments to meet this need are to be hoped for;

in any case, it is important that the potentialities for ecosystem modeling of hybrid as well as digital computers should be fully explored.

Interdisciplinarity—Continued emphasis should be placed on the need for interdisciplinary training. Individuals brought up within one of the traditional disciplines, with only limited and casual contact across the disciplinary frontiers, can contribute to a program in systems ecology only after extensive retraining, formal or informal. We need personnel with a broad training in the biological and earth sciences, who have developed expertise in certain aspects of mathematics and computer science. This is made more difficult by the rather narrow curricula of many universities.

Energy Relationships in Ecological Systems

Energy is essential for life, but since life itself is dynamic rather than static, energy flow must occur at all times. The earth ecosystem functions because of the flow of energy from a source, the sun, to a sink, outer space, after passing through the biosphere. The biosphere, which is that zone of soil, rock, water, and air containing organisms, is at an energy state, or thermodynamic level, that is compatible with life. This energy state is neither too warm nor too cold for life to exist and replicate.

The thermodynamic level of the biosphere fluctuates greatly, with both random fluctuations and periodic cycles. Some portions of the biosphere (polar regions and upper troposphere or lower stratosphere) are relatively cold while other portions (tropical regions and thermal hot springs) are relatively hot. Nevertheless, life has evolved to occupy all of the earth's surface, some of the subsurface, and a good deal of the atmosphere. A part of our understanding of the earth ecosystem and its many subsystems, including spe-

cific biomes (see Figure IX–5), is to understand the passage of energy through the various components and the thermodynamic levels of each and every part.

However, in order to understand and interpret the significance of energy, of energy flow, and of a particular thermodynamic state in the context of ecosystem analysis, one must understand simultaneously the life processes themselves. Ecology is that body of knowledge concerning the relationships between organisms and environment, organisms interacting with one another, and including the effect of man on the ecosystem. Ecosystems are those finite entities of the landscape which include the organisms and the physical environment. One must understand the physiological and biochemical requirements of each species in the ecosystem with respect to temperature, energy, and such effects as photoperiodism, phototropism, and the like. The thermodynamic status of a plant or animal can be appreciated only in the context of its

particular and specific physiological requirements.

Life-Support Systems

Primary productivity in the earth ecosystem is the result of photosynthesis. Each and every species of plant responds uniquely to environmental conditions — to the energy status, to gas concentrations of the atmosphere and water, to pollution, to disease, and so on. The entire food chain, web, or pyramid begins with primary production. A "natural" ecosystem has many species of plants, each collaborating with the others to produce the total primary production of the system but each responding in a special way to the variable conditions. Herbivores consume the plants and each herbivore responds to the variable energy status of the ecosystem in a unique way. Each species of herbivore will have its own physiological requirements and biochemical responses to temperature, light, moisture, gas exchange, pollution, and so forth. Energy is trans-

Figure IX–5 — MAJOR WORLD BIOMES

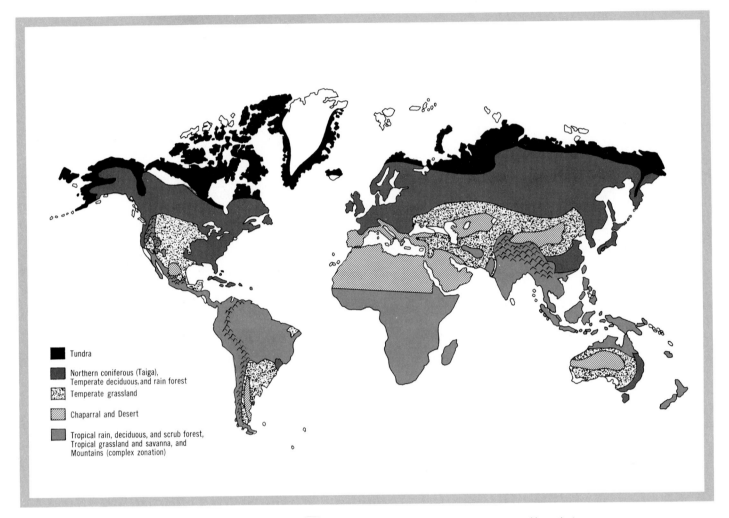

■ Tundra

■ Northern coniferous (Taiga),
Temperate deciduous, and rain forest

▨ Temperate grassland

▨ Chaparral and Desert

■ Tropical rain, deciduous, and scrub forest,
Tropical grassland and savanna, and
Mountains (complex zonation)

This map shows the distribution and location of the world's major biomes. Note that except in the rugged mountainous regions of North and South America, the distribution of biome types tends to be along parallels of latitude. Such a situation suggests the importance of temperature and rainfall, both of which are strongly dependent on latitude. Studies of past climates and biome distributions also support this concept.

ferred from primary producers to secondary producers, but the response of each herbivore depends on the daily and seasonal cycles of temperature, light, moisture, gas concentration, and such. Carnivores and omnivores consume herbivores and primary producers to form higher levels in the food chain (see Figure IX–6), but again it should be emphasized that each and every species responds in a unique manner to the energy state of the system and to

cycles and fluctuations of energy, gas, minerals, moisture, and the like.

Man is now affecting the life-support system of the planet earth to a serious degree. Man is consuming oxygen at a rate that may someday change the concentration of this gas in the atmosphere, and at the same time man is affecting the primary source of oxygen production through pollution and other means. Man is emitting to the atmosphere

massive amounts of carbon dioxide (CO_2); these directly affect plant productivity, since increased CO_2 in the atmosphere implies increased rates of photosynthesis. The increased atmospheric CO_2 concentrations also imply potential changes of climate.

The living, green, photosynthesizing surface of the earth, with all its associated organisms, has evolved in synergism with the atmosphere. Each

Figure IX–6 — PLANT-MOUSE-WEASEL CHAIN

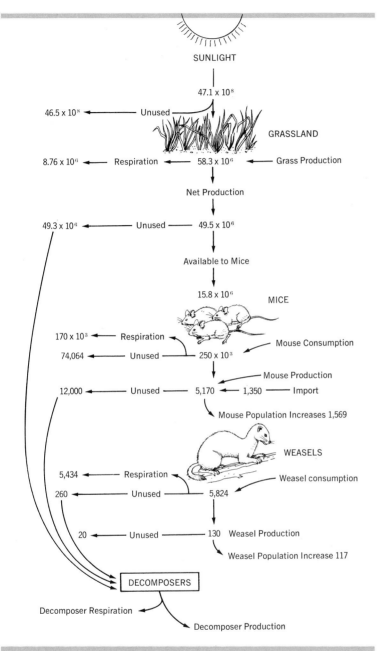

The diagram illustrates an actual energy-flow budget for a plant-meadow mouse-weasel food chain in an old-field habitat. Numerical values are in kilocalories per hectare. About 1 percent of the incoming solar energy is converted into plant tissue. Most of energy represented by this plant tissue is accounted for by respiration and decomposition. Of the remaining energy, the meadow mice consume only 2 percent. The weasels, in turn, utilize 30 percent of the available mouse biomass. Of the energy consumed in each stage of the food chain, the plants use 15 percent in respiration, the mice 68 percent, and the weasels 93 percent. This supports the suggestion that successive stages in food chains exhibit an increased utilization of the energy taken up. However, in this particular food chain, so little of the energy entering the system was eventually utilized in the conversion of weasel flesh that it would have been impossible for the habitat to support a secondary carnivore preying upon the weasels. Because of this tapering off of available energy in a food chain, food chains rarely exceed five steps and commonly have less.

depends upon the other. The present composition of the atmosphere is the direct result of life on the surface, and life itself depends on the particular character of the atmosphere. Ozone in the stratosphere, which screens the surface from the actinic ultraviolet rays of the sun, is a direct photochemical product of the oxygen that comes from plants. Carbon dioxide and water vapor absorb and emit infrared radiation, thereby directly affecting the heat balance of the earth, but these chemical constituents interact intimately with the green photosynthesizing surface. The atmosphere has a narrow semi-transparent spectral window that allows sunlight to flow to the earth's surface and some radiant heat to flow to space.

It is this delicately balanced, unique system of life and atmosphere, in cooperation with the oceans of the world, which is the life-support system for man. Yet man persists in dirtying the atmospheric window and tampering with the energy flow, gas exchange, and life-support system itself.

Energy Relations of Plants

Energy exchange for plants is by processes of radiation, convection, transpiration, and photosynthesis. We now have excellent theoretical, mathematical models to describe how a particular plant leaf is coupled to the climate surrounding it by means of energy exchange. The plant leaf will assume a particular temperature and a particular transpiration rate (the two dependent variables) as a function of the total amount of radiation absorbed by the leaf, air temperature, wind speed, and relative humidity of the air (the four independent variables). The plant's dependent variables are coupled to the environmental independent variables by the absorptivity of the leaf to radiation, the size, shape, and structure of the leaf, and the internal resistance of the stomates to diffusion of water vapor. We understand these matters well but still need much additional work in this area. It is the energy exchange for a leaf which drives all other processes critical to the life of the plant.

The next part of the process, the gas exchange of carbon dioxide and oxygen release, is not well worked out. The chemical kinetics of photosynthesis and respiration are rate processes which depend on light, temperature, and gas concentration and which are driven by the available energy. In order to understand plant adaptation and response to climate and environment, we must understand the entire process of energy exchange, gas flow, photochemistry, thermochemistry, and physiological reaction.

Each species of plant has a biochemical response which is enzyme-controlled. Some plants photosynthesize well at low temperatures and some at high temperatures, some at low light levels and some at high light levels, and so on. More knowledge is needed immediately concerning these enzyme-mediated processes. Schemes are needed to determine the basic biochemical response functions of chloroplasts and mitochondria within whole leaves as a function of leaf temperature, light intensity, and concentrations of oxygen and carbon dioxide. These measurements must be separated from the whole process which involves gas diffusion and the physical environment.

The matter of photorespiration, which occurs in most plants, must be understood much better. We want to know precisely how it is that net photosynthesis productivity depends on the climate conditions of radiation, air temperature, wind speed, and humidity for each specific kind of plant. Only now are we putting together a complete model that incorporates in a self-consistent manner energy flow, gas diffusion, leaf morphology, anatomy, physiology, and biochemistry. Such a model is essential if we

are to understand primary productivity, including the exchange of oxygen, carbon dioxide, water vapor, and other gases including pollutants. This is not only important for our understanding of ecosystems but also for our management of crops for food production.

Energy Relations of Animals

The energy budget of specific animals has been worked out for the first time only in recent years. From the particular properties of a specific animal we are able to predict the climate within which the animals must live in order to survive. Conversely, for a given set of climatic conditions we can predict the metabolic rate required for survival and

this in turn puts limits on the available food supply. Earlier work concerning the response of an animal to climate was highly qualitative and descriptive. (See Figure IX–7) Although useful, this is not sufficient, since we are dealing with an extremely complex response to a multiple set of variables all of which act simultaneously.

Our lack of good physiological knowledge for any particular animal is likely to be enormous. Information concerning metabolic rates, respiratory moisture loss, evaporative water loss, and thermal insulation of animals is usually poor and inadequate. This information is essential to an understanding of the energy balance of animals and their specific response to climate and environment.

Figure IX–7 — ENERGY BUDGET OF A HORSE

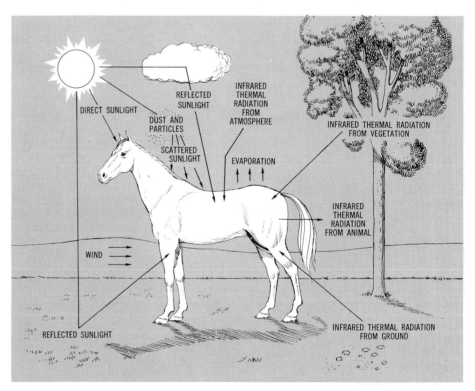

The diagram depicts, simply and qualitatively, the multiple energy inputs and outputs that affect a horse. Although not quantified in the diagram, it is possible to describe each input mathematically so that the energy balance of the animal can be computed. The result can be used further as a part of a larger model describing the energy balance in a field or pasture where grazing takes place.

Yet the ecosystem functions in the way it does because of the specific response of each and every animal in the ecosystem, the totality of which represents the food pyramid or web of life. Understanding of these matters is critical to our understanding of climate and its effect on plant and animal communities of the world.

Greatly improved physiological measurements of metabolic rates and water-loss rates as a function of environmental conditions are needed. It is necessary to know the values of radiation absorbed by the animal, air temperature, wind speed, and humidity during the course of any measurements. The conditions under which the animal was conditioned must be specified. In the laboratory, it would be particularly important that complete energy-budget analyses be done for each set of observations of the animal. In the field, careful observations are needed of metabolic rates and water-loss rates as well as of the microclimate conditions near the animal. These measurements are difficult to make, but must be done and can be done with the aid of telemetry and other modern methods.

Systems Analysis

On the one hand, mathematical analysis of the productivity of individual plant leaves is now being done based on a holistic approach including the use of physics, chemistry, physiology, and biochemistry. On the other, agronomists are working out the energy and gas exchange of a community of simple plants — e.g., corn, wheat, or millet. A great deal of work is required to bridge the gap between these two approaches. A given species has leaves that may occupy various parts of a plant canopy. The leaves forming one part of a canopy are in an entirely different microclimate than the leaves of another part, and the properties of shade leaves are different from the properties of sun leaves of the same species. One can evaluate the individual leaves of each part of a canopy, apply the numbers game for all the leaves of a part of the canopy, and integrate over the entire canopy for productivity, respiration, total water use, and so on. This approach will match up eventually with the approach of the agronomist to the problem of evaluating the whole stand. However, since the ecologist is interested in the role of various species within a stand, it is necessary to take this detailed approach.

Competition and Phenology — The ecologist is interested in competition among the species of a plant community — competition for light, moisture, carbon dioxide, and nutrients, and maybe for wind and air flow, soil bacteria, and other factors. In order to understand competition one must understand the plant response to energy and gas exchange as they affect growth, flowering, seed development, and so on. A closely related topic is phenology — the response of organisms to time-cycles of climate. To understand phenology we need to understand the temperature of a plant as it responds to the climate of soil and air and to realize the significance of events throughout the season that may integrate into plant response. Studies of competition and phenology require good laboratory measurements and good field measurements. It is not so necessary to obtain an abundance of field data, however, as it is to analyze well and completely the field data obtained.

Prediction — As we understand the specific response of animals to energy flow (radiation, convection, conduction, evaporation, and metabolism), we can begin to work out the response of a set of organisms within a community. (See Figure IX–8) It is not sufficient to know the amount of energy transferred through the food pyramid from primary producer to primary, secondary, and tertiary consumers; it is also important to understand the energetics of each organism in the community and the response of each organism to all climate and edaphic factors. Furthermore, behavioral studies of some animal populations often ignore or treat only cursorily the detailed environmental conditions. Animal behavior will often respond to energy flow, as well as to other factors, in an intimate fashion.

Despite an acute shortage of good physiological data for most animals, we can begin to simulate on the computer communities of plants and animals and their response to climate. We can set up simple experimental ecosystems in the laboratory or out-of-doors and check prediction from a model against observation. We need much better evaluations of energy flow through various ecosystems, as well as evaluations of gas exchange and nutrient flow. The biome studies of the International Biological Program will add considerable knowledge, but much remains to be done.

Modern science has the capacity to do a much better job of analyzing energy flow through ecosystems and evaluating specific physiological response. Here is a magnificent opportunity for a strong theoretical discipline to be developed. It must be based on good physiological data from the plant and animal sciences. Theoretical development must be constantly checked by field observations.

Figure IX–8 — RELATION BETWEEN FOOD INTAKE AND CALORIFIC
EQUIVALENCE OF INVERTEBRATES

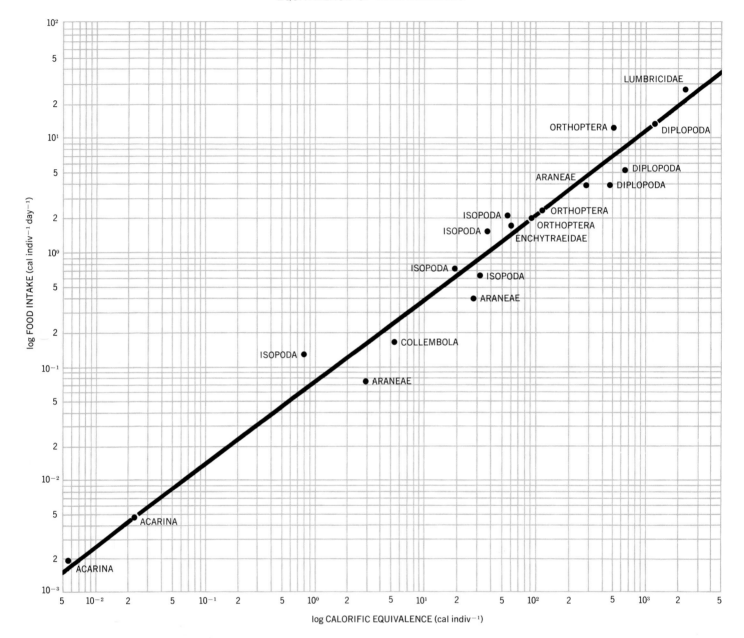

The graph shows the relationship between food intake and calorific or heat equivalence of several invertebrates. This information was obtained from published
material and synthesized to determine the mathematical relationship which then can
be used in a numerical, computerized model to predict the amount of heat that is
produced by a given amount of food.

A Note on Soil Studies

Soil science in the United States is now scientifically stronger than ever before. Virtually each branch of the field is staffed with a sizable number of fundamentalists whose contributions are adding materially to an understanding of the soil system. Primary direction has been toward agricultural production, and results have been impressive. Laboratories are generally well equipped with the most modern instruments.

However, with each step toward increased specialization, we have fewer and fewer investigators who are capable of understanding in depth the entire soil system. Thus, we are developing more and more specialists working in highly technical corners with fewer and fewer investigators comprehending *soils* from the standpoint of the "field effect." Of course, this problem is not unique to soil science.

Status and Needs

In examining global soil resources, we find the subject fairly well documented in the United States, Europe, the western sectors of the Soviet Union, and Australia. Through various international organizations we are getting a more complete picture of soil resources in other locations, such as Africa and South America; but even on these continents the picture is understood in at least general terms. Climate-wise, soil resources in the tropics, deserts, and the polar regions are not too well known. Strengthening the former two is more critical than the third, since congestion in the temperate climates is likely to bring increased population first to the desert sectors and then to the tropics, and only last, if needed, the polar regions.

Water Quality and Quantity — Since water supply and water quality are of great importance not only for agriculture but for all of mankind, the major problem concerns the desert or desert-like areas. Water quality as well as quantity is related to climate, substrate, soil, plants, and so on. The more arid the climate, the more acute the problem of quantity and natural quality of water. For example, drainage waters from desert areas are more likely to be charged with excessive salts for irrigation.

Pollution and Soils — In the more densely populated areas (e.g., eastern North America and Europe), the pollution problem is becoming acute. When potential pollutants enter the soil — whether they be industrial wastes, fertilizers, insecticides, or detergents, among others — we know very little of how they react. More emphasis should be directed to the study of organic matter, types of minerals, aeration, acidity, and so on, to learn how they affect the fate of potential pollutants. Stronger studies are needed on persistence adsorption, translocation, solution, and precipitation of potential pollutants in soils. If there is one area in which a team approach is needed, it is on the problem of ecology and pollution.

Wet Soil Areas — Since most potential pollutants entering the soil eventually find their way, in one form or another, to water courses, lakes, estuaries, coastal sectors, and the like, these locations are all materially affected. There are few soil and substrate studies being conducted in these critical low areas. Traditionally, our soils effort has been confined to farming areas and the growing of crops. Certainly, the problem of the soil system in low, wet areas and in the vicinity of lakes and shores needs to be strengthened. Soil classification in wet soil areas is weak; in general, little attention has been paid to these areas.

Need for Balance

Soil scientists are not now being used to full advantage in the United States. Virtually all ecological and environmental studies involve the soil system in some way. The soil is the link between the organic and inorganic worlds. But we see virtually all important soil research in this country being carried out under the aegis of agriculture, while soil studies dealing with *ecosystems*, a field currently as critical or more critical than agriculture, are poorly organized and poorly staffed.

If we are going to master the pollution problems and problems of ecology and environmental control, then there must be a strengthening of undergraduate and graduate programs in the subject of soil science in non-agriculturally oriented institutions. Soil science should be programed — as are geology, hydrology, climatology, botany, and zoology — as one of the natural sciences. It is not implied that the agricultural effort should be weakened; rather, the non-agricultural viewpoint should be strengthened.

2. FOREST ECOSYSTEMS

The Forest As An Ecosystem

A forest is a natural or artificial vegetation unit encompassing many different tree associations and harboring a multitude of other life forms which use it for food or shelter or both. Man has used the forest since his ascent to a dominant position, either for direct products or indirectly by destroying large areas and converting the land to other uses — mainly food production or urban development. Currently men consider forests and forest areas useful for the following purposes: wood and fiber production; forage production; water production; aesthetic values — with the many ramifications of this subject. In many instances, attempts to convert forests to other land uses have proved unwise, and large areas have gradually reverted to forest use or have been converted by planting of tree species; the species used were often different from the endemic populations and, therefore, the forest ecology has changed.

Generalized Description of Forest

A forest is best regarded as a system. As such, it is composed of subsystems, which can be defined in various ways, depending on the subject under discussion. Here we prefer to consider two principal subsystems: (a) the abiotic, consisting of the nonliving components of the *soil* on which trees and other green plants grow, the *atmosphere* surrounding and interacting with the living members of the system, and *water and nutrient elements*, which are in continual movement through both biotic and other abiotic parts of the forest system; and (b) the biotic subsystem, consisting of living plants and animals.

Trees are the dominant biotic feature of forest ecosystems, constitute the framework of any structure it may possess, and affect importantly nearly all other components, biotic and abiotic. *Shrubs, herbs, and nonvascular plants* such as fungi, algae, mosses, and liverworts make up a smaller proportion of the total biomass of the forest system but play vitally significant roles in its dynamics. Fungi and bacteria, for example, are the principal agents of decomposition, and all known tree roots function in symbiosis with mycorrhizal fungi in the uptake of water and nutrient elements. *Insects, mammals, birds, and other animals* are primary consumers of vegetational biomass manufactured by trees and other primary producers and, hence, affect the functioning of the system importantly; their numbers are affected by numerous predators and parasites.

Where Science Stands Today

To a large degree we are still in the descriptive stage of forest-ecosystem understanding and, in some instances, not very far along in this stage. Most of the higher plants have been described and catalogued for most forests of the world. However, a multitude of other life forms exist and large numbers have not been identified; certainly their function is not understood, except for such common forms as earthworms.

The multiplicity of life forms existing in forest soils is an example of the deficiency in our knowledge. As a more definitive case, if one looks at a tropical forest in detail one soon discovers that major species have been identified by industrious plant explorers but that our knowledge largely ceases at that point. Information on detailed inter-relationships, even those necessary to manage and predict the effects of common manipulations, is largely nonexistent in the case of tropical forests.

For forests of temperate regions, which for the most part have been studied more by man and on the whole used more intensively, we presumably have better information. The complexity of our problems in these forests is reduced because species composition is simpler, especially as it relates to the dominant species. Thus, a northern coniferous forest may be almost a single-species forest whereas several hundred tree species may be found in a few square kilometers in many tropical forests. It is doubtful, however, that the same simplicity applies to all other life forms.

In many instances, man has managed temperate and boreal forests rather intensively for relatively long periods of time to various ends — principally the production of wood. It is not surprising, therefore, that a considerable body of information has been built up relating to growth rates of certain important species in a given environment. In such cases, much is also known about the management of water resources or the provision of forage for wild or domestic animals, and we have frequently acquired considerable practical information on forest insect populations and diseases.

Despite the relatively large amount of work on forests, the conclusions seem justified that much of it has been descriptive, on relatively small areas of a large forest resource, and so far has not materially enhanced our ability to make accurate predictions of important processes occurring in forest ecosystems. For instance, we have no certain road to regeneration of a forest after natural or artificial removal, and many of the problems that develop in management are still unpredictable.

What We Need to Know

An appraisal of present knowledge about forest ecosystems leads to the conclusion that we need to know more about the following subjects in order to understand these systems more thoroughly and make reasonably accurate predictions.

1. Details of many life forms other than trees, especially those using the soils as a habitat;

2. Competitive aspects of forest life;

3. Dynamics of forest populations;

4. Stability of forest environments;

5. Forest growth and forest environmental relationships;

6. Potential utility of different kinds of biomass produced in forests;

7. Total productive capability of forests with improvements man can add;

8. Aesthetic management of forests;

9. Method of coordinating and integrating information collected on forests to answer some of the above questions and predict results of forest changes — in other words, some kind of workable forest-ecosystem model.

In a broad sense, lands devoted to various forest uses are considered to be within public control even though operated by private individuals. This seems to be particularly true of relatively large ownership, in contrast to the small acreages generally referred to as farm woodlots. For example, game, fish, and recreation are considered to be public goods on these private lands and, therefore, subject to some public control and management. In addition, of course, the United States is blessed with large areas of public forest land, managed by various agencies for a variety of purposes.

In assessing the question of how research can do more for the public good in the management of these lands, we should probably look first at the purposes for which the land is to be used and the public good to be served. If a real public need is paper for education, or building material to improve housing of a large segment of the people, then one can make a logical argument for developing research programs that would make at least some of our forest ecosystems as productive in wood fiber as possible.

On the other hand, if the best public need is served by setting aside most of the areas for recreational purposes, then we must develop programs that would enable these lands to be used by large numbers of people but still maintain the recreational and aesthetic aspect of the forest ecosystem. This is a more difficult task than most people realize and one which has had little investigation. For some reason, we have assumed that describing an area as a National Park or a Wilderness sets it up for permanent maintenance of its original state without undue problems. In one sense, the problems imposed by large numbers of people on delicate forest ecosystems are more difficult to predict than uses for wood or water. Therefore, we must know enough about our forest ecosystems to set up the proper public use and then develop the information to manage them for that purpose.

A Note on Hubbard Brook

The study of interrelationships of forests, water, and minerals requires a special study vehicle that allows integration of information from several separate fields. As of now, research levels in the separate fields of forest soils and hydrology are reasonably adequate. Many forestry and conservation schools and federal and state agencies maintain personnel and research facilities suitable to the study of these separate fields. But truly integrative research, which welds the expertise of various disciplines and focuses it on a particular ecosystem, is relatively rare.

The Hubbard Brook Study

The Hubbard Brook Ecosystem Study was conceived and developed as a multidisciplinary study of single, well-defined watershed ecosystems, including both natural and man-manipulated ecosystems. The Hubbard Brook Experimental Forest comprises about 7,500 acres in the White Mountains of central New Hampshire, operated and maintained by the Northeastern Forest Experiment Station of the U.S. Forest Service. It is surrounded by a large, undisturbed tract of the White Mountain National Forest, which consists of a series of discrete watersheds with similar northern-hardwood forest vegetation and a homogeneous bedrock that forms an impermeable base.

The original goals of the Hubbard Brook Ecosystem Study were to understand the energy and biogeochemical relationships of northern-hardwood forest watershed ecosystems as completely as possible in order to propose sound land management procedures. A small-watershed ecosystem approach was used to study hydrologic cycle–nutrient cycle interaction in forest-stream-lake ecosystems. This concept provided an opportunity to deal with the complex problems of the ecosystem on an experimental basis.

Integrated ecological studies of these small, watertight, replicated forested watersheds were begun in 1963 by Likens and Bormann in cooperation with the U.S. Forest Service. The study has involved some 32 senior scientists from ten universities, one national laboratory, and three government agencies. The specific work ranges from studies of complete nutrient budgets, including measurements of inputs of cations and anions in precipitation and losses of cations and anions in dissolved and particulate matter exiting the system, to studies of nutrient cycle–hydrologic cycle interactions, weathering rates, soils, litter accumulation and degradation, biomass measurements, productivity, nutrient turnover within the biota, phenology, energy pathways and relationships, and experimental manipulation (deforestation) of an entire watershed ecosystem. Figure IX–9 illustrates the results of one such study. In addition, a biogeochemical study of a small lake within the general drainage area of Hubbard Brook is under way. Computer simulation and systems-analysis procedures are being developed to facilitate understanding of the complex interrelationship of these ecosystems.

The results of the study to date have been described in numerous publications. The project has been endorsed by the U.S. National Committee for the International Biological Program (IBP), and the study has been accepted as a part of the U.S.

Figure IX–9 — ECOLOGICAL EFFECTS OF DEFORESTATION

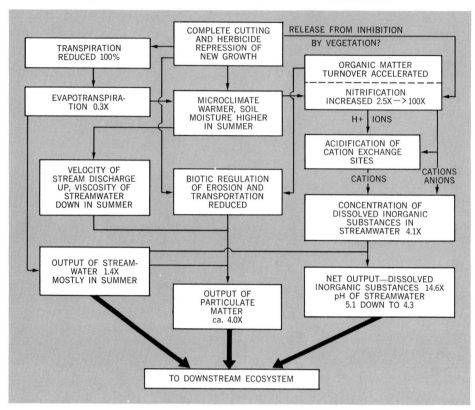

The diagram summarizes some of the ecological effects of the deforestation of Watershed 2 in the Hubbard Brook Experimental Forest. The rates at which the processes are taking place are based on data obtained during 1966-68, and are expessed in terms of increases above those observed before the watershed was deforested. High nutrient concentrations, coupled with the increased amount of solar radiation, have resulted in significant eutrophication. This study is an example of how a known change in one component of an ecosystem can change the structure and function in another section of the same or related ecosystem in an unexpected way.

program for the IBP and the International Hydrological Decade.

The Value of the Small-Watershed Approach

The small-watershed approach has already shown its power to draw together aspects of the fields of meteorology, limnology, geology, soils, hydrology, biology, and ecology into one coherent study on the structure and function of an ecosystem. This type of approach is basic to advancement of knowledge of how landscapes really work. In turn, good land-use planning is dependent on knowledge

of the structure and function of ecological systems.

Although the hydrologic aspects of many types of watersheds, forested and otherwise, are under study, there are relatively few watersheds where comprehensive biogeochemical studies are under way. This is a serious deficiency and should be remedied. Comparative small-watershed studies, where the watersheds are well defined, should be initiated in all major biomes where they are presently not part of IBP planning. Twenty to thirty of these studies scattered throughout the North American continent in various biomes and involving undisturbed and man-manipulated ecosystems would be a modest start.

Other Needed Activity

Several other deficiencies are evident when one considers comprehensive ecosystem studies. One of the major goals of ecosystem study is to improve our capacity to predict the behavior of ecosystems under various kinds of stress. Modeling, ecosystem analysis, and simulation of ecosystems are aimed at improving predictive capacity. Our capacity to meet these needs is growing haltingly, although there is a strong need for a centralized laboratory dealing with the mathematical aspects of ecosystem analysis. This lab could do research on its own and cooperate in modeling, analysis, or simulation of various ecosystem studies under way or planned.

One of the great problems facing teams of scientists analyzing a forest (or other ecosystems) is physical and chemical analysis of thousands of samples of plant and animal tissue, air, water, soil, and the like. Service laboratories charged with these types of analyses and with the development of new sampling techniques would be of great utility in accelerating and expanding studies of the many terrestrial and aquatic ecosystems that make up the continental United States.

Tropical Forests

Tropical forests now cover about 5 billion of the approximately 10.6 billion acres of the world that are still forested. These forests are among the most poorly known areas of the world, especially with respect to their ecology. This condition is particularly unfortunate because there is no other system with comparable productivity that covers more than a small fraction of the area occupied by the tropical forests. Because of our ignorance, these forests remain one of the most poorly used of the earth's resources.

General Description of Tropical Forests and Soils

Evergreen "tropical rain forest," the most productive of the tropical forests, is found in the lowlands where rainfall is high and where dry periods, if they occur, are very short. Evidence suggests that the forest itself appreciably increases its own rainfall through the water that evaporates from its canopy. Semi-deciduous and deciduous forests are found in areas with high humidity but dry seasons of several weeks to months. Dry seasons of several months permit development of a continuous, but relatively dry and less well-developed, forest; if dry seasons are longer, forests can exist only as patches, small groups, or single trees separated by grassland.

The adaptive characteristics of tropical forests (and the problems from man's point of view) are largely the result of interactions between the rather uniformly high temperatures and the amount of rainfall. The physical character of most tropical soils is such that both water and air can move through at least the surface layers relatively easily; thus, as long as the forest canopy is intact, rainfall does not cause much erosion. In over half the tropical land area, however, heavy precipitation has resulted in the solution and leaching away of almost all but the most resistant oxides of iron and aluminum. Where leaching has been extensive, availability of plant nutrients and soil fertility is generally very low.

Tropical trees are successful under these conditions largely because they have developed efficient mechanisms for nutrient cycling. This is accomplished by the shallow root systems, which acquire minerals as fast as they are released from fallen leaves and branches during their rapid decay. Thus, the few minerals obtained from the soil and the rain per unit of time are not allowed to escape. Because of the efficiency with which minerals are captured following their release through decomposition of dead organic matter, the amount of minerals tied up in the vegetation frequently rivals — and for a few elements exceeds — the amount in the soil. (Even so, productivity of many tropical forests is limited by lack of some mineral nutrients; discovery of effective methods of providing more of these minerals could greatly improve forest production.)

Nutrient availability is higher in some of the younger volcanic soils scattered throughout the tropics because there has not yet been time for complete leaching to take place. Some of the relatively shallow soils on steeper slopes are also richer than the deeper soils on level areas because erosion keeps sending the most leached soil down the slope, permitting tree-root systems to penetrate to newer soil formed from the parent rock below. By temperate-zone standards, however, even these relatively rich tropical soils are often of low fertility.

Land Management in the Tropics

Traditional native practice in tropical forests is to cut some or all of the trees in a small area and then to burn them. Nitrogen supplies are lost by this slash-and-burn method, but the ashes contain the other minerals that had been held by the trees and thereby provide enough fertility for one or more years of primitive crop agriculture. After several years, so much of the mineral has been leached away that the land becomes too poor to crop and new land must be cleared. In some slash-and-burn techniques, additional trees are brought in (especially from the slopes) and burned on the cut-over areas along with the normal slash; crop production can then continue somewhat longer than usual because of the increased amount of fertilizing ash provided. In some areas, it is necessary to maintain a cover on the soil at all times if the lateritic soil is not to be destroyed by the combined effect of direct rain and sunlight.

Shifting cultivation (slash-and-burn) techniques can work well enough to support low populations, but they require a great deal of land. Five to fifteen years of forest fallow are needed to allow rebuilding of the trees' mineral supply; this means that, at best, several times the area cropped must be available in order to provide continuous support of a farmer.

Modern Techniques — In general terms, the methods of increasing yields are the same in the tropics as in temperate areas. Nevertheless, attempts to transfer temperate-zone ecology and agricultural practices directly to the tropics have usually met with failure, occurrences which emphasize how much we have yet to learn. Techniques of replacing slash-and-burn methods with carefully designed crop rotation (frequently including care to maintain continuity of a canopy) are now being developed. They show some promise, but a great deal more research is needed. Fertilizers can be very effective, but poor understanding of soils and of plant requirements means that the kinds and combinations of materials that would be most

useful on each are unknown. Requirements and effective methods of application are generally not known for major nutrients or for trace elements.

Water-conservation (and erosion-inhibition) devices such as bunds, terraces, mulches, tie ridges, and so on are useful. Irrigation can be very effective, but there are usually unconsidered costs associated with the use of dams and reservoirs. Perhaps the most important of the latter is the effect that dam-associated flood control will have on downstream lowland alluvial soil such as those along the lower Nile. Fertility of these soils has remained high, sometimes in spite of millenia of intensive farming without fertilizers. This is because of the annual natural mineral input of the deposited flood silt. Comparative costs of maintaining fertility of these alluvial soils in the absence of flooding are unknown.

Rebuilding Degraded Soils — If much produce (lumber, crops, etc.) is to be removed from an area, this will remove the nutrients incorporated in the produce. Where the nutrient cycling is tight, as in tropical forest, crop removal can result in spectacular fertility-loss rates. Even if all the unused parts of the plant are returned to the mineral cycling, the fertility of the soil will decrease. Techniques need to be developed to replace these losses from crop removal and mineral leaching and to learn how to provide additional minerals so that production can be increased. For example, many tropical soils have properties that are especially effective in the making of added phosphorus and some trace minerals.

The extent of forest in many parts of the tropics, especially in the dryer areas, is being reduced by fire and by overgrazing by domestic stock. Grasslands are replacing forests and, partly because grasslands have less close minerals cycling than forests, the quality of these soils is being

degraded. (See Figure IX–10) Activities of man and his stock have already produced large areas of white-sand savannah which have very low productivity. Even if the influence of man and stock were removed, reforestation would be slow because the soils have been so greatly damaged. Efforts must be made to learn how to counter the soil-degradation processes that have produced these areas and how to rebuild the soils that have already been degraded.

Forest Management for Production

Timber — Although tropical areas contain almost half of the world's forests, they produce only about one-tenth of the world's timber. Only about one-sixth of the tropical forest is being exploited for timber, in part because of the inaccessibility of about 60 percent of the forested acres. There are several reasons for this: lack of road networks and vehicles; poor markets, which means that building roads and buying vehicles for timber harvest is uneconomical; low levels of available technology; the fact that many tropical hardwoods are so heavy that they will not float, thus precluding use of rivers to float logs as is common in the higher latitudes; and the diversity of tree species usual in tropical forests. This diversity means either that many kinds of timber must be cut and marketed or that a great deal of effort must be expended to extract only the few species desired from an extensive and highly varied forest.

Much research needs to be done on these problems. If clear cutting is practiced, or even enough trees are taken that the integrity of the canopy is destroyed, soil destruction can occur and erosion may be severe. In some parts of the tropics, soil will, in effect, turn to stone when so exposed. In other areas, siltation from erosion following timber extraction of forest clearing has produced serious problems. For example, silta-

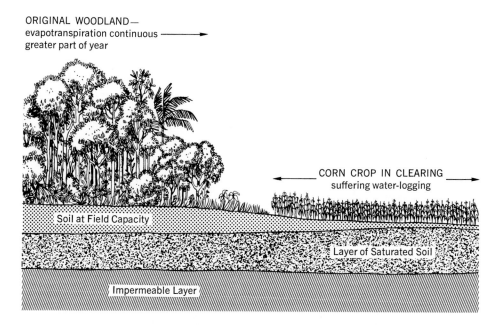

ORIGINAL WOODLAND—
evapotranspiration continuous
greater part of year

Soil at Field Capacity

CORN CROP IN CLEARING
suffering water-logging

Layer of Saturated Soil

Impermeable Layer

The illustration shows the differences between a forested area and an unforested one in Rhodesia. In the forested area, the depth of soil and amount of water are sufficient to support the growth of trees. Evapotranspiration (a combination of water loss by evaporation from the soil and transpiration from plants) is in balance with the available water supply. Once the tree cover is removed, evapotranspiration is reduced, thus allowing the water table to rise and reducing the depth of usable soil. The net result inhibits crop growth.

tion following poor forest-utilization practices has greatly decreased the life expectancy of reservoirs; it sometimes causes problems by silting up irrigation channels and often reduces efficiency and causes damage to pumps through clogging and abrasion. If the silt can be deposited on the cropland, it provides fertilization (but at a high cost). Research needs to be done to find out how best to crop the timber of these forests with minimal damage and promotion of minimal forest-regeneration time.

The relatively little developmental work that has been done on intensive management techniques to increase the timber yield of tropical forests suggests that it will be possible, with more understanding, to raise productivity to at least three times present natural levels. Under some circumstances, natural productivity may be surpassed by twenty times — or pos-

sibly even more. Much research will be required, however, if this goal is to be reached.

Tree Monocultures — Biological mechanisms that operate to control populations of various plants and animals appear to be more prevalent and more effective in the tropics than in temperate and arctic zones. The high diversity of tropical forests may, in part at least, be a response to this condition. When attempts are made to grow monocultures of various tree species or other crops, therefore, tropical populations may be subject to particularly severe biological attack. For example, it has so far proved impossible to establish successful rubber plantations in South America, the home of the Para, or hevea, rubber tree, because of disease problems. Under natural conditions, where rubber trees are widely scattered, disease is transmitted

poorly because of the distance between trees.

The biological attack that many tropical monocultures suffer can be blunted or stopped in some instances, but the problems are frequently severe and a great deal of good research is needed for their solution. The problem has been partly overcome (or avoided) for some species by transporting them to parts of the tropics in which they are not native — with great care taken not to transport simultaneously their diseases or insect pests. The highly productive rubber plantations in Africa and Southeast Asia, for example, were started with South American trees.

This technique can doubtless be useful in the future, but it is of paramount importance that careful, thorough, and appropriate research precede it. Inadequate research could lead to release of species in areas where, in the absence of their natural biological controls, they would spread to become pests of major magnitude. This could produce a catastrophe that would dwarf the disaster that followed the release of prickly-pear cactus in Australia. By 1900, this cactus covered an estimated 10 million acres, and by 1925 it had spread to about 60 million acres; in half of this area, the cactus was so dense that neither man nor horse could enter.

Looking to the Future

Genetic breeding programs for most tropical plants, with a few outstanding exceptions, are not well developed or are not being carried on at all. With respect to forest trees and their yield, enough has been done with a few temperate species to demonstrate that programs of this kind can be of great benefit in increasing yield and decreasing inter-cropping interval. Tropical-tree yield can doubtless be greatly increased as well, and research and breeding pro-

297

grams should be greatly increased. An obvious problem is that breeding programs with trees progress slowly because of the amount of time required for trees to grow to the point where they can reproduce.

Because of their high productivity and even higher potential it might be possible to develop tropical forests as a major new food source. For example, leaf extracts of a number of species have a high protein content and large amounts of digestible carbohydrate. Research is needed to determine the best methods of leaf collection and food extraction and how to handle the disagreeable aromatic, gummy, or other substances that are often produced by tropical trees. Additional work will also be needed to determine how to package, advertise, and sell these products. Traditional food habits of most peoples are hard to change, even when such change could result in a distinct improvement in their nutrition.

Some tropical trees have useful pharmacological properties. About half of the new prescriptions currently written contain one or more plant products as a major active ingredient. The tropics have been an especially rich source of these chemicals and there is no doubt but that

further investigation will be very rewarding.

Several other problems should at least be mentioned. One has to do with the use and misuse of resources provided by animals of the tropical forests in the form of meat, hides, pets, and experimental animals. Another relates to the reservoir of disease, disease vectors, and pests present in tropical forests. A third results from the interaction of vegetation and the hydrologic cycle and on the effects of irrigation, each of which can produce appreciable effects on local (and perhaps distant) rainfall amounts. A fourth concerns the effects of wartime defoliation on large stretches of forests and the problems involved in providing for their rapid recovery (or the development of really good alternative uses of the affected areas).

Although it may not now be much of an immediate problem, the rate at which air pollution is increasing could pose a serious problem to parts of some tropical forests. As a result of efforts of many of the less developed countries (which are primarily tropical) to industrialize, local air pollution may increase rapidly. Many of these countries may be too poor to be willing to pay for unprofitable

pollution-abatement programs and processes.

A possible longer-term problem is related to the fact that tropical species generally are more sensitive to temperature fluctuations than are temperate species. This means that if man's various activities should cause either a warming or, as now seems more likely, a cooling of the climate, the tropical forests could be in real trouble. Removal of these forests could itself contribute to this cooling through resultant increases in albedo and in atmospheric dust. In either event, a useful ecological generalization is that species from stable environments (as in the tropics) are more sensitive to temperature and chemical effects than are those from fluctuating environments (as in temperate zones).

Finally, because of the magnificence and complexity of the biological system that is represented by tropical forests, they will serve as excellent resources in the development of man's understanding of the ecological enterprise and as an area to which he can go for rebuilding and refreshing the human spirit. Efforts should be made to preserve parts of these forests, and to make them readily available for these purposes.

Comparison of Temperate and Tropical Forests

Whether we like it or not, feel it dangerous or laudable, the human race must prepare itself for a gigantic task: managing the earth's surface! This task is not, of course, the concern of any single nation or race, but it is obvious that the highly industrialized nations of the northern hemisphere must take the lead in tackling the job before us, because they have the economic wealth, scientific manpower, and industrial force to begin to undertake the task.

It is natural that we, as a people of the temperate zone, take our own environment, the deciduous forest or grassland biome, as a reference point in trying to understand other terrestrial environmental features. This way of thinking is sometimes dangerous, especially if we try to draw conclusions from management practices in one area and transfer this concept to another. For present purposes, however, it is valuable to start from a few principles common to all

productive areas of the world and elaborate the differences from these.

The State of Scientific Knowledge

The temperate zone has at least three very distinct forest formations in which the ecology, especially the sensitivity to human impact, is entirely different: deciduous forest; chaparral; and laurel forest. Tropical areas are even more complex in this respect. One can distinguish among lowland tropical or equatorial rain forest, subtropical rain forest, seasonal forest, forest savannah, and tropical mountain forest. These forest types all have some common and some unique features, which do not clearly separate themselves into tropical or temperate; for example, evergreenness appears in both regions. A selection of compositional, structural, and functional criteria are compared in Figure IX–11. Here, the discussion will center on comparisons between temperate deciduous forests and tropical rain forests.

Although we know a great deal about the properties of almost all existing vegetation types, we seem hopelessly confused about how much of each vegetation type exists in the world. The terminology for distinct types is weak, and the accounts of different authors conflict. Even in such apparently clear traditional groupings as forest, grassland, desert, and cultivated land there are many discrepancies about areal extent. Total land surface is always the same, of course — 147 million square kilometers. But statistics for various vegetation types gathered within the past fifteen years, including the official calculations of the Food and Agriculture Organization, vary greatly. Thus, one can find the following estimates:

Land Type	Square Kilometers (millions)
Forest	38 - 50
Boreal Forest	12 - 23
Tropical Forest	15 - 20
Grassland	24 - 40
Tundra	6 - 7
Desert	14
Cultivated Land	14 - 17

Discrepancies are even greater with respect to subdivisions of the above-mentioned formation classes.

Figure IX–11 — COMPARISON OF TEMPERATE AND TROPICAL FOREST TYPES

	Properties	Predominantly evergreen leaf cover (yes or no)	Height of stand (feet)	Approx. leaf area index x ground surface covered	Coniferous species present	Functional annual seasonality (yes or no) and ruling force
TEMPERATE	temperate deciduous forest	no	> 100	~ 10	rare	yes; temperature
	chaparral	yes	< 100	5 - 12	present	yes; temperature + rain
	laurel forest	yes	< 100	9	rare	yes; temperature
TROPIC	lowland tropical rain forest	yes	> 180	3 - 11	absent	no
	subtropical rain forest	yes	> 120	8 - 15	rare	yes, weak; rain
	seasonal forest	yes/no	> 100	10 - 22	rare	yes; rain
	forest savannah	no	< 100	?	absent	yes; rain + temperature
	tropical mountain forest	yes	< 100	2 - 8	variable rare to present	no

The table lists several properties of forest types and compares these within the temperate and tropical zones. Note the importance of temperature in the temperature zone and that of rain in the tropics.

Such uncertainty offers a weak basis for world management planning. A new plan must incorporate the evaluation of a new size inventory for whatever the management units might be. These units are fairly easy to establish along the biome concept, which coincides generally with the "zonal vegetation," "climax vegetation," or "vegetation formation" of the phytogeographers.

Classical Models — Any management plan requires a model. The "models" of the ecologically oriented phytogeographers have traditionally included the following categories: (a) altitudinal profile; (b) soil pattern and catena; (c) climatic (microclimatic) pattern; (d) species composition; and (e) successional series.

The correlation between some of these properties is so significant that predictions can be made in the temperate zone and, to a lesser extent, in the tropics. The predictions are usually more reliable for plants than for animals; they are usually better for qualitative statements than for quantitative statements; and they are normally better for dominant species or factors than for the less important components. In the deciduous forest, the traditional models are already refined and commonly used for management practices. In the humid tropics, they are generally an order of magnitude cruder; some are just being elaborated. A generalized model of a succession, including productivity data, is impossible to draw for the humid tropics with any degree of confidence.

Knowledge of tropical and temperate-zone ecology is about equal almost everywhere. However, knowledge in certain geographical regions or with regard to certain factors may be more advanced in the tropics, and the knowledge gained there shows reverberations and applications in the temperate zone.

Mathematical Models — Modeling in the sense that it is used today with regard to systems analysis — i.e., mathematical or computer modeling — exists for partial processes in many cases in the temperate forest area, only rarely in the tropics. No entire ecosystem is yet completely understood and modeled in any biome. This work is just now being undertaken by several thousand ecologists working in different parts of the world.

The Analysis of Ecosystems Program of the U.S. International Biological Program has as its ultimate goal to provide the next generation of scientists with an ecosystems model that gives a satisfactory approximation of the following structural and functional characteristics of the various terrestrial ecosystems: (a) productivity range; (b) turnover rates of matter and nutrients; (c) species diversity; and (d) environmental parameter ranges with special emphasis on energy, temperature, water and substitute levels of nitrogen, phosphorous, potassium; and others. Further, the program will help us to secure sufficiently accurate data for the elaboration of a general ecosystems model that enables us to predict functional and structural responses of any given ecosystem to man-made or accidental changes.

It will take several more years of intensive study to develop predictive models for population changes and chain reactions caused by the elimination or introduction of species or groups of species. These "sensitivity investigations" may provide the most important results from present ecosystems studies. In many cases, changes are surprising and significant but apparent only after several years. It might be easier and quicker, therefore, to study the effects of some interferences in tropical environments rather than in temperate zones, be-

cause development periods are shorter and uninterrupted by a rest period. Genetic studies have applied this principle successfully in many cases, and ecologists should do the same. The results of such studies in tropical areas will provide us with models that will help us to manage our own environment, especially in the southern United States.

For some of the large-scale changes that man imposes upon the environment, predictions are already possible. Thus it is probably safe to predict that, in South America, large-scale *traditional* (temperate-zone) agriculture in the Amazon-Orinoco watershed will fail, that the Rio Negro region will change from a black-water stream to a white-water system, that all sorts of unpredictable changes in the fauna will occur as a result of the removal of several natural environmental barriers, and that fantastic changes will follow in every respect.

It is probably *unsafe*, however, to predict what would happen to the atmosphere if all the tropical regions of the world were cultivated. The data base is too slim for any reasonable prediction. We can only define certain areas that are likely to become problems: for example, the change of tropical air masses from an almost constant carbon dioxide level to an as yet unpredictable fluctuation; or the potential threat of airborne disease originating in the tropics (especially fungal diseases of plants) for plants, animals, and man. The attempt to establish large human settlements in the humid tropics of South America raises problems of unknown magnitude. For example, sanitary sewage disposal in an area saturated with water and at such a temperature level is a gigantic problem, and the prospect of industrial sewage is even more dire.

Needed Scientific Activity

The primary reason that ecology was previously the "Cinderella" of

the biological sciences is the fact that an incredible number of species are ruled by an unwieldy number of forces, and the species in turn influence the forces. The analysis of an ecosystem always seemed an unmanageable task, even assuming that only the most important components were to be studied. The recent development of systems analysis, the teaching of team studies, and the ever growing computer capacities give us a more realistic chance for a valid ecosystem model. But all these tools are useless without a willingness of many scientists from several disciplines to cooperate in one study and generate the necessary data pool for individual cases.

Data Base — The data base for the prediction of human impact is completely incomparable in deciduous and tropical forest areas. From the standpoints of an ecosystems modeler, the data base is totally lacking to unsafe or, occasionally, satisfactory in tropical areas and sometimes sufficient to unsafe in the deciduous forest areas. A general judgment is not possible because the knowledge necessary for the understanding of ecosystems is so different in the various disciplines. It is still necessary to conduct major investigations and collect a sound set of data if one cares about accurate models that are meaningful for management purposes.

Instrumentation — The sensors and techniques to acquire the necessary data are generally adequate, though their reliability and durability are usually better in temperate zones than in the tropics. It is, of course, always necessary to develop new tools for the constantly changing tasks before us. For the elaboration of better and more complete ecosystem models, we foresee the need for simulators and analogue computers of larger dimensions. Many computing facilities today still have only the capacity to confirm the conclusions that people had drawn from hand calculations. How quickly progress will be made naturally depends on the demands of scientists and the adequacy of public support.

Ecosystem Models — The development of ecosystem models is prerequisite to an adequate understanding of environmental problems. A single model is infeasible at the moment, but we see this as a future goal. The development of a set of models is the immediate necessity as a baseline for application in both management and teaching.

The set of models to be developed needs to include all of the classical models mentioned earlier, but better quantification is needed for many parameters. Tropical areas need much more work for the elaboration of such models than temperate zones. Specifically, the following sets of models — in the form of abstract mathematical equations, matrices, or probabilistic or stochastic statements — are needed for understanding and predicting human impact on the biosphere or environment:

1. Global Level

    (a) Production capacity of vegetation; responses to average levels of growth factors like radiation, temperature, water, nutrients, pollutants; utilization of vegetation by animals and man;

    (b) Optimal carrying capacity of the earth for men under various possible management practices;

    (c) Interaction of vegetation and the physical environment; circulation of carbon, oxygen, and other substances through atmosphere, biosphere, hydrosphere, and geosphere; quantity and rate (circulation speed) need to be investigated.

2. Biome Level

    (a) Production rate of vegetation;

    (b) Utilization practices of animals and other consumers;

    (c) Decomposition rate;

    (d) Reasons for homeostasis and the equilibrium level of forces that maintain it;

    (e) Efficiency of energy utilization;

    (f) Man's management practices and their influence on the system's turnover rates.

3. Regional (Landscape) Level

    (a) Production, consumption, and decomposition in biocenoses; reactions to levels and specific fluctuation patterns of external and internal forces like radiation, temperature, water, nutrients, pollutants, animal feeding, etc.;

    (b) Developmental patterns of species in space and time;

    (c) Qualitative responses of the regionally available species pool with regard to different environmental matrices;

    (d) Chemical diversity within the food web.

Such a model can only be developed if comparisons are available from all contrasting biomes, although some biomes are more important than others for the development of a general model. For example, inclusion of a humid tropical forest is essential, since these forests represent either the absolute maximum, optimum, or minimum realized on earth for many of the ruling environmental forces. Turnover of matter and energy in the humid tropics is twice as fast as in the temperate area. Tropical areas contain at least 60 percent of the world's natural resources. Again, the humid tropics are especially susceptible to human impact, since their soils and climate and orographic conditions are highly sensitive. This is especially true for modern agricultural techniques, utilization of high-yielding varieties, and constant shielding with pesticides and insecticides.

3. FOREST ANIMALS

Problems of Animal Ecology in Forested Areas

Traditionally, the study of animal ecology in forested areas of the United States has been concerned only with species that are either injurious to man or to forests or are game animals of interest to the hunter. To these original concerns — i.e., the impact of animals on the forest and the availability of animals for man — we should now add two more: (a) the impact of man on forest animals, and (b) the needs of forest animals for suitable habitat.

Large and small forest animals and birds affect man's aesthetics, economics, and, occasionally, his health. Furthermore, the greatly increasing pressure of man on the wildlife resource of the forests has created serious problems. Sometimes control of animal populations is necessary or desirable; this is true in the urban-suburban fringe as well as in national parks and private recreation areas. At other times, the need is to promote the integration of forest wildlife into the urban and semi-urban scene, where the presence of wildlife provides an antidote to some of the stresses of urban living.

The State of Animal Ecology Research

Forest animals vary greatly in their adaptations, both to the type of forest and to the relative amounts of forest and open land that they require. Many forest animals are more accurately forest-edge animals; the white-tail deer is a prime example, and any consideration of white-tail habitat must involve the relative proportions of forest and opening. In addition, year-to-year differences in environmental conditions may have drastic influences on the animals. The impact of winter weather on the survival

of the ruffed grouse is a case in point. Low temperatures, snow depth, and the conditions of the surface of the snow all play a part in the survival of the bird: that is, ruffed grouse can survive long periods of extreme cold provided that adequate snow is available and uncrusted, so that the bird can penetrate into the snow for night roosting. With deer, light snow permits ready movement but deep snow restricts it. Similarly, environmental differences between locations influence the behavior, feeding ability, and survival of an animal population.

Data Base — A reasonably adequate base of data on forest animals already exists. This is particularly true for those animals important to the hunter and sportsman, such as the white-tail deer, ruffed grouse, wild turkey, and gray squirrel. Data are gradually accumulating on the life histories and behavior of various carnivores, including the black bear, bobcat, coyote (in forest habitats, especially), and timber wolf, as well as on many smaller mammals, both predators and herbivores.

Knowledge of gross food supplies for forest herbivores is readily available, but more important are the data now being gathered pertinent to the calorie content of this food and to the fluctuation in mineral constituents — i.e., on the quality of the animals' food. Much data have been accumulated on browse for white-tail deer, lesser amounts of information on fruits and nuts.

But there are sizable gaps in our understanding of the utilization of food and shelter. Little is yet known of the reasons why certain plant species are consumed in preference to others, nor are the changes in rumen flora of the white-tail deer under-

stood. Virtually no information is available on forms of food materials like forest herbs and aquatics. We are just beginning to discover some of the nuances of the summer food habits of deer, the diversity of foods used (particularly herbaceous materials), and the impact that summer food selection may have on deer habitat. Additionally, although we know that crossbills and finches use seeds of forest trees in quantity, we know little of the relationship of these bird populations to tree seed crops. Food selection, utilization, and availability are thus areas open to considerable work relative to most forest animals and birds.

Instrumentation — The advent of radio telemetry has done much to increase knowledge of the home range and behavior patterns of a number of animals and birds. For example, movement patterns of owls have been studied in Minnesota and the hunting pattern of barred owls delimited. (The owl hunts in one area until prey populations have dropped — i.e., until hunting is unprofitable; it then moves on to another location and another and in time returns to the original spot when mice populations have again reached a suitable level.) Telemetry is also producing information on deer behavior as well as movement patterns for such animals as the grizzly bear and the timber wolf.

The impact of radio telemetry on knowledge of animal behavior is already great, but there is ample room for additional studies of movement patterns and even more opportunity for telemetry of physiological parameters. Improvements are presently being made in the technology, and much information of value will likely be gained thereby.

In the field of habitat research, progress has also been made in improving sampling methods. Low-level, large-scale photography offers excellent opportunities for improving the analysis of wildlife habitat.

Modeling — Mathematical modeling has already shown some value and will undoubtedly be useful in clarifying many animal-habitat relationships. Theoretical formulation of data in forest animal ecology has been relatively slow in developing, however. The lack of suitable quantitative input has been one deterrent; another has been the slow development of modeling techniques.

Needed Scientific Activity

Habitat Research — The single most essential need in forest wildlife ecology is to relate or link the animal to its habitat in detail. Although considerable data are available, the linkages are still far from clear. For example, what is the relationship between food availability and consumption, or between tree cover and energetics. Specifics are needed on the interaction of animals with abiotic environmental factors as well.

Answers to such questions will require both additional field studies and the use of mathematical models that can in turn be tested for accuracy by field investigation. They will also require greater interest on the part of researchers themselves. In the Lake States, for example, despite the great importance of forest wildlife to the recreation industry as well as to the

health of the forest ecosystem, very few individuals are engaged in forest-habitat research.

With suitable additional input, considerable advances could probably be made within fifteen years in the linking of animal to habitat components — both food and shelter. Steady progress toward this end is highly desirable. Population stress and its underlying causes is another area of work that deserves attention. The study of animals as disease vectors, although not a major problem area, should be continued.

Public Understanding — Despite remaining gaps in scientific understanding, present knowledge of the ecology of the larger forest animals probably exceeds the ability of the land manager to use this information. Today's land manager is restricted by lack of popular acceptance of the basic principles of population dynamics and habitat. Like religion and politics, questions having to do with length of hunting season, bag limits, and status of animal and bird populations are not easily settled; nor are they always discussed rationally.

For example, it is difficult to convince the public that changes in habitat and weather are usually much more effective in population control than is the two-legged predator. Thus, controversy always surrounds the question of whether or not female white-tail deer should be hunted. And yet the known reproductive cycle of the white-tail, its responses to weather conditions, the effect of severe winters on reproduction, and the normally high replacement rate

all indicate that it is virtually impossible to exterminate deer save on a very local basis. Other fallacies include (a) the idea that it is possible to "stockpile" populations of ruffed grouse by closing the season one year and thus have more birds the next, and (b) the concept of predator control by bounty.

Perhaps for these reasons, the Great Lakes Deer Group several years ago listed public understanding as among the most important of its problems; the group recommended motivational research to find out what creates public attitudes toward agency programs, a study that should include the sociology and psychology of deer-hunting and other factors regarding the deer herd. In general, the most controversy results from a lack of understanding by a major segment of the public of the ecological requirements for animal development and of animal population dynamics.

One may say with reason that there are no strictly scientific controversies in forest animal ecology, although there is some disagreement as to the relative impact of habitat and predators on populations of certain game animals (specifically, the moose at Isle Royale) and on deer in the Middle West and elsewhere. The scientific base of understanding is far from complete, however, and as gaps in knowledge of the animal, of animal use of the forest, and of forest growth are filled and the information conveyed to the public, scientific management of forest animals may become feasible.

Wilderness as a Dynamic Ecosystem, with Reference to Isle Royale National Park

The major problem of the status of man on earth can be approached in some degree through studies of other living things to assess the influences

of density factors, behavioral homologies, population dynamics, and other phenomena common to many species. Research in these plant-animal com-

munities must produce a better understanding of natural dynamics and life renewal in native types of forest, range, wetland, and aquatic habitats.

To these basic parameters must be added the complicating effects of human culture on both man and his environment.

Gross considerations suggest that the unguided technological culture in the hands of a rapidly increasing population is producing an unmanageable complexity in human society and rapid deterioration in the environment and its component resources. If man is to endure on earth, the entire biosphere must be his ecosystem, preserved and kept productive through conservative use and understanding management.

Since man has never created an enduring, self-perpetuating ecosystem, he has much to learn from the study of natural processes. All conditions relative to human use and management are of interest and should be studied. However, the features of ecosystems that guarantee perpetuation are most clearly effective under primitive conditions. Thus, areas where primitive conditions are still operative are of special scientific interest. The least-modified communities of living things are likely to be found on lands and waters set aside as "wilderness" or natural reserves of one kind or another.

Isle Royale as a Prototype Ecosystem

A roadless island of 210 square miles in northern Lake Superior exemplifies the kind of situation where fact-finding is possible under relatively undisturbed conditions. Isle Royale is a national park and may be visited by some 10,000 people during the tourist season from mid-June to early September. From the end of October to mid-May it is uninhabited except for a research group, using a small aircraft, that is present for seven weeks in February and March.

Animal Populations and Associated Vegetation — Lying 15 miles from the nearest Canadian shore, the is-

land is sufficiently isolated that it has not yet been colonized by certain mammals and birds found commonly on the mainland — especially deer, bear, raccoon, porcupine, and ruffed grouse. Lynx and marten disappeared from the island early in this century, as did coyotes in the mid-1950's. In the latter case, the advent of wolves about 1949 probably resulted in elimination of the smaller competing canid. The fox does not appear to have been affected by such competition.

The boreal forest and hardwood vegetation of Isle Royale was extensively burned over in the past century. Alteration of "natural" conditions by this human disturbance must be considered a matter of degree, since burning also took place in primitive times. The dynamics of forest successions is, in any event, significant. Early successional stages produce food and cover for such creatures as snowshoe hare and beaver, as well as browse for the moose. Thus, burning incident to drought cycles renews the habitat of many herbivores and indirectly supports their dependent carnivores.

The mammal populations of Isle Royale have shown the instability that characterizes simplified animal communities. The moose illustrates this, since it reached the island in the first decade of the century, before its primary enemy, the wolf, was present. As a result, by the mid-1920's, moose had overpopulated and destroyed most of the available browse. In ensuing years, as a result of malnutrition and disease, moose died down to a low level. A fire in 1936 destroyed forest cover and initiated new brush-stage successions on about a third of the island. Moose were building up again when wolves crossed the ice and became established in the late 1940's.

The Meaning of a Dynamic Wilderness — In areas like Isle Royale, the U.S. National Park Service and other land-management agencies have been enabled to get a new view and

concept of "wilderness" as a dynamic condition. Thus, a full spectrum of successional stages and habitat conditions enables a vegetation zone to support a wide variety of animal life. On any given site, animal life must change with maturation of the forest or other vegetation. In terms of land management, this means that agencies charged with the administration of natural areas must regard fire as a part of the primitive scene that should not be totally eliminated, even if this were possible. A strictly applied policy of fire suppression would lead to the development of extensive monotypes representing the "climax," or stability phase, of plant life in a region. This would correspondingly reduce variety in both flora and fauna.

Predator-Prey Relationships — Biological studies carried out by Purdue University on Isle Royale over the past twelve years have been significant in revealing predator-prey relationships. The moose is the largest member of the deer family and the gray, or timber, wolf is its only effective natural enemy. In natural communities, large browsing and grazing animals depend in major degree on their predators for population control, the alternative being range damage and violent fluctuations in number. When it became known in the early 1950's that wolves had reached Isle Royale, it was evident that this was a situation in which natural relationships of the two species could be studied.

The major findings of the ensuing research program elucidate a mutually beneficial relationship between predator and prey, an adjustment of relative stability that, by controlling the moose population, protects the habitat from over-use. As of midwinter, an average population of 22 to 24 wolves is being supported by a moose population of about 900. The beaver is a secondary prey species furnishing 10 to 15 percent of the wolf's food. Numbers of the moose and beaver are limited by the wolf. As in other large carnivores, wolf numbers are self-limited largely through behavioral intolerances. Ordinarily there is one pack, most commonly around 15 animals, in which breeding takes place, and only one female will bear young. There has obviously been a high mortality among young wolves.

The remains of more than 400 dead moose — nearly all wolf kills — have been examined on Isle Royale and their ages determined by tooth characteristics. On this basis, a composite life table and survivorship curve for the moose herd has been constructed.

(See Figure IX–12) This illustrates a relatively high mortality of calves in the first year of life. In the next five years of its life, a moose evidently is at the peak of health and vigor, for it is seldom taken by wolves. From age 6 to the maximum age of 17+, the moose is increasingly liable to be killed; the average adult taken is 9 to 10 years old. Correlated with advancing age and a higher mortality rate is an increasing incidence of physical disorders.

The high selectivity for old and debilitated moose has been evident in the hunting habits of wolves. An average of 12 moose have been approached and brought to bay for every one killed. Vulnerable moose appear to be detected readily, while animals capable of strong defense are quickly passed by. In effect, the wolf culls the moose population and preserves a stock that can utilize the plant food supply most efficiently in producing new generations to support wolves.

Implications of the Isle Royale Findings

This information reveals working mechanisms that confer durability on the ecosystem. It may be pointed out that population stabilization and turnover rate in the wolf could only be studied where this species is protected from unnatural mortality. The natural age structure of the moose herd and the selection effect of the predator could be ascertained only where moose are protected from hunting and exposed to natural predation. Isle Royale National Park is perhaps the only area in the world where these conditions are met at present.

The relationship of predator to prey has other, more direct, implications, since big game herds are most commonly managed in the absence of effective natural enemies. The chief dependence in population limitation is on the gun and such factors as highway kill. Such artificial selection will in time alter the direction of speciation and change the nature of such wild species as the deer. In the preservation of wild fauna and flora, for whatever benefits are to be realized, there are evident advantages in understanding the character and dynamics of the original associations in which living things developed.

Figure IX–12 — LIFE EXPECTANCY AND SURVIVORSHIP OF ISLE ROYALE MOOSE

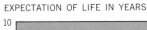

EXPECTATION OF LIFE IN YEARS

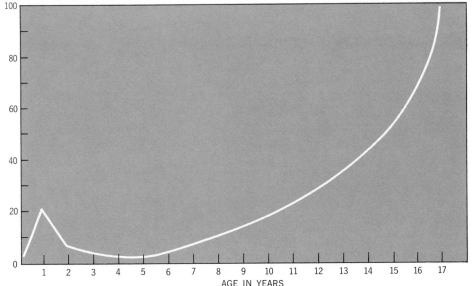

PERCENT MORTALITY

AGE IN YEARS

4. FOREST FIRE

Research into Fire Ecology

Fire is a useful tool in maintaining or modifying many vegetation types. Like all tools, however, it should be used in certain situations and not in others. For example, it should be used only where it can be controlled or where, if it escapes, the potential damage will be minimal or at least considerably less than the benefits. Some vegetation types can be improved by burning, others cannot. Still others, such as certain desert areas, support too little vegetation to carry a fire.

Fire and climate are interrelated to the extent that a specific kind of climate largely determines the kind of vegetation an area can produce. This, in turn, determines the fire-vegetation interrelationships — i.e., the readiness with which an area will burn, the effects of fire on modifying the plant cover, and the effects of this modification on the subsequent potential fire history of the area.

Fire can have various interrelated beneficial effects on forests and grassland as well as on many woodland (low-stature trees) and brushy areas. It may control undesirable woody species, thus promoting the growth of grasses and other herbaceous plants and, as a consequence, increasing the grazing potential. This modification often reduces soil erosion and runoff, since grasses provide a better close ground cover than many woody species. (See Figure IX–13) Other beneficial effects include ease and economy of controlling accidental wildfires; soil fertilization from the ashes; control of ticks, poisonous snakes, and other undesirable animals; control of fungi in the longleaf pine; creation of a better habitat for game animals, including turkeys, quail, and deer; reduction of excessive pine reproduction; maintenance of profitable timber stands.

Evaluation of Current Scientific Knowledge

There is a rather large body of information on forest fire, much of it from foreign countries. In the United States, research is being carried on by the Forest Service at the University of Washington, Seattle, and by the U.S. Forest Fire Laboratory in Missoula, Montana, among other places. Significant recent additions to scientific knowledge include the following:

1. Considerable theoretical work by Anderson and Beaufiat at the Forest Service's Intermountain Research Station at Missoula.

2. Research on the practical aspects of fire behavior by Countryman, working out of the Forest Service Laboratory in Riverside, Calif.

3. Research on quantitative characteristics of fire in the desert grasslands by Claveran and Moreno at the University of Arizona, Tucson.

4. Research on fire temperature, development of mathematical formulations, and effect on mesquite and grasses being carried on out of Texas Tech University, Lubbock.

5. An analysis of fire ecology by Daubenmire.

6. An analysis by Batchelder of quantitative external factors such as air temperature, humidity, and wind in relation to fire behavior.

7. An analysis of fire in relation to the various vegetation types in the United States by Humphrey.

8. An aggressive and expanding program of research and dissemination of information on

Figure IX–13 — EFFECT OF FIRE ON MESQUITE SHRUBS

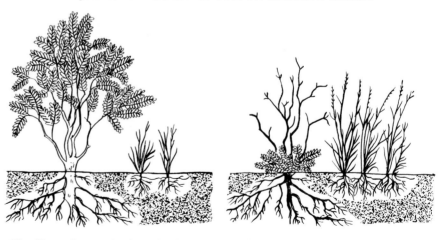

The illustration to the left shows how mesquite chokes out grass under normal conditions. After a fire, the grass recovers rapidly while the mesquite recovers much more slowly. Controlled burning will eliminate the mesquite entirely and maintain the grassland.

fire ecology that has been carried on for several years under Komarek by the Tall Timber Research Station, Tallahassee, Florida.

Despite the extent of the present data base, however, the entire subject of fire ecology has been inadequately studied. Three aspects that are particularly deficient are the reactions of individual species to fire, the effect of repeat burns on species and vegetation types, and mathematical modes of fire-ecosystem component relationships. Although a few data are beginning to accumulate that are serviceable as a base for both theoretical formulation and mathematical modeling, relatively little of the earlier research was suited to this approach. Currently, there appears to be a trend in the direction of quantitative research and a continued increase is anticipated. Much more is needed.

Status of Instrumentation — With a shift from qualitative to quantitative research, one progresses from minimal use of instruments to a need for instrumentation that is often expensive and highly sophisticated. Fire research today is moving in this direction, and, as a consequence, proposed investigations are requiring a budget for equipment that would have been unthought of only a few years ago. Remote-sensing and monitoring equipment to obtain a variety of temperature and moisture measurements with time are particularly useful in these studies. Although much of the basic equipment is currently available, refined techniques or specific situations will necessarily result in some modification or refinement.

Interaction with Other Environmental Systems — Despite the fact that most fire research has been of an applied nature — relating fire to noxious-plant control, forage production, timber yield, soil and water losses, and water yield — surprisingly little is known about the specifics of fire as it relates to other environmental systems. For example, many of our forests and grasslands can be improved for recreation and hunting by the judicious use of fire. These same areas can be rendered less liable to destruction by wildfires when administered under a sensible program of controlled burning. Yet this relationship is almost completely unexplored.

As the use of our wild lands increases consequential to the greater availability of leisure time and the need to escape from urban congestion, these lands are exposed to an ever increasing hazard of destruction from man-caused fires. The possibility of reducing this hazard through a management-by-fire approach needs to be thoroughly investigated. In cities, we stress cleaning up potential fuel in our fire-prevention campaigns; in forests, by contrast, we encourage accumulation of fuel to a point where an accidental fire can become a holocaust.

Because of anti-fire propaganda and the inadequacy of research, there is considerable difference of opinion even in scientific circles on the beneficial and harmful effects of fire in most vegetation types. This controversy extends from the interpretation of historical records, through the long-time effects of previous fires and present fire-control policies on the "climax" vegetation, to the yield of such renewable natural resources as forage, game animals, timber, and water. Obviously, these differences of opinion must be resolved if our lands are to be used most effectively and, in many instances, if we are to prevent their further deterioration or destruction.

Requirements for Scientific Activity

The principal needed scientific advances are: (a) amplification of both qualitative and quantitative studies directed to specific vegetation types and individual species; (b) greater emphasis on man and his effect on the wildland environment as this affects the incidence of fires; (c) research on controlled burning as a means of pretreatment to control wildfires; (d) additional research on the generalities and specifics of fire (controlled and wild) as interrelated with all other aspects of specific ecosystems; and (e) extensive development of theoretical formulation, including mathematical modeling. The current scientific poverty of knowledge on this topic and the rapidly increasing rate of use of our wildlands by man indicate a high degree of urgency for such research.

Necessary significant advances could be made in a minimum of three years. Five years would be adequate to effect a more far-reaching breakthrough. In addition, many ecological studies require a long period of time to evaluate cause-effect relationships properly, and fire studies are no exception. Aside from recovery time following a single fire, fire research often requires repeat burning at periodic intervals over a period of years. Studies of this sort should have a minimum duration of 25 years or more.

The Role of Fire in Forest Management and Ecology

Wildfires destroy vegetation and wildlife, may result in erosion and soil damage, leave unsightly vistas, are costly to suppress, and upset management plans and schedules. Thus, one of the most important tasks of the forest manager is to control wildfire, preferably by prevention. Only if the forest is free of wildfires, can management measures be applied as needed to yield the maximum amount of goods and services the forest is capable of producing.

Prescribed fire, however, can be a useful tool for achieving these ends. It is often one of the measures that may be appropriate in manipulating forest vegetation. But to use fire properly it must be fully controlled.

Because of the great variation in climate, topography, soils, and vegetation in the United States, a comprehensive discussion of the role of fire in forest management and ecology would require much more space than is available here. This discussion will therefore be limited to the loblolly–shortleaf pine–hardwood forest type, which extends from Maryland to Texas through the middle South. It is the most important forest type in the southern timber economy and one in which the fire history encompasses both substantially wild and prescribed fire.

Ecology of Fire

Fire was apparently the major factor in maintaining extensive stands of pine long before the South was settled by man; it can probably be considered a natural ecological factor in southern pines. With the advent of human settlement and, later, extensive logging, it became a frequent, almost annual occurrence over much of the region. Not until the organization of public forestry agencies and the establishment of permanent forest industries was the custom of indiscriminate annual woods burning brought under control. However, wildfire continues to be a frequent occurrence.

Loblolly pine is the most prominent tree species in this type of forest. It usually occurs in relatively pure stands, being a seral species. On drier sites, shortleaf pine is often mixed with it, particularly in the western part of its range in Arkansas, Louisiana, and Texas. Pine is followed by deciduous hardwoods in the plant succession, and the pine stands characteristically have an understory of hardwood tree and shrub species which eventually displace the pine unless a disturbance occurs that again favors pine.

The effect of fire in loblolly pine stands is closely related to the biological requirements and characteristics of the species and to the trend toward hardwoods in the plant succession. The effect of fire on the succession depends on the age of the pine stand and on the intensity, frequency, and season of fire occurrence.

Effect of Fire Intensity — Crown fires at any season of the year completely destroy the pine stand. Fires of this type occur during periods of exceptionally high fire hazard, so that understory vegetation is also killed back to the ground. A burned soil surface is an excellent seedbed for loblolly pine, and the proportion of pine in the new stand depends on the supply of pine seed in the first year or two after the crown fire. Pine becomes established readily in the burned area, and the resulting stand is made up of pine seedlings and hardwood seedlings and sprouts. In one study, pine reproduction equalled hardwoods in basal area but not in number of stems nine years after a crown fire, showing that the pine

stems were growing much faster than the hardwoods and would probably form the bulk of the dominant stand.

Loblolly pine stands become fairly resistant to surface fires at about 10 years of age. Fire usually destroys younger stands completely but surface fires damage older stands very little. Furthermore during the dormant season such fires in older pine stands have very little effect on succession. Litter is consumed and small stems are killed. The hardwood stems are quickly replaced by sprouting and the thin litter permits establishment of pine seedlings, so that conditions quickly become as they were before, except that hardwood stems are probably more numerous.

Effect of Season — In the loblolly pine range, wildfires are most likely to occur in spring, before growth begins, and in autumn, after leaf-fall. Winter fires are less frequent, while summer fires occur only during prolonged and severe dry periods.

Fires during dry periods in the growing season may be very destructive because initial vegetation temperatures are higher, growing tissues are more exposed to heat, and sprouting is less vigorous than that following dormant-season fires. Depending on how much of the overstory is killed, conditions after summer fire range from something resembling those after a crown fire to a reduction in the smaller understory hardwoods only. The succession varies accordingly.

Fires within the first year after harvest cutting differ in their effects, depending on the time of the year they occur in relation to pine seedfall. During the dormant season they destroy not only advance reproduction but also whatever seed is present. Hardwoods are highly favored because a whole growing season must pass before another crop of pine seed is produced. Meanwhile, hardwood sprouts and herbaceous vegetation produce a new mantle of litter that retards pine-seed germination.

On the other hand, fires before seedfall may favor pine establishment if they do not occur too early in the growing season. Hardwood stems killed after early August sprout very little until the following spring. Consequently, fires in late summer before seedfall not only increase favorable seedbed conditions by consuming slash and undisturbed litter, but also give pine seedlings an even start with hardwood sprouts and seedlings the following spring. The earlier that fires occur in the summer, the more nearly the sprout and seedbed conditions approach those following dormant-season fires after harvest cutting.

Effect of Frequency — While occasional fires favor loblolly pine regeneration, fires at intervals of less than 10 years eventually eliminate loblolly pine. Frequent fires repeatedly destroy the pine reproduction, while hardwood stems are multiplied by seedling establishment, sprouting, and suckering. The process becomes relatively rapid when the dominant pine stand is clear-cut or otherwise destroyed. Continued frequent burning may ultimately result in a vegetational type dominated by grasses.

Effects of Fire on Soil

Fire heats the soil only very shallowly, but it affects the surface soil both physically and chemically. Physical effects range from none or negligible to measurable.

The texture of the surface soil may be a factor. Thus, in the coastal plain of South Carolina, a fire-effects study showed no reduction in bulk density, total porosity, or percolation rate down to a depth of four inches, even after ten annual fires. Yet, in other coastal-plain locations, investi-

gators have remarked on the compactness and reduced permeability of the soil surface after burning.

It is logical to expect a greater effect on soils of heavier texture. A difference in effect on plant growth attributable to soil texture and drainage characteristics was found in a study in northeastern North Carolina, where the area occupied by hardwood sprouts increased rapidly for three years after logging and site preparation and then grew more slowly. On soils with poor surface drainage and plastic subsoils, hardwood reached 85 percent ground coverage in five years without burning but occupied only 65 percent in burned areas. On soils with good surface drainage, burning had the opposite effect: hardwood cover increased faster on burned than on unburned areas, reaching about 10 percent greater coverage after five years.

Erosion following fire is not a concern in the flat coastal plain but may be a danger farther inland on more pronounced topography. However, instances of serious erosion following fire in the loblolly pine range have not been reported. It may be that the vegetation grows back fast enough to protect the soil surface when the high-intensity summer storms occur.

Fertility — Burning usually results in an increase in organic matter incorporated in the surface soil. Fire-charred material filters into the upper

layer. In addition, the greater amount of herbaceous vegetation that usually follows burning, especially grasses with their abundant fine roots, may be a source of increased organic matter. These observations are from coastal plain locations. On sloping land, water would tend to carry ash and charred material from the site and organic matter increases might not be so pronounced; organic matter might even be reduced on heavier textured soils.

Soil chemical properties are usually improved for plant growth after fire. Calcium is increased appreciably, with an accompanying decrease in acidity. Other mineral elements may be increased slightly through release from the litter. (See Figure IX–14) Nitrogen is increased, apparently from several sources. Burning releases much of the nitrogen in the litter but some remains in fire-charred material, which is concentrated close to the soil surface. The increase in herbaceous plants includes not only grasses but also legumes, possibly providing a source of nitrogen. However, an observed annual increase of 23 kilograms per hectare in annually burned loblolly pine stands in the lower coastal plains of South Carolina could not be accounted for by the transfer of nitrogen from the litter to the mineral soil.

Soil organisms in the litter and humus layers are destroyed by burning, but the effects have not yet been comprehensively investigated. Ap-

Figure IX–14 — QUANTITIES OF NUTRIENTS RELEASED BY BURNING TROPICAL VEGETATION

	PHOSPHATE	POTASSIUM	CALCIUM	MAGNESIUM
Tropical rain forest (forty years old)	112	731	2,254	309
Savanna woodland	7	41	31	23

The table gives an estimate, in terms of pounds per acre, of several nutrients that are released to the soil by burning vegetation in two different tropical regions.

parently, the population of soil organisms recovers rapidly after burning and is associated with the increase in nitrogen. In the top four centimeters of mineral soil in the South Carolina study, over four grams of nitrogen per hectare per day were fixed in the burned plots while only 0.2 grams were fixed in the unburned plots. However, the individual samples from the burned plots ranged from no nitrogen fixation up to 61 grams per hectare per day, for reasons that were not evident.

Disease — A survey throughout the South showed less *Fomes annosus* root rot on burned areas. This disease spreads by growth of mycelia in the forest floor, or aerially by spores from the fruiting bodies. Consequently, fire may tend to retard the spread of the disease.

Use of Prescribed Burning in the Timber Industry

Prescribed fire has been recommended and widely used in the loblolly pine range for control of understory hardwoods, site preparation for seeding or planting, and for fire-hazard reduction.

Prescriptions for safe burning have been reasonably well developed by research and experience. Favorable conditions are: relative humidity of 40 to 60 percent; a wind steady in direction but under ten miles per hour at four feet above ground; and litter moisture content of 5 to 20 percent. Burning is safest when these conditions are first reached after a rain of half an inch or more.

Backfires are preferred for areas with heavy fuel because they burn more slowly and less intensely. Headfires are used where fuel is light. Igniting the entire perimeter of the area is poor practice, since "hot spots" occur where fires from different directions meet, resulting in crown scorching and sometimes killing trees.

For Understory Control — Because the hardwood understory is a major obstacle to re-establishment of the pine stand after harvest, its control has received a great deal of attention. If hardwoods are allowed to grow unchecked throughout a pine rotation, site preparation for regeneration is difficult and costly; often requiring use of heavy machinery. Periodic burning during the rotation holds this understory in check, with the burning interval determined by the growth rate of the understory sprouts. A prescribed fire will burn hardwood stems up to about two inches in diameter back to the ground. Thus, the burning interval may range from a few years up to ten years, depending on site quality, overstory density, and the species in the understory.

Periodic burning for understory control is usually done in the winter. Summer burns are more difficult to control with several years' fuel accumulation, and winter burning usually fits better into the over-all schedule of seasonally determined forestry operations. Winter fires do not kill the rootstocks, so the population of understory plants is not reduced; in fact, the number of sprouts is usually greater during the first few years after the fire than before.

In contrast to winter fires, summer fires reduce the understory population. When the parent stem is killed or cut in the summer, especially near the end of the spring flush of growth, the sprouts are much weaker than those arising from winter-killed stems. Plants that are not vigorous often die. Thus, two or three successive annual summer fires virtually eradicate the understory. This effect can sometimes be used to prepare loblolly pine stands for regeneration. The first burn is made in winter to lower the fuel level to the ground and make subsequent summer burns safe. Then, two or three summer burns reduce the understory population and leave a favorable seedbed.

With an adequate supply of seed, a new stand is virtually assured.

Prescribed burning for understory control apparently has no detrimental effect on the growth of the overstory pine stand. In South Carolina, even ten successive annual summer fires did not cause any reduction in growth of the overstory. With heavier surface soil, or on slopes where more water would be lost through increased runoff following burning, growth of the overstory might be reduced.

For Site Preparation — Fire is also often used after harvest cutting for site preparation. Logging breaks up the litter and exposes mineral soil on an appreciable portion of the harvested areas, but much of the forest floor and the understory remain undisturbed. Fires for seedbed preparation after logging are most effective in late summer, before pine seedfall, because pine seedlings have an even start with the competing hardwood sprouts the following spring.

Other benefits are realized from periodic burning. The stand is essentially "fire-proofed." Because of greater ease of movement, the costs of timber inventory, tree marking, logging, and timber-sale supervision are reduced. Perhaps more important, the habitat for wildlife, particularly deer, is improved. Without fire, the browse plants grow beyond reach of deer early in the life of the stand. With periodic burning, especially in winter, the browse supply is repeatedly replenished as the understory is killed back to the ground and promptly resprouts.

Use Outside the South — Prescribed burning has been most widely practiced in the South but is now coming into use in other sections of the country. In the Lake States, it is used as a site-preparation measure for jack- and red-pine regeneration and for understory control in red pine. The effects on vegetation seem to be much the same as they are in the South. Sprouting of hardwood species is greatly reduced by summer fires, and several summer fires will virtually eliminate hazel, the most serious and widespread competitor of pine regeneration in Minnesota. Spring and fall burns are less effective and sometimes more erratic in behavior.

Use of fire for seedbed preparation in black spruce has been developed through research and is now being used on a limited scale. Mature black spruce is cut in strips. The strips are burned while the water table is high. The slash and certain mosses, which are a poor seedbed for spruce, are eliminated and a favorable seedbed of burned peat is created on most of the area. Clearcut blocks are also seeded artificially following prescribed burning.

In the West, fire is used mainly in Douglas fir and pine types for slash disposal after harvest cutting, which also prepares the area for seeding or planting.

Needs and Limitations of Prescribed Fire

While fire is a very useful tool, it requires great care to apply properly. Its effects are not known completely, even in the South, and it has sharp limitations. It is applicable for understory control only where the overstory is resistant to fire, which restricts its use for this purpose to the hard pine types. It has somewhat wider applicability for site preparation.

Use of fire in the management of forests has been applied with varying results, some promising, some disappointing. One of the main problems is in understanding the total effects of burning in order to achieve consistent results either for forest reproduction or wildlife management.

To prescribe fire for specified results while avoiding damages to the stand and site, much more information is needed on the relation of fire intensity to weather factors and fuel conditions, and the effect of various fire intensities on the vegetation and soils. While research may show that particular weather and fuel conditions will produce a certain fire intensity, such narrowly specified conditions will occur only infrequently and for limited periods. Thus, the duration of the required weather and fuel conditions determines the acreage that can be burned, which may often be less than planned. In addition, fire intensity will vary with vegetational and fuel types over the burn areas, with corresponding variations in results. Because of these limitations and variations, fire can only be an imprecise tool at best. Consequently, if fire is to be used, information to prescribe it correctly is essential.

Limitations of the Southern Experience — It is not safe to assume the effects of fire on soils observed in the South are applicable elsewhere, for two reasons. The frequent past burning in the South may be a factor in the observed soil effects — any pine area used to study fire effects is likely to have been burned many times in the past. And soils elsewhere are not comparable to those in the southern pinery. Even in the South, however, the available information comes from only a few studies in limited localities. Consequently, the effects of fire on erosion, soil structure, chemical characteristics, and soil biology should be investigated along with studies of vegetational effects and development of techniques wherever fire is to be used. Burning undoubtedly releases mineral nutrients contained in the forest litter, but these might be largely lost on slopes and deep sands. Very little is known about fire effects on soil flora and fauna beyond their immediate destruction in the burned portion of the forest floor, yet they may be very important in longer-term soil productivity and the health of the forest vegetation.

It should be recognized, however, that burning for site preparation is done only once in the life of a forest stand. In southern pines, a rotation (time from establishment to harvest of a timber stand) may be as short as 20 or 25 years. In the North and West, a rotation is much longer. Burning for hardwood control during the rotation is done more frequently and the effects on soils may be more important.

Effect of Smoke — An aspect of prescribed burning that has only recently been recognized is that smoke is an effect that needs to be considered. Weather and fuel conditions satisfying prescriptions for burning may occur simultaneously over extensive areas and many fires may be burning at the same time. Locally, low-lying palls of smoke can reduce visibility enough to make automobile driving hazardous. People in the vicinity may suffer physical discomfort. On a larger scale, one could speculate that weather might conceivably be affected by fire under certain atmospheric conditions. Smoke particles might serve as condensation nuclei, resulting in cloudiness, or the smoke itself might accumulate at temperature-inversion levels, obstructing back radiation and changing temperatures at ground level. Thus, the effects of the smoke alone might preclude prescribed burning in some localities.

Needed Scientific Activity

Several aspects of fire ecology should receive serious attention:

1. Effects of fire or burning are long-range. Published reports are often based on short-term studies, both in management and ecology. Long-term studies with both ecological and management emphasis are needed.

2. There should be more integration of ecological and management research. The two are of-

ten separate schools of thought, and their approaches, methods, and results should be more closely integrated so that management workers would benefit and apply ecological information and ecologists would be made more aware of the possible applications, economics, and practical potentials involved.

3. Fire affects all aspects of the biotic environment, and these,

too, must be investigated, including: soil moisture, temperature, texture, chemistry, soil microorganisms and fauna, seedbed conditions, recovering vegetation including mosses, herbs, shrubs, and trees, affected animal populations, and air and water pollution. Interrelationships among these are important in understanding the total effect of fire.

4. Application of findings from

one forest and soil type to another are usually not practical, and few generalizations can be made. The total picture for each type of situation must be worked out separately.

5. There is need for a careful review and analysis of work done in both ecology and management areas to integrate findings to date and avoid duplication of efforts, a fault of present and past work.

5. POLAR ECOSYSTEMS

Polar Flora and Vegetation

The polar tundra with a permafrost base, as found in the high arctic and antarctic, is one of the most fragile types of world vegetation. As with any ecosystem, the living components in the tundra — the microorganisms, plants, and animals — are in delicate balance with their environment; any change in the environment will result in some changes in the composition and relationships of the living components. Since the number of different types of living organisms in the polar tundra are much fewer than in other ecosystems, even small changes often cause drastic changes in the composition and relationships of the living organisms. For example, depression by heavy vehicles, overgrazing, or trampling by animal herds or humans at certain times of the year can result in complete local destruction of the tundra vegetation. (See Figure IX–15) Recovery to the original vegetation, if it occurs at all, takes at least 100 years.

In the arctic, economic development has already begun and is likely to increase significantly in the future. It is very important that the effects of these developments on the fragile tundra be studied by trained scientists so that an assessment may be made as changes take place. In the antarctic, the only threat to the tundra is from base construction and tourism; these threats have thus far been moderated by the provisions and recommendations of the Antarctic Treaty relating to conservation of antarctic fauna and flora.

Because it appears to be much simpler than the biological systems of the temperate and tropical regions, the polar tundra offers unique opportunities for studying problems involving the interrelations between the environment and the living organisms. This simplicity in appearance results from the lack of large trees, which in other regions make for a distinct multi-level system (the ground, the herb layer, the shrub layer, and several tree-top layers) with many different types of dwelling places for other organisms. In the polar regions, the levels are few, and thus there are fewer complications involved in studying any one of them. Despite this relative simplicity, however, it does not necessarily follow that the processes or interrelations within the tundra are any easier to understand than those in a temperate or tropical forest.

Recent Developments in Polar Studies

In the antarctic, except for areas of the northern Antarctic Peninsula, the tundra is the most depauperate type, composed entirely of nonflowering plants, mostly lichens, mosses, and algae. Even where this tundra is present, it is very spotty, dependent primarily on the availability of water in a land where desert conditions prevail and where most of what water there is is unavailable to plants because it is frozen into snow and ice.

The more humid northern Antarctic Peninsula and the sub-antarctic

Figure IX–15 — A SECTION OF THE TUNDRA BIOME

The photograph shows a section of tundra or marshy plain near Point Barrow, Alaska. The land is characterized by a lack of trees and an upper surface that is spongy and uneven due to the freezing and thawing of the poorly drained land. The picture shows polygons that are 15 to 25 feet across, a result of winter freezing. Beneath the surface, at depths ranging from a few inches to several feet, is the permafrost, or permanently frozen soil, that is the ultimate limit to plant root growth.

313

islands have a tundra more nearly resembling that of the arctic, but containing fewer types of flowering plants. There are only two species of flowering plants native to the Antarctic Peninsula.

The antarctic tundra has been less studied than that of the arctic. However, as a result of the Antarctic Treaty and the international scientific cooperation of the past ten years, great strides have been made in gathering details about the plants and their environments.

Major works have been written or are in the process of being written about flowering plants in all parts of the arctic (Siberia, Scandinavia, and central Canada). Work on the non-flowering plants is less extensive but is also progressing. A good beginning has been made in the understanding of the plants that occur in the antarctic as well. Major flora of the various plant groups — lichens, mosses, and algae — will probably be reported on in the near future. The flora of the sub-antarctic islands are also being studied, and, again, reports on major flora are likely to appear relatively soon.

Thus, it can be said that much of the basic investigation about polar-region plant life is done or soon will be. This cannot be said about the interrelations among the plants and animals and their environments. *This* is the needed area for study.

Needed Scientific Activity

Although, as noted, we know a fair amount about the distribution of the plants and animals in the tundra, we lack detailed information about all of the interrelationships. Ecosystem modeling, a way of mathematically taking into account the various factors of the environment and their interrelationships with the living organisms, requires such detailed information for each component of the model. Once a meaningful model has been made, predictions can be soundly based. (See Figure IX–16)

The Tundra Biome study group of the International Biological Program has proposed that such things as productivity of the plants and of the whole tundra be investigated. Multidisciplinary studies of the sort that have been done at Cape Thompson and Kodiak Island in Alaska would be valuable in providing a better understanding of the tundra ecosystem. There is need to study the ecological interrelationships and the specific changes that are being brought about by planned environmental change. Only then will it be possible to predict meaningful changes that are likely to occur when other environmental changes are made.

Figure IX–16 — FLOW DIAGRAM OF A WET COASTAL TUNDRA ECOSYSTEM

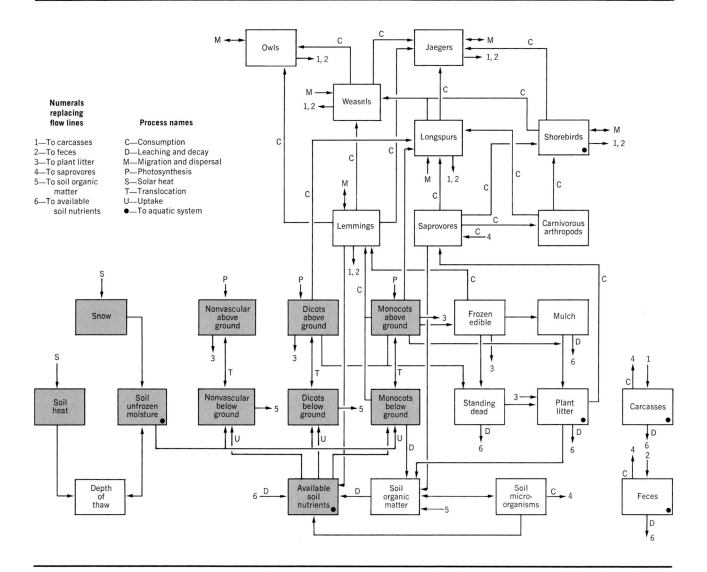

**Numerals
replacing
flow lines**

1—To carcasses
2—To feces
3—To plant litter
4—To saprovores
5—To soil organic
matter
6—To available
soil nutrients

Process names

C—Consumption
D—Leaching and decay
M—Migration and dispersal
P—Photosynthesis
S—Solar heat
T—Translocation
U—Uptake
●—To aquatic system

This is a rather detailed flow chart of a tundra ecosystem representative of the Point Barrow area. The driving variables (shaded areas) are solar heating, moisture availability, nutrient availability, and photosynthesis. The net result is seen as the production and maintenance of such animal populations as weasels, shorebirds, etc. Although the diagram is basically an energy-related chart, the rates of flow of energy between points are not indicated.

PART X

ENVIRONMENTAL CONTAMINANTS

EFFECTS OF ENVIRONMENTAL POLLUTANTS AND EXPOSURES ON HUMAN HEALTH AND WELL BEING

In addition to their often profound ecological implications, man's activities and their by-products have negative as well as positive effects on human health and well being. In some cases, these effects are long-term and only now are beginning to be understood; in other cases, effects are suspected but not yet proved; and in still others, effects as yet unsuspected may exist. The charts below outline the situation as it is at present; however, the current climate of environmental concern is apt to lead to research that will document and modify this outline rather than expand it.

The following listings have been made available through the courtesy of the World Health Organization.

COMMUNITY AIR POLLUTION

(Note: Items in parentheses refer to effects other than those directly affecting human health status)

Agents, pollutants	Definite Effects	Possible Effects
Sulfur dioxide (effects of sulfur oxides may be due to sulfur, sulfur trioxide, sulfuric acid or sulfate salts)	1. Aggravation of asthma and chronic bronchitis 2. Impairment of pulmonary function 3. Sensory irritation 4. (Effects on vegetation)	
		5. (In certain conditions, produces effects on buildings and works of art)
Sulfur oxides and particulate matter from combustion sources	6. Short-term increase in mortality 7. Short-term increase in morbidity 8. Aggravation of bronchitis and cardiovascular disease 9. Contributory role in etiology of chronic bronchitis and emphysema 10. Contributory role to respiratory disease in children	
		11. Contributory role in etiology of lung cancer
Particulate matter (not otherwise specified)	12. Impairs visibility (soils surfaces and materials) 13. (Alteration in incident sunlight)	
		14. Increase in chronic respiratory disease

319

COMMUNITY AIR POLLUTION (continued)

Agents, pollutants	Definite Effects	Possible Effects
Oxidants (including ozone)	15. Aggravates emphysema, asthma, and bronchitis	
	16. Impairs lung function in patients with bronchitis-emphysema	
	17. Eye and respiratory irritation and impairment in performance of student athletes	
	18. Increased probability of motor-vehicle accidents	
		19. Alteration of oxygen consumption
Ozone	20. Irritant to respiratory tract	
	21. Impairs lung function	
		22. Acceleration of aging, possibly due to lipid peroxidation and related processes
Carbon monoxide	23. Impairs oxygen transport function	
		24. Increased general mortality and coronary mortality rates
		25. Impairment of central nervous system function
		26. Causal factor in atherosclerosis
Nitrogen dioxide	27. (Discolors atmosphere)	
		28. Factor in pulmonary emphysema
		29. Impairment of lung defenses such as mast cells and macrophages or altered lung function
Lead	30. Increased storage in body	
	31. (Lethal to animals eating contaminated feed)	
		32. Impairment of hemoglobin and porphyrin synthesis
		33. Probably decreases enzyme level
Hydrogen sulfide	34. Increased mortality from acute exposures	
	35. Causes sensory irritation	
	36. (Damages property (paint))	
		37. Impaired sensory detection or reflexes
		38. (Socio-cultural nuisance)
Mercaptans	39. Sensory irritation (odor)	
		40. Headache, nausea, and sinus affections
Fluorides	41. (Damages vegetation; harms animals)	
		42. Fluorosis of teeth

COMMUNITY AIR POLLUTION (continued)

Agents, pollutants	Definite Effects	Possible Effects
Ethylene	43. (Damages vegetation and hastens ripening of fruit)	
Asbestos	44. Produces pleural calcification*	
	45. Malignant mesothelioma, asbestosis*	
		46. Contributes to chronic pulmonary disease (asbestosis and lung cancer)
Chlorinated hydrocarbon pesticides	47. Stored in body, mostly from milk and animal fats	
	48. (Ecological damage)	
		49. Impairment of learning and reproduction
Organo-phosphorus pesticides	50. Acute fatality	
	51. Acute illness	
	52. Impair cholinesterase	
		53. Impairment of general health, and of adaptation
Other odorous compounds	54. Sensory irritation	
		55. Headache and sinus affections
Hydrothermal pollutants	56. (Can influence local climate and interfere with visibility)	
		57. (Influence on action of hydroscopic pollutants)
Beryllium	58. Berylliosis with pulmonary impairment	
Air-borne microorganisms	59. Air-borne infections	

* These effects have been shown to occur in the vicinity of mining and processing operations. General community exposure may cause these effects, but this has not definitely been proven.

FOOD AND WATER CONTAMINANTS

Agents, pollutants	Definite Effects	Possible Effects
Bacteria	1. Epidemic and endemic gastro-intestinal infections (typhoid, cholera, shigellosis, salmonellosis, leptospirosis, etc.) 2. (Malodor)	
		3. Secondary interaction with malnutrition and with nitrates in water (cf., No. 15)
Viruses	4. Epidemic hepatitis, and other viral infections	
		5. Eye and skin inflammation from swimming
Protozoa and metazoa	6. Amoebiasis, schistosomiasis, hydatidosis and other parasitic infections 7. (Malodor)	
Metals	8. Lead poisoning 9. Mercury poisoning (through food chains) 10. Cadmium poisoning (through food chains) 11. Arsenic poisoning 12. Chromium poisoning	
		13. Epidemic nephropathy
		14. "Blackfoot" disease
Nitrates	15. Methemoglobinemia (with bacterial interactions)	
		16. Methemoglobinemia (bacterial interaction not required)
		17. Nitorsamine effects on mutagenesis and/or carcinogenesis
and/or phosphates	18. (Eutrophication)	
and/or organic matter	19. (Malodor)	
"Softness" factor		20. Increase in cardiovascular disease
Sulfates and/or phosphates	21. Gastro-intestinal hypermotility	
Dissolved solids	22. Impaired potability 23. (Impaired value for irrigation and industry)	
Fluorides	24. Fluorosis of teeth when in excess	
Chlorinated hydrocarbon pesticides	25. (Ecological damage)	
Oil-petroleum	26. Impaired potability	
Thermal (heat) pollution	27. (Ecological damage)	
Phenols	28. Impaired potability	

LAND POLLUTION

Agents, pollutants	Definite Effects	Possible Effects
Human excreta	1. Schistosomiasis, taeniasis hookworm, and other infections	
Sewage	2. Urban filariasis	
	3. Flies and other vectors	
	4. Odor	
Garbage	5. Rat and other rodent infestation	
	6. Flies and other vector-transmitted diseases	
	7. Odor	
	8. Pollution of water and air from disposal practices	
		9. Typhus, plague, leptospirosis, and other infectious diseases
Industrial and radioactive waste	10. Storage and effects from toxic metals and other substances through food chains	
	11. (Loss of vegetation and soil, and altered ecology)	
Fertilizers	12. Ground water pollution effects, surface water pollution effects	
Pesticides (food chain)	13. Contamination of vegetation and secondary foodstuffs	

THERMAL EXPOSURES

Agents, pollutants	Definite Effects	Possible Effects
Cold damp	1. Excess mortality from respiratory disease and fatal exposure or frostbite	
		2. Contributes to excess mortality and morbidity from other causes
	3. Excess morbidity from respiratory disease and morbidity from frostbite and exposure	
		4. Rheumatism
Cold dry	5. Mortality from frostbite and exposure	
		6. Impaired lung function
	7. Morbidity from frostbite and respiratory disease	
Hot dry	8. Heat-stroke mortality	
	9. Excess mortality attributed to other causes	
	10. Morbidity from heat stroke and excess from other causes	
	11. Impaired function; aggravation of renal and circulatory diseases	
Hot damp	12. Increase in skin affections	
		13. Increase in prevalence of infectious agents and vectors
	14. Heat-exhaustion mortality	
	15. Excess mortality from other causes	
	16. Heat-related morbidity	
	17. Impaired function	
	18. Aggravation of renal and circulatory disease	

RADIATION AND MICROWAVES

Agents, pollutants	Definite Effects	Possible Effects
Natural sunlight	1. Fatalities from acute exposure	
	2. Morbidity due to "burn"	
	3. Skin cancer	
	4. Interaction with drugs in susceptible individuals	
		5. Conditional exacerbation in porphyria
		6. Increase in malignant melanoma
Diagnostic X-ray	7. Skin cancer and other skin changes	
		8. Contributing factors to leukemia
		9. Alteration in fecundity
Therapeutic radiation	10. Skin cancer	
	11. Increase in leukemia	
	12. Acute radiation illness	
		13. Increase in other cancers
		14. Acceleration of aging
		15. Mutagenesis
Industrial uses of radiation and mining of radioactive ores	16. Acute accidental deaths	
	17. Radiation morbidity	
	18. Uranium nephritis	
	19. Lung cancer in cigarette-smoking miners [a]	
	20. (Effects on food chains)	
		21. Increase in adjacent community morbidity
Nuclear power and reprocessing plants	22. (Ecological damage due to thermal pollution of water)	
	23. Storage of potentially harmful materials in the body	
	24. (Radioactive contamination of air, land, and water)	
		25. Increase in cancer incidence
		26. Community disaster
		27. Alteration in human genetic material
Microwaves		28. Tissue damage

[a] While this is an occupational exposure, its interpretation is of great importance for community health protection.

NOISE AND VIBRATIONS

Source	Definite Effects	Possible Effects
Traffic	1. Temporary loss of hearing	
	2. Impairment of rest and communication	
	3. Sensory irritation	
		4. Progressive hearing loss
		5. Increased social disorganization
		6. Contributory to cardiovascular disease
		7. Impairment of circulatory function
Aircraft (including sonic boom)	8. Permanent hearing loss	
	9. Temporary hearing loss	
	10. Impairment of rest	
	11. Impairment of communication	
	12. (Damage to property)	
		13. Aggravation or cause of mental illness
Recreational	14. Temporary hearing loss	
	15. Interference with rest	
	16. Interference with communication	
	17. Sensory irritation	
		18. Aggravation of tension-related conditions
Official (bells, sirens)	19. Temporary loss of hearing	
	20. Sensory irritation	
Technological—building construction, paving, etc.	21. Temporary hearing loss	
		22. Progressive hearing loss
Domestic noise	23. Impairment of rest and communication	
		24. Produces tension
Vibrations	25. Discomfort	
		26. Articular and muscular disease
		27. Adverse effects on nervous system

HOUSING AND HOUSEHOLD AGENTS

Agents, pollutants	Definite Effects	Possible Effects
Heating and cooking	1. Acute fatalities from carbon monoxide, fires and explosions, and discarded refrigerators	
		2. Increase in diseases of the respiratory tract in infants
Fumes and dust	3. Acute illness from fumes	
	4. Impaired oxygen transport	
	5. Aggravation of asthma	
		6. Increase in chronic respiratory disease
		7. Increase in heart disease
Crowding	8. Spread of acute and chronic disease	
	9. (Impairment of social interaction and of privacy)	
Structural factors (including electrical wiring, stoves, and thin walls)	10. Accidental fatality	
	11. Accidental injury	
	12. Morbidity and mortality from lack of protection from heat or cold	
	13. Morbidity and mortality due to fire or explosion	
	14. (Impairment of privacy)	
		15. Mental illness and behavioral disorders
Paints and solvents	16. Childhood lead-poisoning fatalities, associated mental impairment and anemia	
	17. Renal and heptic toxicity	
	18. Fatalities and morbidity from fire	
		19. Acute effects of other vapors and paints
Household equipment and supplies (including pesticides)	20. Fatalities from fire and injury	
	21. Morbidity from fire and injury	
	22. Fatalities from poisoning	
	23. Morbidity from poisoning	
Toys, beads, and painted objects	24. Mortality and morbidity	
Urban design	25. Increased accident risks	
	26. (Social disruption and isolation)	
		27. Psychological effects from lack of diversity, accessibility, recreational areas
Acoustical factors	28. Impairment of rest and sleep	
		29. Possible aggravation of tension-related conditions

1. AIRBORNE CHEMICALS

Chemical Contaminants in the Atmosphere

Atmospheric contamination is difficult to define precisely, since "pure air" itself is a mixture. Water contamination is a simple concept, since "pure water" is a single chemical substance. Even with human influences absent, the air has a variable composition in both time and space. There is evidence that there was more oxygen in the atmosphere at the peak of the carboniferous era than there is today; and the atmosphere close to an erupting volcano is bound to be different in composition from the air in the midst of a pine forest.

Definition of Contamination

To discuss the contamination of a mixture it is necessary to define an arbitrary composition as "pure." It is usual to define dry pure air as containing roughly 78 percent nitrogen, 21 percent oxygen, 0.03 percent carbon dioxide, and the remaining 0.97 percent noble gases. (See Figure X–1) Water vapor is present in pure air in highly variable amounts.

Under this definition, all air is contaminated to some degree. Much of the contamination is both natural and beneficial. The development of clouds and precipitation, for example, requires the presence of "nucleation centers," usually consisting of dust, sea salt, and particles formed in the air by reactions between gaseous contaminants.

Some contaminants are intrinsically harmful to things that humans value or harmful in excessive concentrations. If these contaminants are produced directly or indirectly by human activities, they are called air pollutants. In a few instances a pollutant is not, paradoxically, a contaminant. For example, excessive industrial steam meets the usual criteria of a pollutant if it obscures visibility on a major highway; yet strictly speaking it is no more than a part of the variable fraction of water vapor ascribed to "pure" air.

The distinction between a harmful contaminant and a pollutant may be a narrow one. Natural contaminations, such as a rain of volcanic ash or a desert sandstorm, are not classed as pollutants. But when human activity is responsible for their occurring — as it was in the great dust storms of the 1930's — these contaminants are classed as pollutants. We can legitimately consider even a sandstorm in the Sahara as pollution, since the great desert, at least in its present extent, appears to have been caused by overgrazing.

A final case needs to be distinguished in the definition of contamination. Air may be rendered harmful to life, not by the presence of contaminants, but by the absence of oxygen. Since combustion within the 48 contiguous United States now requires twice as much oxygen as all the green plants in the area produce, the hazard of *depleted* air may become acute.

The Environmental Problem

The sources of pollutants are generally well characterized and the composition of most is known. Much less is known about natural contaminants. Many come from enormous areas at miniscule concentrations. For example, air that blows into Barbados from the tropical Atlantic contains a

Figure X–1 — COMPOSITION OF CLEAN, DRY AIR

Component	Content % by volume	ppm
Nitrogen	78.09%	780,900 ppm
Oxygen	20.94	209,400
Argon	.93	9,300
Carbon dioxide	.0318	318
Neon	.0018	18
Helium	.00052	5.2
Krypton	.0001	1
Xenon	.000008	0.08
Nitrous oxide	.000025	0.25

Component	Content % by volume	ppm
Hydrogen	.00005%	0.5 ppm
Methane	.00015	1.5
Nitrogen dioxide	.0000001	0.001
Ozone	.000002	0.02
Sulfur dioxide	.00000002	.0002
Carbon monoxide	.00001	0.1
Ammonia	.000001	.01

The table shows the major and some of the trace constituents of clean, dry air near sea level. The concentrations of some of the gases may differ with time and from place to place. Some of the data are open to question, but the values are meant to indicate the order of magnitude.

minute trace (about one part in two billion parts of air) of sulfur dioxide. In spite of all the sulfur dioxide put into the air by burning high-sulfur fuels, it is unlikely that any of this human contribution reaches Barbados. Instead, some natural, probably maritime, source must be responsible for maintaining the concentration at this level.

It is possible to compute how much carbon monoxide the industries and automobiles of the world release into the atmosphere, and it appears that the worldwide concentration of this gas is about one part in ten million. Knowing these facts, it should be possible to estimate how rapidly carbon monoxide is removed from the air. However, it has recently been discovered that the ocean also constitutes a vast and diffuse source of the gas; thus a much higher removal rate must account for the known concentration. At present the removal process is unknown, yet it must be discovered if environmental management is to be possible. A knowledge of the lifetime of carbon monoxide in air would be a valuable clue from which to begin.

Over-all, one fact is clear. Many pollutants are also released naturally, though at lower concentrations. If there were no natural processes to remove them, the atmosphere would be far more heavily contaminated than it is, even in the absence of human contributions. Hence there must exist an enormous complex of processes which maintain the atmosphere at substantially its present composition. Every component, even most of the minor ones here called contaminants, is present in the global atmosphere as a result of closely balancing processes of generation and removal.

These processes are such that a substantial increase or decrease in generation will be rapidly counteracted, at least in part, by a corresponding change in rate of removal. However, this sort of feedback con-

trol generally has its inherent limits. A very simple example is the ability of living vegetation to remove sulfur dioxide from the air. Studies in Panama show that a very small concentration of this gas is a natural contaminant in the tropics, perhaps emanating from decayed vegetation. If this supposition is correct, then the small natural concentration of sulfur dioxide results from a balance of its release from dead plants and its consumption by living plants.

The balanced system will accommodate a considerable input of sulfur dioxide from pollutant sources, and, in fact, the gas has been shown to absorb rapidly into vegetation. If the added input is too great, however, plants perish, and the system fails.

It is further obvious that all forms of life release wastes to the environment. Wastes by definition are in some degree toxic to the organisms that excrete them; hence, man or any other organism reaching an intolerable population density will pollute the environment with respect to his own survival. Man is far worse than his numbers indicate because he augments his own energies by the synthetic release of energy, thus generating additional wastes. The energy generated in the United States alone is equal to that of 100 *billion* humans. These "equivalent energy slaves" are a measure of our standard of living; they are also a true measure of our impact upon the environment.

Clearly, no acceptable degree of control is imminent for the human population. If both world population and the U.S. living standard were frozen at present levels, and the rest of the world raised to the U.S. standard, a tenfold increase in pollutant emissions would result, assuming constant technology. Yet population cannot be stabilized overnight, and the rest of the world does aspire to the U.S. living standard; although constant technology is a poor assumption, the developing countries have

shown little inclination to avoid the environmental errors of our own past.

These collective considerations delineate the environmental problem. The human impact has reached an alarming level, and much of its force is mediated by the atmosphere. (See Figure X–2) Beyond the above qualitative statement, what is the state of our knowledge?

State of Scientific Knowledge

Frankly, our over-all knowledge is extremely fragmentary. Pate, Lodge, and their co-workers at the National Center for Atmospheric Research have reported on atmospheric composition in the moist tropics in regions far from pollution sources. Keeling and several others continue to measure worldwide distributions of carbon dioxide. At the Stanford Research Institute, Robinson and Robbins have obtained apparently reliable figures for the worldwide concentration of carbon monoxide, and have shown the presence of an unsuspected natural source of this gas in the ocean. Patterson and his group at the California Institute of Technology, by analyzing ice cores from the Greenland Ice Cap and from Antarctica, have documented the worldwide secular increase in atmospheric lead. All of this information is necessary to assess the original state of the system that mankind is now disturbing.

O'Keeffe and his colleagues in the Environmental Protection Agency, Axelrod, Lodge, and others at the National Center for Atmospheric Research, and numerous academic scientists are gradually developing analytical methods of sufficient sensitivity, specificity, and reliability to assess both the reputedly unpolluted and polluted environment. At the University of Washington, Charlson has developed a nephelometer that rapidly assesses local atmospheric haziness and also makes possible

Figure X–2 — POLLUTION — AN ENVIRONMENTAL PROBLEM

The picture illustrates the multiple problems of pollution encountered in a small city in western Pennsylvania. In the first instance, the gaseous effluents from the industrial complex form a cloud over and downwind of the city. This cloud, in addition to causing changes in the local radiation balance and possibly other local changes, is composed of water vapor mixed with pollutants such as sulfur dioxide that cause damage to plants, animals, and man. The city is located on a river into which industrial and municipal wastes are dumped; in earlier days there was no need to worry about the consequences of such action and now, although funds are becoming available to help build water-treatment plants, it is difficult to keep up with the need. The question of solid waste disposal presents yet another unsolved problem. The original city dump along the river only makes the water pollution worse. Incineration causes air pollution. Sanitary land fills use up large quantities of desirable land. Shipping the wastes by rail or barge may help the local problem but does not eliminate it. Furthermore, all these problems spill over into downwind or downstream localities.

laboratory experiments on haziness modification. He has shown that in many typical atmospheres the turbidity measured by his instrument correlates closely with the mass of the particles present.

The Environmental Protection Agency (EPA) maintains monitoring and surveillance activities in most of the major U.S. cities, and some local agencies are measuring their own pollution problems. However, most of the widely used techniques are five to twenty years old and are less effective than most recently developed methods. Nearly all of them lack precision and specificity, and thus the results are affected significantly by the presence of pollutants not being measured.

The Measurement Problem — Before newer techniques are accepted, verifiable standards need to be established for precision, specificity, and accuracy in measuring pollutants at concentrations as low as one part in a billion parts of air and in the presence of equal or larger amounts of all other possible pollutants. This measurement problem is not only unresolved, but there has been no agency with the explicit and exclusive responsibility for evaluating proposed analytical methods. Only recently has a group been created with the responsibility of evaluating existing methods of atmospheric analysis, and it is not yet certain to what extent this group will be successful. Meanwhile, there is a strong tendency to use old techniques, which at least

provide numbers, even though there may be some uncertainty as to the physical meaning of those numbers.

New Attitudes — The immediate past has seen remarkable changes, not so much in the state of knowledge as in the state of mind of the atmospheric research community. Not many years ago, an announcement of plans to study atmospheric chemistry in the tropics invited accusations of junketing from one's colleagues. Only a short time past, many scientists felt that usefulness tainted research results; today "relevant" research topics are eagerly sought by formerly "pure" scientists.

New Methods — Older research tools have been improved and simplified and new tools have been devised. Gas chromatography with more sensitive detectors, atomic absorption, neutron activation, chemiluminescence and fluorescence quenching—all these and others provide the means to analyze even smaller, more dilute, and more complex samples.

This combination of new methods and progressive attitudes in environmental study summarizes the current status of trace chemistry of the atmosphere. While recent achievements are not great, there is now an expectancy and readiness for major scientific advances in this field.

Needed Scientific Activity

This mood of expectancy has led no fewer than a half dozen groups around the world to examine the possibility of routine monitoring of several major contaminants in the air. Carried out at sites remote from local pollution, such work could provide for the first time true "benchmark" measurements against which future changes in the atmosphere can be gauged. Recently, a number of groups within the United States independently concluded that a saturation study is needed of pollution in a single city, ranging from the point of individually emitted pollutants to the far downwind zone where pollutants merge with the general atmosphere.

Studies of (a) urban pollution, (b) analytical methods, and (c) laboratory models of reactions producing, altering, and removing contaminants are three areas of atmospheric chemistry that require immediate attention. These studies alone are not sufficient, however, to solve the environmental problem. Supporting work needed in the biological sciences is lagging for lack of precise methods to assess the ecological impact of contaminants; there must be innovation in city planning, architecture, engineering, and related fields; and behavioral research is essential to understand why people elect to pollute and how they may be dissuaded from polluting. With population increase, restraints inevitably increase; acceptance of these restraints will be necessary to preserve and nourish other freedoms.

Atmospheric Contaminants and Development of Standards

Atmospheric contamination can be considered on the global, national, state, regional, and local scales, each of which has its own vertical and temporal scales. (See Figure X–3) The temporal scales have two aspects — the time-scale of the adverse effects associated with the contaminant, and the time-scale required for effective action for its control. These two time-scales tend to be similar in magnitude for each of the horizontal scales noted above.

One example of the global system is the postulated effects on the earth's temperature when carbon dioxide and particulate matter build up in the atmosphere, affecting global heat balance. Another example is fallout from testing of nuclear weapons in the atmosphere. Neither of these problems can be resolved unilaterally by any one nation. Hence the time-scale for resolution is that of action by international organizations.

On the national scale, which in the United States is synonymous with the continental scale, we are concerned with the buildup of the background contaminant concentration of the non-urban air mass and with interstate transport of contaminants. Experience has shown us that these take years to resolve.

Within the confines of a state, our problems are those of urban-suburban-rural contaminant transport and reactions and of the impact of large, single contaminant sources on the land areas within their range of influence. In such matters, we would expect a state to be able to initiate controls, if not effectively accomplish them, in a matter of months.

In the United States, we are committed to the regional concept of air-pollution control — the region being generally a multi-county area, either intra- or inter-state, which contains the principal sources of its pollution and the principal receptors adversely affected thereby. The principal time-scale with which a region must concern itself is the so-called air-pollution "episode" — the build-up of pollution during a stagnation of horizontal and vertical atmospheric transport mechanisms extending over a matter of several days. Therefore, although the region may adopt a larger time-scale for attack on the basic causes of its contaminant problem, it must also be prepared to react to an occurring episode on a same-day or next-day basis.

The smallest scale is that of the locality, covering several city blocks, in which traffic builds up for several hours each morning and afternoon.

Our concern for atmospheric contamination globally is for the integrity of the earth as a planet on which human life can exist without extinction by freezing, overheating, inundation, or starvation. Nationally, regionally, and locally we see atmospheric contamination as having adverse effects on our health, on vegetation, livestock, materials, structures, and the atmosphere itself. All these elements of damage are associated with costs to society and to our economy; and all the means for control of contaminants have within them certain inherent costs. Our general view is that it costs us more to have pollution than to control it.

Measuring Air Quality

If one views air pollution as a system (see Figure X–4), we find that a convenient starting point is "Sources and Their Control." Our knowledge of the principal pollution sources and

Figure X–3 — ATMOSPHERIC SCALES

Horizontal Scale	Vertical Scale	Temporal Scale
Global	The Atmosphere	Decades
National	The Stratosphere	Years
State	The Troposphere	Months
Regional	The Lowest Mile	Days
Local	The Height of Buildings	Hours

Figure X–4 — A SYSTEM FOR DISCUSSING AIR POLLUTION

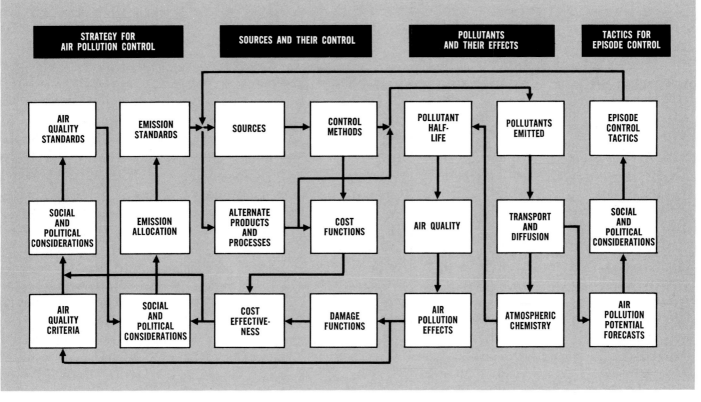

The diagram shows a systems idealization of the problem of air pollution. Each box represents a set of problems about which we may know something, but certainly not enough to solve the problems or to understand exactly how that box may interact with other boxes. It is interesting to note the role of social and political considerations in the over-all air-pollution problem. They dominate our strategy and tactics for the control of air pollution.

the means for their control is quite good, particularly with regard to the contaminants that are emitted to the atmosphere in greatest annual tonnage — namely, carbon dioxide, carbon monoxide, SO_x, NO_x, hydrocarbons, and particulate matter. (In air-pollution parlance SO_x and NO_x mean a mixture of oxides.) Present knowledge of emissions that occur in lesser annual tonnage is less precise; and our control technology is fraught with economic problems.

Some of our apparent control technology has yet to be reduced to commercial practice because of the following dilemma:

1. Application of the untried technology would represent a cost to the user that could be recovered only by raising the cost of the product or service produced.

2. Raising the cost of the product or service would adversely affect the competitive positions of the applier of the technology and will therefore be resisted unless required by law or subsidized by government.

3. There is a reluctance to require by law the application of an untried technology.

This leaves governmental subsidy as the means to introduce untried technology. As yet, we have made only halting steps in this direction.

Once pollutants have been emitted, we are concerned with their fate in the atmosphere and the adverse effects they produce. Their life history in the atmosphere starts with their transport and diffusion from their points of emission to their ultimate receptors, during the course of which they are subject to chemical reaction in the atmosphere and a host of scavenging processes that tend to remove them from the atmosphere. The result of these several processes is measurable at any receptor point in terms of the concentrations of the kinds and forms of contaminants that survive to reach the receptor.

What we measure at a receptor point we call "air quality." Because of seasonal, diurnal, and microscale variations in source strengths and character and in transport, diffusion, reaction, and scavenging factors, air quality will show considerable variability. However, by increasing the averaging time of air-quality data, we can suppress enough of this variability to interpret the data meaningfully.

Technological Shortcomings — There are scientific shortcomings in each stage of the process described above. The transport and diffusion phase takes place in the lower reaches of the atmosphere, above most ground-based instrumentation and below most aircraft and satellite-borne instrumentation. It occurs over populous areas and in airport traffic patterns where we are not free to operate balloons, drones, towers, rockets, dropsondes, and other means of probing the atmosphere for meteorological and pollution information. To the extent that much of our measurement technology lacks sophistication, our knowledge of the phenomenon measured falls short of the optimum desired. Because of the complexity of the potential chemical and scavenging reactions among all the pollutants present in the atmosphere, we have only scratched the surface of understanding these phenomena.

Our knowledge of air quality is limited, furthermore, to just a few places on earth that have been able to afford the installation and operation of air-quality monitoring equipment. Commercial vendors of such equipment have tended to await demand, with the result that there has been a proliferation of instruments to measure a few well-publicized pollutants and a paucity of instruments for monitoring the less "popular" contaminants.

Data Base — We have given the name "air-quality criteria" to tabulations of cause-effect data relating various concentrations of contaminants with the effects observed on people, vegetation, livestock, materials, structures, and the atmosphere. These observations encompass studies in the laboratory and the field and, in the case of people, involve epidemiological and clinical studies. Our "people" data is the weakest because airborne contaminants are only one class among many of stresses on population and the attribution of health effects to any one class is very difficult. Since these latter data form the basis for establishment of "air-quality standards," and thus the base for regulatory control, they are the most controversial of all the data in the whole field of air pollution.

The setting of "air-quality standards," and the derivative establishment of "emission standards" to limit the emission of specific classes of sources, calls forth not only data from the physical and biological sciences, but also involves trade-offs and decisions that deeply involve the social and political sciences and interactions with other elements of the ecological and economic system. Decisions as to how we control air pollution can affect water and land pollution, and vice versa. Decisions on pollutant levels can affect the energy supply for our economy and reflect on the nationwide and worldwide trade in fuels. Considerable public controversy is likely, therefore, as to the desirable uniformity of air quality and national emission standards.

Modeling — To help resolve some of these problems, mathematical modeling is increasingly being applied, both to the gross model of the whole air-pollution system and to more detailed models of individual elements of the system as, for instance, the transport and diffusion model. These latter models have been used extensively in setting the geographic boundaries of the "air-quality control regions" currently being designated by the federal government in various urban areas of the United States.

What We Need to Know

Data — More than anything else, we need to know the effects of pollutants in the atmosphere on the exposed population. Much of our past knowledge has been of the effects of certain pure substances on experimental animals or healthy adults. What we need is knowledge of how the mix of pollutants as they really exist in the atmosphere affects the actual mix of the exposed population.

Technology — Our greatest air-quality measurement and monitoring need is for remote means of probing hundreds or thousands of feet through the air for an information return of pertinent chemical and physical data.

In the area of control technology, our greatest need is to test prototypes and pilot plants preparatory to production and commercial action.

Air-Quality Management — Finally, we need better understanding of air pollution as a system, of the interaction within the system and between it and other systems in the ecological and economic whole. In effect, we need to learn how better to manage the air-quality system.

Institutional Resources — To do these things requires trained people and facilities in which to train them. Much of the money that is now being spent in contract research could be better spent in building and equipping facilities for air-pollution research and training, preferably at universities, of a type that does not now exist in the United States. As an example, the Japanese government has built several large low-velocity wind tunnels for air-pollution research; in the United States, the federal air-pollution authorities have built none. All the large new smog chambers for the study of atmospheric chemical reactions are in the laboratories of private research organizations; they are not available for student training. The list could go on and on. Clearly, a redirection of effort is needed if tomorrow's problems are to be solved.

Modeling the Atmosphere

The purpose of the models in question is to allow quantitative assessment of "air quality" — i.e., the concentration of pollutant gases and particles — at all or chosen points within an area of the order of 100 square miles which contains (and is bordered by) numerous pollutant sources. Models are required both for the assessment of abatement tactics (What sources are responsible for what degree of pollution in what areas?) and for the planning of development (What will be the effect of a new highway or new industrial complex on pollutant concentrations in the area and how, given that a pollutant must be emitted, can its impact be minimized by the siting of the source?).

Existing models, when classified only according to the nature of their output, are of two types: short-term models and long-term models. The objective of a short-term model is to compute air quality averaged over periods of about one hour to one day. Long-term models produce averages of air quality over periods of one month to one year. *Statistics* of short-term averages of air quality may be derived from the output of long-term models by the application of empirical distribution functions. Long-term models are, therefore, applicable to planning and to assessing the broad impact of land-use changes on air quality; but if models are to be used in the day-to-day management of air quality — e.g., during air-pollution alerts and incidents — short-term models are required. Long-term averages and statistics can, of course, be derived by the repeated use of short-term models, at the expense of computing effort.

Physical and Mathematical Basis of Air Quality Models

To compute the concentration of a pollutant, we must know where and in what quantity it is emitted and what happens to it in the atmosphere. If the source inventory is inadequate, the model cannot be expected to be adequate. An adequate source inventory must account for the total emission of pollutant over the area, and it must have the same resolution in time and space as the required output of the models, so that if we require, for example, the one-hour average concentration of sulfur dioxide (SO_2) over an area one mile square, we must have an inventory of emissions of SO_2 hour by hour, averaged over areas not greater than one mile square.

Once in the atmosphere, the pollutant travels with the wind. It may react chemically with other pollutants or normal atmospheric constituents, it may fall out or be washed out, or it may change by radioactive decay. Traveling with the wind is conventionally divided into transport by the average wind (the average being taken over times and areas larger than those resolved by the model) and diffusion by the turbulent eddies (i.e., by wind variations on time or space scales smaller than those resolved by the model).

The mathematical basis of short-term air-quality models is the so-called continuity or conservation equation — a balance sheet of the pollutant in a box in space, with terms representing transport in and out by the mean wind, transport in and out by turbulent diffusion, emissions on the surfaces of and within the box (i.e., the "source inventory"), and chemical or radioactive transformation within and deposition out of the box.

Specification of the mean wind, the coefficients of diffusion terms, and the nature of the transformation, deposition, and decay is the task of the atmospheric scientist. Efficient organization of the calculations calls for mathematical and computational skills. Solution of the continuity equation is essential for a rigorous computation of the concentration of pollutants produced by chemical reaction, such as the oxidants in photochemical smog, but no such model of an extensive area has yet been produced because of the computational complexity of solving a set of simultaneous continuity equations. The short-term models that have been successfully applied have been based on formulae that are formal solutions of a continuity equation with diffusion terms. Such solutions are typified by the "Gaussian plume" distribution of material continuity emitted by a point source. This has the form

$$X(x,y,z,H) = \frac{Q}{2\pi\sigma_y\sigma_z\bar{u}}$$

$$\exp\left[-\frac{1}{2}\left(\frac{y}{\sigma_y}\right)^2\right]$$

$$\left\{\exp\left[-\frac{1}{2}\left(\frac{z-H}{\sigma_z}\right)^2\right] + \right.$$

$$\left.\exp\left[-\frac{1}{2}\left(\frac{z+H}{\sigma_z}\right)^2\right]\right\}$$

where X is the concentration of pollutant at a height z, distant x in a direction along the mean wind and y in a direction across the mean wind from a source at height H emitting material at a uniform rate Q into a mean wind of strength $\bar{u}$. The factors σ_y and σ_z, which measure the diffusive dispersion of the material in the horizontal and vertical directions, depend both on the meteorological conditions and on the distance from the source. They have been determined empirically many times and standard tables exist.

Various integrations of this formula adapt it for use with line sources and sources distributed uniformly over an area. Current air-quality models apply these formulae to all the sources that contribute to the concentration within the chosen "target area" at the chosen time. They differ in the methods by which they insure that only the essential minimum of computation is carried out.

Performance of Air Quality Models

The Gaussian-plume formula has been tested in many field trials in carefully observed weather conditions with controlled sources of a conserved pollutant. Using the standard methods of estimating the diffusion parameters of σ_y and σ_z, it is found that the formulae yield concentrations that are within a factor of 2 of the observed concentrations in about 75 percent of trials.

An elaborate short-term air-quality model has been constructed for the state of Connecticut, with the sources of four pollutants specified for areas 5,000 feet square and two-hour time resolution for four seasons of the year. There are approximately 5,000 separate sources and the program allows computation of two-hour average concentrations of each pollutant over any or all of the squares. In specially conducted trials over 25 days with measurements at 30 points, it was found that 45 percent of the computed two-hour average concentrations of SO_2 were within a factor of 2 of the measurement at a point within the 5,000-foot-square box. Measurement of the average concentration over a 5,000-foot square is not practicable, but statistical examination of the space variability of concentration suggested that the output of the model would be within a factor of 2 of the true area average concentration on 70 percent of occasions. The corresponding figure for a 24-hour average was 90 percent. These figures indicate the

possibilities of the most elaborate of existing short-term air-quality models.

Existing long-term models also use a Gaussian formula with a vertical diffusion term analogous to σ_z. The horizontal diffusion term is replaced by statistics of wind speed and direction at each source. There have been no systematic verifications of the performance of long-term models applied to multiple sources, but in the original application to a single source about 75 percent of the computed seasonal averages were within a factor of 2 of the corresponding observation.

In the application of both short- and long-term models based on the Gaussian formula, two further elaborations are incorporated. The first is an allowance for decay, transformation, or deposition of the pollutant, made by multiplying computed concentrations by an exponential decay factor, characterized by a "half-life." The second adjustment is for the importation of pollutant from the area surrounding the modeled area, for which a detailed source inventory is not available. The long-term models include a uniform "background" term; the short-term models must include a flux of pollutant across the boundary. For example, in the Connecticut model the New York City–New Jersey source, which at times can dominate the air quality over much of the state, is represented by a uniform line-source about 30 miles long — a submodel which quite accurately simulates observed air quality at the state boundary.

Deficiencies of Current Models

Experience with the models shows that, surprisingly, a major source of difficulty is specification of the mean wind field in the short-term models and of wind statistics in the long-term models. Physically, the difficulty arises from the large local variability of measured surface wind, caused by

small-scale topography and phenomena such as sea and lake breezes. Mathematically, the difficulty is to insure that mass continuity is observed when adapting three-dimensional phenomena to a two-dimensional frame. In operating the Connecticut model, best results were obtained by assuming a simple algebraic form for the horizontal streamlines (by inspection of meteorological charts) and modifying them to conform to the large-scale (i.e., large compared with the grid size) topography of the state. Specification of the diffusion terms, particularly the horizontal diffusion, was found to be less critical than specification of the mean wind.

The decay term has a considerable effect on the output and in the present state of knowledge it can only be specified empirically. For example, in the Connecticut model, it was found that the best fit to observation is obtained if a half-life of one to three hours is imposed on emitted sulfur dioxide. The chemistry of sulfur dioxide in the atmosphere is little understood. There is no theoretical support for the adopted value of the half-life. So far as the source inventory is concerned, the indications were that deficiencies were not fundamental in nature but were due to omissions in compilation and a natural reluctance of those emitting pollutants to disclose the magnitude of their contribution.

The major theoretical deficiency is the inability of any model based on Gaussian-type formulae to handle the problem of chemically reacting pollutants and the production *in situ* of secondary pollutants — circumstances typical of the production of Los Angeles-type photochemical smog. This type of pollution is not likely to be successfully modeled until concise computational techniques which can handle several simultaneous continuity equations have been developed. This, and improved knowledge of the chemistry of urban atmospheres, is the main requisite for further advance.

Problems in the Ecology of Smog

In spite of increased concern about the influence of air pollution on man and his environment, the development of firm cause-and-effect relationships has proceeded slowly. Certain conspicuous effects, such as reduction of visibility by pollution particles and irritation to eyes and respiratory-system membranes by the products of photochemical smog have been well documented. Other possible consequences, such as chronic illness and mortality in humans and modification of the temperature and precipitation in urban areas, are less well established, although in some instances the evidence is convincing.

Gaps in Scientific Understanding

Reasonably up-to-date reviews of the effects of smog are available. Reviews of the effects of individual components, such as particulates and oxides of sulfur, are being issued in a series of air-quality criteria by the Environmental Protection Agency (EPA). In neither instance is attention focused on the deficiencies of existing information with a view to defining what studies are required to bring the state of knowledge up to the level required for intelligent planning. Rather, the EPA publications attempt to arrive at estimates of effects from available studies. They conclude that

it is reasonable and prudent . . . when promulgating ambient air quality standards, [that] consideration should be given to requirements for margins of safety which take into account long-term effects on health, vegetation, and materials occurring below the above levels.

Such cautions are appropriate in present circumstances; but at the same time a program of systematic investigations should be promoted, to insure that the margins chosen are really adequate for safety.

Effects on the Natural Environment — The effects on human health, agricultural products, structures, and other materials have received more attention than the effects of smog on the general natural environment and the weather. It has been shown recently that the pine forests of the San Gabriel and San Bernardino mountains are dying because of pollutants from the Los Angeles basin. Vegetation in the neighborhood of all large population centers has probably been similarly affected to some degree. Pollutants may also contribute to the occurrence of higher temperatures in cities than their surroundings, and pollution from cities and industrial complexes may produce anomalous precipitation effects. Definitive investigations of these relationships are necessary.

It is also desirable that more studies be made of the effects of particulate pollutants and trace gases on the weather and climate, both locally with respect to places with high concentrations and globally with respect to the trend in background concentrations.

Elements of Smog — On a global scale, it has been demonstrated clearly that carbon dioxide (CO_2) is accumulating in the atmosphere as a result of combustion of fossil fuels, and the amount of temperature rise to be expected due to modification of the radiation balance has been estimated by theoretical computations. There has been some evidence adduced, less conclusive but nevertheless quite plausible, that concentrations of particulates from pollution are likewise increasing on a worldwide basis. It has been suggested that the increase of particulate pollution tends to produce a cooling which offsets or outweighs the warming effect of CO_2.

Information is lacking on whether or not concentrations of other gaseous contaminants, such as carbon monoxide, sulfur dioxide, and oxides of nitrogen, are similarly rising throughout the world. They probably are, since the removal processes for some contaminants, such as carbon monoxide, are much slower and less efficient than those for CO_2. A general worldwide upward trend in these toxic substances would be of urgent concern. A rise in these background values means that the additional pollution emitted in urban and industrial areas would produce even higher local concentrations. Ultimately, such increases would lead to levels that exceed thresholds for deleterious effects even at large distances from such areas.

It is thus important to establish a network of monitoring stations to measure particulate and gaseous contaminants at representative locations throughout the world, both in and near pollution sources, where almost all present measurements are made, and in remote locations where the background values will be obtained. Furthermore, it is important to measure many contaminants, not just particulates and sulfur dioxide, as is the case at most present-day monitoring stations.

Thermal and Water-Vapor Pollution — A further consideration is thermal pollution and water-vapor pollution. The effects of introducing large amounts of heat into the atmosphere at industrial plants, particularly electric generating plants and in urban areas, are poorly understood. When cooling towers are used, and also in the combustion of hydrocarbons, larger amounts of water are introduced than would evaporate or transpire naturally. This addition of water vapor may have noticeable influence on the radiation balance (temperature effects) and on the occurrence of fog, cloud, and precipitation. Definitive studies of these effects are needed.

Alternative Courses of Action

All of the above considerations are aspects of the general impact of technology on the environment. The concept that technological development constitutes "progress" must be modified so that all effects of the development are weighed, not just the profits to industry and the immediate benefit to the consumer. All the social costs, including the far-reaching consequences to the health of the community, the aesthetic properties of the environment (e.g., visibility), and the soiling of clothes and buildings, among others, must be figured in the benefit/cost ratios that are used to evaluate the desirability of a technological change.

The problems of conservation of natural resources and of waste disposal enter in an interacting fashion. Nonretrievable consumption of resources must be replaced as much as possible by recycling, in which wastes are retrieved and re-used rather than thrown away in the air, water, or soil where they constitute a pollution problem. The whole production-consumption organization of society needs careful study, to develop processes that truly maximize social benefits and minimize harmful consequences. The corollary is that social, political, and economic organization of society will likewise require revision, for under the present pseudo-laissez-faire situation long-range effects will not be given priority over immediate profits in determining the course of action.

Much of the impact of man on the environment has arisen because, as a result of technological advances, the human population has increased exponentially. This increase cannot go on. Even with exploitation and eventual degradation of every part of the earth, a point must be reached when food, air, and water are inadequate to support one additional person at the lowest level of subsistence compatible with life. Figure X–5 illustrates some of relevant variables. We can hope that this stage will never be reached.

We should strive for a stabilization of the population at a level at which the quality of life, as sustained by the quality of the environment, is not merely tolerable but truly enjoyable.

It has been suggested that man will adapt to a polluted environment, just as organisms in general adapt to surrounding conditions by evolutionary processes. However, the changes produced by technology have been too rapid for evolutionary processes to cope with. Long before mutations produce humans whose blood rejects carbon monoxide — rather than having it combine to form carboxyhemoglobin, which limits the transport of oxygen by the blood — the accumulation of carbon monoxide and other toxic substances in the atmosphere may make man extinct.

One alternative is technological adaptation: development of appropriate gas masks, air-conditioned homes and vehicles, or even enclosures of entire cities in which the air is processed to remove toxic substances and protect man from the poisons he puts into the surroundings. But surely it is more sensible to use technology to avoid putting the contaminants into the atmosphere than to apply it to processing the air to remove them before we breathe it.

Figure X–5 — PROJECTION OF PHYSICAL, ECONOMIC, AND SOCIAL RELATIONSHIPS

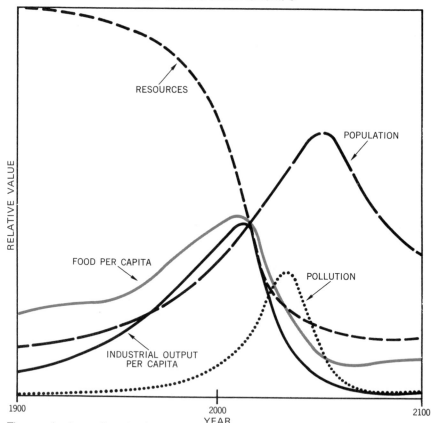

The graph shows five physical quantities plotted on different vertical scales, but combined in the same graph to emphasize their relationship. The variables and their units, projected to the year 2100, are: population (total number); industrial output per capita (dollar equivalent per person per year); food per capita (kilogram-grain equivalent per person per year); pollution (multiple of the 1970 level); nonrenewable resources (fraction of 1900 reserves remaining). Although the model is at best only a first approximation containing many assumptions and gaps of knowledge and data, it does suggest some of the factors that could combine to limit world growth.

2. AIRBORNE BIOLOGICAL MATERIALS

Atmospheric Dispersal of Biologically Significant Materials

An Aerobiology Program has been established within the International Biological Program (IBP). The United States Aerobiology Program under the IBP has been in operation about two years. It is the strongest national aerobiology program, with the Netherlands nearly as active. International collaboration is growing steadily.

The activities of the Aerobiology Program are generating new approaches to studies of biologically significant materials in the atmosphere, such as spores, pollen, fragments of algae and molds, minute insects, and toxic particles and gases. Until now studies of these materials in the atmosphere have been done in highly individualistic ways, with almost no comparison of work by different authors and no theoretical bases for guiding research and organizing the resulting information. There are a few notable exceptions, such as the well-conceived bodies of research in the 1930's and 1940's by Stakman and Harrar on cereal-rust epidemiology on the North American plains. But now there are new pressures to guard food crops against losses, to reduce human disease, to curtail additions to atmospheric turbidity, to clean air of noxious pollutants, and many other tasks involving atmospheric dispersal in ecological systems, all of which are objectives to which aerobiologists can contribute. (See Figure X–6)

The science of meteorology has become "systems ordered," from the research-planning to the data-handling phases, and is fast becoming coordinated on a worldwide scale with respect to observations. Now is a propitious time for aerobiologists to link up with meteorologists for the mutual benefit of their researches and

Figure X–6 — ATMOSPHERIC PARTICULATE MATTER IMPORTANT IN AEROBIOLOGY

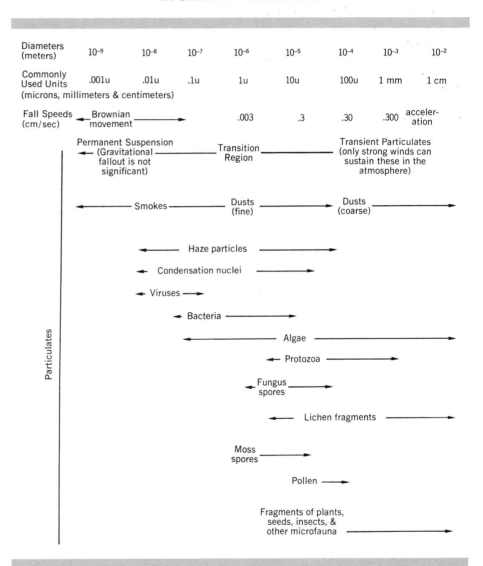

The table gives some physical properties of particulates encountered in aerobiology — diameter, expressed in meters and other commonly used units, and approximate terminal fall speed. From an aerobiological point of view, smokes, fine dusts, haze particles, condensation nuclei, viruses, bacteria, and algae are the atmospheric particulates of greatest concern. This is because gravity does not cause them to fall out of the atmosphere as do most of the heavier particulates in the lower-right-hand part of the table. Instead, they are deposited on surfaces by impaction or are washed out by precipitation.

for aerobiology to derive out of that association help in developing a theoretical framework based on ecological systems approaches.

A planet-wide network for monitoring ecological systems is clearly essential to the human welfare. We need both warning systems that will permit measures for reducing or avoiding injury to ecological systems, and prediction capabilities wherein the potential for injury is shunted aside or eliminated before risk of injury arises. These will inexorably require baseline data against which to measure change, which suggests that we should establish monitoring stations immediately.

One of the most feasible systems to begin with is one for monitoring materials in the atmosphere. Much of the technology for sampling gases and particles in the atmosphere is at a stage of acceptable reliability, and basic stations and networks already exist for observing and measuring fundamental physical parameters. Extensive and costly efforts are already applied to counteract the diseases of plants and animals by airborne agents, human allergies resulting from airborne materials, and insect pests carried on winds.

The necessary data base is less well ordered, however. There is an abundance of information about spores of common plant-disease fungi (smuts, rusts, and the like), and there is a considerable literature on atmospheric pollen sampled by allergists and palynologists. But only scattered studies of other particles of biological origin have been done, and the information on biological particles in general is in an almost completely unordered state. Some good survey data exist on radionuclide particle fallout, but only scattered data of widely different reliabilities concerning other inorganic particulates. Local observations on certain polluting gases have been faithfully recorded for ten years or more in some cities, but the information is mostly uncorrelated with observing stations in other cities or with

other phenomena. In short, virtually all of the data on dispersal of biologically significant materials in the atmosphere is unordered, and there is no data system prepared to receive, let alone store and retrieve it.

By contrast, meteorological data are well ordered and handled in the framework of systems analysis guided by adaptable theory. Furthermore, as consequences of the several International Geophysical Years and agencies such as the World Meteorological Organization, meteorology is organized on a worldwide basis. The aerobiologists can profitably take some cues from the meteorologists.

There follow comments on six major problem areas of aerobiology — the systems approach, plant and animal diseases, airborne allergens, urban and indoor environments, insects and other microfauna, and phytogeography and genecology of "aerial plankton." A concluding section treats the current efforts in aerobiology and prospects for the future of the science.

Systems Approach to Aerobiology

There is abundant information on movements of biological materials through the atmosphere. Nearly all attention to this topic has been *ad hoc* and empirical, however. The time has come when the aerobiologist, the meteorologist, and the applied biologist (e.g., agronomist, forester) or engineer (e.g., sanitation officer, industrial designer) should work together systematically on problems of predicting the time, place, and probability of deposition of given material from the atmosphere. The objective should be to develop functional models of the multiple-parameter problem of the entire process—particle formation, release, takeoff, aerial trajectory, scavenging or deposition, germination (if viable), and effect on biota or environment— so that prediction is based on all observable parameters, with standardized criteria for observations and measurements. (See Figure X–7)

Development of such models will provide schemes for ordering existing information and storing new information in a re-usable and retrievable form. If the models are to have continued and improving usefulness, they must also be suited to feedback corrections so that new information and new solutions improve the validity of the models.

Research Needs — This is a difficult set of theoretical and technical problems from the standpoint of both biology and meteorology. Continued and intensified study of the biology of spore formation and release, questions of survival of living material under different atmospheric conditions, problems of host specificity and conditions favoring epidemics, and similar matters are needed. From the meteorological standpoint there is need for development of joint probability meteorological statistics connected with the favorable conditions for spore release, quantitative transport, and the optimum infection "climate."

Recent advances in measurements of the planetary boundary layer and, in particular, the wind, temperature, and humidity profiles in the near surface layer promise to permit estimates of the critical parameters both from direct measurements and inferences from large-scale meteorology. Especially promising is the development of numerical prediction models from which three-dimensional trajectories of material can be calculated; the direction and speed of transport of the material can be forecast 72 to 96 hours in advance with steadily improving accuracy.

In the absence of current studies to evaluate the frequency of favorable conditions and the subsequent occurrences or non-occurrences of infections, the ability of a total biological-meteorological-agricultural warning system to provide usable and dependable predictions remains to be determined. Contributions toward solving these general problems are increasing.

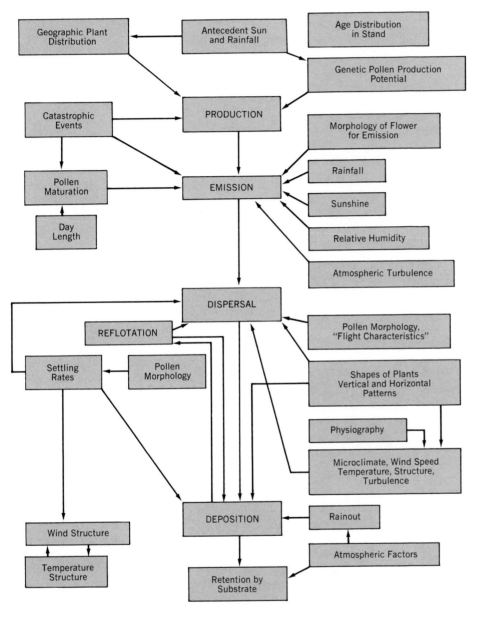

Figure X–7 — COMPONENTS OF A MODEL FOR POLLEN AEROBIOLOGY

Any scheme for modeling, and hence prediction, of pollen concentration must include the many factors shown in the diagram, in approximately that relationship. There are unanswered questions at many points in this conceptualized model, so that accurate predictions of pollen concentration at any point in space and time will not really be available with any degree of accuracy in the near future.

Aerobiology of Plant and Animal Diseases

Plant Diseases — The human food supply of the world depends on row crops, every one of which is subject to diseases or pest attacks that can and do prejudice entire crops over regions of considerable size. (See, for example, Figure X–8) For cereal-grain crops, the answer to rust and smut diseases has been to continue to breed resistant strains, each of which has a useful life of one or two decades, until the parasitic organism develops a form that overcomes the resistance of the host. Can this go on indefinitely, especially since populations of wild ancestors of these horticultural species are disappearing?

For some fungus diseases of crop plants, prevention is exercised by restricting culture to certain climates or special soils. In other instances chemical inhibitors of fungus growth are administered. Similar measures are used against insect pests and sucking insect vectors of virus diseases. The inocula for these diseases and pest attacks are in most instances carried passively by the atmosphere. But only in a few instances do we know in what quantities, in what directions, and with what survival as viable entities the inocula are transported and deposited. The "triangle of epidemiology" — origin, transport or vectoring, and infection—thus depends heavily on information about atmospheric transport. We could learn much about probabilities for transport of many kinds of organisms through full knowledge of the transport of a few that we can readily collect in transit, identify with certainty, and test reliably for viability.

It has been found appropriate for aerobiology, at least in the context of the IBP, to take under its wing certain studies of diseases that are not confined to atmospheric transport considerations. From an ecological viewpoint, diseases of crop plants are exaggerations of natural situations because of ecological imbalances introduced by agricultural practices such

341

Figure X–8 — AVERAGE ANNUAL LOSSES FROM CROP DISEASES
IN THE UNITED STATES

Commodity Group	Loss from potential production	
	% Reduction	Value (in '000 dollars)
Field crops	13%	$1,890,836
Forage crops and pasture ranges	11	808,701
Fruit and nut crops	16	223,505
Ornamental plants and shade trees	12	14,099
Forage seed crops	14	23,584
Vegetable crops	13	2,990,839
Total	13	3,251,114

The figures in this table represent potential production in the U.S. from 1951 to 1960, inclusive — i.e., the production that would have been realized had plant diseases not been present. Most of the losses are due to rusts, smuts, viruses, fungi, and molds that are viable biological material transported in the atmosphere by the wind.

as extensive acreages of monocultures, wide use of genotypically identical populations, unusual growth of foliage or fruit through use of chemical fertilizers and irrigation, and elimination of associated and competing species. Some aerobiologists see opportunities to study the cultural checks and balances of plant diseases at the centers of origin of the crop species, and also opportunities to learn about pathogenic germ-plasm variability, survival, and migration. Out of such studies of "origins and sources" of plant diseases the United States Aerobiology Program is endeavoring to derive new biological information that will constitute improved input for the epidemiological models described above.

Human and Animal Diseases — Although various human and animal diseases are spread by transmission of bacteria, spores, or viruses in the air, most of the atmospheric transport is probably over a short distance and within a water droplet or on some other particle. Studies of these particles have been confined to indoor air, especially of hospitals. However, a number of pulmonary mycotic diseases are acquired by the inhalation of spore-laden dust or other organic particles in the free air indoors or outdoors. Histoplasmosis, coccidioidomycosis, North American blastomycosis, cryptococcosis, and nocaridosis may result from exposure of humans or animals to such infectious materials. The fungi or fuguslike microorganisms causing these diseases are unique in that they are free-living in nature but also find the susceptible mammalian body a suitable growth environment. In a small percentage of cases, the infectious agent disseminates from the pulmonary tract involving a multiplicity of organs and tissues.

From knowledge accumulated to date it appears that some of these etiologic agents exist in certain foci in nature and are often associated with avian or chiropteran species. Some of these agents also exist in sharply demarcated geographical areas, such as a portion of a (Milan, Michigan) schoolyard which was a source of histoplasma infection. Infectious particles become airborne due to winds or mechanical disturbance of soil in which the fungi are present. Most of the work on control has been directed toward eradicating the infectious agent by chemical sterilization of its natural habitat. Some studies have been made on the ecology of these fungi, but much more work remains to be done.

Airborne Allergens

Allergenic pollen and spores in the atmosphere have been under study for nearly fifty years as clinical problems, with varying degrees of attention to botanical sources and phenology of the airborne particles. Greater uniformity in air sampling and reporting techniques, and better organization and availability of accumulated information on the distribution of allergenic particles, are clearly necessary for improved prediction of exposure. Improvements of these kinds are in progress nationally and internationally, fostered by appropriate organizations including the IBP Aerobiology Program.

Research Needs — Especially in connection with urban areas with high levels of gaseous pollutants in the atmosphere, there is need for investigation of possible interactions between biological (spores, pollen, fragments of fungus mycelium, and similar materials) and nonbiological (gases such as sulfur dioxide, hydrogen fluoride, and so on) emissions in transit. Furthermore, the extent to which these two groups of agents may induce synergistic effects on plants and animals is a subject that merits further attention. Regarding atopic allergy, there is strong suggestive evidence that augmented respiratory changes due to simple gaseous irritants may be expected in persons with preexisting inflammatory changes due to exposure to inhalant or ingestant allergens. The concept is growing that specific segments of the general population may be predisposed to experience adverse effects from air pollutants; it would be valuable to explore the possibility that aeroallergens may exert such a selective influence.

An additional aspect of aerobiological health effects that seems to warrant study relates to possible (nonspecific) irritant effects of biological particulates due to vasoactive materials carried by them. Cultures of certain hyphomycetes (molds that produce conidia on loose, cottony hyphae) do synthesize such agents, and it would be useful to know whether airborne spores could do so in the concentrations encountered in nature. Many "allergic" persons report "irritation," hoarseness, and mucous membrane burning following massive exposure to fragments of fungi (e.g., while raking leaves), suggesting the possible action of chemical irritants. Possible direct interactions of eluted materials with the human respiratory flora might also be questioned, since purulent bacterial infection often follows rapidly on such exposures.

Present Urgency — The recognition that precipitating antibody-mediated reactions to biological agents can produce systematic effects and granulomatous lung disease (i.e., farmer's lung, bagassosis, maple-bark disease) provides new incentives for exploring and characterizing the breadth of biological materials in free air. The dearth of even preliminary information regarding incidence and variety of bacteria in free air (apart from hospital wards and operating rooms) is distressing. Similarly, background knowledge and general techniques are at hand for making studies of algal, actinomycete, and protozoan bodies in the "aerial plankton," but scarcely a beginning has been made. Study of algal, insect, and acarid material in air will require development of methods for identifying these components either as individual particulates or as components of bulk samples.

Aerobiology of Urban and Indoor Environments

Assemblages of species and materials in the atmosphere of the urban environment are markedly different from rural and wild landscape assemblages.

Outdoor Environment — One component in urban air has been derived from the local region or from even wider areas, depending on the characteristics of the particles for remaining airborne. Atmospheric concentrations of rust and smut spores from agricultural lands come into urban areas in only slightly reduced numbers. In addition, the urban pollen spectrum is dominated by street and park trees (elm, oak, ash, pine, birch, mulberry) and weeds of alleys and vacant lots (grasses, lambs-quarters and pigweeds, and the ragweed group). There are greatly increased local concentrations of mold spores (conidiospores, conidia, etc.), fragments of algal colonies, and "organic trash" that tends to accumulate in nooks and crannies in masonry and asphalt where normal processes of humification and recycling are ineffective in disposing of it. Soil surfaces, even in the heart of a city, are probably helpful in taking some of these offensive dust components out of the air and converting them into an innocuous humus component of the soil. However, there are only limited soil surfaces in the hearts of cities.

Indoor Environments — Inside dwellings and industrial buildings there are entirely unique and extremely varied assemblages of airborne materials, as one would expect. Old wooden buildings accumulate wood-rotting fungi, molds, and insect and mite populations that make up "house dust," to which certain persons are very sensitive. It was recently reported that North American and European house-dust mites (*Dermatophagoides* spp.) were found in dusts used for commercial extracts in treatment of allergies. Masonry buildings, especially in damp climates, develop mold fungus and algal colonies that populate moving air with spores and fragments. In these structures, parts of dead spiders, mites, insects, and other organic matter become mixed with fungus mycelia to form various substrates for bacterial decay or, in larger masses, sites for insect, mite, or milliped colonies.

Very little specific attention has been given to the airborne plant and animal material of indoor environments. Questions arise with regard to saprophytic, or at least non-invasive, organisms, since reactions to these involving skin sensitizing and precipitating antibodies or delayed (cell-mediated) hypersensitivity may be involved etiologically in diseases presently of unknown origin. Evidence from sampling strongly suggests that domestic humidifiers pose a real hazard for fungus-sensitive patients; careful investigations of indoor allergens is warranted. Forced ventilation through ducts that are not periodically cleaned is a potential source of continuous dispersal of spores, mycelia, and dust. The longer the occupancy, the greater the accumulation of offending materials. Allergists in the United States and Europe are increasingly interested in these aspects of indoor environments. Recent reports of a small epidemic of severe lung disease due to thermophilic antinomycetes (probably *Micromonospora* sp.) contaminating a commercial air-conditioning system underscore the potential value of work in this area.

Atmospheric Dispersal of Insects and Other Microfauna

Transport of insects and other very small animals by wind is proving worthy of special study, not alone for the biogeographical implications but because of the inherent potentiality of pest epidemics and vectoring of diseases. In regions where alfalfa and mixed hay crops are grown, summer winds and disturbance by mowing usually launch great numbers of leaf hoppers, spittle bugs, and other small sucking insects into the air. Once airborne, these insects are carried as much as 100 miles downwind, where they settle down on new crops, in some instances transmitting plant viruses they brought with them. The U.S. Department of Agriculture has worked out many of the disease-transmission possibilities, but we do not yet have enough coordinated observations to be able to assess the significance of such insect transport.

In the tropics, vectors such as the tsetse fly generally show patterns of narrower endemism, and this should be studied against the possibility of human activity inadvertently creating favorable conditions for a dangerous vector in a new area. There is clearly need for assessment of existing knowledge in this area and an effort to determine efficient courses for further action.

"Aerial Plankton" in Relation to Genecology and Phytogeography

A neglected but obvious functional aspect of the aerial transport of pollen and spores, and of all other particles that are propagules, is that this process represents transfer of genetic material from one geographic area to another and, in the event of germination on the new site, injection of more or less different genetic material into a population. If we are to understand the ecological genetics, or "genecology," of populations, quantitative as well as qualitative aspects of atmospheric dispersal of viable propagules and pollen must be studied. Applications having considerable economic importance will follow closely in such activities as breeding of hybrid crop plants and forest trees.

In the course of observing aerial transport of viable propagules, we should be on the lookout for those that would have come from a distant source. This evidence would help to resolve many old arguments for or against long-distance transport as explanations of wide disjunctions of range.

Wind transport of humus and other organic material out of one eco-

system unit and into another has become a matter of concern to ecologists studying productivity in detail. They find this export and import of materials and energy attaining significance in the production budgets of climates that are dry and windy, at least for seasonal periods. Aerobiologists are currently trying to help the ecologists of the IBP Grassland Biome Project in Colorado to obtain reliable measurements of amounts of material in transit at given times and accumulating on different sites over specific time intervals.

Historical Studies—"Microfossil" pollen grains, spores, diatoms, and other small and identifiable organic particles in sediment have been used for over half a century to obtain stratigraphic correlations and paleoecological reconstructions. The most detailed and refined uses are made of late Quaternary microfossils because they are so nearly like the living forms of which we have first-hand knowledge. Several aerobiologists are endeavoring to identify strategically located sedimentation sites and airborne biological forms accumulating in them today in order that the older sediments might, in effect, extend the baseline for environmental monitoring back in time some hundreds or thousands of years. Opportunities may present themselves for linking in time the changes indicated by airborne particles with changes indicated by aquatic-system elements. Some inland lakes are known to have sediments that are annually banded, so that precise dates can be obtained for the record of the past. One such lake in Minnesota has nearly 10,000 annual bands in its sediments.

Prospects for Aerobiology

In his book *Microbiology of the Atmosphere*, Gregory stated:

Our knowledge of the terrestrial air-spora is fragmentary in the

extreme. The air has never been systematically explored simultaneously in different parts of the world by comparable methods. There is a heap of accumulated data.... Here and there are intriguing suggestions of phenomena; but many of the data are uninterpretable, and we need a fresh study of aerobiology as part of a vast terrestrial process.

The IBP Aerobiology Program is initiating just such efforts as a transient, first step. It has sponsored, jointly with the Environmental Protection Agency, a conference entitled "Aerobiology Objectives in Atmospheric Monitoring," at which meteorologists and aerobiologists drew up the first lists of priorities for information acquisition and assessed the practicalities of sampling and data processing. These people will look ahead to integrating these activities into the proposed GNEM (Global Network for Environmental Monitoring). The prospects are that support for worldwide environmental monitoring, in aerobiology at least, will be well repaid by the benefits realized.

The Secretary-General of the United Nations is calling for an international body that will supervise sentinel and warning stations for detrimental changes in environments and biota all over the earth, and the plans for the GNEM constitute the preliminary blueprint. ICSU (International Council of Scientific Unions) and its member organizations — IUBS (International Union of Biological Sciences), in particular — are readying a larger scheme, called the "Man and the Biosphere" program, designed to interpret the changing conditions for man and the organisms sharing the earth and supporting him, and to plan for improvement of conditions for human life in the future.

For at least the decade of the 1970's, organizations serving aerobiological needs must be kept adaptable and responsive to widely different opportunities. This argues for a small, volunteer steering group, representing diverse interests in aerobiology and dedicated to international cooperation. This steering group should have membership from government, academic institutions, and appropriate industrial organizations. A large, monolithic research organization does not seem appropriate, but provisions must be made for receiving, processing, storing, and issuing information, hopefully by a modest addition to some established data center.

Biological Monitoring Techniques for Measuring Aeroallergens

Diseases caused by inhalation of airborne biological particles have long been recognized as important public health problems. These diseases, commonly termed hay fever or pollinosis, are estimated to affect about 10 percent of the U.S. population (a much greater percentage than are known to be medically affected by all man-made air pollutants) and sometimes develop into more serious diseases such as bronchial asthma. In addition to causing considerable discomfort to affected individuals, these diseases cause a substantial economic loss in terms of time lost from work or school, lowered efficiency, and direct medical costs. These diseases are most frequently caused by pollens from anemophilous plants and by a few groups of fungus spores, but other known or potentially allergenic airborne biological particles include spores from ferns and mosses, algae, plant hairs, and insect scales. Aeroallergens vary greatly in size, shape, density, and other physical characteristics, but many are more or less spherical and most have dimensions between 1 and 100 microns.

Aeroallergens are commonly sampled from the atmosphere to determine their presence or absence, relative abundance, spatial distribution, and both seasonal and diurnal patterns of occurrence. Past studies have given considerable qualitative information for a few common particles such as ragweed pollen, but few data have been obtained for many known or potential aeroallergens. Until recent years, sampling devices capable of giving a quantitative measure of concentration for particles in this size class did not exist and even today are little used. However, accurate concentration measurements are necessary for such important studies as the following:

1. Determination of the spatial and temporal changes in distribution of each important aeroallergen and the relationships of such changes to meteorological and other factors.

2. Studies of the relationships between aeroallergen concentrations and the onset or severity of allergic symptoms in susceptible patients.

3. Evaluating the success of medical treatments.

4. Planning and evaluating the results of weed control or eradication programs.

5. Documenting changes in aeroallergen concentrations caused by changing land-use patterns and urbanization.

6. Determining the seasonal and diurnal emission patterns from sources of aeroallergens and relating these patterns to other variables.

7. Determining the efficiency of particle-removal mechanisms such as washout by precipitation and impaction by vegetation.

8. Determining possible synergistic effects between aeroallergens and other air pollutants.

Despite the obvious need for more study of aeroallergens, such research has been hindered by the difficulty of obtaining accurate and representative samples of these airborne particles and by the tedious methods that must be employed to identify and count the samples collected.

Evaluation of Current Scientific Knowledge

Nearly all research on aeroallergens and their relationship to man depends on sampling devices and techniques, but the accuracy of such sampling devices is critically dependent on the characteristics of the particles they are employed to sample.

Data Base — Information on the characteristics of aeroallergens is far from complete. Although the size and shape of airborne pollens are generally known, little useful information exists on their density. The size and density of some pollens are known to change with age or with changes in humidity, but few measurements are available. For example, it is not known whether the bladders on conifer pollens are inflated or deflated while airborne or whether this varies with conditions. Information on fungus spores is more sparse; no density determinations seem to have been made, and many spores sampled from the atmosphere cannot be identified as to source species. Even less information is available on other actual and potential aeroallergens.

The sources of airborne pollens are generally known as to geographic region and habitat (see Figure X–9),

Figure X–9 — DISTRIBUTION OF RAGWEED POLLEN IN THE UNITED STATES

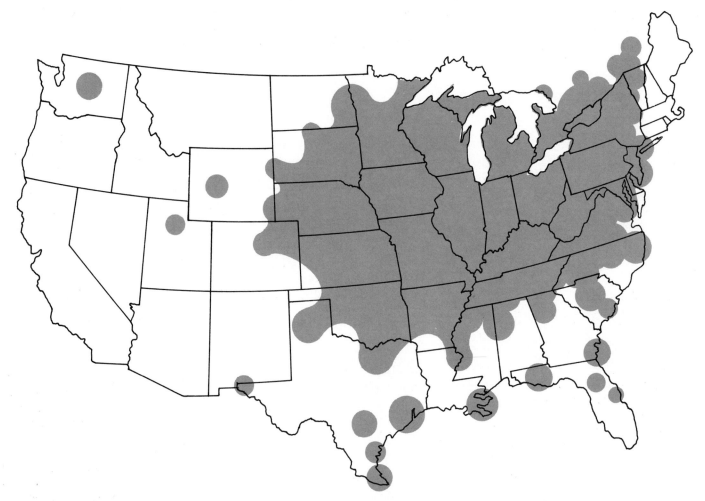

Ragweed pollen is responsible for more than 90 percent of all the pollinosis in the United States. Some 50 species of ragweed are known; they are found in all fifty of the United States, but the highest concentrations are in the North Central and Northeastern states. They grow alongside highways, in plowed fields, and in other disturbed areas. Since there is more and more disturbed soil each year, there is more and more ragweed, and, hence, there are more and more pollen and hay-fever sufferers.

but the location of local sources that affect specific receptors is often not known. Seasonal patterns of occurrence are fairly well documented for most important species, but diurnal patterns have been studied for only a few, and the relationships between these patterns and other variables are little known. Sources of fungus spores are less well known than sources of pollen, and diurnal and seasonal spore concentration patterns have seldom been studied.

Although the dispersion mechanism plus the source strength will determine the concentrations that are sampled at any given point of interest, quantitative studies of pollen transport and dispersion from known sources have been made by only two research groups in this country. These studies have indicated that pollens are dispersed much like inert particles of similar size, and that meteorological diffusion theory may be applied if particle characteristics,

source configuration, and output rate are known.

Concentrations of aeroallergens at sampling locations may vary by at least several orders of magnitude. Close to a local source, such as a field of ragweed, concentrations can average over 75,000 grains per cubic meter during a several-hour period. Short-period peak concentrations probably exceed this value by several times. At locations distant from sources, ragweed pollen concentrations seldom exceed 200 grains per cubic meter during the emission season. Other aeroallergens also vary greatly in concentration, and certain fungus spores are often present in great numbers. These variations in concentration lead to difficulties in choice of sampling methods and periods. An efficient sampler may overload in the presence of high concentrations, while an inefficient one may not take an adequate sample if concentrations are low.

The Limitations of Sampling Methods — Obtaining a sample of airborne particles in the aeroallergen size range may be accomplished by many samplers, but obtaining an accurate or representative sample over all size ranges commonly present is a difficult problem not solved by any sampler in current use. In fact, it can be stated categorically that no single sampling method so far devised is capable of obtaining a representative sample of all aeroallergens from the free atmosphere and that no perfect sampling method exists for any.

The principal cause of difficulty in sampling particles in this size class is the momentum that they acquire in moving air as a result of their mass and velocity. This inertia causes their path to deviate from that of the surrounding air if that air is forced to change speed or direction, as by a sampling device.

With the exception of isokinetic sampling, which has not yet been perfected for use in the free atmosphere, sampling methods in which air and, hopefully, its entrained particles are drawn into an entrance or orifice tend to be inefficient for large particles since these often fail to follow the airstream into the entrance. Since momentum increases with particle size, particle density, and air speed, it follows that such samplers are not only size-selective but vary in entrance efficiency with wind speed.

In general, methods of removing from the airstream those particles

that do get into the entrance are satisfactory. These methods include filtration, impaction, liquid impingement, and electrostatic attraction. Suction-type samplers are sometimes used for sampling aeroallergens, but cannot be recommended except for the smaller fungus spores.

The most common device for sampling aeroallergens is a microscope slide coated with adhesive and exposed horizontally, usually between rain shields. This "gravity-slide," or "Durham" sampler, collects by turbulent impingement and gravitational settling, but is generally unsatisfactory since the volume of air sampled cannot be defined and the catch is a function of wind speed, turbulence, and wind direction relative to the long axis of the slide as well as the concentration of particles and their characteristics. Although still in widespread use and of some value for qualitative purposes, it should be replaced by other samplers where quantitative measurements are desired.

To date, the most satisfactory devices for sampling aeroallergens are those which collect by impaction. Here, the momentum of the particle is used to effect its capture; efficiency increases as particle size, particle density, and wind speed increase. However, efficiency of wind impactors does vary with particle parameters, so that each particle of interest is likely to be sampled with a different efficiency and the efficiency for all will vary with wind speed. In general, samplers of this nature must be accompanied by a sensitive anemometer, and the catch corrected for sampling efficiency. An advantage of wind-impaction methods is that impaction efficiency can be computed mathematically for certain simple geometric shapes like cylinders and spheres if impactor dimensions, particle parameters, and wind speed are known. For a given collector and a single particle type, impaction efficiency can be calculated and graphed as a function of wind speed. (See Figure X–10) Total collection efficiency,

however, depends on both impaction and retention efficiency and adequate adhesive must be used on collecting surfaces to insure good retention of impacted particles. Wind-impaction samplers are usually cylindrical in shape and are commonly mounted on a wind vane so that the sample is taken only on one side. Such samplers have normally been used only in controlled research programs and are not recommended for general use.

The disadvantages of wind-impaction samplers were largely overcome and their advantages retained by the development of powered impaction devices such as the rotorod, rotobar, and rotoslide samplers. In these, the sampling surfaces are rotated through the air at a high rate of speed, giving virtually constant impaction efficiency for any given particle type. Although efficiency may still vary with particle size and density, it is generally much higher than for wind-impaction samplers. Adequate retention requires a thicker or better adhesive, since particles impacting at a high rate of speed tend to bounce off. Since the efficiency of these devices is high and their sampling surfaces small, overloading becomes a problem during prolonged sampling periods at commonly encountered concentrations. This problem is overcome by sequential or intermittent sampling, but the sampling surfaces must be protected from wind impaction when not rotating. Several methods have been devised for this purpose. Rotating impaction samplers are the most satisfactory sampling devices now available for most aeroallergens and are being used by an increasing number of allergists, public health agencies, universities, and research groups.

Aeroallergens collected on sampling surfaces are commonly identified and counted using an optical microscope. Routine counting of a single particle type such as ragweed pollen may be readily accomplished by unskilled workers, but critical identification of many pollens and

Figure X–10 — EFFICIENCY OF CYLINDRICAL COLLECTORS
FOR RAGWEED POLLEN

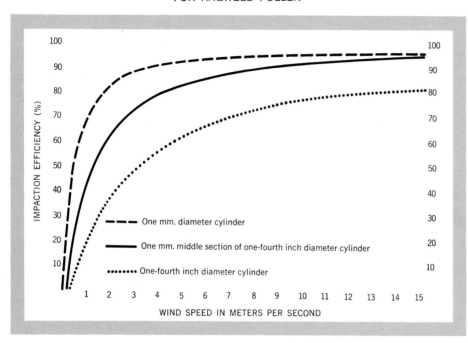

The graph shows a plot of impaction efficiency in percent *versus* wind speed in meters per second for three different-sized cylinders. The smaller the diameter of the collecting cylinder, the higher the impaction efficiency because the stagnation region in front of the cylinder is physically smaller and the particles need less inertia to penetrate it. To overcome the variability in wind speed and wind direction in nature and to operate the samplers at optimum impaction efficiency, samplers are rotated to simulate wind speeds of 10 meters or more per second.

spores requires highly trained experts. At times, concentrations, not only of the species of interest but also of other materials, may be so high that counting becomes difficult and time-consuming. This problem is multiplied when samples are counted for many or all species present. Visual counting is a tedious chore at best, but automatic counting devices have not yet proved their ability to differentiate and count aeroallergens.

Representativeness — Aeroallergens are commonly sampled at a single point over some pre-selected time period, often twenty-four hours. The spatial representativeness of single-station sampling has been little investigated, but it is known that proximity to sources, elevation above the ground, and presence of obstacles to airflow can produce wide differ-

ences in catch over short distances. Even two identical samplers operated side by side may often differ by 10 to 20 percent and sometimes by 50 percent. If concentrations are measured over some time period, they may not represent concentrations over either a longer or a shorter time period. Thus, even a perfect sampler could only measure the mean concentration over some time period at a specific location; extension of the measurement to other locations or periods would be accompanied by some uncertainty.

Requirements for Scientific Study

Sampling of aeroallergens, study of their behavior in the atmosphere, correlation of their presence and abundance with other pertinent variables, and application of the knowl-

edge gained to the pollinosis problem would be greatly facilitated by the development and use of better sampling devices. An ideal sampler would sample the atmosphere nonselectively, capturing particles of all sizes and shapes with equal and known, although not necessarily perfect, efficiency. The samples should also be collected in such condition that identification, counting, and analysis would not be more difficult than with present samplers. Obviously, such a sampler would have wide application in sampling air pollutants of all types. Attempts to develop two samplers having these characteristics are in progress at Brookhaven National Laboratory but neither is yet operational. Further research and development on sampling methods are needed.

Until improved samplers are developed, rotating impactor samplers will remain the most quantitative method of sampling aeroallergens. Only one of these, the rotoslide, has been tested under controlled conditions for collecting efficiency for ragweed pollen. Efficiency determinations for the rotoslide and the other rotating impactor samplers should be made for a wide range of pollen and spore types and sizes. More research is also needed to determine the best available adhesive for these samplers and to develop better methods of application.

Since the efficiency of impaction samplers is a function of particle characteristics, these should be determined for at least the more common aeroallergens. Most needed are measurements of pollen and spore density, but changes in size, density, and the state of conifer pollen bladders with age and humidity also need investigation.

Studies are also needed to assess the temporal and spatial representativeness of single-station samples as a function of surroundings (terrain, vegetation, and man-made structures), distance from sources, meteorological variables, and particle type. Such studies would permit estimation of the probable range of error caused by considering a sample representative of a wider region or a different time period. Peak-to-mean concentration ratios should be studied so that short-period concentrations can be estimated from longer-period means with some statistical reliability.

Finally, the efficiency of the human nose as an aeroallergen sampler should be investigated to aid in relating measurements of ambient concentration to allergic symptoms. Some allergists believe it is more important to determine what is being inhaled than to determine accurately what is in the air. A sampler simulating the human breathing and retention mechanisms should be worth developing.

Further studies involving aeroallergen sampling that might be expected to result in advances in knowledge and methods include:

1. Studies of the relationships between aeroallergen concentrations and pollinosis or other health effects.

2. Studies of the effect of weed-control programs on local concentrations of an aeroallergen. Such studies should include adequate before-and-after sampling with appropriate samplers. Weed-control programs would not seem useful unless preliminary measurements of both locally produced pollen and that transported into the area from outside sources indicate that reduction of locally produced pollen would cause a medically significant decrease in over-all concentrations.

3. Studies of the production, re-lease, transport, dispersion, and removal of aeroallergens from known sources.

4. Studies designed to evaluate the efficiency of natural particle-removal mechanisms such as washout by precipitation or impaction by vegetation (green-belts, shelterbelts, or forests).

5. Surveys of the incidence and concentration of aeroallergens as a function of time, meteorological conditions, and other pertinent variables.

Since individual allergists and their societies have shown a marked reluctance to adopt new and improved methods for sampling aeroallergens, public agencies should set an example by taking the lead in using and recommending the most appropriate of these devices.

3. PESTS AND PESTICIDES

Environmental Pollution and Pesticides

The history of man is a history of his modifying his environment to suit his own needs and desires for food, shelter, and the pleasures of his own leisure. Primitive man lived as an integral part of the living and nonliving environment, but as his proficiency to further his own ends has advanced, he has progressively taken on a more dominant, displacive role. Because of his success and his awesome technology for modifying the world in achieving that success, man now faces the dilemma that if he proceeds as he has been he will destroy or greatly lessen the earth's capacity to sustain life, himself included.

Shortcomings of Present Technology

Among his technologies, some of which embody greater attacks on the biosphere, man has developed an "advanced" technology of pest control. This technology can only buy *time* while we find a solution to the main problem of human population growth and establish a redirection of all our technologies along more compatible ecological lines.

Pest-control technology, through use of modern synthetic chemical pesticides, achieved a high degree of perfection in terms of control of insect pests for a time. It was, however, developed single-mindedly with no real regard for ecological consequences. It was based on the staggeringly false cliché that "the only good bug is a dead bug," and on the incomprehensible premise that each pest problem is a separate one — with no entangling feedback loops disturbing to crop-protection objectives. Thus, we have developed deadly, broad-spectrum, persistent pesticides and used them too indiscriminately

and in ignorance of, and disregard for, ecological consequences of vital concern, often creating pest situations worse than the original ones, to say nothing of ancillary problems of much importance.

Among the adverse consequences of a single-objective pesticide technology are:

1. Resistance has developed in many target species. (See Figure X–11) The more rapid the resurgence, the more rapidly is resistance developed; and re-

sistance to alternate materials then used often develops even faster.

2. Most materials are nonselective, directly affecting the natural enemies of the target pest, often more so than the pest. Rapid resurgence of the pest species then occurs.

3. Destruction of key natural enemies can be indirect, through too severe destruction of the target pest itself (the enemies starve out) and through de-

Figure X–11 — RESISTANCE OF INSECTS AND MITES TO PESTICIDES

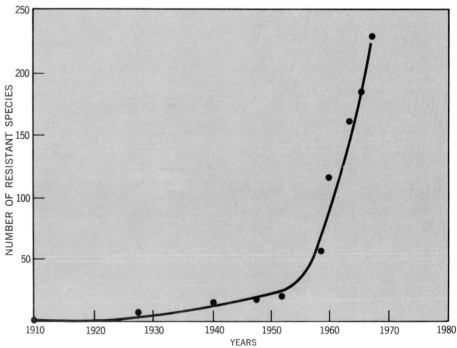

The graph shows that the number of resistant species has been increasing rapidly since the early 1950's and now stands at about 240. The changes in pest species that allow them to survive at higher and higher concentrations of insecticides are genetic and result from natural selection. Unfortunately, the graph tells the story only of known pests. Large numbers of insect species that have not been examined are subject to the same selection for resistance. When and if these insects erupt as agricultural pests, they will already possess a significant resistance to pesticides.

struction of some alternate prey species, perhaps of no economic importance. This can lead to resurgence.

4. Previously secondary pests or entirely innocuous species are commonly unleashed; this has usually been due to disturbing effects on their natural enemies.

5. Destruction of honey bees and other important pollinating insects.

6. Hazards to the applicators (many deaths and much sickness).

7. Hazard to crop culture on the same ground (overload of persistent pesticides in the soil, etc.).

8. Immediate hazards to man and wildlife that enter the treated areas.

9. Hazards to nontarget organisms in places well removed from the treated area. This includes significant influences on birds like pelicans, ospreys, and eagles that feed high on the food chains and especially on ones living around estuaries where DDT, for example, is concentrated; on important estuary anthropods; on grazing livestock and even man himself as a result of residues on crops or range or in fish, etc. DDT, for example, has moved widely in the biosphere — it is found in sea life at the antarctic. Drainage of pesticides into lakes and rivers has caused great kills of fish and much public alarm. The herbicide 2,4,5-T is apparently being withdrawn from the market for fear of adverse effects on man and livestock during pregnancy.

An Enlightened Technology— Integrated Control

An enlightened pest-control technology is one that maximizes benefit/cost relationships and minimizes environmental degradation. The philosophy and methodology of integrated control aims to this end.

The weather is a powerful mortality factor for many pest species, but we cannot manipulate the weather. Natural enemies of pest species are nature's own pest-control specialists, and their use causes neither outbreaks of innocuous species nor environmental degradation. Moreover, such species are quite manipulatable. Their great importance in general is suggested in the very fact that secondary and formerly innocuous species are unleashed and become serious pests when disturbing pesticides are used. Why are only 2 of the 100 phytophagous species on cotton in California found to be serious pests? Why is our natural vegetation so seldom grossly devoured by the myriad of phytophagous species that attack it? Many upsets have followed use of pesticides in these situations and adverse effects on natural enemies is considered the usual reason. Natural enemies should be explored in much greater depth in the enlightened new pest-control technology.

In spite of the repercussions from unwise use of pesticides, pesticides *nevertheless* remain a most useful tool for managing our insect pests in a manner compatible with this objective. Use of *selective* pesticides, *selectively* used, offers our best opportunity of making maximum use of natural enemies, combined with cultural methods, lures, and other schemes. The development of a new form of "biological" pesticide — i.e., hormones — offers new possibilities of selective pesticides. During the time we are learning to better use the residential natural enemies and finding new and better ones for introduction, or perhaps altogether new means of pest control, pesticides will be especially needed. (See Figure X–12) We do not now have adequate natural enemies for all the major pests on many crops (although this might prove to be more nearly attainable

Figure X–12 — PESTICIDE USAGE AND AGRICULTURAL YIELDS

Area or Nation	Pesticide Use		Yield	
	Grams per hectare	Rank	Kilograms per hectare	Rank
Japan	10,790	1	5,480	1
Europe	1,870	2	3,430	2
United States	1,490	3	2,600	3
Latin America	220	4	1,970	4
Oceania	198	5	1,570	5
India	149	6	820	7
Africa	127	7	1,210	6

The table shows the close parallel between rank order of pesticide usage in selected countries and areas and rank order of agricultural yield. Note, however, that Japan produces twice as much food per hectare as the United States, but uses *ten* times the amount of pesticides. Similarly, the U.S. has over twice the African yield per hectare, but uses eleven times as much pesticide. The question is whether such a high ecological cost for food production is unavoidable or the result of a particular agricultural system.

than many think) and we need selective use of pesticides to make the best use of the ones we have.

In developing modern pesticide programs, we need to consider the following:

1. Complete control of the pest is not essential or even desirable. Treatments can be reduced in number and dosage if realistic economic-injury levels are established; natural enemies are then left to dampen resurgence tendencies and the rise of secondary species, the resistance problem is not aggravated, and less toxic material is added to the environment.

2. The faunal elements in the environment are interrelated. The biologies and roles of seemingly insignificant species may be a clue to effective use of a natural enemy against a major pest. Thus, in winter, a tydeid mite is a significant alternate for an important predator of spider mites on grapes in the San Joaquin Valley in California; here, too, the non-economic leafhopper *Dikrella cruentata* found on wild blackberries is essential to the overwintering of the effective parasite of the grape leafhopper, *Erythroneura elegantula*, a key pest of this crop. Planting of small patches of blackberries near extensive vineyards can thus provide the ingredient for control of the pest species on grapes, and the cessation of treatments for this leafhopper can result in the natural solution of the spider-mite problem that the pesticides induce.

3. Using the pesticide at the dosage and manner having the optimal effect in providing immediate relief from damage but causing a minimal ecological disturbance may require a ma-

terial having some persistence. Short-lived alternatives to some persistent materials may be even more objectionable, and more repeated applications may be required, thus magnifying the problems.

4. If effective and practicable pesticides should be used in specific parts of the environment rather than as general coverage materials.

5. Each pesticide should be appraised separately and on the basis of specific use unless, as seems the case for DDT, the general severity of the pollutive accumulation in the environment justifies its demise (aside from public health use in heavily malarial areas, etc.).

6. Natural enemies, cultural measures, traps, and other feasible nonpollutive measures should take priority over use of pesticides, with the latter used to supplement them. Cultural measures may include growing of trap crops or ones harboring alternate hosts of enemies, destruction of pest-harboring refuges, use of planting dates, etc. Releases of sterile insects or use of genetic techniques should be tried when promising for a particularly difficult species, where its solution would open up avenues for better-integrated control of the pest complex. Releases of the pest itself, use of strategic repetitive releases of natural enemies, augmenting techniques, and introductions of *new* natural enemies should be especially explored in depth. It is a fallacy to think that, since crops are highly artificial (unnatural) and grown as simple monocultures, the laws governing the balance of nature and the role of natural enemies are insignificant here. Complex natural communities present a more stable picture than sim-

pler communities because of the greater diversity in trophic links. Yet many of the species of natural enemies accounting for the low numbers of a potentially disturbing (to the community) phytophagous insect are highly host-specific. Such links (host and host-specific enemy) are often transferred to crop situations. Sometimes the pest form has arrived without the natural enemy. Our best examples of biological control have resulted from our seeking out and introducing such natural enemies.

Integrated control, a systems-analysis approach, can be built on the basis given above. The computer is essential in systematizing information and testing hypotheses of how complex systems work so as to arrive at proper manipulating strategies, but it cannot substitute for grass-roots information. Much grass-roots input is needed before any major complex case (crop) can be put on a rational, predictable scheme of management. Key natural enemies commonly present a high degree of predictability for certain major pests (and others can be developed), thus making it possible to develop the system around such a central fact when established. Moreover, we must go on with the task of working out controls while we are gaining additional insights for a full systems-analysis approach. In-depth study of faunal relationships and crop phenology, economic-injury levels, and the like are *musts*.

For an integrated control scheme to be fully effective in achieving the goal described, a revolution in the system of pest-control advisement is essential, and this cannot be accomplished without massive training and re-training of a corps of pest-control ecologists (see below).

Moreover, the whole social, economic, and cultural situation relative to insects or insect parts in foods, as well as the "cosmetic" pests and others, needs changing. Unrealistic marketing standards, consumer attitudes, government regulations, and so forth perpetuate an unrealistic demand for *totally* unblemished, insect-free produce; this demand can greatly complicate an otherwise realistic solution which could provide high-quality produce and high yields at reasonable cost.

The Status of Our Knowledge

The final result of the approach described above should be an enlightened systems-analysis approach to decisions on strategy and tactics of pest control, with due allowances (based on value judgments that society will have to make) for the impact each measure might have, not only for the benefit/cost relationship (to the grower and the consumer), but for the quality of the environment (health, wildlife, aesthetic, etc.).

Research Needs — We need models for depicting the control of a complex of pests on a crop. The modeling of a single pest population in the field has progressed rather far in a few instances. There is, for example, a model of a laboratory population of a grain insect and its parasite over 23 generations, with remarkably good prediction for the whole 23 generations — not just generation by generation. However, this is a simple two-species system in a simple, constant environment. In the field, we need to gain similar insights into the whole environmental complex (biotic and abiotic), especially the natural-enemy performances relative to the climatic regime, the key pest species, and the possible influences of given pesticides on them (and on ones keeping the innocuous species under control). We also need better knowledge of the phenology of the crop and cropping practices relative to the pests. We have only the roughest information on the economic–injury levels for any pest. Of the few we have studied, the numbers of insects required to cause economic injury are much greater than previously considered. This is prerequisite to using pesticides wisely or in not using them and relying more on natural controls or cultural measures.

We need much greater emphasis on means of augmenting the value of natural enemies. Only a beginning has been made relative to use of strategic releases of both pest and enemy species, adding supplemental foods or alternate hosts for enemies in the environment (or nesting sites for avian predators of insects), or using special strains or genotypes of a natural enemy species. The introduction of new natural enemies is a vast, largely untapped resource. The hesitancy in doing so, based on theoretical considerations, is refuted by the record of over seventy years; moreover, new theory confirms past policy and speaks for much wider use of new introductions.

The main reason why more biological control has not been accomplished is that vastly too large a portion of available effort has gone into work on pesticides in the area of single-minded pesticide-use technology. A disproportionate amount has also gone into the development of new ideas (e.g., use of releases of sterile insects) that have succeeded only to a very limited degree and and do not offer prospects for wide-scale commercial solutions. A record of some 70 cases of complete biological control and 250 with at least partial success for the world is a formidable achievement in the light of the effort that has been made on biological control.

Economic and Political Considerations — The pesticides that have been developed are broad-spectrum ones, which is natural since the industry has been motivated by profit. Only token consideration has been given to other aspects (but more so relative to human health). What is needed are pesticides with selective activity — i.e., which act on a group of pest species, with little effect on key natural enemy groups. It is said to cost from several million to $15 million to develop a pesticide and market it. Many more pesticides would be required for the new technology, and sales of each would be limited. The market price would be high. The public must decide if it wants the less pollutive technology badly enough to pay the price in some form of subsidy to develop these materials. Actually, such materials could be nearly self-supporting, since the grower could afford a higher price for them if his total usage of pesticides is thereby greatly reduced.

Use of resistant hosts has been useful in many instances and will be again, but superimposing a pest-resistance requirement on top of the already staggering problems in developing high-yielding, good quality, marketable cultigens means that this solution is not likely to be a general one.

Training Advisers — Lastly, we need to change our whole system of pest-control advisement. In the past it has been based to a large extent on profit from sales. The ecologically untrained, or even the ecologically antagonistic, have often been used as salesmen. There has been great pressure on them to sell. They are the closest "advisers" to the growers, who in many cases have relied on them heavily. Excessive concentration on sales and too little attention to need and consequences has led to the current situation.

What is needed is a corps of well-trained professionals who sell their advice — i.e., advice *not* to treat as well as to treat — but not the pesticide itself. Thus, the system of advising should be separated from profit from sales. Since pesticides constitute a poisonous factor in our environment, reaching beyond the confines of the area treated, it seems necessary that society set up such a safeguard, as it has long since in the dispensing of drugs for medicinal purposes. Whole new programs of training pest-control professionals who will do this advising are needed in the universities.

A General Perspective — It will be necessary that adequate care is taken to assure that the necessary changes in philosophy and methodology are made at each institutional level. The old philosophy and methodology have been entrenched for 40 years, and nothing less than extreme action will alter the picture fast enough.

At the same time, it is wishful thinking to pin hopes on conceptually intriguing new, but generally unproved, ideas of pest control — e.g., use of sterile insect releases, inundative parasite releases, genetic techniques, hormones, special wavelengths, plastic exclusion airdomes, and the like. A planned systems-analysis integration of the long-established techniques of biological and cultural controls, and limited but strategic use of selective chemical controls, offers our best prospect of solutions on a broad scale.

Pesticides and the Pollution Problem

In a broad and complete view of pollution of the earth's biosphere, pesticides are a minor element. Nevertheless, for certain local environments or for certain endangered species, the pollution from *specific* pesticides has become a problem worthy of special attention. In our general concern about this pollution and in our response to other undesirable effects of certain pesticides, it is not rational to condemn all pesticides. Furthermore, it is ill-advised to attempt to ban all pesticides (even all persistent pesticides) in the misguided hope that this will protect birds and other wildlife from the effect of man's disruption and pollution of the environment. Even if all pesticide use were stopped, other activities of man would cause broad and sweeping disruptions of his ecosystems and threaten many forms of desirable life on this planet.

Uses and Limitations of Pesticides

Pesticides remain, in spite of adverse publicity, man's most powerful tool in the management and control of pests. We have no choice, if we insist on even minimal food, health, and comfort, but to control pests. The pesticides developed in the past 25 years are effective and economical and can be marshalled quickly to have immediate impact on a pest population — even over a large area. When pest populations approach economic levels, there is little other than pesticides that we can use to avoid damage and which will have the desired immediate effect. Hence, it seems clear that pesticides must and will continue to be used in a major way in pest management.

The disadvantages or limitations of pesticide chemicals are well known. They have been so emphasized in the press, on radio and TV, in political arenas, and elsewhere that it is now difficult to have a rational discussion that balances the beneficial and the undesirable aspects of pesticides. In brief review, the limitations of pesticide usage are as follows:

1. Selection of pest strains that are not controlled by usual pesticide dosages.

2. Temporary effects on pest populations necessitating repeated treatment (often the pest population quickly returns to a higher level than before treatment).

3. Hazards from residues of the pesticide in the harvested crop.

4. Outbreaks of secondary pests unleashed by destruction of their natural enemies.

5. Undesirable effects on nontarget organisms, including (a) parasites and predators; (b) fish, birds, and other wildlife; (c) honey bees and other necessary pollinators; (d) man and his domestic animals; and (e) the crop plant.

6. Direct hazards to man during the application of pesticides and subsequently in the treated area.

7. Reduction and simplification of the biotic component of the agro-ecosystem.

Factors Affecting Pesticide Use

This formidable list makes it necessary to re-evaluate carefully the appropriate use of pesticides. It also serves as a basic guide to the improved use of pesticides for pest management and control. If we can devise procedures for the use of pesticides which will avoid or minimize these disadvantages or complications, then we will have developed an improved, perhaps even an ideal, methodology for the efficient and effective use of pesticides.

Destruction of Natural Enemies — Ecologists concerned with the control of pest insects have for some time been alarmed at ecological disturbances in agro-ecosystems engendered by the unwise use of pesticides. These are caused by the unintended destruction of natural enemies, which in turn results in rapid resurgence of the target pest species or a secondary outbreak of an unleashed but formerly innocuous insect. For example, where a broad-spectrum pesticide is used (and natural enemies of the pest are also eliminated) or when high dosages of a selective material are used that kill off high percentages of the pest (and thus starve out the natural enemies by eliminating their food), the pest populations can recover quickly without hindrance of natural enemies.

This destruction of natural enemies, as an unfortunate side effect of pesticide usage, has two main consequences. First, the target pest may quickly recover from the impact of pesticide usage and resurge to even higher levels. (See Figure X–13) Second, the resurgence of unleashed secondary pests may occur shortly after the application of the triggering pesticide, or later in the growing season, or even in a subsequent season. In cotton in California, for example,

we have had serious outbreaks of such unleashed secondary pests as beet armyworm, cotton-leaf perforator, and cabbage looper. These secondary pests may be more destructive and more difficult to control than the original target pest. Re-establishing the effectiveness of natural enemies may require two or more years.

Health Hazards — It is obvious that we should not knowingly use pesticides in ways that would constitute a risk to human health. Such hazards can occur to the individual applying the pesticide, or to persons entering the treated area either during the application or at some appreciable time later, or to persons exposed to the residues of the pesticide on or in the harvested crops, or in other more subtle ways. When such a hazard is discovered, procedures should be taken to avoid the risk —

e.g., proper masks and clothing for applicators, minimum time period after treatment before the treated area can be entered, or minimum time after treatment before harvest. In those instances where the risk cannot be avoided, then use of that particular pesticide should be curtailed and a suitable alternative control measure sought. This is not to suggest that all uses of the pesticide be banned but rather that the particular hazardous uses be eliminated. Furthermore, when alternatives are considered, all aspects, both positive and negative, should be carefully weighed.

Limitations of Substitute Materials — In the past year or more, there has been considerable public pressure to eliminate all persistent pesticides. Let us not forget that, if this comes about, society is losing valuable tools for pest control and that there are other problems associated with many of the substitute materials. Basically, each compound should be considered individually as to its peculiar risks on the basis of its specific characteristics together with the exact manner of dosage and place of application.

To date, the substitutes have usually been either organophosphorus compounds or carbamates, though it is difficult to generalize because there are so many exceptions. The substitute materials used so far have shown, first, a frequent pattern of higher acute toxicity, with associated greater immediate risk to man, livestock, and wildlife. Secondly, these substitute compounds frequently have produced serious damage to honey bees and other necessary pollinators; their impact on the California beekeeping industry has been disastrous. Thirdly, they have had a severe impact on insect natural enemies. As noted above, elimination of natural enemies from treated areas frequently permits rapid resurgence of the target pests and outbreaks of previously innocuous species. Finally, the short-lived nature of the substitute materials together with their side effect

Figure X–13 — RESURGENCE OF CALIFORNIA RED SCALE

| Orchard No. | Locality | Population Density—California red scale | | | |
| | | Initial | | Final | |
		DDT-treated	Un-treated	DDT-treated	Un-treated
1	Irvine, Orange Co.	0	2	125	3
2	Sinaloa, Ventura Co.	35*	46*	572	17
3	Sespe, Ventura Co.	1	1	425	7
4	Biological Control Grove UCR, Riverside Co.	8	2	246	8
5	Birdsall, San Bernardino Co.	0	0	67	6
6	Beemer, San Diego Co.	4	5	158	3

*Initially heavy, due to previous upset by ants. Ants were controlled subsequently.

The table shows differences in the density of California red scale between trees left under normal biological control and some experimental citrus groves treated with DDT. The initial counts, comparable in both sets, were made just before DDT was applied; the low ratings (mostly 10 or less) indicate that the scale was scarce and under an excellent degree of natural control. After one or two seasons of treatment with DDT, however, red scale was far more common, whereas the scale on the untreated trees was evidently held in check by natural enemy activity. Ratings above 50 to 100 begin to cause visible, and economically unacceptable, twig and branch kill.

on natural enemies requires repetition of applications. This increases the selection pressure for resistance in some cases and hastens the development of populations resistant to the chemical.

Persistence of a pesticide chemical is not in itself an undesirable quality. Normally, we need some level of persistence for pest control. This is especially true when the pest population moves slowly into a susceptible stage of development or out of hibernation quarters or other inaccessible or untreatable habitats into the area of contact with the pesticide. If the movement into the area to be protected extends over an appreciable length of time, the pesticide must persist over this length of time or else repeated treatments with a non-persistent material will be necessary. In general, the latter procedure will be more costly and more hazardous. Persistence is a disadvantage when it is the cause of undesirable residues on the harvested crop or elsewhere in the agro-ecosystem, or when the pesticide is concentrated through food chains to harmful levels in non-target organisms. (See Figure X–14) Again we must strike a balance between costs of alternative procedures and between the benefits and undesirable effects of these procedures. This comparison should not be made only in narrow economic terms but also with full consideration of the social costs and benefits.

Guidelines for Good Pest Management

Today many decisions with respect to pest control are being made in a political context and with little consideration of the fundamental technological facts upon which sound pest-control decisions should be based. Each pesticide usage should be judged on the basis of the poten-

Figure X–14 — CONCENTRATION OF DDT IN A LAKE MICHIGAN FOOD CHAIN

	DDT in ppm
Water	0.000002
Bottom mud	0.014
Fairy shrimp	0.410
Coho salmon, lake trout	3–6
Herring gull	99

The table shows why minute quantities of DDT in lake water are a serious problem. The rate of accumulation is proportional to the concentration of DDT in the water multiplied by the time of exposure. By the time DDT reaches fish, its level of concentration can cause reproductive failure. These concentrations in the fish in turn become a hazard to the piscivorous birds at the top of the food chain. Retention time for DDT in water averages 30.8 years. No solution to the problem is yet evident.

tial positive values to be achieved by such usage as weighed against the possible negative values occurring from residues on the harvested crop, occupational hazards to humans, hazards to pollinating and other beneficial insects, effects on wildlife, the contribution to total environmental pollution, and other direct or subtle effects. Each use of a chemical must be judged independently. Banning all uses of a chemical is unwise unless it is clear that all uses of that chemical are harmful. Likewise, it is irresponsible to advocate the total replacement of pesticides with sophisticated but poorly tested alternative pest-control techniques. It is a disservice to society to discard the good crop-protection methodology

currently available and to adopt in its place a glamorous new but untested methodology. In the future development of crop protection for a world agriculture, it will be just as important to apply the methodology of traditional pest-control techniques as it will be to find revolutionary new approaches, some of which may be expected to have little or no practical value.

Research — In the interest of a better environment, the integrated control concept must be fostered among pest-control researchers, and research on pest-management systems should expand as rapidly as possible. There is a critical need for information on many aspects of integrated control, including pest economic thresholds, natural control, ecology, phenology, and the nature of agro-ecosystems. Such studies will provide information permitting better timing and placement of insecticidal treatments and will lead to the development of alternative control measures. Studies of this sort are currently being supported by federal and state agencies and some of the commodity groups, but the need exists for greatly expanded support.

Manpower Training — The more sophisticated controls and integrated control systems will create a demand for more highly qualified people in pest control. Consequently, there is an urgent need to develop, simultaneously, training programs for ecologically oriented pest-control advisers. Practicing economic entomologists versed in the principles of integrated control are extremely rare today and badly needed for an ecological approach to pest control. The training of a new corps of researchers and advisers well versed in integrated control will entail careful planning and the development of a new type of curriculum.

4. MARINE CONTAMINANTS

Effects on the Ocean of Atmospheric Circulation of Gases and Particulate Matter

The transport of materials from the continents to the marine environment takes place primarily through wind, river, or glacial systems. The activities of man have added two other paths: (a) introduction, both by intent and by accident, from ships and domestic and industrial sewage outfalls, and (b) introduction by man of materials to the atmosphere, with subsequent impact upon the oceans. The latter path will be emphasized here.

Aerial transport can result in the rapid and widespread dispersal of solids, liquids, and gases. For example, radioactive debris in the troposphere from the Chinese nuclear device tested in 1965 fell back to earth in a latitudinal band following its transport in the jet streams; these materials circled the world twice with an average velocity of 16 meters per second.

The ocean acts as a reservoir for the dissolved phases introduced to it and maintains them for periods of the order of centuries to thousands of millenia. Thus, the impacts of man upon the seas, if measurable today, will also be measurable many, many generations into the future.

There are probably three major responses by the environment to such impingements by man: alteration of its physical nature, alteration of climate, and alteration in the constitution of communities of organisms. Although some of the changes are quite difficult to detect today, nonetheless, on the basis of our knowledge of the types and amounts of materials being dispersed to the air, there is hope for some predictions.

Impact of Man-Made Materials

Managing the discharge of materials to the atmosphere will take on greater importance with time as both population and the material and energy utilizations per capita increase in the world. We have successfully managed, so far, the releases of radioactivity to the environment from nuclear reactors. On the other hand, we have had serious problems with the disposition of pesticides to our surroundings; clear-cut impacts on the communities of birds have been felt. The definition of critical problems in atmospheric release of solids and gases such that appropriate actions can be taken by policymaking bodies is clearly the end-point of the considerations presented here.

Metals — The identification of the materials from fuel combustion and from industrial production is incomplete, especially with regard to the latter category. Metals such as mercury and arsenic, which have volatile forms, are entering the atmosphere — and subsequently the oceans — as a result of mining and extractive metallurgical, industrial, and agricultural operations. High concentrations of atmospheric mercury accompany the smog in the San Francisco Bay region. High arsenic contents of Japanese rain waters have been attributed to the smelting of sulfide ores and fuel combustion. The flow of such substances through our surroundings is poorly defined. About 2.5 percent of the total production of gasoline is lost by evaporation during transfer processes, from production site to vehicles and to storage tanks and through vaporization from the automobile gas tank and carburetor. This amounts to several million tons per year throughout the world. Again, the subsequent activities of this gasoline in the air are as yet undetermined.

Chemicals — Volatile synthetic organic chemicals are dispersed about the atmosphere and their impacts are still described inadequately. The losses of dry-cleaning fluids and freon, though not necessarily the most important emissions, are nonetheless illustrative of the types of material flows that should be studied. The evaporation of dry-cleaning solvents must be of the same order of magnitude as their production — several hundred thousand tons per year. The most widely used substance is perchloroethylene.

A similar amount of dichloro-difluoro-methane (Freon-12) enters the air following its use as a propellant in the bombs containing shaving cream, deodorants, paints, and so on. Do such materials retain their identity before entering the oceans or are they degraded as atmospheric gases? The gas chromatograms of liquid air condensates from the atmosphere contain many unidentified peaks, perhaps volatile synthetic organic compounds. A systematic investigation of possible inputs, based on production figures and field observations, would be most rewarding.

Fuels — The greatest single source of man-introduced materials to the environment encompasses the products resulting from combustion of the fossil fuels—coal, oil, and natural gas. Since 1850, the amounts burned have doubled about every fifteen to twenty years. Carbon dioxide is the principal gas released in such processes; its rate of increase at the present time is 0.8 parts per million per year for an atmosphere containing about 320 parts per million. About 40 percent of the carbon dioxide so introduced still remains in the atmosphere.

The main sink for this added carbon dioxide has not yet been established, although it is most probably the deep ocean. There have been suggestions that land plants, through more extensive growth, have accommodated this additional carbon dioxide. Whether such introductions have increased plant productivity in the sea through the input of additional carbon dioxide to the surface waters and whether the earth's temperature has increased through the "greenhouse effect" created by this excess carbon dioxide are questions not yet resolved.

The search for the sinks of the products of fossil-fuel combustion has widened our knowledge of natural phenomena. For example, at one time it was thought that the fate of carbon monoxide, resulting from the incomplete combustion of fossil fuels, was either an atmospheric oxidation or an uptake by seawater. Surface seawaters have carbon monoxide concentrations ten to forty times higher than atmospheric equilibrium values and the marine environment turns out to be a source for carbon monoxide. Mid-tropospheric concentrations in the subtropics display no marked differences between the two hemispheres, indicating that the source of the carbon monoxide is natural and that the atmospheric lifetime of the gas is of the order of a year or longer. Higher values of carbon monoxide have been found in the air over open ocean waters as compared to the air over bay and river waters.

Preliminary calculations of the oceanic output give a value of the order of ten million tons per year, about five percent of the 200 million tons annually generated by the burnings of fossil fuel. The sources of the carbon monoxide in the oceans are probably biological — through the bacterial or photochemical oxidation of organic matters in surface waters or through the direct production by marine algae, "Portuguese Men of War," or siphonophores.

The disposition of the carbon monoxide in the atmosphere is not yet known. The principal sink will probably turn out to be stratospheric oxidation by OH, H_2O_2, or HO_2 radicals. Another possible fate of the carbon monoxide may be an oxidation to carbon dioxide by soil bacteria.

Insights into Natural Processes

The researches with carbon monoxide illustrate a common result of environmental studies — we learn about natural processes through investigations of pollutants. Such was the case with the radioactive species introduced through the detonation of nuclear devices both in the atmosphere and in the oceans; our knowledge of mixing processes within these two geospheres was decidedly enhanced. In addition, marine ecological research has been sponsored primarily by atomic-energy agencies that are concerned about the interactions of radioactive species produced by fusion and fission reactions with members of the biosphere.

Complementarily, guidance as to the fates of man-introduced materials to the atmosphere-ocean system can come from knowledge about the natural substances involved in the major sedimentary cycle.

Atmospheric Transport — Over the past decade, the transport of solids to the marine environment by atmospheric paths has become a most attractive area of research. More than a century ago, Darwin had suggested that major expanses of sediment on the open ocean sea floor are the result of an atmospheric transport from continental arid regions. Yet only recently have we been able to state with some confidence that most sedimentary solids in the North Pacific, North Atlantic, and Arabian Sea are derived from the continents by wind transport. Perhaps more important is the observation that the geographic distribution patterns of diagnostic minerals in the deposits moderately well define the bounds of the wind systems. For example, in the North Pacific the concentration gradients of the clay mineral illite and of quartz in the sediments closely parallel the gradients in the intensity of the jet stream averaged over a year. Similarly, off the west coast of Australia, the prevailing southeasterly winds are recorded in the sediments by high concentrations of the clay mineral kaolinite that they carried from the Tertiary laterite deposits on land.

Atmospheric Dust — Removal of solids from the atmosphere takes place through scavenging by precipitation, rain, snow, sleet, and rime and by gravitational settling, with the former process being the more important. Since the average time between rains in many parts of the world is counted in weeks, transport of suspended particles can take place over great distances. Dust collected on the island of Barbados originated in the European-African continents with a transport by the northeast trade winds. Such materials were also picked up further along their transport path in the glaciers of Mexico.

The industrial activities of civilization are recorded in such dusts. Many atmospheric solid samples collected in the Atlantic are gray to dark gray in color due to pollution by carbon and fly-ash spherules. Increases in the rate of dust accumulated in the Caucasus glaciers have been related to the mechanization and industrialization of eastern Europe. The dust accumulation rate clearly shows marked increases beginning in 1950, which parallels the growth in the Soviet economy. (See Figure X–15)

Possibly, a more pertinent case for the impact of man upon the marine

Figure X–15 — COMPARISON OF CAUCASIAN DUST FALL
AND THE SOVIET ECONOMY

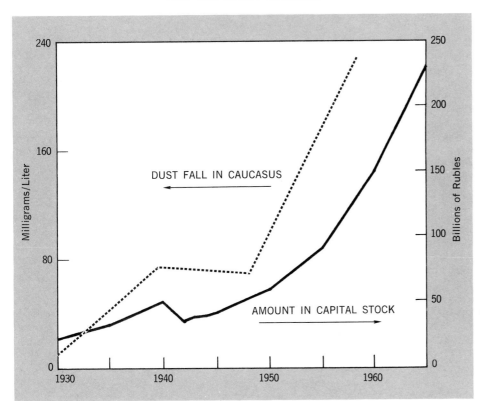

The diagram shows a close correspondence between (a) measurements of fallout of atmospheric dust in milligram per liter, as measured in glaciers of the Caucasus mountains, and (b) the amount of capital stock (equivalent inventories, building and livestock) in the Soviet economy expressed in billions of 1937 rubles.

environment may be seen in the finding of talc as a common constituent of atmospheric dusts. This mineral is rare in land soils, but appeared ubiquitous in solids collected from air masses, as well as in glacial snows deposited before 1946. This talc arises from its use as a carrier and diluent for pesticides in surface and aerial spraying of agricultural crops.

Direct measurements of chlorinated hydrocarbon pesticides and their residues have followed the discovery of talc in these domains. Comparisons of the contributions of river-borne and atmospherically transported pesticides to the marine environment have been made and both appear to be of the same order of magnitude. The atmospheric estimates based on

particle collection are clearly underestimates, inasmuch as some of the pesticides are carried to the marine environment in the vapor phase. Nonetheless, these mechanisms for conveying pesticides to areas of the oceans where river influxes appear to be slight do explain the increasing levels of chlorinated hydrocarbons appearing in birds and fish.

Interactions of Contaminants and the Atmosphere-Ocean System

The interactions of airborne contaminants with the marine biosphere are more speculated upon than established. The scientific literature is replete with tales of woe concerning the possible effects of pesticides on

the photosynthetic activities of marine algae and a consequential loss of oxygen from our atmosphere. Recent investigations do indicate that photosynthesis and growth of some species of marine phytoplankton can be adversely affected by exposure to chlorinated hydrocarbons; others show a complete insensitivity. But to extrapolate such findings to a possible elimination of all photosynthetic activity in the oceans appears unwarranted, inasmuch as the factors governing the gross production of organic matter in marine plants are still incompletely determined.

On the other hand, present-day experimental and monitoring data do suggest that there is a significant decrease in the productivity of estuarine fish and shellfish as a result of the ingestion of DDT and its residues, some of which is airborne from the continents. Further, it appears that the resistant surviving animals are able to concentrate and transmit toxic quantities of these residues in the food chain. The reproductive successes of seabirds has decreased due to interferences with their normal calcium metabolism by the high body burdens of these halogenated hydrocarbons. These birds, feeding on marine fish, are at the upper levels in the food chain. The marine fish are building up levels of these pesticides that equal, and sometimes exceed, those of their freshwater counterparts. The ocean waters act as a reservoir for these river- and wind-transported materials, while the rebirth of rivers every year often results in lower concentrations even though the rivers are closer to their points of origin.

These studies with DDT and its residues are providing a most important pattern to study the polycholorinated biphenyls (PCBs) — another industrial chemical group, most probably dispersed through the atmosphere, that is appearing in marine fish and birds. Manufactured since 1929, PCBs are used as plasticizers, transformer fillings, solvents for paint, and components of caulking materials. They probably behave similarly to the halogenated hydrocarbons in organisms, and there is great concern over their buildup in the marine environment. (See Figure X–16) Such materials will receive a good deal of attention in the coming years. But of greater importance will be the identification of other chemicals that are building up in organisms of the sea and that are capable of altering their life processes.

Deleterious effects due to the entry of man's artifacts to the atmosphere-ocean system have been documented in only a few cases, such as those of pesticide residues on the reproductive success of some marine birds. We can expect other catastrophic episodes in the future, however. To react rationally and effectively to such events and to minimize their recurrences, it will be important to have a past record of man's inputs to his environment, especially of substances that we do not now monitor for one reason or another.

Use of Glaciers in Atmospheric Monitoring

The idea of utilizing permanent snowfields (glaciers) to provide such information is not new. Yet researches on the glacial records of man's activities at the earth's surface have so far been small and limited, even though permanent snowfields exist below all of the major wind systems and maintain sequential records of atmospheric fallout for centuries and even for millenia. Work on lead concentrations in ice layers from northern Greenland and from the interior of Antarctica have shown increases beginning at 800 B.C. to the present, with the sharpest rise occurring after 1940.

These increases are ascribed mainly to lead smelteries before 1940 and to burned lead tetra-ethyl and lead tetra-methyl in internal combustion engines after 1940. In both cases, lead was introduced to the atmosphere and brought back to the surface of the earth primarily in precipitation.

The surface sea waters today show much higher lead concentrations than their deeper counterparts, an effect that diminishes as the open ocean is is approached. Predictions as to the future lead concentrations in the ocean can be made on the basis of extrapolated industrial activity and of models of the oceanic mixing processes. Very important is our knowledge of the wind transport of lead aerosols in the past through our reading of the glacial record.

The concept that the amounts of pesticides contributed to the tropical Atlantic by the trade winds are comparable to those carried to the sea by major river systems was triggered by analyses of both pesticides and their carrier talc in permanent snowfield records as well as in direct analyses of river and atmospheric samples.

Finally, the glaciers have recorded the inputs of sulfur dioxide to the atmosphere through the burning of fossil fuels. The excess sulfur in the atmosphere is now at least several times natural levels.

Examples such as these point out one most important direction to go for obtaining benchmark data to study man's relationship to the chemistry of the surface of the earth.

Figure X–16 — PCB RESIDUE IN FISH, BIRDS, AND MAMMALS

Type	Organ	Location	Concentration (ppm)
Herring	Fat	Baltic	0.5–23
Salmon	Eggs	Sweden	7.7–34
Pike	Muscle	Sweden	6.0–48
Eider duck	Liver	Holland	2.1–96
Heron	Liver	Britain	0–900
Heron	Fat	Stockholm	9,400
Dolphin	Fat	Sargasso	33
Seal	Fat	Baltic	16–44

The table shows the ranges of concentration in parts per million that have been measure in various organs of several species of fish (cf., Figure X–14 for DDT). PCB's are not destroyed by usual waste-disposal methods. They enter the aquatic environment through sewage effluents, land runoff from industrial wastes, and condensation following incineration. PCB's have properties similar to DDT, but they are more persistent and stable.

Oil on the Sea Floor

Recent observations concerning the fate of oil in the ocean after spills and leaks such as those in the Santa Barbara channel and from the S.S. *Torrey Canyon* off the English coast have led some investigators to conclude that dispersal methods that involve removing the oil from the surface by overpowering its natural buoyancy (thus transferring it to the sea bottom) are potentially more harmful to the environment than methods that leave the oil dispersed but floating on the ocean surface.

Since sinking methods involve the use of extremely cheap agents (sand, ashes, and the like) and since they generally remove the oil before it can contact beaches, yacht hulls, and other recreational surfaces, there are strong economic and aesthetic arguments in favor of their continued use.

On the other hand, if it could be shown that the transferral of toxic petroleum constituents to the sea floor would result in damage to demersal fisheries, there are strong arguments for establishing an effective international regime to control both drilling for and seaborne transportation of petroleum, wherever the possibility exists that it may be deposited in quantity upon the sea surface, and to fix responsibility, assess damages, and compensate those economically injured in case such an event occurs.

Status of Scientific Knowledge

Current scientific knowledge relevant to the problem of petroleum on the sea surface and sea floor is far from adequate with respect to reliable predictions of the possible harmful effects of removing petroleum or petroleum residues from the sea surface by sinking them to the sea floor.

Amounts of Hydrocarbons in Marine Sediments — We do know already, from extensive investigations of the chemical composition of ocean sediments in many parts of the world, that detectable quantities of paraffins, aromatics, and asphalts — chemically indistinguishable from petroleum fractions — are present in ocean sediments. (See Figure X–17) Ironically, these investigations have been carried out primarily to determine the sources of oil in sediments, not the fate of oil in the sea.

Emery summarized much of this work in 1960 in his book *The Sea Off Southern California*. He found the greatest rate of accumulation of hydrocarbons in marine sediments to be in certain stagnant basins, where they could amount to as much as 0.15 percent of the dry weight of sediment. Emery's calculations showed that about 880 tons of such material were deposited annually in the sediments over an area of 78,000 square kilometers, compared to an annual production of 135,000 tons of similar materials by the phytoplankton over the same area. Disregarded entirely in this computation is the possibility that any of the hydrocarbon material currently being deposited in the sediments is reworked from the numerous seeps in this region of the California coast.

Recent work by Horn, Teal, and Backus of Woods Hole Oceanographic Institution not only shows that floating lumps of petroleum residue are common on the sea surface but suggests two methods by which the constituents of such lumps can be transferred to the sea floor through natural processes as well as a natural method for disposing of the material at the sea surface.

Natural Sinking Processes — Goose-neck barnacles, which at certain seasons of the year attach themselves to any suitable firm substrate near the sea surface, were found adhering to floating lumps of petroleum. Since these creatures secrete a calcareous exoskeleton, they are significantly heavier than sea water;

Figure X–17 — PETROLEUM HYDROCARBON CONTAMINATION IN THE MARINE ENVIRONMENT

SEDIMENTS	
Location	ppm
West Falmouth, Mass., USA	up to 12,400 (dry wt.)
West Falmouth, Mass., USA	21–3,000 (wet wt.)
Narragansett Bay, Rhode Island, USA	50–3,560 (dry wt.)
Chedabucto Bay, Canada	0–6.8 (dry wt.)

The table shows some measurements of petroleum hydrocarbons found in sediments of coastal waters. Studies have shown that marine organisms are adversely affected by petroleum and that complex mixtures of petroleum hydrocarbons are present both in sediments and marine organisms. It is estimated that the input to U.S. coastal waters of petroleum hydrocarbon via sewage effluents ranges from 12,000 to 150,000 metric tons per year.

thus, as they grow they unquestionably transfer lumps of petroleum residue to the sea floor by adding weight. It is in all probability this effect and not slight toxicity that accounts for the observation that the largest barnacles attached to oil lumps were 8 millimeters long, whereas barnacles attached to pumice reached 11 millimeters.

The existence of floating pumice itself suggests another possibility in the transfer of floating oil to the sea bottom. Floating pieces of pumice on the sea surface are observed to decrease continually in size as the result of abrasion through wave action. The abraded particles in turn conceivably can be accumulated by (or accumulate) petroleum particles to the extent that the mixture is heavier than sea water and hence sinks to the bottom.

Surface Removal Through Bacterial Action — The mechanism for removal at the surface is bacterial oxidation. Horn and his colleagues found oxygen consumption of a floating oil lump at $10°$ centigrade to be about the equivalent of oxidation of 7×10^{-6} $g/hr^{-1}/cm^{-2}$ of petroleum. Since a sphere has a surface:volume relationship of $3/r$, this observation tells us that floating oil with a density of 1.0, if divided into spherical particles of radius 21×10^{-6} cm, will be completely consumed in one hour at $10°$ centigrade. One can reasonably expect this value to increase to 42×10^{-6} cm at about $18°$ and to double again at about $26°$ centigrade. By the same arithmetic, a film of oil 7×10^{-6} centimeters thick will be consumed in an hour if the bacteria thrive only on one surface at $10°$ centigrade, but in half this time if they can attack both surfaces at once.

It may be more illuminating to consider these rates in terms of years (8,765 hours). At $10°$ centigrade, a layer of oil attacked on only one surface will be consumed at the rate of 0.6 millimeters per year. This figure may be compared with Emery's 880 tons per 78,000 square kilometers in

a year, which is about 1.1 to 10^{-5} millimeters per year, or his 135,000 tons per year of petroleum-like substances produced by phytoplankton, which is 1.7 to 10^{-3} millimeters.

These rate computations allow us to draw several conclusions. One is that the practice of adding emulsifiers to floating oil to facilitate its dispersal into small units will also facilitate its natural oxidation as long as the emulsifiers are not bactericidal. Another is that keeping the oil at the sea surface, where ambient temperatures are highest, will minimize the time required for its natural oxidation. And another is that oil will be more persistent in polar latitudes than in temperate or tropical latitudes. Still another is that both "natural" accumulations of petroleum components in marine sediments and production of similar compounds by phytoplankton take place at rates much below the "natural" ability of the systems at the sea surface to oxidize floating oil residues.

Inasmuch as bacteria form an important food source for the ciliary and mucus feeders in the marine plankton, then, and since observation shows that bacterial growth is enhanced in the presence of the combination of solid surface and source of fixed carbon offered by floating oil lumps, it seems inconsistent to refer to their presence as "chronic pollution."

Additional Sinking Agents — In shallow coastal water, supposing that oil is delivered to the sea surface at a rate greater than that at which it can be naturally oxidized, it seems likely that airborne dust and other solid residues will act as additional agents in increasing the density of floating oil and causing it to sink to the bottom. A layer of tarry residue will then exist on the bottom in such localities, its thickness increasing with time at a rate equal to the rate of delivery of oil minus the rate of oxidation *in situ*. Such layers can indeed be observed on the bottoms of industrial harbors.

Needed Scientific Activity

Although present knowledge tells us that, at least in some cases, no harmful effects can be attributed to the presence of petroleum on the sea — the sea off southern California, for all its dozens of oil seeps, is one of the more productive fishery areas in the world — it would be a mistake to assume that we already have all the information required to settle the question of whether oil on the sea floor is preferable to oil at the sea surface. For one thing, crude petroleum varies widely in its chemical makeup. We need, therefore, to examine the relative toxicity of crudes from a variety of sources to marine plants and animals, pelagic and benthic. We need also to examine the rate of bacterial oxidation of various crudes and to establish the effect of temperature on these rates.

We need also to study bottom conditions in the vicinity of oil terminals and tidewater oil refineries as compared with control areas lacking such industrial activity to determine the extent to which areas of the ocean floor have already undergone the type of modification that has been observed in New York's East River — where there is a thick layer of "blacktop" in the vicinity of the Brooklyn Navy Yard — and the influence that incorporation of petroleum residues into bottom sediments has had on the benthic biota. And we need to map the various areas of the continental shelves and slopes of the world, down to the depth below which bottom conditions are without influence on fisheries, and to evaluate their productivity in terms of current fishing operations.

At depths greater than about 750 meters, the sinking method of oil dispersal can presumably be used without fear of harmful effects. Over lesser depths, where important demersal fisheries exist, only laboratory studies of the effect of sunken oil on the biota can provide pollution-control authorities with the information that will enable them to evaluate whether removal of floating oil through causing it to sink to the bottom is economically preferable to attempting to collect it on the surface, to speed its natural removal by spreading emulsifying agents, or letting it drift ashore.

The observation of Horn, Teal, and Backus that barnacles thrive attached to floating petroleum lumps and that a pelagic isopod preferentially associates itself with the same items suggests that the components of such lumps are not toxic to these groups of crustacea. It is generally supposed that the lower-molecular-weight constituents of petroleum are more toxic than those of higher molecular weight. It is also true that the vapor pressure and solubility in water of these constituents both decrease markedly with increasing molecular weight. It seems likely, therefore, that natural processes in the ocean may act rather rapidly in the case of floating petroleum residues to leave only the more inert, heavier fractions at the sea surface, the lighter fractions having been either volatilized to the atmosphere or dissolved in the mixed layer of the ocean above the thermocline. Some direct observations of the change in composition with time of floating oil spill seem highly desirable in this regard.

Horn and his colleagues further suggest that toxic petroleum components find their way into the food chain through fish like the saury, which appear to be voracious feeders of anything they may encounter at the sea surface. It would appear to be relatively easy to sample saury from the catches of the wide-ranging Japanese fishing industry, as well as apex predators such as dolphin (*Coryphaena*), swordfish, and tuna, to determine if, in fact, any accumulation of undesirable compounds originating in petroleum can be detected. Porpoises, also mentioned by Horn, can be readily sampled through the individuals that are captured accidentally in tuna-seining operations.

5. ENVIRONMENTAL DISEASE

Malaria

Malaria in humans continues to be a major problem in many parts of the world. Uncritical enthusiasm generated in the period immediately after World War II, occasioned by the unexpected appearance on the scene of the chlorinated hydrocarbons, led to the belief that global eradication of malaria was a possibility. National and international agencies invested large sums of money in sweeping programs, built upon the observations that the residual effects of long-persisting insecticides, when these had been applied to the walls of dwellings, would serve to interrupt the transmission of malaria by cutting short the lives of the vector anophelines, thus denying to the parasite the chance to infect new hosts.

There were early victories in regions where the habits of the specific vector species led, in a certain few instances, to actual eradication of the vector or, in other instances, to interruption of transmission and eradication of malaria. In still other instances victory was partial, and marked reduction in incidence of malaria could be noted. (See Figure X–18) In other instances, notably in Africa, parts of Asia, and parts of South America, results have been disappointing.

In the large-scale campaigns, emphasis was placed almost entirely on control procedures and the intricate logistic problems relating thereto. For a period of two decades, there was a decided slump in the volume of basic malaria work carried on; fundamental studies on parasite biology, host-parasite interactions, drug prophylaxis and therapeusis, and the biology of the anopheline vectors were neglected.

The recognition that resistance to insecticides was emerging in anopheline vectors (not as serious a problem

Figure X–18 — CHANGES IN MALARIA MORBIDITY
BEFORE AND AFTER MOSQUITO CONTROL

Area	Year	Number of Cases
Mauritius	1948	46,395
	1969	17*
Cuba	1962	3,519
	1969	3
Dominica	1950	1,825
	1969	Nil
Dominican Republic	1950	17,310
	1968	21
Grenada and Carriacou	1951	3,233
	1969	Nil
Jamaica	1954	4,417
	1969	Nil
Trinidad and Tobago	1950	5,098
	1969	5
Venezuela	1943	817,115
	1958	800
India	1935	more than 1,000,000
	1969	286,962
Bulgaria	1946	114,631
	1969	10*
Italy	1945	411,602
	1968	37
Romania	1948	338,198
	1969	4*
Spain	1950	19,644
	1969	28*
Turkey	1950	1,188,969
	1969	2,173
Yugoslavia	1937	169,545
	1969	15*
China (Taiwan)	1945	more than 1,000,000
	1969	9

*Imported or induced cases.

The table shows the effectiveness of selected mosquito-control programs, most of which use DDT. Over 1,000 million people have been freed from the risk of malaria through such programs.

yet as that seen in *Aedes aegypti*) provided signals that difficulties could be anticipated in the application of standardized control procedures in regions where earlier work had been successful. Furthermore, malaria parasites have emerged markedly resistant to the commonly used antimalarials. This has spurred the search for new antimalarial agents and has indicated the need for extension of more basic parasitologic studies.

The problem of drug resistance is particularly acute in Southeast Asia. The U.S. Army Research and Development Command has established a broadly based program of research, largely monitored through the Walter Reed Army Institute for Research, with the collaboration of the U.S. Armed Forces Epidemiological Board and the U.S. Public Health Service. Research efforts have also been intensified in a number of other countries.

The State of Scientific Knowledge

Further discussion requires subdivision into a series of topics, often intricately interassociated.

Malarial Parasites — Earlier beliefs that malaria was exclusively limited to humans have been modified, since it has been shown that *P.falciparum*, *P.vivax*, and *P.malariae* can all be passaged to subhuman primates, can establish infections, and that anophelines can be infected from such sources and can transmit further to primates. The owl monkey (*Aotus trivirgatus*) of South America has been particularly useful in these studies, though, unfortunately, it is not readily obtained in large numbers. Passage of the parasite in such hosts provides material for detailed studies of the host-parasite relationship, and is of great value in providing quantities of the parasite for *in vitro* cultivation and laboratory-controlled studies on parasite metabolism, enzyme studies, morphological studies, preparations of antigens, and the like. The importance of extra-

human cycles for maintenance of the parasites in nature is of obvious interest in epidemiology, and awaits critical assessment.

Detailed morphological studies have provided new insights into the anatomy of the parasite. They promise to provide powerful tools for direct observation of the mechanism of action of antimalarial agents on the parasites. Such studies, coupled with studies of the enzyme systems involved in drug action, should point the way to rational development of antimalarial drugs. These studies are intimately related to studies on the basic structure and biology of the red blood cell.

There has been a considerable extension of knowledge relating to the exo-erythrocytic cycle of development of malaria parasites in the vertebrate host. This is a particularly important field, since it relates to problems of malaria prophylaxis and to the radical cure of the established infection. Failures in prophylaxis and therapeusis of the non-drug-resistant parasites may be due to failure of the drug to get to the parasite, or the parasite form itself may be less sensitive. The former is the likeliest hypothesis.

The recognition in recent years that strains of *P.falciparum* are markedly resistant to 4-aminoquinolines and to widely used antimalarials has produced a spurt of new research. Projects involve the coordinated efforts of synthetic chemists, biochemists, pharmacologists, clinicians seeing drug-resistant cases (particularly in troops), and clinical-laboratory groups studying the new drugs and combinations of drugs under controlled conditions. Several different drug combinations are being used to treat drug-resistant cases; in addition to chloroquine, they employ certain sulfones and certain anti-folic acid agents such as amodiaquine and related compounds. The immediate problem, control of the infection in the individual, has in large part been met, but there is much

unresolved in studies of comparative efficacy and in evaluation of the possibility that the parasite will develop resistance to a further range of antimalarial drugs.

Intensive search for new antimalarials — not just relatives of known antimalarials — has involved the elaboration of drug-screening procedures of several types: rodent malaria systems; avian malaria systems; systems monitoring the development of parasites in mosquitoes or mosquito organs, human malaria parasites, using *in vitro* systems, and, ultimately, malaria parasites of humans in humans. Promising leads include phenanthrenes and naphthoquinones, but they are few in relation to the total effort. The "one shot" antimalarial is still a dream.

Human Host — A prominent question remains unsolved: What factor(s) cause febrile paroxysm? Newly developed techniques for fractionation of parasites and for fractionation of infected red blood cells may lead to a resolution of this question.

The sickle-cell trait in humans has been well established as exerting a protective effect in *P.falciparum* infections. A similar situation has been postulated for the G-6-PD deficiency state, but supporting evidence is not convincing. Further combined field and laboratory studies are indicated.

The possible relationship of malaria to Burkett's lymphome has been advanced on epidemiological grounds; this possibility is currently being studied intensively in East Africa.

The problem of hemolysis in G-6-PD deficient subjects treated with 8-aminoquinolines has been prominent in troops in Southeast Asia, and the subject of detailed studies. Other drug-treatment problems have been recognized, particularly the development of irreversible scotomata following prolonged chloroquine therapy, and agranulocytosis following diaminodiphenyl-sulfane therapy.

These latter reactions, although so far few in number, often terminate in death. It is suspected that they may be related to decomposition products in aged stores of the drug.

Diagnosis — The classical procedure of diagnosing malaria on the basis of finding the parasite remains unchallenged. The paucity of technicians able to apply the established procedures accurately reflects the lack of interest in most medical schools and training centers in tropical medicine in general and malaria in particular.

Direct immunofluorescence using tagged immunoglobulins to signal the malaria parasites in blood smears is a workable procedure, but it is not extensively used, and not likely to be.

Indirect immunofluorescent procedures utilizing prepared malaria smears, sera being examined for presence of antibody, and tagged antiglobulins to the host serum have shown much promise, particularly in permitting study of the immune status of populations. It is not probable, however, that such techniques will find application in the diagnosis of the immediate malarial illness in a human.

Further refinements are to be anticipated, involving the application of newer techniques to obtain purified, or separated, parasite and serum fractions. Practical application of such methodology by routine diagnostic laboratories will come slowly, if ever.

Vectors — The maintenance of malaria in the human community is a reflection of vector-host-parasite interaction, as well as environmental factors. (See Figure X–19) The vector must have an association with humans, and the parasite must be available. This relationship is highly complex put nonetheless subject to analysis by construction of models which can be adapted to computer analysis. Macdonald's contributions to such a model are well known.

It becomes apparent that many or most of the variables introduced into the equation are ill defined, and that many of these relate to the mosquito vectors. A single model can only apply to a single vector, and there are several dozen well-recognized vectors. For each vector, field information is necessary relating to distribution, densities, longevity, flight range, feeding habits vis-à vis humans as contrasted to other blood or food sources, resting habits, frequency of refeeding, susceptibility to insecticides, and susceptibility to the malaria parasite in question. As such questions are explored, there is frequently need for more specific taxonomic detail, and certain of the earlier recognized vectors, such as *Anopheles gambiae*, have been split into a series of recognizable entities (races? species?) with distinctly different biology.

Control — This topic must be considered with respect to the several accessible components: the parasite, the host, and the vector.

The finding of drug-resistant parasites complicates greatly the already complex problem of control through direct attack on the parasite through mass chemotherapy of human populations. Drug-resistant parasites have thus far not been recognized in Africa. Should they be transplanted there through migrations of parasitemic humans, or through development locally, the result would be disastrous.

The host can be approached through immunization procedures. Recent work in rodent malaria systems on developing immunogens derived from sporozoites is encouraging enough to merit extension of such studies to humans. Other approaches to the host, apart from such obvious measures as use of protective clothing, bed nets, and insect repellents — all of limited effectiveness unless conscientiously employed — have centered largely on the insect-repellent aspect. An approach through development of systematic insecticides or repellents, which have had some success in pro-

Figure X–19 — AREAS OF MAJOR MALARIA POTENTIAL

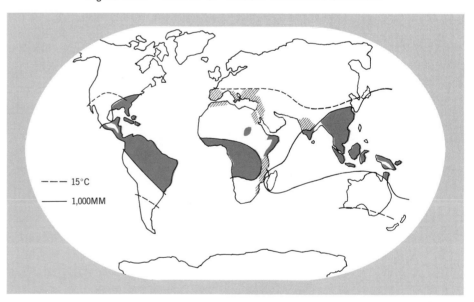

Malaria mosquitos cannot survive in areas where temperatures fall below 15° centigrade and annual rainfall is less than 1,000 millimeters. By combining the 15° centigrade isotherm (broken line) and the 1,000-millimeter isohyetel (solid line), one can determine the areas where mosquito survival is continuous (shaded sections), with consequent heavy risk of malaria, and the areas (hatched sections) where unusually heavy rainfall can permit mosquitos to survive and malaria to spread.

tecting livestock, does not hold much promise for human use. More effective repellents are being sought, but prospects for compounds appreciably more effective than those now used are dim.

Vector-control programs through the application of residual insecticides have had distinct success; there have also been failures. In part, the failures have resulted from development of resistance to insecticides; but in greater part failures have been due to biological behavior patterns of the anopheline species in question, precluding effective exposure to residual insecticides. Larviciding techniques, particularly including low-volume aerial application of insecticides, are in a phase of reassessment.

New techniques of vector control, using genetic manipulation, insect pathogens, antimetabolites, and insect hormones are currently attracting much attention. Genetic manipulation includes male sterility induced by irradiation of chemosterilants, cytoplasmic incompatibility, and translocation semisterility. Successful application of

such techniques will require much more comprehensive knowledge of the biology of each anopheline species under consideration than now exists. In this connection, the biology of the nonbiting males of the many species has received little attention in the past but may well be critical in attempts at genetic manipulation of populations.

A related approach involves attempts to replace a vector population of one species by a nonvector population of a different species through competitive displacement. Such an experiment is now under way on a Pacific atoll, attempting to displace the filaria vector species. The concept could also be applicable to displacing a parasite-receptive clone of a vector species by a parasite-resistant clone of the same species.

Epidemiology — Studies relating to the central problem — the understanding of the epidemiology of malaria in human populations — are indicated at various points in the preceding discussion. It must be further pointed out that epidemiological

studies today are greatly embarrassed by the various types of partial control which may be operating in a field locality, including partially effective drug therapy with many drugs, changing agricultural and living habits of populations, and partially effective vector-control programs. In the process of measuring, variables change and the picture changes. This situation cannot be controlled and will not change.

Need for Trained Manpower

Especially important is continuing training of field epidemiologists, with enough background to permit them to work effectively on actual field problems of malaria in overseas locations. This should include medical personnel, entomologists, and control experts. Most of the medical schools in the United States and in the world do not meet this problem adequately, and attention should be given to the strengthening of several centers that can be recognized as training centers for tropical diseases in general and malaria in particular.

Other Parasitic Diseases

Many parasitic infections are, in fact, zoonoses with significant interrelation between man and domestic or wild animals — e.g., hydatid disease, American trypanosomiasis, leishmaniasis, and fascioliasis. Study and control of such parasitic diseases are seriously neglected though they cause immense losses — both social and economic.

These are diseases of the poor and ignorant, which can, in part, explain the neglect since those people have little political leverage. Nevertheless, the fund of information on the diseases and their control has run ahead of the development of sound and useful control programs. Most existing

control programs are weak and inadequate despite the gravity of the problems. Somehow this pattern of neglect has to be broken.

Schistosomiasis

Schistosomiasis is a worldwide scourge in regions containing about 592 million people. (See Figure X–20) About 125 million people are infected. About 2.6 million are totally disabled by it and 24.8 million are partially disabled. In Brazil alone, approximately 15.5 million people live in affected regions and 5.8 million are infected; 116,600 are totally disabled and 1.4 million are partially disabled. The

estimated economic loss to Brazil due to the "loss of resources" (i.e., loss due to reduced productivity of goods and services alone) is estimated to be about $106 million per annum.

The disease is out of control in almost all endemic areas and has spread or increased in prevalence in Africa, the Philippines, and Brazil in recent years. In these areas, the increase has been due to migration of infected people, opening up of new areas for settlement, or water resources development schemes.

Schistosomiasis demonstrates particularly well the complex feedback among human health, agriculture, in-

Figure X–20 — WORLD DISTRIBUTION OF SCHISTOSOMIASIS

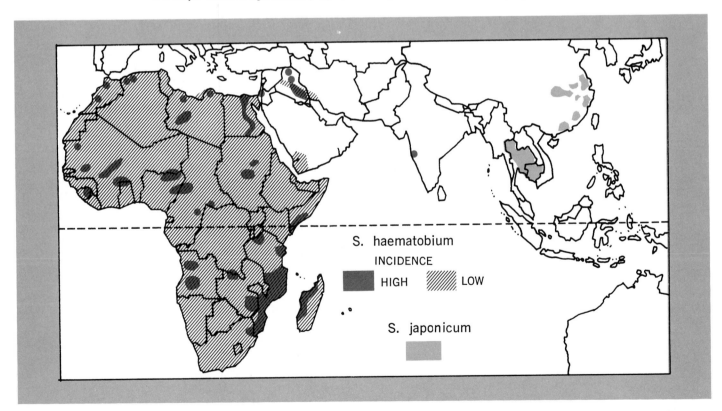

The maps show the distribution of various forms of schistosomiasis. The disease is a major block to agricultural progress in many of the world's developing nations.

dustry, social structure, social change, and economic development. The disease affects mainly the poorer people closest to the soil. Low economic status promotes the disease because it forces people to live in unsanitary conditions. Ignorance is also a major factor in lack of sanitation. The disease causes significant illness and debility in a large proportion of the infected population. These people compete less well and are less productive. The disease, then, holds them down. Farmers, because of the nature of their work, are more often exposed to the infection. Urbanization reduces the danger of spread of the disease, but water resources development schemes — with their dams, irrigation systems, and water-level-stabilization activities — promote the transmission of the disease. Water resources development schemes that can produce significant economic and social advancement can be severely weakened by the spread of this disease that can result directly from the changes the schemes require.

Current Scientific Knowledge — We know enough to control schistosomiasis in most of the endemic zones. The way to do it is by reducing snail populations and contact of man with "infected" water. New molluscicides offer a reasonably economical opportunity to reduce transmission drastically. New drugs are in development that offer for the first time a hope for easy treatment with reduced toxicity. There is no reasonable prospect of a vaccine or other means for control of the disease except, perhaps, for use of competitor snails in some localities.

Needed Activity — The technical base is thus reasonably good. Of course, more information would help. Safer drugs, easier snail control, and a way to vaccinate against the disease can be hoped for. Recently, there has been a series of efforts to produce mathematical models for analysis of transmission problems and for prediction. They are in the exploratory phase and are not really predictive yet. Figure X–21 is one input to such a model.

But control schemes will need more trained people, support, and — perhaps hardest to get — good national organizations devoted to the problem. We have spent enough time "finding out" what we need to know about the problem. We need to get on with control schemes and continue to learn as we go along. A strong push could work wonders in control of the disease in a number of countries.

Chagas' Disease (American Trypanosomiasis)

Chagas' disease occurs in almost all American countries and exists in regions inhabited by about 35 to 40 million people. At least 7 million are usually considered to be infected, though the number is sometimes estimated to be as high as 10 million. In some endemic zones, 50 percent or more of the people are infected; of these, 10 to 20 percent have significant cardiac damage or intestinal-tract damage due to the infection. Morbidity and mortality data are not very good. One careful study of the causes of death that occurred in Ribeirão Prêto, Brazil, over a two-year period showed that the disease was the cause of 29 percent (40 out of 139) of the male mortality in the 25 to 44 year age group — a shocking figure. Argentina considers that it has 2 million infected citizens and 400,000 with heart damage or other significant consequences of the infection. Venezuela has about 2.8 million people exposed to the infection in the endemic zones and about 560,000 infected persons, of whom about half have significant cardiac damage as a result.

Chagas' disease is a disease of the poor, ignorant, and badly housed. It is primarily rural, though some cities are heavily affected in the poorer parts. Poverty and lack of sophistication results in construction of bad houses of poor materials and in poor maintenance of houses. Such houses are excellent harborages for the insect vectors. The disease produces, in a proportion of its victims, acute illness followed by delayed cardiac or digestive-tract damage. These can terminate in heart failure, invalidism, and loss of productivity. The disease strikes particularly hard among young adults in their most productive years and when their families are most vulnerable to economic stress. The circle of poverty-ignorance-sickness-economic failure is a difficult one to break.

Venezuela is the only country with a control program of a size and significance commensurate with the size of the problem. A few other countries have limited control programs (particularly Chile, Brazil, and Argentina). Many countries do not know the magnitude of their problem with any accuracy at all though in many of them there is undoubted widespread morbidity due to the disease.

Current Scientific Knowledge — Knowledge of the disease is now adequate for effective control. What is needed is the decision that control is worth the cost and that it must be undertaken. Systematic use of insecticide (benzene hexachloride or dieldrin) can cut the transmission rate to a low level. Spraying costs $5 to $10 per house and may have to be repeated every two to three years. This is relatively costly, considering the political and economic status of the people affected and considering the inability of most of the countries to spend large sums on disease control.

In a number of countries, it is necessary to determine the importance of the problem. This can be done by systematic sampling to determine prevalence of infection (serological test) and prevalence of significant morbidity (electrocardiogram). Both are technically feasible in any country.

Figure X-21 — EJECTION OF SMALL DROPLETS INTO THE
ATMOSPHERE BY BURSTING BUBBLES

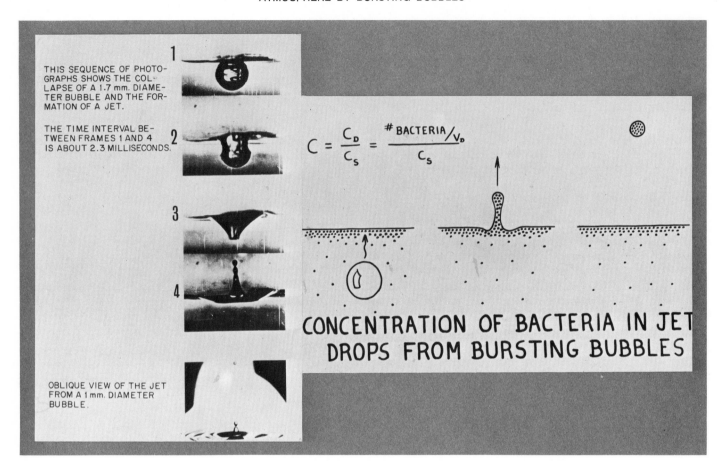

The diagram shows how disease-laden water vapor can enter the atmosphere. When a droplet of water such as rain falls out of the atmosphere through a surface of water, its shape changes and shortly triggers a jetlet, which is then ejected upward from the water surface. A droplet of water from the jetlet remains in the atmosphere, while the rest of it collapses. A similar situation occurs when bubbles formed beneath the water surface, as by decomposition, rise to the surface and burst. If, in either of these cases, the water surface is contaminated, then contaminated droplets enter the atmosphere and may be transported great distances. It is thought that hoof-and-mouth disease spreads in this manner.

Needed Activity — Priorities for research include:

1. Improved and more economical diagnosis; a simpler serological test.

2. Expanded exploration of possibilities for a vaccine.

3. A breakthrough on measures for vector control, particularly since the insecticides now relied on may have to be discouraged because of their cumulative toxicity in the environment. (One household may require several kilograms of 5-percent benzene hexachloride for each spraying, and some houses have been sprayed several times. The rate of application is 0.5 gram of the active insecticide per square meter of surface inside and out.

Latin America has enough well-qualified people in the subject. Those in research need financial help. If they are in national control programs, they need advice and support. Most countries need to be pushed into more aggressive control efforts. The immunological studies can be supported both in and out of the endemic zones. Internationally supported control campaigns to improve, not replace, houses and to spray houses could have a dramatic impact on the disease.

PART XI

HUMAN ADAPTATION TO ENVIRONMENTAL STRESS

GENETIC ADAPTATION TO THE ENVIRONMENT

An evaluation of man's adaptation to the environment depends, obviously, on the use of the two key words, adaptation and environment. To begin with the latter, its use in connection with adaptation usually brings to mind the physical environment — climate, etc. — but the biological environment of a species, in the form of disease or predators, is also well known. Furthermore, many of the important problems of man's adaptation are now concerned with the psychological or social environment. People are as much a part of the environment as sunlight and rainfall, and the problems of man's intraspecific aggression and population control must take into account adaptations to this environment.

If the definition of environment is extremely general, even nebulous, the definition and uses of the concept of adaptation are even more so. In fact, there is considerable confusion as to the nature of man's "adaptations" because of the very loose use of the term. General systems theory, for which adaptation is a central concept, can be applied to everything from physical systems or phenomena to cultural change. Even within the biological sciences there are many uses of the term adaptation. However, the most general use is to define genetic adaptations, which are changes in the gene frequency of a population in response to or as a result of differences in the fitness of the genotypes. Adaptation will here be used only in this restricted, genetic sense.

Darwinism Revived

As an explanation of human genetic differences, the concept of adaptation — or, what is synonymous, natural selection — has only assumed its rightful place in the past twenty years — even though it was Darwin's major contribution to biological science. For almost 100 years after Darwin, biologists and anthropologists concentrated on constructing taxonomies and phylogenies, which were based on the similarities and differences among populations of organisms and were based, implicitly and explicitly, on the assumption that these similarities and differences were "non-adaptive."

In anthropology, the switch to adaptive explanations began about 1950, with Coon and others, and was concerned with the visible, measurable features of individuals that are commonly called racial traits. At about the same time, there was new work and rediscovery of old work on the association of the ABO blood groups and various diseases. The rediscovery of the work done in the 1920's was comparable in a way to the rediscovery of Mendel, in that its significance was now recognized. This recognition was due to the rediscovery of natural selection as a major factor in the evolution of human differences.

Again in the early 1950's, research showed that sickle cell anemia and thalassemia varied in frequency in different "races"; they occurred with extremely high frequencies in some populations. Since these diseases were known to be due to homozygosity for a single gene (the situation is somewhat more complicated now) and were extremely severe if not lethal, their prevalence raised some knotty problems for population geneticists. With such selection against these genes, there had to be some other force balancing this adverse selection and thereby causing the high frequencies. Although there is still some disagreement — mostly as to details — it is generally accepted that heterozygotes for the sickle-cell gene have a resistance to falciparum malaria; thus, adaptation, or natural selection, is the major explanation for differences among human populations in the frequency of the sickle-cell gene. This example is so striking that it is used in just about every textbook.

Science, like the rest of human endeavor, evolves by a pendulum process. Thus, when these three trends re-introduced adaptation into the study of human genetic variation, adaptive explanations began to be proposed for most genetic differences. The result was an exaggeration of the concept that was almost as faulty as its total absence had been in previous work. In the sickle-cell example, the racial and polymorphic traits that were explained by adaptation required this concept; they were obviously genetic differences, and other explanations seemed inadequate due to problems such as the extreme selection against the sickle-cell gene. After the pendulum swung, explanations by adaptation were extended to all genetic differences and to many behavioral differences between populations. These extensions raise two questions: (a) how many genetic differences are explained primarily by selection, and (b) how many of the functional or behavioral differences between populations are primarily genetic and due to different adaptations?

Selection as an Explanation for Genetic Difference

The first question is now being hotly debated by geneticists. The debate began with Muller's discussion of "our land of mutations" and was continued with his paper in association with Morton and Crow. One could almost label this "the American position," which considers most genetic loci, or the allelic variability at most loci, as due to a balance between mutation from the normal allele and selection against the abnormal variants. The statement that most loci are generally described in this way is reasonable;

but Morton and others have gone beyond this position to say that most selection, and particularly that increased by inbreeding, is associated with this type of locus and acts to reduce genetic variation. The other position is that many loci are balanced polymorphisms in which the selection against the two homozygotes balance each other and result in genetic variability; the sickle-cell locus (β hemoglobin chain) is the most obvious example.

Both sides agree that both kinds of loci exist. The questions are how many of each and how important for human genetic disease are the two kinds. Recent estimates of the number of polymorphic loci — in other words, loci with at least two different alleles with appreciate frequencies in a significant number of human populations — have ranged around 30 to 35 percent of all human loci. Thus, while the majority of loci may well be mutational, problems and arguments must still be resolved in order to explain the 35 percent that are polymorphic.

How much of this polymorphism is due to adaptation or natural selection, and how much is simply "neutral" variation? This is one of the major concerns at present. Again, the Americans (and the Japanese, following Kimura) are working on the assumption that most of this variation is "non-adaptive," while the British are more skeptical. The argument seems to go back to the famous encounters between Fisher and Wright on the significance of random genetic drift. In addition, the assumption of "non-adaptive" differences among human populations is basic to the reconstruction of phylogenies or taxonomies; recent work on the adaptive significance of racial differences thus tends to cast doubt on previous work on race.

However, the opposite position — that all polymorphic differences are adaptive — also rests on thin ground. For example, in European populations

the frequencies of cystic fibrosis approach those which would be labeled polymorphic; in Eastern European Jewish populations the frequency of Tay-Sachs disease does, too. For these two loci there has been considerable speculation on the adaptive significance of the abnormal allele, although one need not assume selection for the abnormal allele in these cases. Much work has also been done on blood-group systems other than ABO in an attempt to demonstrate the action of natural selection. Selection against heterozygote Rh babies due to maternal-fetal incompatibility obviously exists, but the attempts to show selection in relation to environmental factors have not been very successful. Thus, the position that almost all genetic differences among human populations are due to adaptive selection cannot be said to have been proven; on the other hand, to assume that any locus is "non-adaptive" because we cannot demonstrate the selection that may be involved is also tenuous.

How much selection would be necessary to develop the human genetic differences we observe? To a great extent, the answer appears to be "infinitesimal" — or certainly within the range of error of the measurements on modern human populations by which we are trying to detect selection. This is due to the uncertainties of sampling and the limited size of the most significant human populations presently under study, such as the Yanomama Indians of Brazil and Venezuela (see Figure XI–1), who are among the few remaining hunters and primitive horticulturalists. And yet we know that human populations do change. Despite their seemingly small genetic differences (see Figure XI–2), Yanomama and Japanese are clearly very different human types. Given this dilemma, we are likely to decide between competing theoretical positions on the basis of their ability to explain the totality of human genetic variation as it exists today and not on the basis of hoping that we will ever

be able to measure the amount of selection that existed 10,000 or 20,000 years ago. And our explanations will contain both instances where genetic drift, or the "founder effect," were far more important factors of gene-frequency change than selection and vice versa.

Adaptation to Explain Behavioral Differences

So much for the increased effect of our knowledge of adaptation on known genetic differences. We now turn to the other extension of the concept of adaptation. To recapitulate, adaptation was revived as an explanation of human genetic differences because there were certain differences among human populations that could not be explained without it. Adaptation was then extended to most other widespread genetic differences; it was also extended by anthropologists, physiologists, psychologists, sociologists, and even educators to other biological or behavioral differences among groups. If a group could be shown to be genetically different in one trait, it was assumed to be different in many other traits and, in addition, any differences that were found among such groups were implicitly assumed to be genetic.

The resurgence of Darwinian thinking has been pronounced in behavioral studies. These include a great number of studies of physiological responses to environmental stresses such as temperature as well as studies of the intellectual functioning of the organisms, which usually fall under the heading of behavioral genetics. There is an important difference between these studies and earlier ones concerning human differences that required adaptive explanations. The latter involved known structural differences that could be related to gene action. For example, the differences in skin color among human populations are very pronounced, are known to be genetic, and, although some investigators do not think it is

Figure XI-1 — DISTRIBUTION OF THE YANOMAMA INDIANS IN SOUTH AMERICA

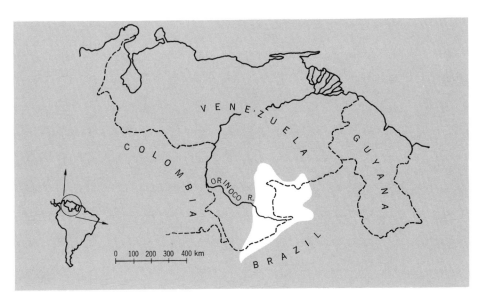

The small map shows the general location of the Yanomama Indians. The large map shows the detailed location of their villages. Two villages located near the Venezuelan-Brazilian border are those from which blood samples for the cytogenetic studies were obtained.

proven, require some adaptive differences in the skin-color genotypes in various environments to explain them. The physiological basis of this selection has not been demonstrated, but there is still no other reasonable explanation in genetic theory for these differences. The fact that skin color seemed to be a climatic adaptation may have given rise to the idea that there must be many more climatic adaptations in man. At first it was hypothesized that gross structural differences may exist; but studies have shown that the number of eccrine sweat glands as well as the number of melanocytes are about the same, and their distribution on the body is also the same in all groups of men.

Although human structures and basic responses to climatic stresses are about the same everywhere, many physiological studies have shown dif-

Figure XI-2 — CYTOGENETIC FINDINGS IN 49 YANOMAMA INDIANS FROM TWO VILLAGES IN VENEZUELA

	Males	Females	Totals	In Jungle Controls	Japanese Controls
Number of Cases	32	17	49	2	174
Number of Cells Examined	3175	1700	4875	250	16,035
Per Cent Cells with 46 Chromosomes	96.7	97.1	96.8	97.0	95.6
Number of Cells with One or More Abberrations:					
Total	139 (4.38%)	61 (3.59%)	200 (4.10%)	5 (2.00%)	157 (1.0%)
Single chromatid breaks	80 (2.52)	32 (1.88)	112 (2.30)	4 (1.60)	105 (0.65)
Isochromatid breaks	20 (0.63)	13 (0.76)	33 (0.68)	1 (0.40)	23 (0.14)
Free fragments	13 (0.41)	6 (0.35)	19 (0.39)	0 (0.00)	10 (0.06)
Dicentrics	3 (0.09)	1 (0.06)	4 (0.08)	0 (0.00)	1 (0.006)
Rings	1 (0.03)	0 (0.00)	1 (0.02)	0 (0.00)	0 (0.0)
Translocations, inversions	0 (0.00)	0 (0.00)	0 (0.00)	0 (0.00)	8 (0.05)
Chromatid exchanges	3 (0.09)	4 (0.24)	7 (0.14)	0 (0.00)	5 (0.03)
Centromere breaks	2 (0.06)	2 (0.12)	4 (0.08)	0 (0.00)	5 (0.03)
No. of Complex Cells	17 (0.54)	4 (0.24)	21 (0.43)	0 (0.00)	0 (0.0)

The table shows cytogenetic differences between some Yanomama Indians and several control populations. The data are compatible, since the same culture methods were used except that the Japanese control cultures were not delayed in the initiation of the 72-hour cultures. Complex cells include those with multiple, exchange-type aberrations.

ferences. Australian aborigines lose heat to permit a lower temperature in their extremities; Eskimos quickly warm their fingers in an ice bath; Africans sometimes sweat less in response to heat. All of this is blithely called adaptation, with the presumption that it has a genetic basis. This work is comparable in method, theory, and genetic bias to the studies of psychological differences, many of which have involved "IQ" tests that purport to find racial differences in intelligence. The logic of such studies is that genetic adaptations to environmental differences must exist, and the only problem is to discover them.

The result of these extensions of the concept of genetic adaptation has been to take a well-defined concept and make it a hodgepodge for anyone to use. To an extent, this is characteristic of areas of science that are developing rapidly or are in ferment — and behavioral and physiological genetics are certainly doing that. The major confusion results from the use of structural differences — i.e., genes — to describe functional or behavioral differences, without recognition that vast differences in behavior are the result of the environment or of other kinds of "adaptation" to the environment.

Perhaps we are back to the old nature-nurture controversy, but there has been some progress. Great strides have been made in the analysis of behavior by the methods of quantitative genetics, and these methods can be applied to physiological differences to some extent. But the measure of genetic determination — heritability — applies only to the population studied and to the differences among the individuals within it. Within any population, as well as between populations, individuals vary in response to any biological and psychological test. William has continually stressed the uniqueness of the individual for just about anything biological that one can measure. And it is true that tests of biological relatives indicate that some of this variation is due to

heredity. But it is a totally different problem to explain differences between populations. It seems reasonable to most people that these differences must also have about the same genetic component; but that is not the case.

We are only just beginning to realize how powerful environmental influences are in affecting the total functioning of the individual. "Adaptation" — whether to temperature change, to disease, to crowded conditions, to learning school work — results from spending one's lifetime in a particular environment; putting two different groups in the same cold chamber, school, or hospital for a day, a week, or even a year is not a "controlled" experiment that will prove genetic or racial differences. For example, it was long thought that "natives" had a natural resistance to some diseases and whites to others such as TB. However, we are now seeing that resistance is a function of previous exposure, amount of exposure, and age at exposure; simplistic notions of racial immunities are not very realistic.

One cannot say, however, that significant differences do not exist or that there are no genetic factors involved. American Negro troops in Korea *did* suffer four times as much from frostbite as whites; this is a problem that needs explaining. American and West African Negroes do seem to have an almost total resistance to vivax malaria, which also seems to be genetic. Many of the populations in Europe and Africa that depend on milk for subsistence have an active lactase enzyme (among adults), while most of the rest of the world's populations are lactase deficient. Nevertheless, most of the behavioral differences among populations that have been called adaptations do not require or demonstrate genetic differences; rather, they have been proposed on the basis of tenuous data and a misunderstanding of the populational significance of adaptations.

Applicability of Animal Ethology

There is one other area of research in which the concept of adaptation has played an important role. This is the application of animal ethology to human characteristics. Lorenz on aggression, Ardrey on territoriality, Morris on sexual behavior, and others on all other kinds of behavioral traits have attempted to develop adaptive, or "Darwinian," explanations for these traits. Ethology in its methods and theories is quite comparable to behavioral genetics, although the latter concentrates on human data while the former generalizes to man on the basis of analogy with animals.

To show that man is comparable to the other animals in many ways is commendable, but it is still impossible to explain the variation in human behavior among populations by biological or genetic factors. Aggression is not universal among human populations; and it is the variability in this characteristic that is the anthropologist's problem. To disregard this variability—as does Morris, for example, by saying that the rest of the world's cultures are evolutionary backwaters — is simply fatuous.

As any other species, however, man does have some species-specific characteristics; and these are undoubtedly due to a long period of adaptation to a common ecological niche, which in his case was hunting with tools on the savannahs of the Old World. But again, to explain what is "wrong" with human societies today by genetic lag is not adequate. If it were, then all human societies should have these aggressive genes stemming from our carnivorous past. But not all societies are as aggressive as ours. Most ethology-oriented scientists seem to view man's cultural evolution as simply social change which adjusts culture to man's biological "needs." This view tends to detract from the power of the environment to change human characteristics — if one can view cultural pressure as the environment. It also tends to overemphasize the significance of genetic adaptation for the survival of populations.

Adaptation and the Future of Human Society

Because fitness expresses the ability of individuals to survive — as well as to reproduce — fitness differences among individuals or genotypic differences among populations are usually assumed to have considerable effect on the population's survival in the course of evolution. However, genotypic evolution has minimal effect on a population's ability to survive. The huge variation in mortality and fertility rates among human population has practically no relationship to genetic variation. Darwinism seems to have given rise to such statements as "the polar bear survives in the arctic because it is adapted to that environment"; but in terms of the course of evolution, the opposite is true—that is, the polar bear is adapted to the arctic because it has survived there. Again, Coon has stated that Negroes survived in malarial environments because they had the sickle-cell gene. But why do several African populations have high frequencies of this gene? Because they have survived for centuries in a malarial environment. (See Figure XI–3) If, with a simple model for this sickle-cell locus, one compares the average fitness of a population with a high frequency of the sickle-cell gene to that of one with no sickle-cell genes, the difference is at most 5 percent per generation. In terms of a difference in mortality rate, this is about 2 per 1,000 per year—which is insignificant when compared to the vast differences in African mortality rates that are due to cultural differences.

Genotypic evolution is the result of competition between individuals within a population and has little effect on population competition. Similarly, genes have little effect on other aspects of culture. Cultures can make any kind of martyr, from kamikaze pilot to celibate, any time

one is needed; genetic differences in behavior traits are thus not the major, or even a minor, cause of cultural evolution. Even within a population it is usually considered that such traits as dominance are genetically determined; but recent research is pointing to the opposite view: that the greater size, intelligence, aggression, etc., of dominants is the result of being dominant and not vice versa. This is only more evidence that "adaptations" that are almost automatically assumed to be genetic may actually be environmental.

In summary, there have been considerable advances in our knowledge of genetic adaptation where the actual genes are known, although its effect vis-à-vis the other determinants of genetic change is being debated. On the other hand, the extension of the concept of genetic adaptation to other human characteristics is still much in limbo. This review has been mostly critical of such work — not because it is valueless but because of its very significance for our knowledge of human society. Already, some are saying that genetic in-

Figure XI–3 — FREQUENCY OF SICKLE-CELL GENE IN LIBERIA

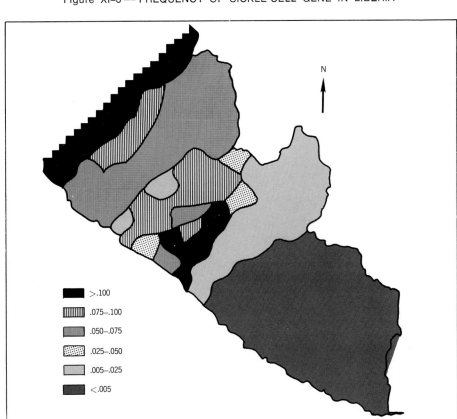

> .100
.075–.100
.050–.075
.025–.050
.005–.025
< .005

The map shows the percentage frequency of occurrence of the sickle-cell gene in the Liberian population. The malaria parasite has been endemic throughout most of Liberia, but the sickle-cell gene varies greatly among tribal populations. The latter variation may be due to the length of time that different Liberian populations have been exposed to malaria. *P. falciparum*, the malaria parasite is spread by the mosquito *Anopheles gambiae*, which cannot breed in heavily shaded rain forests. Thus, it—and malaria—were able to advance where rain forest was destoyed to provide land for agriculture. Slash-and-burn practices began in northern Liberia and gradually spread southward. Today, the gradation of the sickle-cell gene follows this same pattern, thus illustrating on a microscale how the evolutionary process operates. The highest frequency of the sickle-cell gene exists where the rain forest has been opened up for the longest time.

equality is somehow incompatible with "all men are created equal," or that the division of labor is based on "natural inequalities." Thus, the political doctrines of our society are

considered to be based on unsound biological assumptions. On the other side, there seems to be resistance to the idea that any racial characteristic is adaptive; this is the result of ex-

tending the concept of genetic fitness to an ideal of individual worth. In any case, the entire controversy is, or ought to be, irrelevant to the ideology or aims of our society.

ASPECTS OF MAN'S ADAPTATION IN THE TROPICS

From our vantage point in the temperate zones, we look upon man in the tropics as having undergone extensive adaptations. In fact, however, man probably arose in tropical zones, living in small bands in the rain forest; from the standpoint of evolutionary biology, it is we of the highly civilized countries who are now making adaptations to a rapidly changing world.

In recent years, some groups of investigators have undertaken extensive, multidisciplinary studies of the surviving groups of primitive man, these almost without exception in tropical or subtropical zones. In the broadest sense, it is the purpose of these studies to define the population structure of primitive man, and to appreciate the various pressures (disease, nutritional, etc.) which, interacting with that structure, provided the milieu within which human evolution has occurred. It seems appropriate to point out that, in many respects, ours is the first generation of scientists to have the facilities for studies of much deeper significance than those of the past, and the last generation to have the opportunity, since relatively undisturbed primitive man is rapidly disappearing from the face of the earth.

With respect to this matter of understanding better the population structure of primitive man in the tropics, the geneticist is concerned with such matters as: the amount of inbreeding; the extent of polygyny; birth rates; neonatal, infant, and child death rates; marriage patterns, etc. These factors define the stric-

tures that are placed on the evolutionary process.

Genetic Differentiation

The studies of most groups of investigators agree in suggesting that early man in the tropics was characterized by high levels of inbreeding. They suggest that infertility was uncommon and the reproductive performance of woman relatively uniform. On the other hand, because of the institution of polygyny, male reproductive performance was somewhat more variable than in the United States today. The health of the children appears to have been better than those of most peasant populations.

Studies of the frequency of a variety of genetic markers in the isolated villages that comprise most tribal populations reveal a marked degree of genetic microdifferentiation — i.e., there are rather large genetic differences between the villages that compose a tribe. These villages are engaged in a constantly shifting pattern of hostilities, one with the other; that is, competition between demes is a varied risk. This population structure is one that population geneticists feel is particularly conducive to rapid evolution.

Health Patterns

With respect to the matter of interaction with agents of disease, members of these tropical populations have unusually high levels of gammaglobulin. Because of transplacental

transfer, a child thus comes into the world with considerable resistance to local pathogens, conferred on it by its mother. As the child comes into active contact with the many disease agents in its surroundings, it will to some extent be protected by placentally transmitted maternal antibodies, so that it may have an opportunity to build up its own resistance more slowly.

The commitment of many of these primitive groups to regulation of population numbers is noteworthy. By a variety of means — intercourse taboos following the birth of a child, prolonged lactation, abortion, and infanticide — the entry of new life into the population is rather rigidly controlled. Under these circumstances, an infant may be nursed for as long as three years; in general, the nutrition of children is quite excellent. In this respect, many civilized communities may have lost an adaptation well recognized by primitive man.

Goiter — With respect to specific diseases, a number of examples may be cited as to how markedly many of these people differ in their physiological adaptations from ourselves, and how rapidly these adaptations are altered by acculturation. An outstanding example is with respect to iodine. Some of the least-touched groups of South America live in areas where iodine is in very short supply, and yet they do not show goiter. On the other hand, endemic goiter is a prominent feature of civilized populations living under conditions of short iodine supply. Studies indicate that at least one primitive group in South America (the Yanomama) has very high uptake levels of radioactive iodine, levels that, in civilized areas, are characteristic of people with quite large goiters. It begins to appear that the development of goiter in the so-called endemic areas involves more than simple iodine shortage, that there is some environmental factor which interferes with the utilization of iodine but which can be offset by the use of doses of iodine.

Diabetes — A second example is provided by diabetes mellitus. In some of the Indian groups of southwestern United States, diabetes is appearing with a great frequency and many complications. Although the evidence is scanty, the disease does not seem to be particularly

prevalent among unacculturated Indians. The most obvious difference between Indian groups with high rates of diabetes and those with low rates is the greater amount of obesity and the lesser amount of exercise of the former. Thus, diabetes mellitus may represent a breakdown in adaptation to a changing way of life.

Caries — For a third and final example of how the adaptations of primitive man in the tropics are altered by acculturation, one might mention the well-known example of caries. Most relatively untouched groups of primitives are almost caries-free. But within a few years of acculturation, caries often become rampant. The reason is still not clear. Understanding of any of these

three phenomena would contribute greatly to our knowledge of man's adaptation in the tropics as well as in other regions.

There is a widespread feeling that, given today's rapid changes in man's way of life, the selective forces that shaped him and brought him thus far are rapidly being altered. Studies such as the ones briefly sketched here can provide concrete insight into the way these forces are being altered. Many of the conclusions will have to be inferential rather than demonstrated. Even so, it is hoped that such studies will provide a perspective on the extent of the changes now occurring in man's way of life and some of its problems and consequences.

ADAPTATION TO HIGH ALTITUDE

In the autumn of 1967, two international conferences were held to assess the state of knowledge about high-altitude effects on man. One of these was sponsored by the U.S. Army Medical Research and Development Command, the other by the World Health Organization (WHO), the Pan American Health Organization (PAHO), and the U.S. International Biological Program (IBP). Between the two conferences, all major laboratories and research groups working in this problem area were represented. Results were reported of a decade of intensified research effort in the United States and abroad.

Information Level as of 1967

The basic physiological and psychological effects of altitude on lowlanders moving rapidly to high altitudes had been described and verified by the late 1950's. In the early 1960's, research proceeded along these lines:

1. Intensified physiological research on the consequences of

moving men rapidly from low to high altitude.

2. Study of the physiology and general biology of high-altitude natives in Peru, Nepal, and the United States.

3. Investigation of medical problems peculiar to men living at high altitude.

The details of the findings available from these pre-1968 studies are too lengthy to cite in a short report, but some of the highlights were:

1. A detailed description of the physiological and psychological limits of low-altitude man's altitude tolerance. This included a partial knowledge of how much improvement could be expected in performance capability with time and some knowledge about the utility of drugs in modifying altitude tolerance.

2. The study of high-altitude natives demonstrated them to be

different from lowlanders in a number of general biological and specific physiological parameters. These differences included an increased incidence of neonatal deaths, different growth patterns, an oxygen-consumption capacity above that of the lowlanders going to altitude even for an extended time (see Figure XI–4), and, finally, a number of unusual disease characteristics including a remarkable lack of adult cardiovascular disease.

3. The study of medical problems at altitude had provided a basic physiological description of the two direct altitude-related diseases. These are an acute form producing high-altitude pulmonary edema (HAPE) and a chronic form which causes a runaway polycythemia. Anesthesiological and surgical procedures suitable to high altitude had been partially developed and it had been discovered that many drugs have altered action

Figure XI–4 — CHANGES IN OXYGEN CONSUMPTION CAPACITY OF
LOWLANDERS UPON UPWARD MIGRATION

Population	Number	Sex and Average Age	Max VO$_2$ (l/Min/Kg) STPD		% Decrease
			Low Altitude	High Altitude	
U.S. White Researchers	12	Male 27	50.4 (300 m.)	38.1 (4000 m.)	24.4
English Mountain Climbers	4	Male 32	50.0 (sea level)	39.7 (4000 m.)	20.6
U.S. White Soldiers	24	Male ?	40.4 (sea level)	32.1 (4300 m.)	20.5
Peruvian Sailors	10	Male 18-21	39.0 (450 m.)	31.4 (4500 m.)	19.5
U.S. White Runners	6	Male 20	64.2 (300 m.)	46.6 (4000 m.)	27.2
U.S. White Runners	5	Male 15-17	65.2 (300 m.)	49.4 (3100 m.)	25.1
Peruvian Quechua (High Altitude Heritage)	10	Male 22	49.3 (100 m.)	44.5 (4000 m.)	9.7

The table shows the maximum oxygen consumption capacity of people who normally inhabit lowlands (below 1,000 meters) and then the percentage decrease in their ability to consume oxygen upon moving above 3,000 meters. The decreases are striking except in the last category, those who were children of people acclimated to high altitudes. Decrease in oxygen consumption is reflected as a significant loss in work capacity.

on men living in the low oxygen pressures found at altitude.

The formal publication of results on man's adaptational problems at altitude has been substantial since the beginning of 1968, although since that time few new major research efforts have been launched.

Significance of High-Altitude Research on Man

The relevance of high-altitude research to the 25 million people living above 8,000 feet is obvious because of the multiple health effects. The same is true for those who travel up and down from these altitudes. Less can be said about the problem for the much larger number of people living between 5,000 and 8,000 feet, since the effects are more subtle and less well known.

Of perhaps much greater importance, the study of human populations living under the drastically reduced oxygen pressures found at high terrestrial altitudes can provide data of major importance for both such basic scientific problems as the mechanisms of human evolution and such applied problems as the causes of cardiovascular disease. For this reason, scientists from practically every discipline involved in the study of man have been concerned with high-altitude research. While it may, therefore, be suggested that research on man at altitude is needed because it may help us discover cures for adult cardiovascular disease or im-

prove the health of a significant segment of the world's population, the major scientific justification is the use of the environmental contrast as a research tool.

Research Recommendations

At the 1967 WHO-PAHO-IBP Meeting of Investigators on Population Biology of Altitude, a detailed set of research recommendations was developed. These needs have not been met. The following research therefore remains of priority interest:

Physiological Adaptation and Acclimatization to Altitude Introduction — Several studies have indicated that there are important differences in a variety of structural and functional characteristics among people who can be identified as: (a) highlanders for many generations; (b) lowlanders acclimatized to altitude; (c) new arrivals at altitude; (d) highlanders acclimatized to sea level; and (e) lowlanders.

It is not clear what these differences mean. We do not know, for example, whether these differences reflect simple adaptations to a new environment or are the result of selective adaptive processes or even, in some instances, are detrimental to the individual.

For the people who now live at high altitude, and for those who will move there, the most important area of altitude physiology is that which has to do with natural and acquired acclimatization. Study of these processes should direct particular attention to the functional adaptation of people of both sexes, of all ages, and of those living under different working conditions.

Of lesser importance to human populations as a whole is the study of the acute adaptive mechanisms, which are of concern to the much smaller groups of people moving between high and low altitude and for whom residence at high altitude is usually brief.

Physiology of Exercise and Work Capacity at Altitude — A number of human populations at various levels of altitude have for many generations lived and worked while exposed to low levels of ambient oxygen content, although they have not necessarily been exposed to continued tissue hypoxia. The physical performance capacity of these populations is not adequately established.

Studies were suggested on: the basic work capacity of highlanders; the maximum oxygen consumption of altitude populations; the metabolic response to work in various highlander populations (see Figure XI–5); the effect of age and sex on work capacity in altitude populations; the relationship between heart rate and

oxygen consumption in indigenous highlanders.

Altitude Limits for Acclimatization — There is a need to specify altitude tolerance limits for human and other animal species. The temporal maintenance of normal functional integrity of organ systems, behavioral activity, and physical and mental performance should be evaluated.

Environmental Factors — Studies are needed to determine the significance of environmental factors other than hypoxia in altitude acclimatization such as the climatic conditions and the socio-economic environment.

Respiration — An important adaptation of the resident to altitude, which is different from the lowlander, is his pulmonary ventilatory response to different concentrations of both

Figure XI–5 — OXYGEN CONSUMPTION CAPACITY AMONG HIGH-ALTITUDE NATIVES

Population	Location and Altitude	Number	Sex and Average Age	Max VO$_2$ (l/Min/Kg) STPD
Quechua Peasants	Nunoa, Peru 4000 m.	25	Male 25	49.1
University Students "White"	Puno, Peru 3800 m.	13	Male 23.5	42.8
University Students "Quechua"	Puno, Peru 3800 m.	10	Male 23.8	46.8
Trained Quechua	Puno, Peru 4000 m.	9	Male 21.1	48.2
Quechua Miners	Morococha, Peru 4540 m.	?	Male ?	51.2
Aymara Natives	Chile 3500-3650 m.		Male 18.0	49.1
Sherpa Natives	Nepal 3400 m.	6	Male 17.8	51.9
Aymara Natives	Chile 3500-3650 m.		Male 25.6	45.4
Sherpa Natives	Nepal 3400 m.	11	Male 24.6	50.4
Aymara Natives	Chile 3500-3650 m.		Male 34.8	46.3
Sherpa Natives	Nepal 3400 m.		Male 34.0	47.4
Aymara Natives	Chile 3500-3650 m.		Male 44.8	44.0
Sherpa Natives	Nepal 3400 m.		Male 43.6	43.8

The maximum oxygen consumption capacity of native highlanders at high altitudes is comparable to that of native lowlanders at low altitudes (see Figure XI–4). Thus, the work capacity of the two groups is similar in their native habitats, although lowlanders are at a disadvantage when they migrate to high levels.

oxygen (O_2) and carbon dioxide (CO_2) in the air he breathes. The native highlander is relatively less sensitive to low levels of O_2 in alveolar air than is the lowlander; it is not clear whether this decrease in sensitivity is an advantage or a disadvantage at altitude.

Analysis of the important adaptive respiratory process should include study of: age and sex differences, neurological factors, acid-base factors, chemoreceptor sensitivity and thresholds, as well as tissue responses to hypoxia. In addition, it would be of importance to study regulation of ventilation during the performance of physical work at altitude and during sleep. Sleep and associated periodic hypoventilation, as well as performance of hard exercise, increase hypoxic exposure.

Circulatory Mechanisms of Altitude Acclimatization — Although circulatory responses in man at altitude have received more study than other physiological responses, we do not know the criteria upon which we could advise healthy people whether they should or should not live at high altitude, or at what stage of morphological or functional alterations they should move to low altitude. The following areas of investigation are of importance in answering this problem:

1. Epidemiology: Much needs to be known about the prevalence and incidence of cardiovascular disease at altitude. Ecological factors other than altitude should be identified which affect normal cardiac function in highlanders. In addition, we do not know the circulatory response to physical work at different ages.

2. Cardiac Muscle Metabolism: The basic inability of cardiac muscle to work under anaerobic conditions makes it vulnerable to hypoxia induced by high work loads at altitude. Before

optimal and maximal levels for work at altitude could be recommended, further studies are necessary on coronary blood flow and cardiac muscle metabolism during work and rest at altitude.

3. Microcirculation: Whether increased capillarity and anastomotic vascularity in cardiac or skeletal muscle is an anatomical feature of the acclimatization process needs further study. The possible role of changes in the microcirculation in the development of chronic mountain sickness has not been determined.

4. Pulmonary Hypertension: Longitudinal observations are needed in highlanders who develop pulmonary hypertension and right heart hypertrophy. Control measurements are needed that cover both sexes and a wide age range. Special study is needed of the factors that lead to high-altitude pulmonary edema.

5. Circulation Dynamics: More information is needed on the expected changes in cardiac dynamics at altitude. Included under this heading are observations on cardiac output, cardiac work, peripheral resistance, heart rate, stroke volume, blood pressure as well as the role of changes in blood volume, hematocrit levels, and pulmonary circulation. Partitioning of blood flow through vital organs under various conditions at altitude is also an important area to be studied.

Cellular and Tissue Mechanism of Altitude Acclimatization — The biochemical mechanisms underlying high-altitude acclimatization are inadequately understood. Respiratory and vascular adaptations to altitude that permit an adequate delivery of O_2 and removal of metabolites at the

cellular level during rest may not be adequate for sustained hard work by healthy men or, for that matter, sedentary life in the elderly and infirm. There is a need to determine the adaptive processes at the cellular level in the highlander as well as in newcomers to altitude.

We need to know what role is played in these cellular responses by changes in the amount of myoglobin, the number of mitochondria, and the capacity of the cytochrome and electron transporting system. More information is needed on possible adaptive increases in enzymes favoring both aerobic and anaerobic metabolism. We need to know the degree to which rate-limiting neurohumoral-endocrine mediators affect these cellular functions. And finally, we need to know whether genetic factors are operative in the adaptation at the cellular and subcellular level.

Other Areas of Altitude Physiology Requiring Further Study — Available knowledge is inadequate concerning nutritional requirements of those with natural or acquired acclimatization or in those acutely exposed to altitude. Further nutritional and metabolic studies are necessary to establish optimal nutritional allowance for high-altitude residents and for those who wish to reside at altitude.

The factors regulating redistribution of fluid and electrolytes among the various fluid compartments need further elaboration.

In the long-time resident at altitude we need to know more about the possible role of adaptive tissue and vascular responses in the aging process. It is also possible that high-altitude residence has an effect on man's immunological responses and on the types and frequency of infections that he harbors.

The sequential changes that occur during the period of adaptation of the newcomer to high altitude are poorly understood. Accurate time-tables are not available that show rate of adjustment for each organ system including the respiratory, cardiovascular, digestive, endocrine, renal, and neuromuscular systems.

The time course of the de-acclimatization process should also be studied, particularly in those who are exposed intermittently to altitude.

The working group suggested that a handbook of physiological values be developed which uses standardized terminology. A collection of data on normal and abnormal biological values for different altitudes is urgently needed.

Human Biology at High Altitudes

The working group considered the problems posed by the biology of human populations living at high altitudes, which could also, and equally importantly, be relevant to many fundamental problems of human biology in general.

It seems appropriate to present the recommendations for these two approaches separately, although in practice the methods used and observations made will be closely similar.

The Characterization of High-Altitude Populations — Using compositive methods of approach and standardized procedures, information should be obtained in the following categories:

1. Fertility and the Components of Fertility: (a) by demographic methods; (b) by methods used in the reproductive physiology of man and of animals, which could be applied to human population studies.

2. Growth, Development, and Aging: With a focus on age changes and variability in characteristics thought to be (a) of adaptive value at high altitude; and (b) related to the somatic fitness of individuals. Such studies should not be divorced from the psychological and intellectual changes that occur during development.

3. Nutrition: In all cases, the nutritional assessment of the populations studied should be made in as detailed a manner as possible, commensurate with the resources available. Such assessments should include: (a) the nutritional status of individuals; (b) detailed nutritional surveys, where possible; and (c) biochemical studies related to nutrition.

4. Special Problems Relating to Work Capacity: Both physiological and psychological methods should be used.

5. Epidemiology: In all cases, the pattern of disease distribution in populations should be studied. Where additional demographic information is available, it is highly important that more vigorous epidemiological studies should be made. It is of great importance that demographic methods should be developed which would enable the relationships between age, disease, and morbidity to be ascertained.

6. Genetics: Further information is required on: (a) the distribution of polymorphic systems in high-altitude populations; (b) the heritability of quantitative varying traits, particularly those presumed to be adaptive in nature; and (c) congenital defects, especially those presumed to have a genetic component.

All these studies must include as precise as possible an analysis of all biological and physical aspects of the environment. (See, for example, Figure XI–6) Adequate precautions must be taken to insure statistical representation and control situations, which will often mean the study of lowland populations. And finally, the demographic background of the populations under study must be ascertained in as great a detail as possible.

Altitude Studies in General Human Biology — The ecological situations of high-altitude populations often afford unique opportunities for the study of fundamental human biology. In particular, the following problem areas can be investigated:

1. Developmental Flexibility: The determination of the magnitude and biological significance of normal environmentally induced responses.

2. Genetic Structure of Human Populations: Isolated groups, where it may be presumed that factors such as genetic drift may be operative, are particularly important objects of study. Problems involving gene flow and the effects of selective migration may also be encompassed.

3. Natural Selection: Of the variety of ways by which the problem of detecting natural selection may be approached, it was thought that particular attention should be devoted to the analysis of the comparative fertility and mortality of different phenotypes and, where possible, genotypes. Such investigation could be made most appropriately in both stable high-altitude populations and in those which have recently changed their altitude.

These three topics deal with fundamental problems of human biology and thus conflict with the objectives of categorizing the biology of high-altitude population, as discussed

383

Figure XI-6 — GROWTH RATE DIFFERENCES BETWEEN
NUÑOA AND U.S. CHILDREN

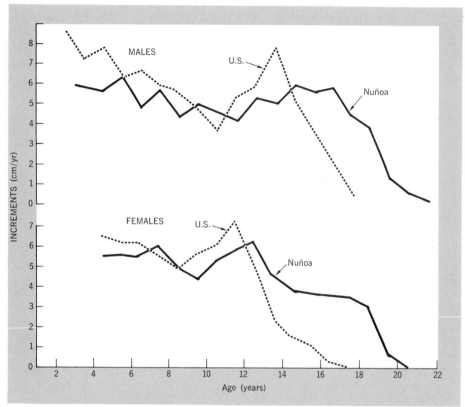

The graph shows differences in rates of general body growth between Nuñoa and U.S. children. The Nuñoa children are primarily of Indian derivation and live in an area of about 1,600 square kilometers whose minimum altitude is 4,000 meters and whose maximum altitude is above 5,500 meters. The Nuñoa children have a slower rate of general body growth than is standard in the U.S., but their growth rate continues over a longer period of time.

chronic mountain sickness or high-altitude pulmonary edema. Simple laboratory methods for determining the sensitivity of the carotid body and respiratory responses to various stimuli including hypoxia should be devised. Other screening tests should be evaluated on sea-level subjects who will later be exposed to high altitude.

Epidemiology, Therapy, and Prevention of High-Altitude Pulmonary Edema — By means of questionnaires and interviews, the importance of factors such as reascent, length of stay at sea level, and slow ascent upon the occurrence of HAPE will be assessed. Field trials of prophylactic drugs, using a double-blind technique, will be carried out, preferably in troops. In selected patients during the acute stage the hemodynamic effect of selected drugs will be investigated. Ventilation-perfusion characteristics will be examined sequentially in the acute stage and during recovery.

Congenital Malformations of the Newborn at High Altitudes — Preliminary studies have shown that the incidence of congenital abnormalities of the heart and other structures is increased at high altitude. Whether this is a genetic abnormality or due to maternal hypoxia at a critical stage of fetal development is not known. Since maternal hypoxia can be prevented or minimized, studies at high altitude are indicated. The causative factors can be evaluated by employing a standard, highly objective method of examination in a prospective study of newborn infants and schoolchildren at selected levels of altitude in different countries. Countries to be included are those where the appropriate facilities are available. The administration of oxygen to newborns should be carried out at high altitude with suitable controls to determine its late effect on the incidence of PDA and the cardiovascular system.

earlier. However, their study demands a large-scale multidisciplinary approach in selected areas, in which the various characteristics itemized earlier would still have to be subjects.

Health Aspects of Altitude

Ischemic Heart Disease at High Altitude — There is evidence that the incidence of ischemic heart disease in high-altitude populations is lower than at sea level. Experimental studies indicated increased resistance to myocardial necrosis in altitude-acclimatized animals. A controlled epidemiological study of the incidence of ischemic heart disease in high-

altitude populations will be carried out using suitable sea-level controls and standardized techniques of investigation. Risk factors for ischemic heart disease will be evaluated and correlated with necropsy data. Adaptive mechanism of the heart to high altitude pertinent to acute cardiac necrosis will be examined in experimental animals. Careful investigative techniques of population analysis will be employed and, depending on initial results, preventive trials may be initiated.

Development of Prognostic Tests for Altitude Sickness — It is important to be able to identify individuals who are likely to develop acute or

High-Altitude Medicine — Despite the fact that over 25 million people live at high altitudes, no information regarding their special medical problems is available. The following subjects need to be treated: (a) high-altitude diseases such as acute and chronic mountain sickness and high-altitude pulmonary edema; (b) modification by high altitude of diseases that are common at sea level such as pneumonia, coronary disease, and shock; (c) action of drugs such as opiates and anesthetics that are modified by high altitude; (d) occupational diseases at high altitudes. The emphasis should be on clinical medicine rather than physiology.

Evaluation of the Effects of Pulmonary and Cardiac Disease upon Cardio-Respiratory Function at High Altitude — Pulmonary function and hemodynamic studies should be carried out in high-altitude residents with silicosis, stanniosis, and following pneumonectomy. The working capacity of such patients should be evaluated by appropriate methods.

Techniques of early detection of industrial pulmonary disease at high altitude should be evaluated and applied to workers.

Factors Affecting Biliary Cholelithiasis in Native Highlanders — Cholesterol stones are commonly observed at high altitude, with probably a different sex incidence than usually observed at sea level. Since this is an important cause of illness, the causative factors should be studied. The study should include an investigation of dietary habits and serum lipids of patients with proven cholelithiasis compared to control subjects living in the same area with normal cholecystograms.

Drug Action at Different Altitudes — Drug action is probably significantly modified in the hypoxic high-altitude environment. Toxicity may be enhanced or diminished and the therapeutic effect may be altered. Studies should be made and known information collected regarding the effect of selected drugs at various altitudes in the world. Drugs such as narcotics, anesthetics, analgesics, opiates, pressor drugs, and cardiac glycosides should be investigated.

Vital Statistics in Relation to Altitude — Vital statistics of WHO are arranged for countries according to many categories — but not altitude. Such information is necessary in order to determine the effect of altitude upon the incidence of disease and mortality.

Functional and Intellectual Correlates of Altitude Hypoxia in Children — It is important to determine if the development and function of the central nervous system is adversely affected by the chronic hypoxia of high altitude. Suitable physiologic tests should be developed to quickly determine the degree of chronic hypoxia in children. Tests of central nervous system functions that could be affected by chronic hypoxia should be designed that would be suitable for field studies.

ADAPTATION TO SMOG AND CARBON MONOXIDE

Smog is a vaguely defined word, certainly not a well-defined chemical species. In general, it means the totality of community air pollution, though it has been applied more specifically (a) to sulfur oxide and particulate pollution, occurring chiefly in coal-burning areas, and (b) to photochemical air pollution, common in southern California, which is affecting an increasing number of urban cities with intense pollution from motor-vehicle exhaust.

Smog in southern California has not been shown capable of increasing the short-term fatality rate, but both types of community air pollution cause respiratory irritation, both can aggravate asthma (though they probably do not cause it), and both are suspected of a part in the development of chronic respiratory disability — emphysema in the case of photochemical pollution, and chronic bronchitis in the case of sulfur oxide and particulate pollution. Readily measurable impairment in airway resistance and other respiratory functions occurs among the populations most likely to show increased frequencies of chronic bronchitis and emphysema. The distinction between the two diseases as causes of death is largely related to the extent to which there are adaptive mechanisms in the airways causing increased secretion of mucus.

Man is exposed to carbon monoxide (a) in cigarette smoking, (b) in occupational exposures to combustion products, (c) in connection with community air pollution, (d) in confined areas contaminated by motor-vehicle exhaust, and (e) when household cooking and heating appliances are not adequately vented. Carbon monoxide can and does kill, especially in association with occupational exposure and poorly vented appliances. There is growing suspicion that the excess mortality from coronary heart disease among cigarette smokers may be due to carbon monoxide, a major toxic constituent of cigarette smoke. (See Figure XI–7) There is also a suspicion that carbon monoxide, as a community air pollutant, may interfere with the survival of patients with acute myocardial infarction (heart attacks), and that it may play a role in impairing the operation of motor vehicles.

Figure XI–7 — POSSIBLE EPIDEMIOLOGICAL AND PATHOPHYSIOLOGICAL
MECHANISMS RELATING CARBON MONOXIDE
AND MYOCARDIAL INFARCTION

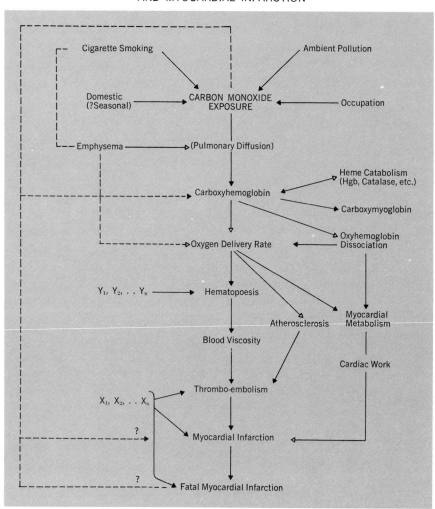

The figure shows, on the right-hand side, possible biochemical and physiological mechanisms and, on the left-hand side, possible epidemiological associations. Solid arrows indicate an increase; open arrows, a decrease or impairment of the mechanism. This scheme is qualitative and some of the reactions shown may be of insignificant magnitude.

Testable hypotheses relating carbon monoxide and myocardial infarction from a clinical and mechanistic view are numerous, but testable hypotheses relevant to the epidemiological approach are few. And yet an investigation of the epidemiological approach would produce observations on biological and physiological processes as well as studies of disease frequency.

Scientific opinion increasingly tends to the view that air-pollutant exposures, whether smog or carbon monoxide, do not generally *cause* a specific disease, but rather that they contribute to the aggravation, and possibly to the causes, of several possible diseases. In an excessively simplistic way, the main target organ for smog is the respiratory system. The main target organ for carbon monoxide is the circulatory system, with the central nervous system being a secondary target.

The human processes of adapting to these agents produce alterations in function and may also be the same mechanisms that lead to their contributions to chronic disease and disability. Should this suspicion be borne out by research over the next five to ten years, the likelihood of a substantial reduction in two very common classes of chronic disease would be greatly advanced. Since heart disease accounts for about 20 percent and chronic respiratory disease for about 2.5 percent of all deaths in California from 1965 through 1967, even a small diminution in the burden attributable to them from adaptive reactions would be well worthwhile.

Present Scientific Data Base

One major piece of evidence relating the finding of symptoms of persistent cough and sputum and impairment of respiratory function with the likelihood of developing chronic respiratory disease is a study by Gregg, a general practitioner, of patients in a relatively unpolluted sector of London. Cigarette smokers in his practice who had persistent cough and sputum when first examined had a more rapid deterioration of pulmonary function during the ensuing five years and also a lower initial function than persons with a similar smoking history but no symptoms. In the case of carbon monoxide exposures, the much higher frequencies of coronary heart disease among cigarette smokers suggest a relationship between carbon monoxide exposures and the chronic diseases associated with lipid deposition in the main blood vessels. So, too, does the demonstration by Astrup in Denmark that, among persons with well-advanced atherosclerotic disease who were smokers, there were much higher levels of carboxyhemoglobin than among those with similar smoking histories but who did not have atherosclerosis.

Recent findings may help to identify those individuals in a population who are susceptible to the chronic diseases associated with maladaptation to inhaled pollutants. These include, in particular, the demonstration that a diminution in trypsin inhibitor in the serum (the so-called alpha₁ anti-trypsin deficiency syndrome) predisposes individuals who were homozygotically deficient to the early onset of pulmonary emphysema. Such individuals are infrequent in the population; studies so far report finding only about one in 3,000. However, it is not yet known whether *heterozygotically* deficient individuals (who may comprise 5 to 15 percent of the general population) are also more prone to chronic respiratory irritants. In a few pilot studies, heterozygotically deficient individuals who were also cigarette smokers showed evidence of chronic respiratory disease in a very high proportion, namely 31 out of 33.

Needed Scientific Activity — Adaptation to carbon monoxide involves, to a substantial degree, the study of populations of cigarette smokers, since their exposures to this agent are very common and of substantial magnitude — that is, sufficient to inactivate from 5 to 15 percent of the oxygen-carrying capacity of the blood for moderately heavy smokers who inhale. Similarly, there is evidence that cigarette smoking increases the risk of chronic respiratory conditions and respiratory impairment in persons exposed both to the sulfur oxide and particulate type of pollution and to photochemical smog. (See Figure XI–8) Thus, we are unable to speak logically of the epidemiologic aspects of studying human adaptation to carbon monoxide and to smog without considering cigarette smoking.

Beyond this, however, we must also consider occupational exposures and relevant and related exposures that occur in the home and during recreation and transportation. While there are large numbers of human subjects exposed to both carbon monoxide and smog, a longitudinal study, necessary to obtain the best type of data for the study of adaptation, has rarely been undertaken for either of them. In the case of occupational

exposure to carbon monoxide, some longitudinal data have been obtained; there are, however, few longitudinal data in the case of carbon monoxide associated with cigarette smoking, since the importance of this exposure has been appreciated only since 1960. In the case of smog, there are populations occupationally exposed to two of the major ingredients that have toxic properties — namely, ozone and nitrogen dioxide — but results of the study of occupational groups are not sufficiently clear-cut for an evaluation of adaptation.

Short-term adaptive mechanisms have a more abundant data base. There is a small data base from experimental human studies, and a somewhat larger one from experimental animal studies, of adaptive mechanisms for ozone and nitrogen dioxide exposures. Data for carbon monoxide are more abundant, but for neither is the data set adequate.

Limitations — The data base for studying adaptation to these agents is unfortunately impaired by the view of one sector of the scientific community that adaptation is solely a beneficial process, one that does not carry with it the risks of the long-term consequences suggested above. Thus, a number of scientific papers have cited the ability of patients to increase the oxygen transport in response to carbon monoxide exposure as evidence that community or cigarette-smoking exposures to carbon monoxide are of little consequence to health.

Recent Scientific Findings

Impairment of Respiratory Function — It has been demonstrated that nitrogen dioxide, a major product of photochemical smog, is an effective agent for producing emphysema in experimental animals when exposures

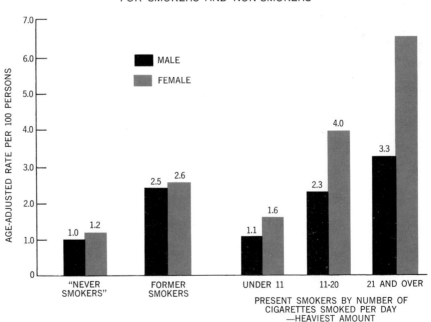

Figure XI–8 — RATES OF CHRONIC BRONCHITIS AND EMPHYSEMA FOR SMOKERS AND NON-SMOKERS

The diagram shows the substantial contribution of cigarette smoking to chronic respiratory conditions. Heavy smokers have as much as five times the excess morbidity of non-smokers. For females this excess is even greater than for males. The rates are adjusted for age and include data on subjects 17 years of age and over.

are long term and at concentrations as low as from 0.8 to 4 parts per million. The work has been reported by Freeman and his colleagues and has been demonstrated in rabbits, rats, mice, and monkeys.

Closely related is the finding of Mueller, Buell, and Thomas, at the California State Department of Public Health, that structural changes in proteins can be produced by exposures to low levels (0.25 to 5 ppm) of either nitrogen dioxide or ozone for a short period of time, and that these changes revert slowly. The mast cells reversibly disappear from the respiratory airways on exposure to nitrogen dioxide; nitrogen dioxide and ozone inhalation can lead to lipid peroxidation in the pulmonary parenchyma. These changes are all presumably adaptive in nature, but their consequences for long-term effects are certainly suggestive, since lipid peroxidation has also been associated with the aging processes.

Balchum, Armstrong, and Ury have reported the impairment of respiratory function in persons already having chronic respiratory diseases who were exposed to elevated levels of photochemical smog occurring in Los Angeles. The lung-function test most consistently responding was that of airway resistance, and its increase reflects the likelihood that persons with chronic respiratory diseases would have to expend more energy to ventilate their lungs during smoggy periods than during normal ones.

Toyama in Japan and Holland, Douglas, Waller, and Lunn in England have shown that schoolchildren exposed to pollution, mostly in the forms of sulfur oxide and particulates, have impaired respiratory function during periods in which the pollution is elevated and have a greater frequency of respiratory conditions. The finding, which has been confirmed in Italy, should also be studied in other countries. It seems quite reasonable to assume that these changes in schoolchildren represent adaptation, and with it the risk of developing chronic respiratory disease. At a meeting in Geneva in 1969 of the Directors of Cooperating Laboratories of the World Health Organization's International Reference Center on Air Pollution, the recommendation was adopted that first priority for additional comparative epidemiologic studies in air pollution should be given to studies of the effects of air pollution on schoolchildren.

Impairment of Circulatory Function — Astrup has shown that the exposure of rabbits on a high-cholesterol diet to increasing amounts of carbon monoxide will increase the atherosclerotic changes in the large blood vessels. Similar changes can be produced by placing the animals in a chamber with low oxygen tension. The findings that smokers with atherosclerosis have higher levels of carboxyhemoglobin, implying higher or more intense exposures to carbon monoxide or greater retention from smoking, than do individuals with similar smoking histories but without atherosclerosis, is strongly suggestive of the role of carbon monoxide in this process. Yet human populations at high altitude, where the oxygen tension is low, have a *lower* frequency of atherosclerosis, lower blood pressure, and lower cholesterol. Accordingly, it has been most valuable to have an experimental comparison of the effects of high altitude and of repeated carbon monoxide exposures in healthy experimental subjects reported by Astrup and Pauli.

They studied eight subjects divided into two groups of four; each group was exposed both to sufficient carbon monoxide to produce 15 percent carboxyhemoglobin and to altitude at 11,225 feet (roughly equivalent in terms of oxygen saturation). The major findings were that with *carboxy*hemoglobin exposure, the *oxy*hemoglobin saturation curve shifted to the left (i.e., the available oxygen would be given off less readily at the tissue level under these circumstances), whereas with altitude the curve shifted to the right (i.e., the hemoglobin would *more* readily give up its oxygen at the tissue level). Carboxyhemoglobin exposures did not increase the respiratory rate, but altitude did. Both types of exposure increased the rapidity with which new red blood cells were produced. Both types of exposure, if sufficiently intense and prolonged, are capable of leading to an increase in the hematocrit. Thus, the major difference in adaptation to altitude and roughly equivalent carboxyhemoglobin levels produced by exposure to this agent is that men adapt to changes in oxygen delivery in the case of altitude; in the case of carbon monoxide exposures, the changes that occur in oxygen delivery appear to be maladaptive. There is a respiratory volume compensation for decreased oxygen-carrying capacity in the case of altitude, but there is none for carbon monoxide.

Ayres, among others, has shown that different portions of the circulatory system have different ways of adapting to the impairment of oxygen transport produced by carbon monoxide exposures. (See Figure XI-9) In particular, the myocardin adapts to increased demand of the heart by increasing the blood flow, since its oxygen-extraction ratio is usually much higher than other tissues. That is to say, the heart normally takes out of the blood that circulates through it a high fraction of the available oxygen in relation to the pattern for other organs. Hence, impairment in oxygen delivery by carbon monoxide requires an increase in the blood flow through the heart muscle. In the case of people with coronary heart disease, however, there is no way in which the heart can increase its blood flow. Thus, according to Ayres' data, it is demonstrable that in persons with coronary heart disease, carbon monoxide drastically interferes with the metabolism of the heart muscle, shifting it from an oxidative to a less efficient form

Figure XI–9 — HEMODYNAMIC AND RESPIRATORY RESPONSES OF FIVE NORMAL SUBJECTS TO CARBOXYHEMOGLOBIN (COH$_b$)

Subj.	COHb (% sat)	Pressure (mm-Hg) LA (wedge)	PA (mean)	Ar t_{O_2}	Ven t_{O_2}	Ar-ven diff (% by vol.)	Cardiac output (lit./ min)	Vent (liter)	t_{CO_2} (mm-Hg)
1	0.48	28	9	89	45	3.40	5.23	4.23	34
	8.84	28	9	81	42	3.82	4.46	4.23	36
2				86	37	3.96	4.37	4.68	36
	6.29			80	30	4.55	4.35	5.72	36
3		3	14	74	42	3.92	4.31	2.55	36
		3	12	68	37	4.24	4.17	3.11	40
4	0.37	9	13	84	49	4.00	5.32	5.43	39
	4.95	9	13	79	42	4.66	6.54	7.36	38
5	0.96	7	12	77	41	4.02	6.00	4.87	36
	9.69	11	18	72	35	4.81	4.68	4.24	39

The table shows that the oxygen tensions of arterial and mixed-venous bloods decreased between 7.3 and 13.3 percent, respectively, when the carboxyhemoglobin rose to between 4.95 and 9.69 percent of saturation. Cardiac output, oxygen consumption, and body-surface ventilation per minute did not change consistently, but the difference in arterial and venous blood, reflecting extraction of oxygen by tissue increased in all five subjects. In the one patient who received the greatest amount of carbon monoxide, left arterial pressure rose and cardiac output fell, indicating abnormal left ventricular function. These studies show that small amounts of carboxyhemoglobin do indeed decrease oxygen tension in the blood which in turn may cause other problems related to the supply of blood throughout the body.

The first line of each set of data shows value before breathing CO at 0.4 percent in air; the second after breathing. Abbreviations are: sat, saturation; LA, left atrium; PA, pulmonary artery; AR, arterial; t_{O_2}, oxygen tension; Ven, mixed venous; Ar-ven diff, arterial-venous difference; Vent, ventilation per square meter of body-surface area per minute; t_{CO_2}, carbon-dioxide tension.

of metabolism. Such individuals cannot adapt efficiently to carbon monoxide exposures.

Permutt and Farhi have worked out a theoretical example of the compensations needed to maintain tissue oxygenation in the presence of 9 percent carboxyhemoglobin, which would correspond to a continuous exposure of a normal subject at sea level for several hours to carbon monoxide (CO) at 70 parts per million. Such a CO hemoglobin saturation would have an effect equivalent to that found with a 23 to 46 percent decrease in the oxygen pressure available for supplying the needs of the body, and a 13 to 37 percent decrease in blood flow or decrease in the amount of circulating hemoglobin. In order to compensate for this amount of COHb, an increase of from 19 to 39 percent in blood flow would be required. This analysis has forcefully driven home the high physiologic cost of adapting to carbon monoxide.

The Risks of Long-Term Exposures — Long-term exposures of animals, particularly small rodents, have shown that ozone will increase pulmonary fibrosis, just as long-term exposure of other animals will increase pulmonary emphysema. It has also been shown by Stokinger and his colleagues that the exposure of experimental animals to brief, low levels of ozone protects them from subsequent high-level exposure which would otherwise be fatal. This is doubtless a useful adaptive mechanism, but its cost may be to increase the risk of chronic respiratory disease. Stokinger and his group have also shown cross-tolerance between ozone and other oxidants. However, tolerance in man has not been demonstrated.

Bennett has reported on long-term exposures of small numbers of human subjects to 0.5 parts per million of ozone, 3 hours a day, 6 days a week, for 12 weeks. The individuals so exposed had a gradual decrease in the forced expiratory volume in one second which began to occur after 8 weeks of exposure and continued to be depressed for 8 weeks after the termination of exposure. A lower dose failed to produce this effect.

Prevailing Controversy and Needed Research

Cohen, Deane, and Goldsmith, utilizing data obtained for other purposes, studied the possible effect of carbon monoxide exposure on the case fatality rate among persons admitted to Los Angeles hospitals with myocardial infarction. They showed that the rate increased during the high pollution period and in the higher of the two pollution areas of Los Angeles County. Without additional studies, however, they were reluctant to attribute this increase only to carbon monoxide. Controversy also exists concerning the effect of carbon monoxide on the central nervous system and, hence, its possible role in the performance of complex tasks requiring accurate time evaluation, such as driving an automobile. There has been no decisive evidence concerning the role of carbon monoxide in general in motor-vehicle accident frequency.

The interaction of the various components of both forms of smog in producing health effects remains controversial. Of particular interest is the hypothesis recently put forward by Pitts, among others, that one of the essential mechanisms in the early oxidation of nitric oxide to nitrogen dioxide is the absorption of energy by atmospheric oxygen and conversion of some of the normal triplet oxygen to a singlet delta form that may have a finite half-life and could be of biological importance.

A cross-sectional study of the frequency of emphysema in several cities in relation to the history of smoking and of pollution exposure is going to be necessary in order to resolve some of the questions about the effects of smog on chronic respiratory disease. The identification of active atmospheric species produced by photochemical processes is an important one that may have powerful interactions with radiological health and carcinogenesis. Closely related is the possibility that agents in photochemical smog may be mutagenic or teratogenic, though such reactions would scarcely be considered adaptive ones.

Relationship to Environmental Management

It is clear that community exposure to carbon monoxide would be substantially diminished if automobiles in operation were decreased either in number or in the amount of carbon monoxide that they emit. Reduction in emissions of hydrocarbons and oxides of nitrogen should also have a substantial effect on the intensity of photochemical smog, although the effect will take a number of years to be fully evident. Since 1956, the United Kingdom has greatly reduced the amount of particulate matter in many of its urban areas, and since 1967 there has been a pronounced decrease in sulfur oxide and particulate emissions in coastal cities of eastern United States. Studies by Fletcher and his colleagues have shown that, in parallel with the decrease in particulate matter in London, there has been a decrease in the frequency of chronic bronchitis and in the amount of sputum produced by groups of people who had comparable smoking exposures all during this period.

The attention paid to atmospheric pollutants is responsive largely to public concern with air pollution as a menacing and offensive substance. The public has not felt it necessary to know the precise health effects. The possibility exists, therefore, that some questions that are of great scientific importance will never be answered, since it is hoped that the increasingly vigorous control measures advocated by the Environmental Protection Agency will reduce community exposures and thus make some of the longitudinal studies unlikely to reflect present or increased exposures.

Thus, the greatest priority should be given to the specific exploration of the hypothesis that pollutant exposures which lead to impairment of function may also increase the risk of developing chronic cardiac and respiratory disease through the mechanisms of adaptation which they provoke. Longitudinal research on exposed populations and their adaptive mechanisms has been inadequately supported because of the difficulty of assembling teams of competent investigators over the longer periods of time necessary for this sort of research. From two to ten research groups, some of which are not in the United States, will be needed to plan and carry out longitudinal studies to evaluate the adaptation of human subjects to smog and to carbon monoxide.

SUMMARY AND RECOMMENDATIONS

Reprinted from the Third Annual Report of the National Science Board *Environmental Science—Challenge for the Seventies* (NSB 71–1).

Modern civilization has reached the stage where, henceforth, no new use of technology, no increased demands on the environment for food, for other natural resources, for areas to be used for recreation, or for places to store the debris of civilization, can be undertaken to benefit some groups of individuals without a high risk of injury to others. No environmental involvement of man can any longer be regarded as all good or all bad. Problems can be mitigated, but absolute solutions are probably unattainable. The best that can be sought, therefore, is to optimize, to try to achieve the wisest cost-benefit decision for society for each action contemplated. Such a strategy requires a strong base of scientific knowledge and understanding of the environment, ability to predict reliably its future course, and, especially, the ability to construct models through systems analysis of the environment and of man's interaction with it on a scale never previously achieved.

It is within this perspective that the present status of Environmental Science has been examined. *Environmental Science is conceived in this report as the study of all of the systems of air, land, water, energy, and life that surround man. It includes all science directed to the system-level of understanding of the environment, drawing especially on such disciplines as meteorology, geophysics, oceanography, and ecology, and utilizing to the fullest the knowledge and techniques developed in such fields as physics, chemistry, biology, mathematics, and engineering.* Included, therefore, are such diverse matters as climate, air turbulence, the air-sea interface, estuaries, forests, epidemics, earthquakes, and groundwater. These environmental systems contain the complex processes that must be mastered in the solution of such human problems as the maintenance of renewable resources (water, timber, fish), the conservation of non-renewable resources (fuels, metals, species), reducing the effects of natural disasters (earthquakes, tornadoes, floods), alleviating chronic damage (erosion, drought, subsidence), abating pollution by man (smoke, pesticides, sewage), and coping with natural pollution (allergens, volcanic dust, electromagnetic "noise").

Environmental Science is now exceedingly vigorous, considered in relation to its development over many centuries. Notable advances are being recorded at an accelerating rate New tools and techniques, borrowed from all of science and technology, are being brought to bear on the problems of observation, measurement, and analysis. Across all of environmental science there is a heightened awareness of the essential nature of the environment and the directions that scientific effort should take. Nevertheless—and it is the principal conclusion of this report—

Environmental science, today, is unable to match the needs of society for definitive information, predictive capability, and the analysis of environmental systems as systems. Because existing data and current theoretical models are inadequate, environmental science remains unable in virtually all areas of application to offer more than qualitative interpretations or suggestions of environmental change that may occur in response to specific actions.

There are two primary reasons for this state of affairs. One involves the nature of environmental science itself, the other the resources available for its advancement.

(1) The natural environment is not a collection of isolated events and phenomena, but rather a vast, integral, mutually interacting system. The recent advent of new technology and technique (satellites, advanced computers, instrumentation of many types, and the methods of systems analysis) for the use of environmental science has, indeed for the first time, provided feasibility for attacking the scientific problems that this environmental system presents. The tasks ahead, however, are of unprecedented magnitude and difficulty.

(2) The trained scientific manpower available to meet this challenge is extremely limited in each of the essential aspects of environmental science. More serious is the fact that this manpower is spread exceedingly thin, both with respect to the manifold problems presented and to the institutions within which research is conducted, new scientists are educated, and scientific results are applied to the solution of problems of the public interest. Indeed, the institutions of environmental science, as here defined, remain in an early stage of development.

This situation constitutes a crisis for the Nation. While environmental problems are so diverse and diffused that virtually every activity of civilization interacts with the environment, few persons can be aware of the full scope of challenge that lies ahead. The current mismatch between capability and need is at least comparable to any other challenge to science and technology that was encountered during this century.

To meet this situation the National Science Board offers five groups of recommendations:

1. NATIONAL PROGRAM

Several factors emphasize the urgency of establishing a national program for advancing the science of environmental systems: (a) New organizations formed at the highest level of the Federal Government, the Council on Environmental Quality and the Environmental Protection Agency, have been charged with responsibilities that include the assessment of the environmental impact of civilized man. These agencies must foresee secondary effects and compare quantitatively the multiple consequences of alternative courses of action. Such efforts are severely limited by the present level of understanding of the behavior of environmental systems. They would become progressively more feasible as advances in environmental science increase man's predictive power. (b) The use of energy and the processing of material by man are doubling every 14 years.* Correspondingly, the number and severity of environmental problems will increase, while the adequacy of *ad hoc* piecemeal expedients will decrease. (c) As population grows, and with it the artifacts of civilization, the human and economic losses due to sporadic natural disasters, already great, will increase in scale. (d) At the same time, the intensification of man's needs for both renewable and non-renewable resources requires even greater manipulation and mastery of the natural and man-made systems that constitute the environment.

It is, therefore, recommended that this urgency be recognized through the early development of a comprehensive national program to expedite the progress of environmental science.

The problems with which environmental science must deal, however, do not respect local, State, or even national boundaries. It is thus further recommended that this national program explicitly provide for the essential Federal role in encouraging and supporting the work of environmental science, quite apart from the role the Federal Government is already exercising with respect to improving and protecting the environment (e.g., programs of soil conservation, sewage treatment, air and water pollution control, etc.). Both nationally and in matters of international cooperation the Federal Government must assume leadership in fostering scientific advance.

This national program should be based on three efforts:

(1) Emphasis should be given to projects, manned by coordinate teams, directed to intermediate scale or "mesoscale" problems, that is, problems on the scale of lakes and estuaries, urban areas, regional weather systems, and oceanic fisheries. Advances on this scale will provide immediate benefits to man.

(2) At the same time, the program must ensure continued effort on global problems, even though their solution may require the resolution of smaller scale issues. In the long run it is the global constraints that will shape and delimit the future development of civilization.

(3) Finally, the program should ensure the continued vigor of those aspects of disciplinary research and graduate education needed to provide the specialists and new knowledge required for environmental science.

The remaining recommendations form an important part of the total recommendation of a national program. The entire program should be established at the earliest practicable date, if progress during this decade and its culmination during the following decades are to be commensurate with the urgency now faced.

2. PRIORITIES

One of the inescapable conclusions of this report is that the number and complexity of scientific problems, both theo-

retical and experimental, that confront environmental science far exceed the capability of available manpower to attack all of them effectively at the same time. If these resources remain distributed as they are, scattered and fragmented, and if problems to be solved are selected largely on the basis of the perceptions of individuals or small isolated groups, progress in environmental science cannot meet the needs of expressed national goals and purposes.

Accordingly, it is recommended that early consideration be given to strengthening arrangements whereby priorities for environmental science can be set, matched to existing and required scientific and engineering manpower, and changed as circumstances warrant. In setting such priorities appropriate weight must be given to the feasibility of achieving scientific solutions in a reasonable time and to the social and economic costs and benefits that could accrue if solutions were attained.

3. ORGANIZATION FOR ENVIRONMENTAL SCIENCE

The scope encompassed by the national program, proposed above, the Federal role inherent in this broad effort, and the patent need for establishing priorities raise serious questions of the adequacy of present arrangements within the Federal Government for planning, coordinating, managing, and reviewing programs of environmental science. As for all science, environmental science today is the responsibility of many agencies, often with conflicting interest under differing agency missions and responsive to many Congressional committees. At the same time the problems to be solved are broader, more difficult, and more dependent upon the coordinated use of scientific resources than those faced in the earlier development of nuclear energy, radar, and space exploration.

For these reasons, it is strongly urged that the Federal responsibility for environmental science, and for its promotion, organization, and support, be considered as important as the corresponding but separate responsibility for environmental quality. In particular, arrangements for Federal decisionmaking must be especially effective for the following activities:

(1) The setting of priorities affecting all research and development in environmental science supported by the Federal Government.

(2) The determination of appropriate and feasible time schedules for the projects of the national program and ensuring that projects are managed in accordance with such schedules.

(3) The provision of full coordination of the efforts of all Federal agencies engaged in the support or performance of research in environmental science, quite apart from efforts in application or regulation.

(4) The establishment of organizational and employment incentives suitable for the types of projects that are characteristic of environmental science through the support of national centers and specialized institutes.

---

*Both activities have shown 5% average annual growth rates for the last 20 years, as reported in *Man's Impact on the Global Environment: Assessment and Recommendations for Action*, MIT Press, Cambridge, Mass., 1970. The total consumption of fossil fuel in the United States also grows about 5% per year; the conversion of an increasing fraction of fossil energy to electrical energy leads to a higher annual growth rate in the utilities.

(5) The encouragement of State and local governments and private supporting organizations to subscribe to the national program, as it is developed, and to the pattern of priorities adopted.

With respect to the organizations where the work of environmental science is done, several considerations are of the greatest importance.

Environmental science, as defined in this report, should be viewed as a distinctive type of activity lying between the extremes of traditional, basic science, on the one hand, and the organizations established by society for the application and use of science and technology. It shares the scientific motivations of the former and the multidisciplinary and organizational complexity of the latter.

Various types of organizational structures should thus be attempted, as experiments in the management of environmental science. Two conclusions are especially important:

(a) In academic institutions, which employ two-thirds of the manpower in environmental science, the need for strong departmental structures has historically hindered the development of effective interdepartmental programs. Within the last few years, however, new capability and experience in systems management, often combined with central funding for complex problems, have given a new vitality to multidisciplinary efforts. A few research institutes and national laboratories have also begun ambitious multidisciplinary studies of environmental problems. These experiments in organization should be continued, expanded, and followed closely.

(b) Industry possesses great capability in systems analysis and systems management, but rarely offers the broad array of scientific competence needed in environmental science. Government has additional strengths, particularly in the application of environmental science to environmental management. A more effective use of these resources can be made by combining the talents of industry, government, and universities in new types of research organizations and by seeking new approaches to the management of environmental science.

4. FUNDING FOR ENVIRONMENTAL SCIENCE

If progress in environmental science is to be made at an acceptable rate it is essential that additional manpower be made available both through education and through transfer from other fields and activities. This will occur only if appropriate employment opportunities and incentives are provided. The *character* of funding is especially important to this end.

In addition to the opportunity provided by new types of organizations, as recommended above, provision should be made for continuity of funding of programs of environmental science as being one of the principal means for attracting the best talent.

It is further recommended that the funding of equipment, facilities, and logistics for environmental science be consistent with scientific needs and opportunities. The highest priority should be given to the needs of multidisciplinary teams engaged in the study of environmental systems.

5. DEVELOPMENT OF ADDITIONAL MANPOWER

While it is essential that the disciplinary strength of academic institutions be maintained and increased across all fields of science, these institutions also have a responsibility specifically with respect to the manpower of environmental science.

Although competent specialists transferring from related disciplines can constructively enter fields of environmental science through on-the-job training, the process can often be faster and more effective if retraining opportunities are available within the educational context. Hence, it is recommended that colleges and universities consider appropriate means for supplementary education in environmental science for scientific and technical personnel.

Of special importance to implementing a national program for environmental science is the existence of an informed citizenry, both as a source of future scientists and as the necessary basis for national understanding and motivation of the entire program. The colleges and universities thus have a special opportunity to contribute by the development of new curricula in which to present the perspective of environmental science, as well as of new courses and programs, especially directed to the undergraduate.

Manpower needs related to environmental science are not confined to the scientists, engineers, technicians, and others who contribute to scientific progress. As environmental science advances, there will be an increasing need for "natural resource administrators" to serve in local, State, or Federal governments. The education of these public administrators involves two types of interdisciplinary training. On the one hand, scientists and engineers must gain a better understanding of the social, economic, legal, and political environment within which practical action must be sought. On the other hand, students of public administration must gain a better perception of the scientific process and a better understanding of how scientists can contribute effectively to the practical solution of environmental problems. It is recommended that substantial and adequate funding be made available for these purposes.

———◆———

Even with the implementation of these recommendations only gradual progress can be anticipated. Environmental science is too difficult, too broad in scope, and too near the beginning for an effective match with societal need to be achieved during this decade. But, correspondingly, the stakes are too high to miss the opportunity for making the 1970's the base on which a constructive future for mankind will be established.

SELECTED REFERENCES

The following references are furnished to enable the reader to go beyond the material presented in this book. Most of the references are readily available, although there are some that, of necessity, are in more abstruse scientific journals. In some cases, classics in the field are cited because of their importance. These references are by no means all-inclusive or exhaustive. They serve only as a bridge to more complete and comprehensive information in the several areas discussed.

I. THE SOLAR-TERRESTRIAL ENVIRONMENT

Chamberlain, J. W., 1961: *Physics of the Aurora and Airglow.* Academic Press, Inc., New York, N.Y.

Committee on Solar-Terrestrial Research, 1969: *Physics of the Earth in Space: The Role of Ground-Based Research.* National Research Council, National Academy of Sciences, Washington, D. C.

Kavanaugh, L. D., Jr., L. W. Schardt and E. C. Roelof, 1970: "Solar Wind and Solar Energetic Particles: Properties and Interactions," *Reviews of Geophysics and Space Physics,* 8, 389-460.

King, J. W. and W. S. Newman (eds.), 1967: *Solar-Terrestrial Physics.* Academic Press, Inc., New York, N.Y.

Space Science Board, 1971: *Priorities for Space Research 1971-1980.* National Research Council, National Academy of Sciences, Washington, D. C.

Whitten, R. C. and I. G. Poppoff, 1965: *Physics of the Lower Ionosphere.* Prentice Hall, Inc., Englewood Cliffs, N.J.

Williams, D. J. and G. D. Mead (eds.), 1969: "International Symposium on the Physics of the Magnetosphere," *Reviews of Geophysics and Space Physics,* 7, 1-459.

Wolfe, J. H. and D. S. Intriligator, 1970: "The Solar Wind Interaction with the Geomagnetic Field," *Space Science Reviews,* 10, 511-596.

II. DYNAMICS OF THE SOLID EARTH

Aggarwal, Y. P., L. R. Sykes, J. Armbruster and M. L. Sbar, 1973: "Premonitory Changes in Seismic Velocities and Prediction of Earthquakes," *Nature,* 241, 101-104.

Committee on Geological Sciences, 1972: *The Earth and Human Affairs.* National Research Council, National Academy of Sciences. Canfield Press, San Francisco, Calif.

Division of Earth Sciences, 1969: *Resources and Man.* National Research Council, National Academy of Sciences. W. H. Freeman & Co., San Francisco, Calif.

Division of Earth Sciences, 1969: *Toward Reduction of Losses from Earthquakes.* National Research Council, National Academy of Sciences, Washington, D. C.

Drake, C. L., 1970: *The Geological Revolution.* Condon Lectures, Oregon State System of Higher Education, Eugene, Ore.

Frye, J. C., 1971: *A Geologist Views the Environment.* Environmental Geology Notes (No. 42), Illinois State Water Survey, Urbana, Ill.

Gass, I. G., P. J. Smith and R. C. L. Wilson (eds.), 1971: *Understanding the Earth.* The Open University, The Artemis Press, Sussex, England.

Geodynamics Committee, 1971: "Geodynamics Project: Development of a U.S. Program," *EOS, Transactions, American Geophysical Union,* 52, 396-405.

Geophysics Research Board, 1964: *Solid-Earth Geophysics: Survey and Outlook.* National Research Council, National Academy of Sciences, Washington, D. C.

Geophysics Research Board, 1969: *The Earth's Crust and Upper Mantle.* National Research Council, National Academy of Sciences, Washington, D. C.

Robertson, E. C. (ed.), 1972: *The Nature of the Solid Earth.* McGraw-Hill Book Co., Inc., New York, N.Y.

Sanders, H. J. (assoc. ed.), 1967: "Chemistry and the Solid Earth," *Chemistry and the Environment, the Solid Earth, the Oceans, the Atmosphere,* 2A-19A, American Chemical Society, Washington, D. C.

Schmidt, R. G. and H. R. Shaw, 1972: *Atlas of Volcanic Phenomena.* U.S. Geological Survey, Department of Interior, Washington, D. C.

III. CLIMATIC CHANGE

Brooks, C. E. P., 1949: *Climate Through the Ages.* Dover Publications, Inc., New York, N.Y.

Budyko, M. I., 1972: "The Future Climate," *EOS, Transactions, American Geophysical Union, 53,* 868-874.

Lamb, H. H., 1966: *The Changing Climate.* Methuen and Co., Ltd., London, England.

Lamb, H. H., 1970: "Volcanic Dust in the Atmosphere with Chronology and Assessment of Its Meteorological Significance," *Philosophical Transactions of the Royal Society, 266,* 425-533.

Landsberg, H. E., 1970: "Man-Made Climatic Changes," *Science, 170,* 1265-1274.

Lorenz, E. N., 1970: "Climatic Change as a Mathematical Problem," *Journal of Applied Meteorology, 9,* 325-329.

Mitchell, J. M., Jr., 1968: "Causes of Climatic Change," *Meteorological Monographs, 8,* 1-159.

Sellers, A. D., 1969: "A Global Climate Model Based on the Energy Balance of the Earth-Atmosphere System," *Journal of Applied Meteorology, 8,* 392-400.

Shapely, H. (ed.), 1953: *Climatic Change: Evidence, Causes and Effects.* Harvard University Press, Cambridge, Mass.

Study of Critical Environmental Problems (SCEP), 1970: *Man's Impact on the Global Environment.* The MIT Press, Cambridge, Mass.

Study of Man's Impact on Climate (SMIC), 1971: *Inadvertent Climate Modification.* The MIT Press, Cambridge, Mass.

IV. DYNAMICS OF THE ATMOSPHERE-OCEAN SYSTEM

Bater, D. J., 1969: "Models of Ocean Circulation," *Scientific American, 221,* 114-121.

Bjerknes, J., 1969: "Atmospheric Telecommunications from the Equatorial Pacific," *Monthly Weather Review, 97,* 163-172.

Changnon, S. A., Jr., 1969: "Recent Studies of Urban Effects on Precipitation in the United States," *Bulletin of the American Meteorological Society, 50,* 411-421.

Committee on Atmospheric Sciences, 1966: *The Feasibility of a Global Observation and Analysis Experiment.* National Research Council, National Academy of Sciences, Washington, D. C.

Dutton, J. A. and H. A. Panofsky, 1970: "Clear Air Turbulence: A Mystery May be Unfolding," *Science, 167,* 937-944.

Haltiner, G. J., 1971: *Numerical Weather Prediction.* John Wiley & Sons, Inc., New York, N.Y.

Manabe, S. and K. Bryan, 1969: "Climate and the Ocean Circulation," *Monthly Weather Review, 97,* 739-827.

Munk, W. H., 1966: "Abyssal Recipes," *Deep Sea Research, 13,* 707-730.

Newell, R. E., 1971: "The Global Circulation of Atmospheric Pollutants," *Scientific American, 224,* 32-42.

Petterssen, S., 1956: *Weather Analysis and Forecasting* (2nd ed.) (2 volumes). McGraw-Hill Book Co., Inc., New York, N.Y.

Shuman, F. S. and J. B. Hovermale, 1968: "An Operational Six-Layer Primitive Equation Model," *Journal of Applied Meteorology, 7,* 525-547.

Stewart, R. W., 1969: "The Atmosphere and the Ocean," *Scientific American, 221,* 76-86.

Stommel, H., 1965: *Gulf Stream: A Physical and Dynamical Description.* University of California Press, Berkeley, Calif.

Stommel, H., 1970: "Future Prospects for Physical Oceanography," *Science, 168,* 1531-1537.

Sverdrup, H. U., M. W. Johnson and R. H. Fleming, 1942: *The Oceans.* Prentice-Hall, Inc., Englewood Cliffs, N.J.

V. SEVERE STORMS

Chalmers, J. A., 1967: *Atmospheric Electricity* (2nd ed.). Pergamon Press, Inc., New York, N.Y.

Dunn, G. E. and B. I. Miller, 1964: *Atlantic Hurricanes* (2nd ed.). Louisiana State University Press, Baton Rouge, La.

Flora, S. D., 1954: *Tornadoes of the United States.* University of Oklahoma Press, Norman, Okla.

Fujita, T. T., 1965: "Palm Sunday Tornadoes of April 11, 1965," *Monthly Weather Review, 98,* 29-69.

Gentry, R. C., 1969: "Project Stormfury," *Bulletin of the American Meteorological Society, 50,* 404-409.

Gentry, R. C., 1970: "Hurricane Debbie Modification Experiments, August 1969," *Science, 168,* 473-475.

Kessler, E., 1970: "Tornadoes," *Bulletin of the American Meteorological Society, 51,* 926-936.

Musil, D. J., 1970: "Computer Modeling of Hailstone Growth in the Feeder Clouds," *Journal of the Atmospheric Sciences, 27,* 474-482.

Orville, R. E., 1968: "A High-Speed Time-Resolved Spectroscopic Study of the Lightning Return Stroke," *Journal of the Atmospheric Sciences, 25,* 827-856.

Palmén, E. H. and C. W. Newton, 1969: *Atmospheric Circulation Systems: Their Structure and Physical Interpretation.* Academic Press, Inc., New York, N.Y.

Rosenthal, S. L., 1970: "A Circular Symmetric Primitive Equation Model of Tropical Cyclone Development Containing an Explicit Water Vapor Cycle," *Monthly Weather Review, 98,* 643-663.

Sulakvelidze, G. K., 1969: *Rainstorms and Hail* (translated from Russian). U.S. Department of Commerce (TT 68-50446), National Technical Information Service, Springfield, Va.

Uman, M. A., 1969: *Lightning.* McGraw-Hill Book Co., Inc., New York, N.Y.

VI. PRECIPITATION AND REGIONAL WEATHER PHENOMENA

Appleman, H. S. and F. G. Coons, Jr., 1970: "The Use of Jet Aircraft Engines to Dissipate Warm Fog," *Journal of Applied Meteorology, 9,* 464-466.

Battan, L. J., 1967: "Silver-Iodide Seeding and Precipitation Initiation in Convective Clouds," *Journal of Applied Meteorology, 6,* 317-322.

Beckwith, W. B., 1968: "An Analysis of Airport Fog Dispersal Operations with Giant Hygroscopic Nuclei," *Journal of Applied Meteorology, 7,* 860-869.

Biswas, K. R., R. K. Kapoor, K. K. Kanuga and B. V. Ramanta Murty, 1967: "Cloud Seeding Experiment Using Common Salt," *Journal of Applied Meteorology, 6,* 914-923.

Carlson, T. N. and J. M. Prospero, 1972: "The Large-Scale Movement of Saharan Air Outbreaks over the Northern Equatorial Atlantic," *Journal of Applied Meteorology, 11,* 283-297.

Committee on Atmospheric Sciences, 1966: *Weather and Climate Modification: Problems and Prospects.* National Research Council, National Academy of Sciences, Washington, D. C.

Fleagle, R. G. (ed.), 1968: *Weather Modification, Science and Public Policy.* University of Washington Press, Seattle, Wash.

Flowers, E. C., R. A. McCormick and K. R. Kurfis, 1969: "Atmospheric Turbidity over the United States, 1961-1966," *Journal of Applied Meteorology, 8,* 955-962.

Jiusto, J. E., R. S. Pilie and W. C. Kocmond, 1968: "Fog Modification with Giant Hygroscopic Nuclei," *Journal of Applied Meteorology, 7,* 860-869.

Mielke, P. W., L. O. Grant and C. F. Chappell, 1970: "Elevation and Spatial Variation Effects of Wintertime Orographic Cloud Seeding," *Journal of Applied Meteorology, 9,* 476-488.

Namias, J., 1966: "Nature and Possible Causes of the Northeastern United States Drought During 1962-65," *Monthly Weather Review, 94,* 543-554.

Ramage, C. S., 1971: *Monsoon Meteorology.* Academic Press, Inc., New York, N.Y.

Riehl, H., 1954: *Tropical Meteorology.* McGraw-Hill Book Co., Inc., New York, N.Y.

Simpson, J. and V. Wiggert, 1970: "Rainfall Enhancement by Dynamic Cloud Modification," *Science, 170,* 127-132.

Sugg, A. L., 1968: "Beneficial Aspects of the Tropical Cyclone," *Journal of Applied Meteorology, 7,* 39-45.

Taubenfeld, H. J. (ed.), 1970: *Controlling the Weather: A Study of Law and Regulatory Processes.* The Dunnellen Co., Inc., New York, N.Y.

VII. WATER RESOURCES, FORESTRY AND AGRICULTURE

Bormann, F. H., G. E. Likens, D. W. Fisher and R. S. Pierce, 1968: "Nutrient Loss Accelerated by Clear-Cutting of a Forest Ecosystem," *Science, 159,* 882-884.

Bosselman, F. and D. Callies, 1972: *The Quiet Revolution in Land Use Control.* Council on Environmental Quality, U.S. Government Printing Office, Washington, D. C.

Byerly, T. C., 1966: "The Role of Livestock in Food Production," *Journal of Animal Science, 25,* 552-566.

Calder, R., 1962: *Common Sense about a Starving World.* MacMillan Co., Inc., New York, N.Y.

Coffman, W. P., K. W. Cummins and J. C. Wuycheck, 1971: "Energy Flow in a Woodland Stream Ecosystem: I Tissue Support Trophic Structure of the Autumnal Community," *Archives of Hydrobiology, 68,* 232-276.

Guy, H. P., 1970: *Sediment Problems in Urban Areas.* U.S. Geological Survey Circular 601-E, U.S. Department of Interior, Washington, D. C.

Hayami, Y. and V. W. Ruttan, 1971: *Agricultural Development: An International Perspective.* The Johns Hopkins Press, Baltimore, Md.

Kneese, A. V., 1965: *Economic and Related Problems on Water Resources Management.* Resources for the Future Reprint 55, Washington, D. C.

Loomis, R. S. and W. A. Williams, 1963: "Maximum Crop Productivity: An Estimate," *Crop Science, 3,* 67-72.

Oglesby, T. R., C. A. Carlson and J. A. McCann (eds.), 1972: *River Ecology and Man.* Academic Press, Inc., New York, N.Y.

Panel on the World Food Supply, 1967: *The World Food Problem, Vols. I and II.* President's Science Advisory Committee, U.S. Government Printing Office, Washington, D. C.

Schmitt, W. R., 1965: "The Planetary Food-Potential," *New York Academy of Science Annals, 118,* 645-718.

National Water Commission, 1973: *Water Policies for the Future.* U.S. Government Printing Office, Washington, D. C.

Watt, K. E. F., 1967: *Ecology and Resource Management: A Quantitative Approach.* McGraw-Hill Book Co., Inc., New York, N.Y.

VIII. AQUATIC ECOSYSTEMS

Bardach, J. E. and J. H. Ryther, 1968: *The Status and Potential of Aquaculture, II, Particularly Fish Culture.* U.S. Department of Commerce (BP 177-768), National Technical Information Service, Springfield, Va.

Barnes, H., 1964-72: *Oceanography and Marine Biology, An Annual Review.* George Allen and Unwin Ltd., London, England.

Coker, R. E., 1962: *This Great and Wide Sea.* Harper and Row, Inc., New York, N.Y.

Costlow, J. D., Jr. (ed.), 1971: *Fertility of the Sea, 1 & 2.* Gordon and Breach Science Publishers, Inc., New York, N.Y.

Gannon, J. E., 1969: *Great Lakes Plankton Investigations: A Bibliography.* Special Report 7, University of Wisconsin Center for Great Lakes Studies, Madison, Wis.

Hardy, A., 1965: *The Open Sea, 1 & 2.* Houghton Mifflin Co., Inc., New York, N.Y.

Hedgpeth, J. W. (ed.), 1957: *Treatise on Marine Ecology,* Vol. 1. Memoir of the Geological Society of America, Vol. 67 (No. 1), Boulder, Colo.

Hill, M. N. (ed.), 1963: *The Sea* (Vol. 2). John Wiley and Sons, Inc., New York, N.Y.

Hutchinson, G. E., 1957: *Treatise on Limnology, 1.* John Wiley and Sons, Inc., New York, N.Y.

Jorgensen, C. B., 1966: *The Biology of Suspension-Feeding Organisms.* Pergamon Press, Inc., New York, N.Y.

Marshall, S. M. and A. P. Orr, 1955: *Biology of a Marine Copepod.* Oliver and Boyd, London, England.

Milway, C. P., 1968: *Eutrophication in Large Lakes and Impoundments.* Organization for Economic Cooperation and Development, Paris, France.

Moiseev, P. A., 1969: *The Living Resources of the World Ocean* (translated from Russian). U.S. Department of Commerce (TT 71-50026), National Technical Information Service, Springfield, Va.

Planning Committee for the International Symposium on Eutrophication, 1969: *Eutrophication: Courses, Consequences and Correctives.* National Academy of Sciences, Washington, D. C.

Raymont, J. F. G., 1963: *Plankton and Productivity of the Oceans.* Pergamon Press, Inc., New York, N.Y.

Revelle, R., 1969: "The Ocean," *Scientific American, 221,* 54-65.

Ruttner, F., 1952: *Fundamentals of Limnology.* University of Toronto Press, Toronto, Canada.

Ryther, J. H., 1969: "Photosynthesis and Fish Production in the Sea," *Science, 166,* 72-76.

Ryther, J. H. and J. E. Bardach, 1968: *The Status and Potential of Aquaculture, I, Particularly Invertebrate and Algae Culture.* U.S. Department of Commerce (BP 177-767), National Technical Information Service, Springfield, Va.

Steele, J. H. (ed.), 1970: *Marine Food Chains.* University of California Press, Berkeley, Calif.

IX. TERRESTRIAL ECOSYSTEMS

Andrewartha, H. G. and L. C. Birch, 1954: *The Distribution and Abundance of Animals.* University of Chicago Press, Chicago, Ill.

Cooper, C. F., 1961: "The Ecology of Fire," *Scientific American, 204,* 150-160.

Darling, F., 1960: "Wildlife Husbandry in Africa," *Scientific American, 203,* 123-138.

Darlington, P. J., 1957: *Zoogeography.* John Wiley and Sons, Inc., New York, N.Y.

Dasmann, R. F., 1968: *Environmental Conservation* (2nd ed.). John Wiley and Sons, Inc., New York, N.Y.

Ehrlich, P. R., 1968: *The Population Bomb.* Ballantyne Books, Inc., New York, N.Y.

Ehrlich, P. R. and A. H. Ehrlich, 1970: *Population, Resources, Environment: Issues in Human Ecology.* W. H. Freeman and Co., San Francisco, Calif.

Hairston, N. G., F. E. Smith and L. B. Slobodkin, 1960: "Community Structure, Population Control and Competition," *American Naturalist, 94,* 421-425.

Hardin, G., 1968: "The Tragedy of the Commons," *Science, 162,* 1243-1248.

Hazen, W. E., 1964: *Readings in Population and Community Ecology.* W. B. Saunders Co., Philadelphia, Pa.

Huffaker, C. B. (ed.), 1971: *Biological Control.* Plenum Press, New York, N.Y.

Hutchinson, G. E., 1970: "The Biosphere," *Scientific American, 223,* 44-53.

Kendeigh, S. C., 1961: *Animal Ecology.* Prentice-Hall, Inc., Englewood Cliffs, N.J.

Kormondy, E. J. (ed.), 1965: *Readings in Ecology.* Prentice-Hall, Inc., Englewood Cliffs, N.J.

Lack, D., 1954: *The Natural Regulation of Animal Numbers.* The Oxford University Press, London, England.

Odum, E. P. (ed.), 1971: *Fundamentals of Ecology.* W. B. Saunders Co., Philadelphia, Pa.

Odum, E. P., 1963: *Ecology*. Holt, Rinehart and Winston, Inc., New York, N.Y.

Odum, H. T., 1971: *Environment, Power, Society*. John Wiley and Sons, Inc., Interscience Publishers, New York, N.Y.

Van Dyne, G., 1969: *The Ecosystem Concept in Natural Resource Management*. Academic Press, Inc., New York, N.Y.

Workshop on Global Ecological Problems, 1972: *Man in the Living Environment*. Institute of Ecology Report, University of Wisconsin Press, Madison, Wis.

ENVIRONMENTAL CONTAMINANTS

Agricultural Board, 1972: *Pest Control Strategies for the Future*. National Research Council, National Academy of Sciences, Washington, D. C.

Blanchard, D. C. and L. D. Syzdek, 1972: "Concentration of Bacteria in Jet Drops from Bursting Bubbles," *Journal of Geophysical Research, 77*, 5087-5099.

Brittin, W. E., R. West and R. Williams (eds.), 1972: *Air and Water Pollution*. Colorado Associated University Press, Boulder, Colo.

Butcher, S. S. and R. J. Charlson, 1972: *An Introduction to Air Chemistry*. Academic Press, Inc., New York, N.Y.

Cairns, J. Jr., G. R. Tonza and B. C. Parker, 1972: "Pollution Related Structural and Functional Changes in Aquatic Communities with Emphasis on Freshwater Algae and Protozoa," *Proceedings of the Academy of Natural Sciences of Philadelphia, Pa., 124*, 79-127.

Committee on Plant and Animal Pests, 1969: *Insect Pest Management and Control*. National Research Council, National Academy of Sciences, Washington, D. C.

Division of Medical Sciences, 1962: *Tropical Health: A Report on a Study of Needs and Resources*. National Research Council, National Academy of Sciences, Washington, D. C.

Eagen, B. A. and J. R. Mahoney, 1972: "Applications of a Numerical Air Pollution Transport Model to Dispersion in the Atmospheric Boundary Layer," *Journal of Applied Meteorology, 11*, 1023-1039.

Garlick, J. P. and R. W. J. Keay, 1970: *Human Ecology in the Tropics*. Pergamon Press, Inc., New York, N.Y.

Goldberg, E. A. (convener), 1972: *Baseline Studies of Pollutants in the Marine Environment and Research Recommendations*. The IDOE Baseline Conference, May 24-26, 1972, New York, N.Y.

Gregory, P. H., 1973: *Microbiology of the Atmosphere* (2nd ed.). Halsted Press, New York, N.Y.

Hidy, G. M. and J. R. Brock, 1970: *The Dynamics of Aerocolloidal Systems*. Pergamon Press, Inc., New York, N.Y.

Leighton, P. A., 1961: *Photochemistry of Air Pollution*. Academic Press, Inc., New York, N.Y.

Ocean Science Committee, 1971: *Marine Environmental Quality*. National Research Council, National Academy of Sciences, Washington, D. C.

Olson, T. A. and F. J. Burgess (eds.), 1967: *Pollution and Marine Ecology*. John Wiley and Sons, Inc., Interscience Publishers, New York, N.Y.

Pimental, D., 1971: *Ecological Effects of Pesticides on Non-Target Species*. Office of Science and Technology, U.S. Government Printing Office, Washington, D. C.

Rabb, R. L. and F. E. Guthrie (eds.), 1970: *Concepts of Pest Management*. North Carolina State University Press, Raleigh, N.C.

Singer, S. F. (ed.), 1970: *Global Effects of Environmental Pollution*. Springer-Verlag, New York, N.Y.

Stern, A. C. (ed.), 1968: *Air Pollution* (2nd ed.). Academic Press, Inc., New York, N.Y.

Sykes, G. and F. A. Skinner (eds.), 1971: *Microbial Aspects of Pollution, A Symposium*. Academic Press, Inc., New York, N.Y.

Wood, D. L., R. M. Silverstein and M. Nakajima, 1970: *Control of Insect Behavior by Natural Products*. Academic Press, Inc., New York, N.Y.

XI. HUMAN ADAPTATION TO ENVIRONMENTAL STRESS

Aiger, J. S., 1971: "Early Cultural Identification in Southwestern Alaska," *Science, 171*, 87-88.

Baker, P. T., 1969: "Human Adaptation to High Altitudes," *Science, 163*, 1149-1156.

Baker, P. T. and J. S. Weiner (eds.), 1966: *The Biology of Human Adaptability*. Oxford University Press, London, England.

Chagnon, N. A., 1968: *Yanomama: The Fierce People*. Holt, Rinehart and Winston, Inc., New York, N.Y.

Cohen, S. I., M. Deane and J. R. Goldsmith, 1969: "Carbon Monoxide and Survival from Myocardial Infarction," *Archives of Environmental Health, 19*, 510-517.

Goldsmith, J. R., 1969: "Air Pollution Epidemiology," *Archives of Environmental Health, 18*, 516-522.

Goldsmith, J. R., 1970: "Contributions of Motor Vehicle Exhaust, Industry, and Cigarette Smoking to Community Carbon Monoxide Exposures," *Annals of the New York Academy of Sciences, 174*, 122-134.

Hanna, J. M., 1971: "Responses of Quechua Indians to Coca Ingestion during Cold Exposure," *American Journal of Physical Anthropology, 34,* 273-277.

Little, M. A., R. B. Thomas, R. B. Mazess and P. T. Baker, 1971: "Population Differences and Developmental Changes in Extremity Temperature Responses to Cold Among Andean Indians," *Human Biology, 43,* 70-91.

Livingstone, F. B., H. Gershowitz, J. V. Neel, W. W. Zuelzer and M. D. Solomon, 1960: "The Distribution of Several Blood Group Genes in Liberia, the Ivory Coast and Upper Volta," *American Journal of Physical Anthropology, 18,* 161-178.

Milan, F. A., 1968: "The International Study of Eskimos," *Arctic, 21,* 123-126.

Neel, J. V., 1970: "Lessons from a Primitive People," *Science, 170,* 815-822.

Neel, J. V., W. R. Centerwall, N. A. Chagnon and H. L. Casey, 1970: "Notes on the Effect of Measles and Measle Vaccine in a Virgin-Soil Population of South American Indians," *American Journal of Epidemiology, 91,* 418-429.

Ward, R. H. and J. V. Neel, 1970: "Gene Frequencies and Microdifferentiation among the Makiritore Indians, IV—Comparison of a Genetic Network with Ethnohistory and Migration Matrices: A New Index of Genetic Isolation," *American Journal of Human Genetics, 22,* 538-561.

Wohlwill, J. F. and D. H. Carson (eds.), 1972: *Environment and the Social Sciences: Perspectives and Applications.* American Psychological Association, Inc., Washington, D. C.

World Health Organization, 1972: *Health Hazards of the Human Environment.* World Health Organization, Geneva, Switzerland.

Youseff, M. K., S. M. Horvath and R. W. Bullard, 1972: *Physiological Adaptations: Desert and Mountain.* Academic Press, Inc., New York, N.Y.

INDEX

A

Absorption
  radiation aerosols, 58, 89
  water in forest canopy, 202
Abyssinian Plateau, Africa, 123
Accademia del Cimento, Florence, Italy, 51
Acclimatization: high altitudes, 380, 381, 382
Accumulation: cloud zone, 149, Fig. V–13
Acoustic waves: volcanic eruptions, 44
Actinic rays in urban areas, 117
Adaptation
  climatic
    high altitude, 379–385
    skin color, 375
  genetic
    see Natural selection
  human
    limitations, 387
    to air pollution, 338, 385–390
    to high altitude, 379–385
    to tropical climates, 378
  technological, 338
Adelie penguins, 232
A-disciplinary problems
  see Multidisciplinary problems
Advection in water cycle, 202
AEC, see Atomic Energy Commission, U.S.
Aerobiology, 339–349
  particulates, Fig. X–6
Aerobiology Program, U.S. (IBP), 339, 342, 344
Aerosols
  in atmosphere, 55, 58, 69
    effect on circulation, 89, 91
    effect on climate, 64, 116
    effect on precipitation, 192
    effect on radiation balance, 67, 68
  in troposphere, detection by radar, 112
    see also Nucleating agents; Nuclei; Particulates
Aesthetics
  Corpus Christi Bay, Fig. VIII–10
  forest management, 293
  lakes, 260
  of the environment, 338
  oil on ocean surface, 361
Africa
  agriculture, 74, 215, 220, 242, 291, 297
  arable land, Fig. VII–8
  atmosphere-ocean system, 82, 191, 192, 193, 194, 358
  climatic change, 51, 52, 69, 72
  data networks, 59
  earth processes, 27, 28, 32, 33, 44
  environmental contamination, 217, 329, Fig. X–12, 364–367
  human adaptation, 376, 377
  severe storms, 123, Fig. V–1, 154, Fig. VI–10
  tropical research facilities, 185
Aging processes
  human
    air pollution, 388
    at high altitudes, 382, 383
  lakes, 268

Agricultural planning
  crop management, 288
  soil studies, 291
  tropical areas, 295–298, 301
  urban-induced weather changes, 115
Agriculture, 215–221
  cattle, 74
  crop rotation, 296
  effects of parasitic disease on labor, Fig. X–20
  effects of smog, 337
  lessons from fossil plant studies, 74
  pesticides and yields, Fig. X–12
  polluting drainage, 248, 261, 273
  water use, Fig. VII–1, 204
  see also Agricultural planning; Farming; Land use; Soils
Agriculture, U.S. Department of
  aerobiology research, 344
  agricultural science, 218
  lighting research, 160
  see also Forest Service, U.S.
Air: composition, 329
Air Force, U.S., 13, 15, 102, 181
  see also Air Weather Service, U.S. Air Force
Air pollution, see Pollution, Atmospheric
Air quality
  control regions, 334
  measurement, 333, Fig. X–4
  models, 335–336
  standards, 334
Air-sea rhythms, see Ocean-atmosphere system
Air Weather Service, U.S. Air Force, 13, 102, 103
Aircraft
  cloud seeding, 154, 173, 176
  fog seeding, 180, 181, 182, 183
  jets, 65, 69, 103
  lightning and, 157–158
  radar, 111
  turbulence and, 105, 106, 107, Fig. IV–10
  weather monitoring, 98, 124, 129, 193, 194
  see also Aviation
Airports
  air pollution measurement, 334
  fog dispersal, 181, 182, 183
  weather prediction needs, 101, 102, 103, 104
Aitken, J., 193
Aitken nuclei, 193
Alabama, 147
Alaska, 32, 69, 87, 181
  earthquakes, 35, 40
  marine areas, 242, 244, 246
  polar ecosystems, Fig. IX–15, 314, Fig. IX–16
  volcanoes, 41, 42, 44, 46
  weather modification, 101
Alazani Valley, Caucasus Mts., 151
Albedo of the earth, 66–69, Fig. III–7, 70, 71
  atmospheric constituents, 89
  climate and, 51, 52, 55
  effect of dust, 194

tropical forests, 298
  urban areas, 116
Alberta, Canada, 41, 154
Alder (tree), 208
Aleutian Islands, 35, 36, 44, 46
Alewives
  trophic dynamics of Great Lakes, 227, 228, Fig. VIII–2, Fig. VIII–14, 262, 263, 264, 266
Algae
  air pollution, Fig. X–6, 343, 345
  Great Lakes, 264, 270
  in chert deposits, 52
  in forest ecosystem, 292
  in harbors and lagoons, 233
  in oceans, 236
  Lake Washington, 272, Fig. VIII–17
  macroscopic, in aquaculture, Fig. VIII–11
  trophic dynamics, 225, 226, 227, 228
  tundra 313, 314
Allergens, Airborne, 340, 342, 345–349
Alpha Helix, R.V. (ship), 233
Alpine glaciers, 52
Alps: plate deformation, 28
Altitude: human adaptation, 379–385
Aluminum oxides in tropical forests, 295
Amarillo, Texas, 204
Amazon River, 34, 187, 300
Amchitka Island, Aleutians, Alaska, 46
America, see United States
Amery Ice Shelf, Antarctica, 84
Amitrole herbicide, 207
Ammonia: volcanoes, 43
Anaerobic basins, 55
Anakawa, Akio, 88
Anchovy fisheries
  food potential, 237, 238
  Peru, 234
Andean Mts., S.A., 32
Anderson, J. P., 306
Anemometers, 347
Angell, James K., 109
Angstrom, A. J., 71
Animals
  energy budget, 289
    horse, Fig. IX–7
  ethology, 376
  experimental
    air pollution studies, 387–388, 389
    high altitude medicine, 384
  fish protein as food for, 227–247
  in forest ecosystems, 292, 302–305
  fire and, 310, 312
  tropics, 298
  water quality and, 212
  in tundra ecosystems, Fig. IX–16
  plant eaters, 225
  response in ecosystem, 289
  source of food for man, 74, 217, 218
    in oceans, 236
  see also Carnivores; Game animals; Herbivores; Livestock; Mammals
Anions: forest ecosystems, 294
Antarctic Treaty, 313, 314

Antarctica
    contamination, 330, 360
    ecosystems, 313, 314
    food chain, Fig. VIII–6, 351
    food production, 217, 241
    glaciation, 53, 54, 55
    oceanic circulation and, 78, 83–84,
        Fig. IV–3, 98, 231–233, 239
    see also Krill
Anticyclones
    drought, 165, 167
    prediction of, 93, 94
Apollo missions, 14, 158
Appalachian Mts., 31, 118
APT, see Automatic Picture Transmission
Aquaculture prospects, 250–253
Aquatic ecosystems: modeling, 282
Aquatic plants, 236, 302
Aquifers, 203
Aquitards, 203
Arabian Sea, 358
Arcata, Cal., 181
Arctic regions, 78, 79
    air-sea rhythms, 86, 87
    ecosystems, 313–315
    food production, 217
    pack-ice behavior, 58
    see also Antarctica
Ardrey, William B., 376
Argentina, 154, 241, 242, 369
Argonne National Laboratory (AEC), 257
Arid regions
    Africa
        source of dust in western hemisphere,
            191
        source of hurricanes, 123
    maintenance of the biosphere, 280–285
        gramagrass output, Fig. IX–4
        mosquito submodel, Fig. IX–3
    subtropical anticyclones, 165
    water supply, 198
Arizona
    groundwater, 204
    range management, 74
    seismic refraction profile, 29, 31
    University of, 306
Arkansas, 308
Armed Forces Epidemiological Board,
    U.S., 365
Armenia, 152
Armstrong, Bruce W., 388
Army, U.S., 136
Army Air Force, U.S., 46
Army Medical Research and Development
    Command, U.S., 365, 379
Aromatics, 361
Arsenic poisoning, 322, 357
Asama volcano, Japan, 45
Asbestos, 320
Ash, Volcanic
    as contaminant, 55, 56, 68, 71, 72, 329
    falls and flows, 40, 41, 42, 44, 45
Asia
    agriculture, 220, 238, 251, 252, 297
    climatic change, 57
    data networks, Fig. IV–7
    environmental contamination, 364, 365
    precipitation, Fig. VI–10, 185

Asphalts, 361
Assimilation capacity of lake water, 270
Asthma, 319, 385
Astrup, Paul, 386, 388
Atlanta, Ga., 189
Atlantic coast, 38, 135
Atlantic Ocean
    air-sea system, 78, 83, 84
    climatic change, 57, 58
    conservation, 246
    data measurement, 79, 86, 91, 360
    drought, 165, 167, 188
    earth processes, 27, 28, 33, 53, 55
    environmental contamination, 191, 192,
        194, 329, 358
    precipitation, 189
    severe storms, 123, Fig. V–1, 126, 132, 147
    weather forecasting, 185
Atlas, D., 109
Atmosphere, 3, 34, 52 158, 257
    behavior, 62, 63
    composition, 55, 286, 287
    upper, 3, 10, 11–13, 167, 175
    see also Pollution, Atmospheric
Atmospheric circulation, 89–92
    global, 64, 72
    indicated by tree rings, Fig. III–5
    topics, 125, 188
        dusts, 192
        monsoons, 184
    urbanization effects, 116
Atomic Energy Commission, U.S., 46,
    Fig. VI–11, 259
    see also Argonne National Laboratory;
        Brookhaven National Laboratory
Auroral electrojet, 10
Auroral substorms, 5, 8
Australia
    agriculture, Fig. VII–8, 219
    air-sea system, 358
    climatic change, 57
    earth processes, 44
    ecosystems, 291, 297
    human adaptation, 376
    precipitation, 184, 185
    water resources, 242
    weather modification, 188
Automatic Picture Transmission (APT), 185
Avalanches, 42, 212
Aviation
    accidents, 108, 111, 117
    noise pollution, 326
    weather forecasting for, 101, 102, 103
    weather reporting from, 105, 106
    see also Aircraft
Axelrod, Herman D., 330
Ayres, S. M., 388
Azerbaidjan, U.S.S.R., 152
Azores Islands, 35, 135

B

Backfires in forests, 310
Backus, Richard H., 361, 363
Bacteria
    air pollution, Fig. X–6, 342
    in forest ecosystem, 292

oxidation of floating oil lumps, 362
soil, oxidation of CO, 358
Baja California, 240
Balchum, Oscar Joseph, 388
Baldwin Hills Dam, Los Angeles, Cal., 204
Baltic Sea, 52
Barbados, Antilles, 191, 193, 194, 329,
    330, 358
    see also BOMEX
Barnacles, 241
    on petroleum lumps, 361, 362, 363
Basalt, 29
Basin and Range Province, Nevada, 29, 31,
    204
Batchelder, Arthur R., 306
Bears, 302
Beaufait, William R., 306
Beaver, 304
Bees and other pollinators, 351, 354, 355
Behavioral differences among populations,
    373, 374, 376
Benchmark stations, 59, 331
Benefit/cost analysis
    effects of technology on the environ-
        ment, 338
    environmental management, 283
    fog dispersal at airports, 180-181,
        Fig. VI–9, 183
    forest management, 206
    pest controls, 351, 353, 356
    water quality in Great Lakes, 270
    weather changes, 172
Bengal, Bay of, 184
Bennett, Dudley W., 389
Benthic marine communities, 231, 232
Benzene hexachloride, see Dieldrin
Bering Sea, 74, 242, 244, 246
Bermuda, 191
Bermuda High, 165
Berry, Lester J., 219
Beryllium, 321
Bezymianny (volcano), 40
Biological effects
    air contaminants, 332
    pesticides, 351
    thermal discharges in lakes, 259
Biological extinction of animals
    climatic changes and, 73-74
    magnetic field reversals and, 25
    Stone Age hunters, 74
Biological materials as air pollutants, 339
Biomes, Major world, 285, Fig. IX–5
    deciduous forest, 298
    tundra, Fig. IX–15, 314, 315
    see also Grassland ecosystem
Biosphere, 3, 301
Birds
    malaria systems, 365
    pesticides and, 351, 353, 357, 359
Bishop tuff, Cal., 42
Bivalves, 232, 237
Bjerknes, J., 167, 189
Black spruce, 311
Blackberries, 352
Blast waves from solar flares, 6
Blind areas for weather observations, 98
Blood groups, 373, 374
Bobcat, 302

BOMEX (Barbados Oceanographic and Meteorological Experiment), 125, 185, Fig. VI–11
Bormann, F. H., 294
Boundary layer of plant evaporation, 200, 201
Braham, Roscoe R., 171
Brazil
  air-sea system, 190
  climatic change, 52
  drought, 188
  environmental disease, 367
  human adaptation, 374, Fig. XI–1
  mineral deposits, 33
  range management, 74
Breton Island, Miss., 136
Bristlecone pine: tree ring studies, 61
Bronchitis, 319, 385, Fig. XI–8, 390
Brook, J., 139
Brookhaven National Laboratory (AEC), 348
Brooklyn Navy Yard, New York, 362
Browning, Keith A., 149
Brownsville, Texas, 135
Bryan, Kirk, Jr., 87
Bryozoa, 232
Budyko, M. I., 67, 68
Buell, P., 388
Building codes
  earthquake hazards, 39
  hurricane protection, 136
Buildings and structures
  effects of air pollution, 319
  effects of smog on, 337
  polluting capacity of houses, 327, 385
  see also Construction industry
Buoys, 90, 190
  ocean studies, 78, 79, 80, 82, 84, 87, 100
Bureau of Reclamation, U.S., 171, 172
Burkett, Howard B., 365
Burma, 184, 185

C

Cactus, Prickly-pear, 297
Cadmium poisoning, 322
Calcite, 193
Calcium
  chloride, 174
  increase in Great Lakes, 268
California
  crust of earth, 29, 30, Fig. VII–3, 204
  earthquakes, 26, 28, 30, 31, 33, 35 36, 37, Fig. II–7, 39, 40
  environment 336, 337, 351, 352, Fig. X–13, 385, 386, 390
  fog dispersal, 181, 182
  forests, 61, 207, Fig. VII–5
  ocean areas, 87, 231, 240, 242, 245, 361, 362
  trees, 61
  volcanoes, 40, 41, 44
  water, 33, 166, 199, 204, 211
California, University of, 66
California current: data measurements, 78
California Institute of Technology
  contamination research, 330

Cambrian era, 52
Cambridge Research Laboratories (U.S. Air Force), 13
Cameroons, W. Africa, 192
Canada
  air-sea system, 106
  climatic change, 73
  earth processes, 39
  ecosystems, 314
  environmental contamination, 267
  severe storms, 133, 147, 151
Canton Island, Pacific, observatory, 84, Fig. IV–4, 86, 87, 88
Cape Cod, Mass., 135
Cape Thompson, Alaska, 314
Cape Verde Islands, 135
Carbamates, 355
Carbon, 22, 32
  carbon 14
    insecticides, 234
    measure of productive capacity of the sea, 236
  circulation in forest ecosystems, 301
  lake nutrients, 272
  pollution particles, 358, 362
Carbon dioxide (CO_2)
  advection in photosynthesis, 202
  cloud seeding, 173, 174, 175
  fog seeding, 180, 182, 183
  hailstorm seeding, 153
  heat balance of the earth, 287
  in atmosphere, 34, 55, 56, 57, 58, 64, 89 120, 329, 333, 337, 357–358
    amounts present, 67, 68, Fig. III–9, Fig. III–10, 72
    high altitudes, 382
    moist tropics, 330
    ocean absorption, 82, 233
    urban areas, 119
  land cultivation and changes in, 300
  plant growth, 288, 289
  quantity affected by man's activities, 286
Carbon monoxide (CO)
  air pollution and, 320, 330, 333, 337, 338, 358
    human adaptation, 385–390
Carboniferous era, 329
Carboxyhemoglobin, 338, 388, Fig. XI–9
Caribbean Sea
  atmospheric dust, 191, 192
  earth processes, 53, 54
  severe storms, 123, Fig. V–1, 135
  weather forecasting, 185
  weather modification, 188
Carnivores
  food chain, 225, Fig. VIII–11, 286, Fig. IX–6, 304
Carp in Great Lakes, 261, 263, 266
Cascade Range, Wash.-Cal., 40
CAT, see Clear air turbulence
Catfish, 251
Cations
  forest ecosystems, 294
Caucasus Mountains, U.S.S.R., 151, 152, 358, Fig. X–15
Cenozoic era, 52, 55
Center for Short-Lived Phenomena, Cambridge, Mass., 47

Central America, 35, 123, 246
Central Plains: weather, 146, 165
Ceraunograms: tropical weather forecasting, 187
Cerra Negro (volcano), Costa Rica, 44
Chad Lake, Africa, 52
Chagas' disease, 217, 369–370
Chain reactions
  ecological balance of Great Lakes, 261
  forest ecosystem response to population changes, 300
  hurricane development, 125
  ocean-atmosphere system, 88
Changnon, S. A., Jr., 152
Chaparral, 298
Charleston, S. C., 38
Charlson, Robert J., 330
Chemicals
  atmospheric pollutants, 118, 119, 332
  marine contaminants, 357–360
  see also Fertilizers; Insecticides; Pesticides; Pollution, Atmospheric
Chemiluminescence quenching, 331
Chert deposits, 52
Chicago, Ill., 113, 119, 257
Children, Growth of
  air pollution and, 388
  high altitudes, Fig. XI–6, 385
  tropical regions, 378
Chile, 240, 241, 242, 369
China, 184, 185, 186, 216, 357
China Seas, 184
Chitin, 240
Chlorinated hydrocarbons
  use on forest lands, 206
  water-vapor pollution, 337
  see also Insecticides; Pesticides
Chlorine in Great Lakes, 268
Chloroplasts, 288
Cholesterol stores, 385
Christmas Island, 87
Chromium poisoning, 322
Chromosphere, 5
Chubs, see Ciscoes
Chukchi Sea, 246
CIC (Committee on Institutional Cooperation), 269
Cigarette smoking: health hazards, 385, Fig. XI–8, 387, 388, 390
Cincinnati, Ohio, 114
Circular storms, 123
Circulatory diseases, 388
Ciscoes: Great Lakes, 261, 262, 263, 264
Citrus groves, 355
Clathration process: fog dispersal, 183
Claveran, Ramon, 306
Clay minerals
  ice nuclei, 192
  in ocean sediments, 358
Clear air turbulence, 105–112
Clear cutting
  forests, 207, 210, 213
  tropical areas, 296
Climate, 13, 34, 59, 62, 72
  aerobiology, 344
  affected by
    air-ocean system, 82, 85
    gravitational field, 51

hurricanes, 133
 volcanic ash, 41
 water supply, 198, 212
change, 51–74, 180
 regional, 57, 60
 models, 64, 120
control, 55, 57, 58, 89
urbanization and, 113–120
vegetation fire and, 306
world's major biomes, Fig. IX–5
see also Precipitation; Weather
Cloud seeding
 hail suppression, 151–155
 hurricane modification, 126
 lightning control, 158, 160–161,
 optimum conditions, Fig. VI–5
 possible results, 57
 precipitation changes, U.S., 170–179
 Project STORMFURY, 128–132
 seeding materials, Fig. VI–6, 178
 simulation, Fig. VI–6
 see also Seeding techniques for fog
Clouds, 68, 108, 113, 174, 175
 albedo of the earth and, 66, Fig. III–7,
  68, 69, 71
 atmospheric circulations, 89, 165
 billow, 109
 cirrus
  contrails and, 69
  satellite measurement of, 103
 cumulonimbus
  Caribbean area, 188
  hailstorms and, 154
  monsoon areas, 187, 188
  tornadoes and, 138, 144
 cumulus
  atmosphere-ocean system, 67, 91
  cloud seeding, Fig. VI–6
  dust and, 191, 192
  hailstorms and, 150
  hurricanes and, 125, 128, 130
  nuclei, 170
 cumulus congestus
  tropical areas, 188
 lightning from, Fig. V–15
 modification, 188
 monsoon areas, 187
 nucleation centers, 329
 predictions, 102, 103
 stratus clouds
  precipitation, 173
 studies
  clusters, 126
  via satellites, 87, 123
  weather forecasting, Fig. IV–6, 95
 water vapor and, 337
Coast Ranges, Cal., 29, 30
Coastal areas
 damage by hurricanes, 128, 133, 135
 entrapment of water, 255
 lakes
  upwelling, Fig. VIII–12
 marine productivity, 233, 235, Fig. VIII–7
 pollution, 254
 tundra ecosystem, Fig. IX–16
 see also Shore zones
Coastal Studies Institute, Louisiana State
  Univ., 134

Cobalt: lake nutrient, 272
Coffee cultivation, Fig. VII–9
Cohen, S. I., 390
Cold fog, 180, 182
Colorado
 cloud seeding, 171, 172, Fig. VI–5
 hail storm research, 154
 seismic monitoring, 31, 39
Colorado Plateau, 29
Columbia, Md., 118
Columbia Plateau, Wash., 29
Columbia River, Wash.-Ore., 40
Commerce, U.S. Department of, Fig. VI–11
Commission for Climatology, World
  Meteorology Organization (WMO), 59
Community air pollution, 319–321
Competition among plant species, 289
Computers
 ecosystem modeling
  analogue, 281
  digital, 281, 285
  hybrid, 281, 285
 forest ecosystems, 300
 simulation
  atmosphere-stagnation periods, 118
  ocean productivity, 233, 235
 use, 16, 352
  space efforts, 16
  weather forecasting, 91, 94, 97, 99, 101,
   103, 104, 125, 141, Fig. V–10, 185
Condensation: fog dispersal, 181
Congenital defects, 383, 384
Conglomerate rocks, 203
Coniferous forests, *see* Forests
Connecticut, 73, 336
Conservation
 air quality models, 335
 aquaculture and, 251
 gene pool, 278
 water, 259
Constance, Lake (Ger.-Aus.-Switz.), 52
Construction industry
 impact of climatic change, 58, 59
 structures resistant to
  earthquakes, 39
  hurricanes, 136
  tornados, 145
 weather forecasting for, 101
Contaminants
 environmental, 329–370
 Great Lakes, 264
 marine, 330, 357–363
 see Pollution, Atmospheric;
  Pollution, Water
Continental drift, 26, 32, Fig. II–4
Continental margins: sea floor discontinuity,
  29, 31
Continental shelf: storm damage near,
  28, 135
Continentality, 52, 64, 190
Continuity equation for air quality models,
  335
Continuous culture theory: oceans, 233
Convection
 earth's crust, 22
 energy exchange for plants, 287
 models, 47, 66, 67, 91, 140
 precipitation stimulation, 173, 179

turbulence and, 108, 111
 urban areas, 116, 119
 water resources and, 200
 weather, 96, 128, 186, 187
Cooling towers, 259
Coon, Carleton S., 373, 377
Copepods, Fig. VIII–5
 in food chain, 237
Copper, 32, 272
Coral reef, 232
Coral Sea, 186
Cordillera Mountains, S.A., 31, 32
Coriolis force, 254, 258, 269
Corn
 hybrid, 218
 maize, 217
 systems analysis of growing, 289
Corona of the sun, 3, 5
Corpus Christi Bay, Texas, 249
Costa Rica
 gas deposits, 43
 mud flows, 42
 volcanic eruptions, 40
 volcanic science, 44
Costs, *see* Benefit/cost analysis;
  Economic effects
Cotton production
 dependence on water supply, 204
 pesticides and, 351, 355
Coulter, M. W., 228
Coulter method, 228
Council on Economic Growth, Technology
  and Public Policy, Committee on
  Institutional Cooperation (CIC), 269
Countryman, Clyde, 306
Cowan, J. Ritchie, 202
Cox, Charles S., 82
Coyote, 302, 304
Crater Lake, Ore., 40, 41
Crete, Greece, 44
Crossbills, 302
Crow, James F., 373
Crustaceans
 trophic dynamics, 226, 228, Fig. VIII–2,
  237, 252
 petroleum lumps and, 363
Cryogenics: fog modification, 183
Cultural enrichment of bodies of water,
  see Eutrophication
Currents
 coastal, 128
 lakes, 254, 255, 256, 270
 lightning strokes, 161
 ocean, 79, Fig. IV–2
 tornadoes, 139
Cyanide: water contamination, 272
Cycles
 air-sea, 84–88
 antarctic ocean currents, 84
 biospheric, 285
 climatic change, 57, 59–61
 definition, 60
 diurnal and seasonal, 51
 glacial/interglacial, 51
 motions of the earth, 54
 ocean surface temperatures, Fig. III–2
 stratospheric winds, 51
 sunspots, 52

Cyclones
  cellars, 135
  drought, 165
  prediction, 91, 93, 94, 98, 144
  synoptic systems and, 128
  tropical, 184, Fig. VI–12
  see also Tornadoes
Cystic fibrosis in European populations, 374
Cytogenetic studies of Yanomama Indians,
    Fig. XI–1, Fig. XI–2

D

D region of ionosphere, 9, 10–11
Dakar, W. Africa, 194
Dallas, Texas, 140
Damage/destruction
  by contaminants, 329
  by forest fires, 207
  by hailstorms, 151, Fig. V–12, 154
  by hurricanes, 123, Fig. V–4, 128, 130,
    133, 136, Fig. V–6
  by lightning, 157, 160, 161
  by solar energy, 8
  by tornadoes, Fig. V–6, 144
  by volcanoes, 42, 43, 44
  by weather changes, 115
  see also Disasters
Daphnia, 227, 228, Fig. VIII–2
Darwin, Charles
  natural selection, 373, 374, 376, 377
  sea floor contamination, 358
Data bases
  adaptation to air pollution, 387
  adaptation to drought, 219–220
  air-quality criteria, 334, 340
  climatic statistics, 120
  cloud seeding technology, 171, 175
  drought prediction, 167
  ecosystem modeling, 282
  estimates of water supply, 197
  forest ecosystems, 300
    animal ecology, 302
    fire, 307
  hurricane surveillance, 131
  marine environments, 231
    North Pacific Ocean, 242
    Puget Sound, 249
  measuring aeroallergens, 345
  sea-air system, 78, 80, 82, 87–88
  trophic dynamics of Great Lakes, 227
  urban-affected weather changes, 114
  water quality of Great Lakes, 264, 268
  weather forecasting, 90–92, 93,
    Fig. IV–7, Fig. IV–8, 98, 103
    pilot reports, 106
    tornadoes, 146
    tropical areas, 188
Daubenmire, Rexford, 306
Davis, Margaret B., 73
Davis Sea, 232
DDD in lakes, 228
DDE in lakes, 228
DDT
  in antarctic animals, 241
  in birds, 351, 359
  in fish, 228, 359
  in lake waters, 272

in oceans, 233, 245
in pesticides, 352, Fig. X–13, Fig. X–14,
    Fig. X–18
phytoplankton and, Fig. VIII–3
temperatures and effects of, 57
use in forest areas, 207, 213
Deane, Margaret, 390
Death rates, 377, 378
  air pollution and, 385
Deaths
  Chagas' disease, 369
  high altitude, 379
  hurricane caused, 127, Fig. V–5, 136
  lightning caused, 157, 158
  tornado caused, 137, 138
Decay term for air pollutants, 336
Deciduous forests, see Forests
Decomposition in forest ecosystems, 292
Deer, White-tail, 302, 303, 305, 306, 310
Defense, U.S. Department of
  air-sea system, 108
  BOMEX support, Fig. VI–11
  data networks, 23
  volcano technology, 47
  see also Air Force, U.S.; Armed Forces
    Epidemiological Board, U.S.; Army,
    U.S.; Army Medical Research and
    Development Command, U.S.;
    Cambridge Research Laboratories;
    Naval Electronics Laboratory Center;
    Navy, U.S.
Defoliation: effects on forests, 298
Deforestation
  ecological effects, Fig. IX–9
  effect on climatic changes, 55
Dendroclimatological studies, 59
Denmark, 386
Density of water in lakes, 254
Dental caries, 379
dePena, R. G., 151, 152
Desalination of sea water for equatorial
    areas, 187
Desert areas
  arid America, 73–74
  ecosystem model, Fig. IX–3
  monsoons and, 184, 186
  soil studies, 291
  solar radiation in, 55, Fig. III–10
  see also Arid regions
Dessens, J., 152–153
Detroit River, 263, 266
Developing nations
  agriculture, 218
  effects of parasitic disease, Fig. X–20, 369
  polluting technology, 330
deVries, A. L., 232
Diabetes, 379
Diablo Range, Cal., 29, 30
Diamonds, 22
  deposits, 32
Diatoms, Fig. VIII–4
Dieldrin, 369
Diet, see Nutrition
Diffusion
  air quality, 334, 335
  lake waters, 256, 257, 259
  tornado modeling, 140
  water within forest canopy, 202

Dinoflagellates, Fig. VIII–4
Disasters
  cactus growth in Australia, 297
  marine monitoring, 231
Discover, USS (ship), 194
Diseases
  airborne, 340, 341, 343
  causation
    contamination, 319–324, 327, 342,
      343, 369
    noise, 326
    radiation, 325
  environmental, 364–370
    altitude-related, 379, 380, 383, 384, 385
  genetic, 216, 373, 374
  in animals, 217, 298, 303
  in plants, 297, 300, 310
  resistance to, 376, 378–379
  smog and CO related, 385–390
  see also Allergens, Airborne; Health; and
    names of specific diseases
Diversion of water, 198, Fig. VII–1
Diving, 232, 233, 245
Djakarta, Indonesia, 86, Fig. IV–5
DOD, see Defense, U.S. Department of
Dolphins
  toxicity in food chain, 363
  tuna fishing and, 246
Douglas, J. W. B., 388
Douglas fir, 311
Drilling
  continental, 21–25, Fig. II–1, 30, 31, 57, 59
  ocean, 53, Fig. III–3, 55
Dropsondes: air quality measurement, 334
Drought, 165–168
  adjustments to, Fig. VII–10
  agriculture and, 218–221, 278
  air-sea interactions, 86
  definition, 166
  tropical areas, 184, 188
Drug action: effects at high altitudes,
    379, 384, 385
Dunbar, M. J., 231
Dust
  Africa, 191–194, Fig. VI–13
  effect on climate, 55, 56, 57–58, 59,
    Fig. III–10
  nucleation centers, 329
  pollution factor, 327, Fig. X–6, 343, 358
  solar radiation and, 55, 67, 68, 71
  Soviet economy and, Fig. X–15
  tropical forests and, 298
  see also Aerosols
Dust Bowl, Great Plains, 165
Dwarfism in crop yields, 216
Dynamo effect of earth's core, 24–25
Dynamo region of ionosphere, 10
Dzerdzeevskii, B. L., 72

E

E region of ionosphere, 9, 10
Earth
  continental U.S., 28, 31
  crust, 21, 27
  shock wave, from solar wind, 5
  sun's influence on, 3–17
  see also Earthquakes; Volcanoes

Earthquakes, 21, 22, 35–39, 135
  effect on water quality, 212
  locations, 26, Fig. II–3, 28, 30
  tidal waves, 81
  volcanic eruptions and, 43
  see also Seismicity of the earth
Earthworms, 292
East, Edmund, 218
East River, New York, 362
EASTROPAC Program, 87, 88
Echinoderms, 232
Eclogite, 29
Ecology, 21
  climatic change and, 34, 72
  definition, 285
  precipitation management and, 173, 175
  surveys, 231
  see also Ecosystems
Economic effects
  aquaculture, 250–253
  climatic changes, 57, 59
  Corpus Christi Bay, Fig. VIII–10
  costs of contaminants in air, 332, 333, 338
  fisheries of Puget Sound, 249
  fog modification, Fig. VI–9, 183
  hail-suppression, 151, 154
  hurricane modification, 128
  lightning-caused damage, 160
  long-range weather forecasting, 97–98, 100
  parasitic diseases, 367, 369
  pesticides, 353
  precipitation management, 172, 173, 175, 177
  subsidence in oil and water
      bearing formations, 203, 204
  threat to tundra of developments, 313
  tropical storms, 187–188, 189
  turbulence, 108
  urban-induced weather changes, 115
  see also Benefit/cost analysis
Ecosystems
  definition, 285
  freshwater, 225–229
  marine, 230–235
  models, 209
  studies of IBP, 58
  terrestrial, 226
Eddy processes: ocean circulation, 80
Ekman, V. W., 79
Electrojets of ionosphere, 10
Electromagnet radiation
  lightning, 157
  tornadoes and, 138–139
  urbanization and, 113
Electrons: concentration in ionosphere, 9
Elephant-seals, 240, 241
Emery, K., 361, 362
Emiliani, Cesare, 54
Emphysema: air pollution and, 319, 385, Fig. XI–8, 387, 389, 390
Emulsifiers for floating oil, 362
Energy
  hailstorms, 149
  hurricanes, 124, 125
  lightning, 157
  monsoons, 186

needed for food production, 216
  sun, 51, 52, 55
  tornadoes, 145
  volcanic explosions, 44
  waste generation, 330
Energy budget
  affected by urbanization, 116
  clear air turbulence, 105, 106
  cloud systems, 171
  drought, 167
  Great Lakes, 269
  horse, Fig. IX–7
  tropical areas, 187, 191, 194
  water evaporation, 200
Energy transfer
  ecosystems, 225, 285–291, 301
    forests, 294, 300
    tundra, Fig. IX–16
  food chain, Fig. IX–6
  leaves, 288
  world oceans, 236, 237
England, 185, 390
  air-sea systems, 53, 56, 57, 69, 77, 87, 106
  environmental contamination, 361, 390
  human adaptation, 374, 386
  severe storms, 149
  urbanization, 113, 117, 119
  weather forecasting, 100
  weather modification, 181
  see also London, Eng.
Environment
  alteration by volcanoes, 44
  definition, 60, 373
  design, 272–280
  management, 283, 298
    impact of technology, 338
Environmental Protection Agency, U.S., (EPA), 330, 331, 337, 344, 390
Enzymes
  high altitude adaptation, 382
  plant growth and, 288
EPA, see Environmental Protection Agency, U.S.
Equator
  climate, 165, 166, 167
  drift of pollutants across, 190
  dry zones
    meteorological observations, 187
  magnetic, 10, 135
  Pacific area
    drought prediction, 168
Erie Canal, 261, 262
Erosion
  after fire, 306, 308, 311
  environmental management, 283
  forests, 207, 208, 211, 214
    tropical areas, 295, 296
  lake aging, 268
  precipitation augmentation, 177
  steep slopes, 211, 212
  surface water and, 204
Eskimos, 246, 376
Estuaries
  ecosystem, 248–253
  marine productivity, 235, 243
  storm damage, 133
Ethology, Animal: application to humans, 376

Ethylene, 320
Eugeosynclinal belts of rock, 31
Euler, Ferdinand K., 26
Euphausia superba, see Krill
Euphausids, see Krill
Europe
  agriculture, 291
  air-sea system, 66, 86, 87
  climatic change, 51, 52, 55, 57, 58, 68
  data measurement, 59, Fig. IV–7
  earth processes, 41
  environmental contamination, 69, 193, 271, 343, 358
  human adaptation, 374, 376
  severe storms, 149
  urbanization, 113, 114, 119, 226
Eutrophication, 209, 322
  beneficial, 217
  deforestation, Fig. IX–9
  Great Lakes, 267–270
  Lake Washington, 270–273
Evaporation
  effect on water supply, 198, 200, Fig. VII–2, 202
  fog dispersal, 181
  Lake Michigan, Fig. VIII–13, 259
Evapotranspiration, Fig. VII–1, Fig. VII–2
  tropical forest, Fig. IX–10
Evolution, Cultural, 51, 377, 378
Exosphere, 11
Expendable Bathy-Thermographs (XBT), 87
Extreme ultra violet radiation, 4, 9, 10

F

F region of ionosphere, 9, 10
FAA, see Federal Aviation Administration, U.S.
Farhi, Leon E., 389
Farming
  aerobiology and, 343
  climatic changes and, 57, 58, 59
  cultural pest control, 354
  hail damage, 154
  marketing specialists, 250, 251
  precipitation, 177
  slash and burn technique, 296, Fig. XI–3
  subsistence, 218
  see also Agriculture
Faults, 30, 31
Fawbush, Ernest J., 101
Federal Aviation Administration, U.S. (FAA), 158
Feedback
  atmospheric temperatures, 56
  causes of weather changes, 97
    drought, 165
  human ecosystem, 278
  parasitic diseases and whole life of
      affected individual, 367, 369
  pest-control technology, 350
  pollution control by nature, 330
    models, 340
  precipitation mechanisms, 170, 171
  sea-air rythms, 86, 87
  see also Interactions

Fertility
human populations, 377, 378
high altitudes, 383
soil, 40, 45
tropics, 295, 296, 297
Fertilization of forest areas, 208, 209
Fertilizers
chemical, 278
human and farm sewage, 251
pollution effects, 323
runoff affecting water quality
Great Lakes, 265, 268
rivers, Fig. VIII–15
FIDO, see Fog Investigation and Disposal
Operation
Finches, 302
Finger Lakes, N. Y., 262
Finley, J. P., 138
Fire
forest areas
effects, 207, Fig. VII–5, 212, 213
fire ecology, 306–312
Isle Royale, 304
lightning-caused, 157, 158, 160, 161
slash burning, 208
incineration
of wastes, Fig. X–2
spread of pollutants, Fig. X–16
Fish products, 239, 241
Fisher, R. A., 374
Fisheries
aquaculture, 250–253
climatic changes and, 57, 58, 79, 82
ocean data collecting, 87
distribution throughout world, Fig. VIII–7
food sources, 217
world ocean, 236–247
lakes, 228, 254, 273
Great Lakes, 261–267
Lake Michigan, Fig. VIII–14
leisure activity, 293
management models, 234
ocean floor sediments and, 362
Puget Sound, 248–250
purse seine, Fig. VIII–9
species selection for aquaculture, 250
water flow to the oceans, 200
Fishes
adaptation to cold water, 232
effects of water pollution, 356, 359
in Great Lakes, 227
water quality required, 205, 206
see also names of specific species
Fletcher, C. M., 390
Floods
effect on water quality, 212
rain-caused, 128
tropical areas, 184, 296
Florida
agriculture, 252, 253
air-sea system, 79
climatic change, Fig. II–7, 57
data measurement, 68
ecosystems, 307
environmental contamination, 191, 194
severe storms, 135, 147, 189
weather modification, 166, 171

Florida Power and Light Company, 252
Florida Straits, 79
Flounder, 253
Fluid dynamics
atmospheric circulation, 56
earth core studies, 22
lakes, 256
Fluid-flow instability in upper air:
models, 106
Fluorescence quenching, 331
Fluorides, 320, 322
Fluorometer, 256
Flushing rates of lakes, 266
Fly-ash: pollution by, 358
Fog, 180–183
industry-induced, 337
urban-induced, 113, 114, 117
Fog Investigation and Disposal Operation
(FIDO), 181
Food and Agriculture Organization, 299
Food chain, Fig. VIII–1, 234, 285, 286,
Fig. IX–6, 289, 301
Antarctic, Fig. VIII–6
aquaculture, Fig. VIII–11
in Puget Sound, 248, 250
in sea, 236, 244
pollution from DDT, Fig. X–14, 359
pollution from petroleum compounds, 363
pollution from toxic metals, 322, 323
Food pyramid, see Food chain
Food supply, World
contaminants, 322
protection from, 217
losses to, 339
diseases of plants, 341
production
fish, 228
potentials and problems, 215–218
world oceans, 233, 236, 237
projection, Fig. X–5
small number of crops and livestock,
217–218
sources
forested areas, 302
tropical areas, 298
Food web, see Food chain
Foraminifera, Planktonic, 53
Forest ecosystems, 292–301
animal ecology, 302–305
polluted precipitation and, 119
regeneration, 293, 297, 310
see also Fire
Forest Laboratory, U.S., Missoula, Mont.;
Riverside, Cal., 306
Forest management, Fig. VII–4, 205–212
land ownership, Fig. VII–4, 293
reforestation, 296
water quality and, 212–214
Puget Sound, 248
Forest Service, U.S.
fire ecology, 306
forest lands, 205
lightning research, 160
monitored ecosystems, 283
watershed research, 294
Forests
coniferous, 292, 308, 310, 337
deciduous, 295

comparison with rain forests, 299–301
seral stages, Fig. IX–1
fog benefits, 180
timber production, 292
tropical regions, 296, 297
fire and, 306, 307
trophic dynamics, 226
tropical, 292, 295–298
compared with temperate forests,
298–301
oxygen and, 34
rain forests, 295, 299–301, Fig. XI–3
Fort Tejon, Cal., 38
Fort Wayne, Ind., 114
Fossils
fuels, 68, 71
lake sediment, 344
mammals, 73–74
Founder effect, see Genetic drift
Fox, 304
France, 153, 154, 181, 183
Freeman, A. R., 388
Freezing, Shock-induced: cloud seeding, 153
Freon
fog-seeding nucleant, 180
air pollution, 357
Frequency management in radio
communication, 14, 17
Fronts, Weather
turbulence, 105
urbanization and, 113
Fuels
toxic effects, 357–358, 360
see also Oil/Petroleum
Fuginaga, Motosako, 251
Fujita, T. T., 130, 145
Fumaroles, 43
Fungi
airborne, 340, 343, 345, 346
crop diseases, 341, Fig. X–8
fire and pine fungi, 306
in forest ecosystem, 292

G

G-6-PD deficiency, 365
Gaivoronskii, I. I., 151, 152
Game animals
disease resistance, 217
forests, 293, 302–303, 305
Gamma globulin in tropical populations, 378
Gamma rays, 33
Gannon, John E., 227
GARP, see Global Atmospheric Research
Program
Gary, Ind., 119
Gas chromatography, 331
Gases, 67, 329, 337
air pollution, 339, 340, 357
in clean, dry air, Fig. X–1
volcanoes, 40, 41, 43
Gasoline, see Oil/petroleum
Gauging stations of U.S. Geological
Survey, 197
Gaussian plume, 335, 336
Geiss, Johannes, 54
Genecology, 344

Generators, Ground-based
  for cloud seeding, 170, 175, 176
  for fog-seeding, 180, 183
Genetic drift, 374, 383
Genetics
  gene pool, 278
  high altitude populations, 383
  pest control, 352, 354, 367
  plant breeding in tropics, 297, 300
Geological Survey, U.S., 29, 45, 46, 197
Geomagnetic tail, 7, 8, 10
Geomorphic changes by hurricanes,
  133–136
Geophysical Fluid Dynamics Laboratory,
  (NOAA), 66, 68, 82, 87
Georgia, 147
Geosphere, 301
Geosynchronous satellites
  see Satellites, Geostationary
Geothermal heat, 33
German Atlantic Expedition, 187, 189
Germany
  agriculture, 215, 241
  climatic change, 57
  severe storms, 154
  urbanization, 119
Glaciation
  atmospheric monitoring, 358, Fig. X–15,
    360
  boundaries, 52
  causes, 52, 53, 54, 55
  control of, 55
  cycles, 62
  ocean surface temperatures and, 53
  volcanic activity and, 45
Global Atmospheric Research Program
  (GARP)
  data collection networks, 59, 88, 91, 95,
    96, 97, 100, 101, 107, 126, 167, 190
  monsoon forecasting, 184, 189
Global Network for Environmental
  Monitoring (GNEM) 235, 344
Global techtonics, 21–33
  earthquakes and, 26, Fig. II–3,
    28, 35, 36
"Globigerina ooze," 53
Glomar Challenger, D.V. (ship), 53, 55
Glover, Kenneth M., 106
Glowing avalanches: damage by, 42
GNEM, see Global Network for
  Environmental Monitoring
Goiter, 378–379
Gold deposits, 32
Golden Gate Park, Cal., 117
Goldfish in Great Lakes, 263
Goldman, Charles R., 272
Goldsmith, John R., 390
Goose Creek, Tex., 203
Grand River, Mich., 270
Grand Traverse Bay, Mich., 269
Grape growing, 352
Graphite, 22
Grassland Biome Project, Colorado
  (IBP), 344
Grassland ecosystem
  fire ecology, 306, 307
  model, Fig. IX–2
    blue gramagrass, Fig. IX–4

temperate regions, 298
tropical regions, 296
Graupel, 150, Fig. VI–6
Grazing practices
  effects of fire, 306
  energy balance of a field, Fig. IX–7
  environmental management, 283, 296
  overgrazing
    forest lands, 210, 214
    tundra, 313
Great Lakes
  circulation patterns, 82, 254–256
  marine ecosystems, 225–228, 229, 230
  pollution, 257, 259, 261–270, 272
Great Lakes Basin Commission, 268, 269
Great Lakes Deer Group, 303
Great Lakes Fishery Commission
  (U.S.-Canada compact), 266
Great Lakes Fishery Laboratory,
  U.S. Dept. of Interior, 266, 267
Great Plains, U.S.
  cereal-rust epidemiology, 339
  drought studies, 219
  hail storms, 149, 154
  tornado models, 147
Greece, 35
Green Bay, Wisc.: lake pollution, 257,
  263, 269
Greenhouse effect
  CO₂ and, 82, 358
  radiation balance of the earth, 70, 71
Greenland
  climatic change, 52, 53, 54, 55, 57
  data measurement, 360
  ice cap, 330
Gregg, Ian, 386
Gregory, K. F., 344
GROSSVERSUCH III, Canton Ticino,
  Switz., 152, 153
Groundwater levels, as part of water
  supply, 197, 204
Grouse, Ruffed: survival, 302, 303
Guiana, S. A., 33
Gulf Coast
  ocean systems, 81
  severe storms, 133–135
Gulf of California, 33
Gulf of Mexico, 133, 135, 136, 147, 253
Gulf Stream, 78, 79
Gunn, R., 139

H

Habitat research, 303, 306, 310
Hailstorms
  hailstones
    formation and growth, Fig. V–11, 151
    modeling, 154
  hailstreak, 152
  modeling, 149, Fig. VI–6
    cloud modeling, 154
  predictions, 94
  suppression and control, 147
    experiments, 151–154
HAILSWATH, Project, 153
Harbors
  pollution in, 223
  debris in, 34
  engineering models, 81

Hardwoods
  and pine forests, 308, 309, 310
  summer fires, 311
  tropics, 296
Hardy, Kenneth R., 106, 109
Harrar, J. George, 339
Hawaii
  earth processes, 27, 28
  urbanization, 40, 41, 44
  volcano technology, 35, 43, 45, 46
  weather forecasting, 185
Hawaiian Volcano Observatory, 43, 45, 46
Hay fever, see Allergens, Airborne
Hazards
  air pollution, 385, 386, 387
  drought, 218
  ocean pollution
    food sources, 244, 245
  pest controls, 351, 354, 355
  to aviation, 108, 180
  toxic wastes in near shore regions, 233
  water quality in forest areas, 207, 209
  see also Radiation hazards
Haze, 67, 68
  air pollution, 192, Fig. X–6
  assessed, 330–331
  urban-induced, 117
Hazel, 311
Headfires, 310
Health
  effects of air quality on, 334, 337, 338, 349
    biological contaminants, 339
    see also Allergens, Airborne
  effects of smog and CO, 385–390
  high altitude living, 379–385
  see also Diseases; Hazards
Heart diseases, 379, 380, 382, 384, 385
  carbon monoxide and, Fig. XI–7, 390
Heat
  antarctic waters, 84
  distribution in the atmosphere, 105
  lightning, 157
  relation to food intake, Fig. IX–8
  storm forecasting, 138
  see also Pollution, Thermal; Thermal
    bar; Thermal engine; Thermal plume
    in lake water
Heat balance, see Solar radiation
Heat effects, 324
  fog modification, 181, 182
  tundra ecosystems, Fig. IX–16
  urban areas, 113, 116, Fig. IV–12
Heat transfer
  from earth's interior, 22
  global circulation, 91
  hurricanes, 125, 126, 128, 129, 131
  ocean-air system, 78
Heathcote, John G., 219
Hekla (volcano), Iceland, 41
Helicopters, 181
Helium, 10, 11, 51
Helmholtz, H. v., 109
Hemispheric interchange
  atmospheric circulation, 188
Herbicides
  forest areas, 205, 207
  lake contamination, 272
  2,4,5-T hazard, 351

Herbivores, 74
  balance of nature, 280, 285, 286
  forest ecology, 302–305
  trophic dynamics, 225, 226
    marine, 237, 239
  see also Game animals; Livestock
Herculaneum (historic), 40
Heredity
  adaptive traits, 383
    high altitude, Fig. XI–4
Herring, 238, 363, 264
Heterozygosity, 373, 374
Hewlett, John D., 211
Hicks, Steacy D., 109
High Altitude Hydrometeorological Service,
  Nalchick, U.S.S.R., 151, 152
High Plains, U.S., 154, 204
Hilo, Hawaii, 41, 46
Himalaya Mts., 184, 186
HIRS (High Resolution Infrared
  Radiometers), 69
Hoecker, W. H., 140
Holland, Joshua Z., 82
Holography: fisheries management, 244
Homozygosity, 373
Honolulu, Hawaii
  modeling, 185
  oceanographic cruises, 87
Hoof-and-mouth disease, 370
Hormone pesticides, 351
Horn, Ralph, 361, 362, 363
Horse: energy budget, Fig. IX–7
Houghton, Henry G., 183
Housing: disease control in Latin America,
  370
Housing and household agents
  polluting effects, 327, 385, 387
Hubbard Brook, N. H., 208, 293, Fig. IX–9
Hudson River, 262
Human factors
  aggression, 376
  air quality standards, 337
  food chain, 225
  forest ecosystems, 301
    incidence of fires, 307
  geomorphic coastal changes, 136
  impact on environment, 223, 277, 334,
    Fig. X–5
  in climatic change, 58, 59, 63–64, 65,
    67, 68, 69, 70–71, 101
  in storm forecasting, 138
    volunteer spotters, 147–148
  in weather forecasting, 97, 99, 102,
    104, 165
    tropical areas, 185
  labor in agriculture, 216
  water quality, 211, 212, 213
  water supply, 198, 218
  see also Adaptation: human;
    Pollution, Atmospheric: man-made
Humboldt Current, 167
Humidity
  cloud formation and, 165
  fog modification, 181
  forest fires, 306, 307
  in atmosphere, 178
  plant growth, 287, 288
  prescribed burning, 310

tropical forests, 295
  urbanization and, 113
  water cycle, 200, 201, 202
Hungary, 33, 216
Humphrey, Robert R., 306
Hunt, James L., 201
Huntington Beech, Cal., 203
Hurricane Alix (1960), 134
Hurricane Audrey (1957), 134, 136
Hurricane Betsy (1965), 127
Hurricane Beulah (1967), 123, 124
Hurricane Camille (1969), 127, 133,
  Fig. V–5, 136
Hurricane Carol (1954), 133, 135;
  (1960), 134, 135
Hurricane Debby (1969), 126, 128, 129, 130
Hurricanes, 123–136, 191
  effect on water quality, 212
  forecasting, 94, 95, 98, 102, 103
    models for, 91
  modification
    eye-wall seeding, 146
    see also STORMFURY, Project
  role in tropical weather, 188, 189
Hutchinson, G. Evelyn, 254
Hutton, James P., 22
Hydrochloric acid: volcanoes, 43
Hydrofluoric acid: volcanoes, 43
Hydrogen, 10, 12
  atomic
    in thermosphere, 11
  earth's mass, 51
  fluoride, 342
  ion activity, 212
  sulfide
    air pollution, 320
  volcanoes, 43
Hydrologic cycle, Fig. VII–2
Hydrology, Stochastic, 197–198
Hydrosphere, 3
  circulation in, 301
Hydrothermal pollutants, 321
Hygroscopic particles
  seeding cold clouds, 175
  seeding warm clouds, 174
  seeding warm fog, 181, 182, 183
Hypoxia: in high altitudes,
  381, 382, 384, 385
H.V.O., *see* Hawaiian Volcano Observatory

I

Ibadan, University of, Nigeria, 185
IBP, *see* International Biological Program,
  U.S.
Ice
  ages, 32, 120
  cores
    analysis, 58
    atmospheric lead, 330
  crystals
    formation, 192, 193
    precipitation formation, 174, 182
    structure, Fig. VI–3
  fogs (Alaska)
    modification, 181, 182
  tundra, 313
Ice-seals, 246

Iceland
  air-sea system, 86
  climatic change, 52, 57, 72
  earth processes, 27, 33, 41, 47
ICSU, *see* International Council of
  Scientific Unions
Idaho, 29, 31
IDOE, *see* International Decade of Ocean
  Exploration
Igneous rocks, 30
IGY, *see* International Geophysical Year
Illinois, 31, 216, Fig. VIII–15
Illite
  ice nuclei, 192
  in ocean sediments, 358
Immunofluorescence
  malaria diagnosis, 366
Imperial Valley, Cal., 33
Inbreeding, 374, 378
India
  agriculture, 217, 218
  earthquake prediction, 37
  hailstorms, 149
  monsoons, 184, 186
  see also Institute of Tropical Meteorol-
    ogy; National Council of Economic
    Advisors
  see also Rajasthan Desert
Indian Ocean
  air-sea system, 78, 82, 84, 167
  expedition, 82
  severe storms, 134, 184
  water resources, 236
Indians, American, 379, 384
Indonesia
  aquaculture, 238
  data measurement, 86
  earth processes, 35, 40
  monsoon forecasting, 184
  urbanization, 43, 44
Indoor environments: aerobiology, 343
Industrial revolution, 113
Industry
  effect on water quality, 199, 213, 214, 337
  radiation damage, 323, 325
  see also Pollution, Industrial;
    Pollution, Thermal
Inertia: tornado modeling, 140
Infrared radiation
  heat balance of the earth and, 287
  spectrometry, 141
  weather predicting, 103
Inland waterways, 82, 265
Insecticides
  Chagas' disease, 369, 370
  effect on terrestrial ecosystems, 301
  forest areas, 207
  malaria transmission and, 364–367
  phytoplankton sensitivity to, Fig. VIII–3
Insects
  air pollution, 339, 340, 341, 343, 345
  pesticide resistance, Fig. X–11
  population model, 353
  problem of agriculture, 216, 217
  tropical plants, 297, 298
  see also Malaria
Institute for Atmospheric Physics, National
  Research Council, Italy, 153

Institute of Marine Sciences, University of
  Miami, 253
Institute of Tropical Meteorology,
  Poona, India, 185
Instrumentation
  animal ecology, 302
  atmospheric circulation, 90, 334
  balloon-borne, 90, 98, 190
  climatology, 108
  fisheries management, 244
  forest ecosystems, 300
    fire ecology, 307
  hail research, 156
  infrared thermometer, 256
  ocean characteristics, 78, 80, 87
  photomonitoring equipment for
    antarctic waters, 233
  physical limnology, 255, 256
  severe storms, 95, 132, 147
  tropical region studies, 188
  urban effects on weather changes,
    114, 115
  weather modification, 170, 175, 176, 178
  weather observations, 106
  weather predictions, 103, 104
Insurance: hail damage, 154
Intelligence testing, 376
Interactions
  air pollutants, 342, 343
  atmosphere and its lower boundary,
    89, 91, 97, 101
  crust and mantle, 21
  fire studies, 307
  Great Lakes
    fish species, 264
    man and fisheries, 263
  heat balance of the earth and
    photosynthesis, 287
  host-parasite insects, 364, 366
  hurricane formation, 125, 126, 128, 131
  insect species and pesticides, 352
  lake water mixing, 254
    internal waves and turbulence, 256
  man and climate, 57, 115, 177
    drought, 218
    smog, 390
  marine biological system and its
    environment, 233
  ocean-atmosphere, 77–88
    contaminants, 359
    rainfall, 165, 167
  pollution control and economic
    system, 334
  Puget Sound, 248, 249
  radioactive species, 358
  sea floors and continental margins, 29
  submodels developed separately, 282
  temperate forests
    animals and environment, 303
    water-nutrient cycles, 294
  tropics, 187
    temperature and rainfall, 295
    vegetation and environment, 301
    vegetation and water cycle, 298
  tundra ecosystems, 313, 314
  waste disposal and conservation, 338
Interdisciplinary problems, see
  Multidisciplinary problems

Interglacial periods, 53, 54, 55
Interior, U.S. Department of, Fig. VI-11,
  266, 267
  see also Great Lakes Fishery Laboratory
International Biological Program, U.S.,
  (IBP)
  aerobiology program, 339, 341, 342, 344
  ecosystem studies, 58, 233, 279, 283, 289,
    294, 300, 314, 344
  human adaptation, 379, 380
International Council of Scientific Unions
  (ICSU), 80
  Global Atmospheric Research Program
    (GARP), 91
  International Union of Biological
    Sciences, (IUBS), 344
  International Union of Geological
    Sciences (IUGS), 31
  Inter-Union Commission on Solar-
    Terrestrial Physics, 15
  Scientific Committee on Ocean
    Research, 80
International Decade of Ocean
  Exploration (IDOE), 82, 88, 167
International Geophysical Year (IGY), 88,
  190, 340
International Hydrological Decade, 294
International Hydrological Program,
  International Field Study, 270
International Joint Commission
  (Can.-U.S.), 267
International Reference Center on
  Air Pollution (WHO), 388
International Union of Biological Sciences
  see under International Council of
    Scientific Unions
International Union of Geological Sciences
  see under International Council of
    Scientific Unions
Intertropic Convergence Zone, 194
Invertebrates: relationship of food and
  heat, Fig. IX-8
Iodine, 118, 378
Ionization: created by radiation from
  sun, 9
Ionosondes, 15
Ionosphere, 3, 5, 8–11, 13–14, 17
  electric field from earth, 158
  storms, 10
Irazu (volcano), Costa Rica, 42, 43
Iribarne, J. V., 151, 152
IRIS (Infrared Interferometer
  Spectrometer), 90
Iron, 35
  content of dust over tropics, 193
  deposits, 32
  earth's core, 23
  lake nutrient, 272
  oxides, 295
Irrigation
  health hazard, 217
  in agriculture, Fig. VII-8, 220, 221
  tropical regions, 296, 297, 298
  water from Great Lakes region, 265
  water use, Fig. VII-1, 204, 291
Isle Derniere, La., 135
Isle Royale ecosystem, 303–305

Isotopic studies
  core samples, 55, 57
  lead, 30
  oxygen ^{18}O, 53
  sea water, 84
  strontium, 30
Italy, 153
  earth processes, 33, 44, 53
  human adaptation, 388
Ivory Coast, Africa, 192

J

Jagger, Thomas, 45
Japan
  aquaculture, 238, 241, 242, 251, 252
  earth processes, 30, 35, 37, 43, 44, 135
  environmental contamination, 334,
    Fig. X–12, 357, 363
  human adaptation, 374, Fig. XI–2
  oceanographic research, 240
  weather prediction, 45, 100
Japanese Meteorological Agency, 81
Java, 41, 43, 44
Jet streams
  hailstorms, 149
  heat distribution in the atmosphere, 105
  low-level, 108
  pollution transport, 357, 358
  prediction of, 93, 94
  subtropical, 86, 189
Jones, Donald, 218
Jones, H. L., 139

K

Kailua-Kona, Hawaii, 44
Kamchatka Peninsula, Russia, 40
Kansas, 216
Kaolinite, 192, 358
Kapaho, Hawaii, 44
Kartsivadze, A. I., 151, 152
Kaskaskia River, Ill., Fig. VIII-15
Kates, Allan H., 219
Keeling, Charles D., 330
Kelp, 240
Kelut Volcano, Java, 42, 43
Kelvin-Helmholtz waves, 109, 110, 111
Kelvin type waves, 255
Kenya, Fig. V–12
Kericho, Kenya, 153
Kilauea Volcano, Hawaii, 40, 43, 44, 45, 46
Kimura, Kazuo K., 374
Kinzer, G. D., 139
Kiska Volcano, Aleutians, 46
Kitumbe Estate, Kenya, 153
Kodiak, Alaska
  polar ecosystems, 314
  volcanic ash, 41
Komarek, Edwin Vaclav, 307
Köppen, Wladimir, 54
Krakatoa Volcano, Sumatra, 41, 44, 45
Krill
  in food chain, 232, 237, Fig. VIII–6,
    240, 241, 242
Kung, Ernest C., 105
Kuo, Hsiao-Lan, 82, 140
Kuroshio Current, 79, 244
Kutzbach, John E., 72

L

La Jolla, Cal.: oceanographic cruises, 87
La Porte, Ind., 119
Lactase deficiency, 376
Lahars, *see* Mudflows
Lake Erie
  circulation patterns, 254
  pollution, 262–268, 272, 273
  urbanization, 226
Lake Huron, 262, 263, 265, 266, 267, 268
Lake Maracaibo, Venezuela, 203
Lake Michigan, 227, 228, 257, Fig. VIII–13,
    259, Fig. VIII–14, 262, 263, 264, 265,
    266, 267, 268, 270
Lake Ontario, 255, 261, 262, 263, 264, 265,
    266, 267, 268, 270
Lake St. Clair, 263, 266
Lake Superior, 257, 262, 263, 264, 265, 266,
    267, 268, 304
Lake Tahoe, 272
Lake Victoria, Africa, Fig. III–1, 52, 72, 220
Lake Washington, 270, Fig. VIII–16, 272,
    Fig. VIII–17
Lakes, 294, 344
  contaminants, Fig. X–14
  dynamics of, 254–260
Laki (volcano), Iceland, 41
Lamb, H. H., 72
Land Grant College system, 218
Land surface: world total, 299
Land use
  affected by climatic changes, 72, 73
  arable areas and world population,
    Fig. VII–8
  droughts and, 167, 220
  effects of changes in, 34
  forest ecosystems, 294
  urbanization and, 278
  water quality and, 205, Fig. VII–7, 213
Landslides, 212
Langmuir, Irving, 154, 183
Langmuir spirals, 226
Larval ecology, 231
Lasers, 112, 194
Lassen Peak, Cal., 40
Latin America, 215, 370
Laurel forest, 298
Lava, 22, 27, 40–43
  evidence of earth's magnetic field
    reversals, Fig. II–2
  water storage, 203
Leaching of minerals
  tropical forests, 295, 296
Lead
  iodide (PbI_2), 118, 151, 152, 174
  isotopic studies, 30
  poisoning, 322, 327, 360
  pollutants in the air, 320, 330
    content of dust, 193
    urban-produced, 118
  toxic waste in lakes, 272
Legal implications
  building codes
    hurricane protection, 136
  hurricane modification, 132
  precipitation management, 173, 178

Leisure science, 280
  see also Recreation and leisure time
Liberia, Fig. XI–3
Lichens: tundra, 313, 314
LIDAR (Light Detection and Ranging),
    58, 112, 147, 194
Life support systems, *see* Food chain
Lightning, 157–161
  light from, 157
  research, 158–159
  tornadoes and, 138
Likens, G. E., 294
Lilly, D., 140
Limestone, 203
Limnology, 254
  Great Lakes, 269
  Lake Washington, 273
List, R., 150, 151, 152
Lithosphere, 3, 29
Liverworts, 292
Livestock
  effect on water quality, 210, 214
  for western ranges, 74
  horse energy budget, Fig. IX–7
  protection against malaria, 367
  see also Herbivores
Loblolly pine forests, 308, 310
Lodge, J. P., 330
Lominadze, V. P., 152
London, Eng., 53, 113, 117, 386, 390
Lone Pine, Cal., 38
Long Beach, Cal., Fig. VII–3
Lorenz, Edward Norton, 63, 120
Lorenz, Fred W., 376
Los Angeles, Cal.
  air-quality models, 336
  destructive earthquakes, 38
  environmental contamination, 337, 388,
    390
  fog disposal operation, 181, 182
Louisiana
  fire ecology, 308
  severe storms, 133, 134, 135, 136, 147
Lozowski, E. P., 152
Lubbock, Texas, 204
Lubec, Maine, 135
Ludlam, F. H., 109
Lumbering and logging
  water quality and, 210, 213
  fire and, 308, 310
Lung disease and functioning
  high altitudes, 381, 382
  see also Pulmonary edema
Lunn, J. E., 388
Lynx, 304
Lysimeter studies, 209

M

Macdonald, Eleanor Josephine, 366
Machta, Lester, 64
McMurdo Sound, Antarctica, 232
Magma, 40, 43, 48
Magnetic field of the earth, 21
  core and, 3, 23
  earthquakes and changes in, 37
  reversals, Fig. II–2, 25, 27, 28
  study of, 5

Magnetic fields: interplanetary, 4, 6
Magnetite-chalcopyrite, 31
Magnetopause, 3, 7
Magnetosheath, 3, 7
Magnetosphere, 3, 5, 6, 7–8, 9
Maine, 118
Malaria, 364–367
  control and eradication of animal
    diseases, 217
  DDT and 352
  resistance to, 376
  see also Sickle cell anemia
Malaya, University of Kuala Lumpur, 185
Malaysia, 238
Mammals
  extinct types, 73, 74
  marine, 239, 240–241, 245, 247
Mammauthus columbi,
  (extinct mammal), 73
Manabe, Syukuro, 64, 67, 69, 87
Manam Volcano, New Guinea, 43
Manganese deposits, 32
Manpower
  air pollution research, 334
  interdisciplinary training
    environmental designs, 285
  training
    air-sea studies, 79, 82, 101
    aquaculture, 251
    pest control, 353, 356
    malaria, 367
    tropical meteorology, 185, 188
Mantle of the earth, 21, 23, 26–34
  see also Earthquakes; Sea floor: spreading
Maps, climatic anomalies, 88
Mariculture, *see* Aquaculture
Marine invaders, Great Lakes, 262–263
Marketing specialists, *see* Farming
Marten, 304
Martinique, West Indies, 42, 44
Maryland, 308
Masaya (volcano), Nicaragua, 43
Massachusetts Institute of Technology, 183
Materials changes, due to stresses, 36
Mauna Loa (volcano), Hawaii, 41, 44, 46, 64
Mauritius Island, Indian Ocean, 134, 135
Measurements
  aerobiology, 340, 345–349
  air quality, 331, 333, 334
  crustal velocity, 29
  sea-air movements, 100
  sound wave propagation, 112
  windborne dust tranport, 191, 193
  urbanization and weather changes, 115
Medical problems
  high altitudes, 379–385
  tropics, 364–370
  see also Diseases
Mediterranean Sea
  air-sea system, 86, 106, 109, 254
  earth processes, 35, 44
Mendel, Gregor, 373
Merapi Volcano, Java, 42
Mercaptans, 320
Mercury, 272, 322, 357
Mesopause, 11
Mesosphere, 3, 11, 12
Mesozoic era, 29, 30, 31, 55

Mesquite: fire and, Fig. IX–13
Metabolism
 at high altitudes, 381
 heart disease, 388–389
Metaldehyde, 174
Metallogenic maps for North America, 31
Metals: toxic effects, 322, 357
 see also specific names
Meteoric material in ionosphere, 10
Metropolitan Problems Advisory
 Committee, Seattle, Wash., 271
Mexico, 74, 147, 358
Mexico City, Mexico, 204
Miami, Fla., 191, 194
 University of, 253
Mice, see Rodents
Michigan, University of, 269
Microfossils, 344
Microminiaturization
 equipment for weather research, 104
Micropaleontological analysis of
 core samples, 53
Mid-Atlantic Ridge, 26, 27
Mid-Ocean Dynamics Experiment
 (MODE), 80
Middle East, 280
Midwest (U.S.)
 animal ecology, 303
 atmospheric dust, 192
 climatic change, 69
 cyclone defense, 135
 lake pollution, 271
Migration: marine mammals, 246
Milankovitch, M., 54
Milkfish, 251
Miller, Robert C., 101
Millet, 289
Minerals
 forest soils, 296
 mining, 214
 prospecting, 28, 30–32
Mining of water, 204
Ministry of Agriculture and Forests,
 Italy, 153
Minnesota, 302, 311
Minoan civilization, (Crete), 44
Mintz, Yale, 88
Mississippi Valley, 31, 38, 147
 hurricanes, 133, Fig. V–5, 136
Missouri, 31, 38, 170
Mites: pesticide resistance, Fig. X–11, 352
Mitochandria, 288
MODE, see Mid-Ocean Dynamics
 Experiment
Models, Laboratory
 lakes, 254, 269
 lightning, 159, 160
 tornadoes, 140, 141, 146
 urban-induced weather change, 119
Models, Mathematical
 air pollution, 334, 340, Fig. X–7, 335–336
 antarctic marine life, 232
 atmosphere-ocean systems, 58, 59, 64,
  Fig. III–6, 68, 70
 atmospheric circulation, 89–91
 forest ecosystems, 293, 294, 295, 299,
  300, 301, 307
  animal-habitat relationships, 303

hailstorms, 149, 150, 154
heat-food relationships of invertebrates,
 Fig. IX–8
lake circulation, 255, 269, 270
lightning behavior, 159
ocean currents, 79, 80, 81, 82–83, 87
pest control, 353, 366, 369
physical, economic and social
 relationships, Fig. X–5
plant-energy exchange, 287, 288
tundra ecosystem, 314, Fig. IX–16
volcanic activity, 46, 47
weather modification, 174, 175, 176,
 Fig. VI–6, 178, 181, 182
Models, Predictive
cloud seeding, 171, Fig. VI–3
drought, 167, 168, 220
for estimating water supply, 197, 198,
 201, 202
for weather forecasting, 104, 114–115
 dynamic-iterative, 96, 98, 99, 100, 106
 statistical-physical-synoptic, 100
 tropical meteorology, 185, 186, 187,
  188, 189
hurricane, 95, 124, 125, 126, 128, 129,
 131, 132
lake circulation, 254
solar activity and geophysical response,
 16–17
tornado, 139, 140, 141
trophic dynamics of Puget Sound, 249
watershed research, 211
Models, Simulation
ecosystems, 281, 282
 grassland, Fig. IX–2
 mosquito submodel, Fig. IX–3
 oceans, 233, 234, 235, 244
 validation studies, 283, Fig. IX–4
Great Lakes, 269
upper atmosphere, 3, 14
volcanic processes, 46–47
watershed management, 211
Models, Submodels
ecosystems, 281, Fig. IX–3, 284
Mohorovicic discontinuity, 29
Mojave Desert, Cal., 29, 204
Molds
air pollution, 339, 343
crop diseases, Fig. X–8
Mollusks: aquaculture, Fig. VIII–11
Molybdenum, 215
Monitoring
air pollution, 331
climatic changes, 51, 58, 68
ecosystems
 forest fires, 307
 model validating, 283, Fig. IX–4
for atmospheric contaminants, 337
Great Lakes water quality, 264, 266, 270
tornadoes, 138, 140–141
volcanoes, 44, 46, 48
weather stations, 137
Monocultures
domesticated plants and animals, 278
tropical regions, 297
Monsoons, 184–187, Fig. VI–10, 220
Montana, 31, 160, 306
Monte Nuovo (volcano), Italy, 43

Montmorillite, 192
Monzonite, 29
Moon, Fig. I–3
Moose, 303–305
Moreno, Eudoro, 306
Morgan, B., 139
Morris, Dale Duane, 376
Mortality rates, see Death rates
Morton, Newton E., 373, 374
Mosquitos: submodel, Fig. IX–3, 364–367
Mosses
in forest ecosystem, 292
tundra, 313, 314
Motor vehicles: air pollution, 319, 385, 390
Mount Agung, Bali, 56, 68
Mount Baker (volcano), Wash., 44
Mount Katmai (volcano), Alaska, 41, 44
Mount Lassen (volcano), Cal., 40, 44
Mount Mazama (volcano), Ore., 40
Mount Peleé (volcano), Martinique,
 42, 44, 45
Mount Ranier (volcano), Wash., 44
Mount St. Helens (volcano), Wash., 44
Mount San Salvatore, Switz., Fig. V–14
Mount Shasta (volcano), Cal., 44
Mount Wilson, Cal., 41
Mountain sickness, 382, 384, 385
Mountainous regions: clear air turbulence
 over, 106
Mudflows, 207
volcanic, 42–43
Mueller, Peter Klaus, 388
Muller, H. J., 373
Multidisciplinary problems
environmental design, 279
Hubbard Brook Ecosystem Study, 293-295
human biology evolution, 378, 384
Museums, 231
Mussels, 241, 251
Mutations, 338, 373
Mysids, 238

N

Nairobi, University of, Kenya, 185
Namias, J., 166, 167
Naples, Italy, 43
NAS, see National Academy of Sciences,
 U.S.
NASA, see National Aeronautics and
 Space Administration
National Academy of Sciences, U.S.
 (NAS), 91
 see also National Committee for Clear
  Air Turbulence
National Aeronautics and Space
 Administration (NASA), 47, 69,
 112, Fig. VI–11
National Bureau of Electrical Energy,
 Italy, 153
National Center for Atmospheric Research
 (NCAR)
 BOMEX support, Fig. VI–11
 environmental contamination, 330
 modeling, Fig. III–6, 66, 68, 235
National Committee for Clear Air
 Turbulence, U.S., (NAS), 108

National Council of Economic Advisors, India, 217
National Hail Modification Program, (NSF), 155
National Hail Research Experiment (NHRE), (NSF), 151, 155, 156
National Hail Suppression Field Test, (NSF), 153, 155
National Hurricane Center, (NOAA), 125
National Hurricane Research Laboratory, (NOAA), 130
National Marine Fisheries Service, (NMFS), (NOAA), 87, 253
National Maritime Commission, U.S., 189
National Meteorological Center, Wash., D. C., 139
National Oceanic and Atmospheric Administration (NOAA), 13, 16
  modeling, 66, 68, 81, 82, 87
  project STORMFURY, 128
  see also Geophysical Fluid Dynamics Laboratory; National Hurricane Center; National Hurricane Research Laboratory; National Marine Fisheries Service; National Severe Storm Forecast Center; National Severe Storms Laboratory; National Weather Service; Space Environment Laboratory
National Park Service, U.S., 304
National Science Foundation (NSF), Fig. VI–11
  see also National Hail Modification Program; National Hail Research Experiment; National Hail Suppression Field Test
National Severe Storm Forecast Center, (NOAA), 138
National Severe Storms Laboratory, (NOAA), 138, Fig. V–8
National University, Taipei, Taiwan, 185
National Weather Service, (NOAA), 81, Fig. IV–9, 102, 103, 136, 138, 141, 168, 171, 197
Natural enemies of pests, 350, 351, 352, 353, 354, 355, 356
Natural factors
  in climatic change, 63, 64
  contaminants, 329, 330
Natural gas, 33, 357
Natural selection, 72, 373–378, 383
  pests and pesticides, Fig. X–11, 354
Naval Electronics Laboratory Center, San Diego, Cal., 109
Navy, U.S., 81, 102, 128
NCAR, see National Center for Atmospheric Research
Negro, 376, 377
Nepal, 379
Nephelometer, 330
Netherlands, 339
Nevada, 29, 31, 204
New England
  data measurement, 31
  drought, 165
  severe storms, 133
  urbanization, 119
New Guinea, 43
New Hampshire, 293

New Jersey, 336
New Mexico, 31, 74, 204
New Orleans, La., 135
New York, 38, 53, 119, 336, 362
New Zealand, 33, 35, 44, Fig. VII–8
NHRE, see National Hail Research Experiment
Niagara
  falls, 262
  river, 254, 255
Nicaragua, 43
Nickel sulfide ores, 31
Nigeria, 192
Nile River, 296
Nitrogen
  as fertilizer
    in agriculture, 215
    in forest areas, 209
  cycles, 282
  enrichment of lake waters, 226, 228, 268, 272
    Lake Washington, Fig. VIII–17
  forests, 300
  in soil of tropical forests, 295
  in the air, 329
  nitrogen oxides
    air pollution, 320, 337, 388, 390
    contaminants, 322
    in groundwater, 200
    in Lake Washington, 272
    in rivers, Fig. VIII–15
  mesophere, 12
Nitrogen fixing
  burned-over soils, 310
Nitrogen-fixing plants, 208
  trophic dynamics, 227
NMFS, see National Marine Fisheries Service, U.S.
NOAA, see National Oceanic and Atmospheric Administration
Noise and vibrations: effects of exposure, 326
North America
  air-sea system, 86
  climatic change, 53, 55, 57, 73
  drought, 167
  earth processes, 30, 31, 35, 44
  ecosystems, 286
  pollution, 267
  severe storms, 160
  urbanization, 226
  water resources, 291, 294
  weather forecasting, Fig. IV–9, 115, 119
North Carolina, 309
North Sea, 33, 79, 81
Northern hemisphere
  climatic change, Fig. III–4, 61
    monsoon winds, 184
    temperature variation, Fig. III–8, Fig. III–9, Fig. III–10
    weather forecasting, 90, Fig. IV–7, 98, 101
Norway, 78, 241, 246
Norwegian Sea, 78, 102, 103, 104
NSF, see National Science Foundation
Nuclear reactors
  effects on water quality, 231
    estuaries, 248

  lakes, 259, 268
  oceans, 245
  see also Heat; Power-generating plants
Nucleating agents, 174
  cloud seeding, 176
  effect on hurricanes, 191, 193
  fog dispersal, 180, 181, 182, 183
  1,5-dehydroxynaphthalene, 174
  see also Ice: crystals; Silver iodide
Nuclei
  condensation, Fig. X–6
  freezing, 117, 118, 174
  hygroscopic, 153
  ice, 153, 170, 171, Fig. VI–7, 181, 182, 193
  precipitation, Fig. VI–2, 170, 329
  see also Cloud seeding
Nuées ardentes, see Glowing avalanches
Nuñoa Indians, Fig. XI–6
Nutrients
  forest ecosystem, 292, Fig. IX–9, 295, 301, 311
  Great Lakes, 269, 270
  Lake Washington, 271, 272
  tundra ecosystem, Fig. IX–16
Nutrition
  human, at high altitudes, 382, 383, 385
  plant
    crop production, 215
    forest streams, 208, 209
    phytoplankton, 234
  requirements for aquaculture, 251
Nyamuragira Volcano, Africa, 44

O

Oasis effect: water cycle, 202
Observatories
  for solar activities, 15, 17
  seismographic stations, 23
Ocean-atmosphere system, 77–120, 287
  BOMEX project, 125
  drought prediction, 165
  marine contamination in, 357–360
  models, 65–72
  monsoons, 186
  phytoplankton and, 233
  weather forecasting and, 101
Oceanography, 254
  role in weather forecasting, 82, 100
Oceans
  basins, 26
  CO₂ sink, 358
  circulation, 77–88, Fig. IV–2, Fig. IV–3, 234
    models, 68
  currents, 78, 79, 83, 84
  floor
    Globigerina ooze, 53
    oil on, 362
  formation, 21, 24
  heat sink, 257
  source of carbon monoxide, 330
  surface, 52, Fig. III–2, 58, 64, 100
  thermal pollution, 34
  tropical areas, 189
  weather predicting over, 96
Ogallala Formation, 204
Ohio, 69

Oil from marine animals, 240, 241, 242
Oil/petroleum
  gasoline vaporization, 357
  prospecting
    Alaska, 32
    continental shelves, 28
    flow of wells, 47
    worldwide, 31, 33
  sea floor contamination, 361–363
  subsidence of rock formations, 203
  water pollution, 322
    effect on marine mammals, 245
O'Keeffe, Andrew E., 330
Oklahoma, Fig. V–7
Olivine in mantle, 29
Omnivores: food chain, 286
Opik, Ernst, 52
Oregon, 40, 204
Organophosphorus compounds, 355
Orinoco River, S.A., 300
Orographic clouds, 175
Orographic lifting and tilting, 111
Orville, H. D., 150
Ostracods, Fig. VIII–5
Ottersten, Hans, 106
Overgrazing, see Grazing practices
Owens Valley, Cal., 38
Owl monkey, 365
Owls, 302
Oxidation
  carbon monoxide, 358
  floating oil lumps, 362
  of soil humus, releasing CO_2, 71
Oxides, 319, 333
Oxygen
  atomic
    in mesosphere, 12
    in thermosphere, 11
  consumption by biosphere, 286
  forest ecosystem, 301
  from plants, 287, 288
  human consumption at high altitudes,
    379, Fig. XI–4, Fig. XI–5, 382
  newborns, 384
  in atmosphere 34, 320, 329
  in forest streams, 206
  in lakes, 263, 264, 268, 270
    in Lake Washington, 271
  in ocean water, 83, 84, 233
    antarctic, 232
  in the blood, 387
  oxygen isotope (^{18}O)
    ice-caps of Greenland, 57
    in foraminiferal shells, 53
    in sea-core dating, Fig. III–3
Oyster-farming: U.S., 252
Ozone (O_3), 11, 12
  in atmosphere, 89, 319, 320
    health hazard, 387, 388, 390
    urban areas, 117
  in stratosphere, 55, 58, 287
    monitoring, 69
  volcanic gases and, 41

P

P-waves, 29
Pacific Northwest, 209

Pacific Ocean
  air-sea system, Fig. IV–1, 78, 83–87, 165,
    167, 358
  coral reefs, 232
  data measurements, 79, 81, 98, 100
  earth processes, 28, 30, 31, 35, 37, 38, 45
  environmental contamination, 367
  severe storms, 123, 189
  water resources, 233, 236, 242, 244
  weather forecasting, 101, 168
PAHO, see Pan American Health
  Organization
Paleozoic era, 31, 52
Pan American Boeing 707, 158
Pan American Health Organization
  (PAHO), 379, 380
Panama City, Fla., 253
Panofsky, Hans A., 105
Paraffins, 361
Parameterization
  cumulonimbus convection, 189
  hurricane modeling, 126, 128
Parameters
  animal ecology, 302, 304
  ecosystem modeling, 282, 283
    forests, 300, 301
  hydrological
    fisheries, 242, 249
    ocean circulation, 234
  physico-chemical, 340
    Great Lakes, 227, 266
  statistical
    water cycle, 198, 201, 202
Parasites
  in forest ecosystem, 292
  malaria-spreading, 364, 365
  world ocean mammals, 245
Paricutin Volcano, Mex., 41
Particulates
  air pollutants, 319, 333, 337, 339, 385,
    387, 388, 390
  radionuclides, 340
  see also Aerosols
Patagonia, S.A., 53
Pate, John B., 330
Patterson, Claire C., 330
Pauli, Hannes, 388
Pawnee site, 284
PCB (Polychlorinated biphenyls)
  in fish, birds and mammals, Fig. X–16
  in fish in lakes, 228
  in oceans, 233, 359
Penguins, 232, 241
Penman, H. L., 201
Pennsylvania, Fig. VI–8, Fig. X–2
Perch, 261, 263
Perchloroethylene, 357
Peridotite in mantle, 29
Permutt, Solbert, 389
Persistence
  adsorption of pollutants, 291
  drought-producing systems, 165
  forecasting, 99, 102
  pesticides, 352, 356, Fig. X–16
  water contamination in forest areas, 206
  water currents in lakes, 255
Peru, 234, 379

Pesticides, 350–356
  effect on food chain, 244, 245, 323
  effect on terrestrial ecosystems, 301
  effect on water quality
    forest areas, 206, 207
    Great Lakes, 264, 265
    lake eutrophication, 268
  pollution effects
    chlorinated hydrocarbons, 320, 322,
      333, 359
    phosphorus, 321
  2,4,5-T, 207, 213
  see also Insecticides
Pests, 350–356
  see also Insects; Pesticides
Petroleum, see Oil/petroleum
Petroleum hydrocarbons: marine
  contaminants, Fig. X–17
Petrology, 46, 47
Pharmacological properties of tropical
  trees, 298
Phenology of plant species, 289
Phenols, 322
Phenotypic selection in crop-breeding, 216
Phenoxy herbicide, 207
Philippine Islands
  conservation, 251
  earth processes, 35, 44
  environmental contamination, 367
  research facility, 185
Philippines, University of the, 185
Phlegrean Fields, Italy, 43
Phloroglucinol
  cloud seeding nucleant, 174
  fog seeding nucleant, 180
Phosphates
  contaminants, 322
  Lake Washington nutrient, 271
Phosphorus
  enrichment of lake waters, 226, 228, 272
  excess in Lake Erie, 264
  forests, 296, 300
  Great Lakes, 268
  Lake Washington, Fig. VIII–17
Phosphorus-fixing
  mineral soils, 209
  trophic dynamics, 227
Photochemistry
  air pollution, 385
  ionosphere, 10
  plant growth, 288
Photosynthesis
  aquatic plants, 225, 226, 236
  evolution of processes, 34
  Lake Washington, 272
  life support systems and, 285, 286
  marine contaminants and, 359
  modeling, 282
  plant energy exchange, 287, 288
  tundra ecosystem, Fig. IX–16
Phytogeography, 344
Phytoplankton, Fig. VIII–4
  absorption of nutrients, 234
  in aquaculture, Fig. VIII–11
  in lakes, 226, 227
  in oceans, 233, Fig. VIII–6, 359, 361, 362
  sensitivity to insecticides, Fig. VIII–3
Pike, Blue, 261, 263

Pine trees, 310, 311
    air pollutants and, 337
    Bristlecone, 61
    Loblolly, 308, 310
    Longleaf, 306
    Shortleaf, 308
Piscivores, 227
Pitts, Grover C., 390
Planktivorous fish, 227, 228
Plankton, 53, 231, 340, 344
    see also Phytoplankton; Zooplankton
Plant-water relationships, 219–220
Plants
    aerobiology and, 343
    antarctic, 313, 314
    aquatic, 236
    arctic, 314
    diseases, 341, Fig. X–8
    food chain, Fig. IX–6
    food production, 216
    growth, 288, 289
    leaves, systems analysis, 289
    spore reproduction, Fig. XI–1
Plasma physics, 3, 5, 8
Plasmapause, 8
Plate techtonics, see Global techtonics
Pleistocene era, 62, 73, 74
Pliocene age, 204
Plum Island, Mass., 133, 135
Polar bear, 377
Polar caps
    absorption, 11, 14
    magnetopause, 7
Polar front zone, 84
    precipitation, 165
Polar regions
    ecosystems, 313–315
    effect of aerosols, 68
    floating oil, 362
    ice melting possibilities, 119
    information lack on magnetopause over, 7
    ionosphere and, 10
    radio communication over, 11, 14–15, 17
    shipping in, 82
    soil studies, 291
    see also Antarctica; Arctic regions
Polar wind: in F region of ionosphere, 10
Political considerations
    air pollution control, Fig. X–4, 334
    pesticides, 353
Point Barrow, Alaska, 313, 315
Pollen
    aerobiology, Fig. X–7
    air pollution, 339, 340, 343, 345–349
    profiles
        climatic change and, 59, 60, 61,
            72, 73, 74
Pollinosis, see Allergens, Airborne
Pollution
    programs, 232
    projection, Fig. X–5
    worldwide, 190
Pollution, Atmospheric
    abatement by precipitation augmentation,
        177, 178
    biological, 339–349
    chemical, 319, 320, 321, 327, 329–338, 357
        pesticides, 354–356

effect on temperature, 194
forecasting of, 101
forests, 298
    fire in, 213, 311, 312
    Great Lakes area, 264, 268
    hemispheric interchange of air, 188
    lake eutrophication, 268
man-made
    influence on climatic changes, 55, 57,
        65, 66, 68, 69, 71, 72, 115
    urban effects, 113, 116, 117, 118, 119
models
    dispersion, 89, 96
    weather forecasting, 93
natural causes
    influence on climatic changes, 55, 69, 72
    volcanoes, 21, 55, 56, 68, 71, 72, 329
nuclei for precipitation, 192, 193
radioactive elements, 33
regional controls, 332
smog, 385
turbulence and, 108
    acoustic monitoring, 112
upper atmosphere, 65, 69
    see also Carbon monoxide
Pollution, Chemical
    estuaries, 248
    Great Lakes, 264, 265, 268
    pesticides, 354–356
Pollution, Industrial
    atmosphere, 55, 357, 358
    chemicals
        Great Lakes, 264
    from petroleum products, 248
    lake eutrophication, 268
Pollution, Noise, 326, 327
Pollution, Radioactive, 33, 323, 325
Pollution, Soil, see Soils
Pollution, Thermal, 34, 199–200, 255,
        Fig. VIII–12, 322, 337
    coastal areas, 248
    fish culture and, 252
    lakes, 254
        Great Lakes, 263, 264, 266, 268
        Lake Michigan, 257–260, Fig. VIII–13
    oceans, 245
Pollution, Water
    abatement by precipitation augmentation,
        177
    antarctic, 241-242
    coastal areas, Fig. VIII–7
    enrichment of Great Lakes, 227, 228
    forest areas, 206–207, 209, 312
    lakes, 254, 257
    sea farming and, 251
    world ocean, 79, 82, 83, 244, 245,
        Fig. VIII–8
    see also Pollution, Thermal; Sewage
Polygons: arctic tundra, Fig. IX–15
Polygyny: population structure and, 378
Polymorphism, 373, 374
Pompano, 250
Pompeii, 40
Pond culture of fish, 217
Population density
    arable land in relation to, Fig. VII–8
    cause of pollution, 330, 350
        effect on forest and, 293

control of numbers, 373, 378
    environmental design and, 278–280
    modification of earth's albedo, 71
    soil fertility and, 40, 45
    water use factors, 198
Porometer, 201
Porpoises, see Dolphins
Port Louis, Mauritius Isl., 135
Portales, Texas, 204
Potash, see Potassium
Potassium, 32, 215, 300
    eutrophication in Great Lakes, 268
Power-generating plants
    thermal water discharges, 199–200, 249,
        254, 257, 325, 337
        benefits for aqua farming, 252
        Great Lakes, 263, 268
        influence on Lake Michigan,
            Fig. VIII–13
Prairies
    solar radiation in, 55
    climatic change, 73
Precambrian rocks, 30
Precession of the earth, 54
Precipitation
    atmosphere-ocean system, 67, 360
    biological particulates, Fig. X–6, 349
    climatic records, 51, 58
    dust removal by, 358
    fluctuations, 57
    forecasting, 100, 102
    forest land, 205
    in forest ecosystems, 294
    indicated by tree rings, Fig. III–5
    models, 89, 95
    modification, 169–179, Fig. VI–2
    nucleation centers, 329
    urbanization and, 113, 117, 118
        pollution in, 119, 337
    water cycle, 198, 200, Fig. VII–2
        lake eutrophication, 268
    world-wide, 165, Fig. VI–1
    see also Rainfall; Snow
Precipitation stations
    National Weather Service, 197
Predators
    balance of nature, 280
    control of, 303
    in forest ecosystem, 292, 302
    modeling, 282
    see also Isle Royale ecosystem
Predictions
    air turbulence, 111
    change in shallow-water communities,
        230–231
    climatic changes, 59, 61
    droughts, 165–168, 172, 221
    earthquakes, 35, 36, 38
    forest stream temperature, 206
    injury to ecological systems, 340, 342
    lead concentrations in ocean, 360
    long-range effects on biosphere, 280
    processes in forest ecosystems, 292–293
    responses of ecosystems to changes, 300
    responses within ecosystems, 289
    sea-air rhythms, 78, 79, 80, 81, 89
    solar activities, 5, 6, 11, 13, 16–17
    volcanic eruptions, 43–45

water supply, 197–202
weather, 94, 95, 97, 100
  hurricanes, 123–124, Fig. V–3, 135, 136
  severe weather, Fig. V–10
  tornadoes, 137–138, 146
  see also Weather forecasting
President's Science Advisory Committee
  (PSAC), 215
Pressure
  atmospheric
    climatic records, 51, 58
    cloud seeding, 129
    ocean currents and, 78
    sea level, model, Fig. III–6
    sea temperature and, Fig. IV–5
    tornadoes, 137, 144, 145
    tropical regions, 188
    weather, 95
  effect on materials, 22, 23
  subsidence, 203
Primates: malarial infection, 365
Primitive man, 74, 378
Princeton University, 87, 88
Propane, Liquified: fog-seeding nucleant,
  180, 183
Protactinium-231, 53
Proteins
  chemical changes in, 388
  in marine animals, 239, 240–242
Prudhoe Bay, Alaska, 32
PSAC, see President's Science Advisory
  Committee
Public Health Service, U.S., 365
Puerto Rico, 135
Puget Sound, 248, 249, 250, 270, 271
Pulmonary edema (HAPE), 379, 384, 385
Pumice, 362
Punta Arenas, Chile, 241
Purdue University, 304
Purse seine, Fig. VIII–9
Pyroclastic material, 40

Q

Quail, 306
Quartz
  in dust over tropical areas, 193
  in ocean sediments, 358
Quaternary volcanoes, 45, 63, 344
Quizapu (volcano), Chile, 41

R

Rabbits, 304, 388
"Race": human differences, 373, 374
  376, 377, 378
Radar, Acoustic
  ultra-high resolution, 108, Fig. IV–10
  WIT detection, 112
Radar, Coherent laser, see LIDAR
Radar, Doppler, 95, 110, 140–141, 144, 147
Radar, Frequency modulated
  continuous wave, 109, 110, 111
Radar, Incoherent scatter, 9–10
Radar, Pulsed microwave
  cloud measurements, 170, 176
  observations, 108
    air-borne, 111, 129–130
    ground-based, 111

hook-shaped echoes, Fig. V-7
  weather modification, 178
storm detection, 94, 95
  tropical areas, 187
weather prediction, 103, 104, 109, 138,
  141, Fig. V–8, Fig. V–9, 147, Fig. V–10
Radiation belt, 6, 8
Radiation hazards
  man in space, 5, 14, 25
  effects, 325
Radio waves
  commnications, 3, 4, 5, 8, 11, 14
  lightning, 157
Radioactivity
  dating techniques, 53, 54, Fig. III–3, 58, 72
  fallout, 332, 340
  wastes, 323, 335, 357
Radiometric sounders, 87, 90, 96, 98
Radiosondes, Fig. IV–6, Fig. IV–7, 98
Radon-222, 193, 194
Ragweed pollen, 345, Fig. X–9, 347,
  Fig. X–10
Rainfall
  air-sea rhythms and, 85–86
    Canton Island, Fig. IV–4
  areas of malaria potential, Fig. X–19
  causes, 165
  cloud seeding model, Fig. VI–6
  for prescribed fire in forests, 310
  generation, 170
  hurricane carried, 126, 128, 131, 133
  in ecosystems, Fig. IX–5
    tropical forests, 295, 298, Fig. IX–11
  lightning and, 160
  tornadoes and, 139
  tropical areas, 186, 187, 189
  typhoons, 140
  urban-induced, 115
  see also Monsoons
Rajasthan Desert, India, 58
Ramage, Colin S., Fig. VI–10
RAND Corporation, The, 68
Rapid City, S. Dak., 153
Raschke, K., 202
Rawinsonde networks
  tornado warnings, 146
  weather analysis, 101, 104
Reaction rates
  ocean layers, 89
  precipitation mechanisms, 169
Recreation and leisure time
  effect on water quality, 205, 209, 210, 214
  factor in environmental design, 279, 280
  forest wildlife, 303
  game laws and aquaculture, 251
  hunting, 293, 307
  noise pollution, 326
  tourism in arctic, 313
  water use, 200, 254, 257
  see also Aesthetics
Recycling of resources, 338
  environmental design, 278
  food chain, 226
Red crab, 240
Red scale, Fig. X–13
Redondo Beach, Cal., 203
Reducers: trophic dynamics, 225

Reflectivity of the earth,
  see Albedo of the earth
Regional effects: urban-induced weather
  change, 115, 119
Regional Meteorological Center,
  Darwin, Australia, 185
Residence time
  air pollutants
    carbon monoxide, 358
  water pollutants, 267
    DDT, Fig. X–14
    Great Lakes, 269
    ocean-floating oil lumps, 362
    oceans, 357
Resistance
  children to disease, 378
  pest species, 350
    malarial insects, 364, 365, 367
Resources, Nonrenewable: projection,
  Fig. X–5
Respiration
  air pollution and, 385, 386, 387, 388
  high altitudes, 381, 385
  plants, 288
Revelle, Roger (R. D.), 82
Reynolds numbers, 269
Rh babies, 374
Rhodesia, 297
Ribeirão Prêto, Brazil, 369
Rice production, 218, 220
Richardson, L. F., 107, 109, 110
Richardson number (Ri), 107, 109, 111
Richter scale, Fig. II–7
Rio de Janeiro, Brazil, 41
Rio Grande River, 31
Rio Negro River, S.A., 300
Riometers, 15
Rivers
  as a water supply, 187
  impact on lakes, 270
  nitrate concentrations in, Fig. VIII–15
  nutrient-rich, 268
  thermal pollution, 34
Robbins, Robert Crowell, 330
Robinson, Elmer, 330
Robinson, George D., 68
Rockets
  pollution, 65, 69
  used in cloud seeding, 151, 152, 153
Rocketsonde programs: weather
  forecasting, 101
Rocky Mountain Arsenal, Col., 39
Rocky Mountains
  earth processes, 28, 29, 31
  precipitation, 166, 204
  severe storms, 160
  weather forecasting, 38
  weather modification, 177
Rodents
  in food chain, Fig. IX–6, 302
  malaria systems, 365, 366
  rat middens, 73
Rosenthal, S. A., 128
Ross Sea, Antarctica, 84
Rossby, Stig A., 13, 102, 103
Rossow, V., 139
Rotation of the earth, see Coriolis force
Rotifers, 228

Royal Observatory, Hong Kong, 185
Royal Society, London, Eng., 51
Rubber, Fig. VII–9, 297
Rubidium in isotopic studies, 30
Russia, 68, 358, 359
    fishing, 232, 241, 242, 246
    Moscow, 41, 53
    oceans, 82, 239, 241, 244
    soil, 220, 291
    Ukraine, 216
    volcanoes, 44
    weather, 69, 100, 106
        hail, 149, 151, 152, 154, 155
Rusts (plant diseases), Fig. VII–9,
    339, 340, 341, Fig. X–8, 343

S

S-waves, 29
Saarinen, Thomas Frederick, 219
Saginaw Bay, 263
Sahara (desert), Africa, 52, 192, 193, 329
St. Lawrence River, 261, 262
St. Lawrence Seaway, 259
St. Louis, Mo., 113
St. Pierre, Martinique, 42, 44
St. Vincent (island), Lesser Antilles, 42
Salmon, 266, 271
    Atlantic, 261, 262
    coho, 228, 263
Salmonella, 217
Salt
    cloud seeding, 174, 192, 329
    deposits, 28
    in blood of fish, 232
    in haze, 68
    in irrigation waters, 291
    in ocean waters, 83, 84
Salton Sea, Cal., 33
Samoa, 87
Samplers, Aeroallergen
    Durham, 347
    impaction, Fig. X–10
    rotoslide, 348
San Andreas Fault, Cal., 26, 30, 36, 37
San Bernardino Mountains, Cal., 337
San Diego, Cal., Fig. IV–10
San Francisco, Cal., 35, 38, 39, Fig. IV–12,
    357
San Gabriel Mountains, Cal., 337
San Joaquin Valley, Cal., 204, 352
San José, Cal., 204
San Juan, Puerto Rico, 44
Sand, 135, 329
Sandstone, 203
Santa Barbara, Cal., Fig. VII–5, 361
Santa Clara Valley, Cal., 204
Sardines, 237, 238
Saskatchewan, Can., 32
Satellites
    APT, 185
    atmospheric circulation, 90, 96
    cloud cover monitoring, 68–69
    drag, 14
    effect of radiation, 8
    instrumentation, 87, 90, 96, 98
    observations from, 5, 7, 15, 22, 97, 98, 104
    radiation monitoring, 58, 59, 66

sea-air studies, 78, 81, 84, 87, 100
weather forecasting, 103
    tropical areas, 187, 188, Fig. VI–12, 190
Satellites, Geostationary
    ATS-3
        atmospheric dust, 191, Fig. VI–13
        hurricane surveillance, 129, 130, 134
        storm tracking, 94, 95
        weather forecasting, 101
Satellites, Polar orbiting
    ESSA-3, 124
    hurricane pictures, 95, 123, Fig. V–1,
        Fig. V–2
    ITOS-I, 69
    Nimbus-3, 90, 98
    Nimbus-4, 69
    Nimbus-F, 69
    weather forecasting, 101
Sauger in Great Lakes, 263
Saury, 363
Savannah, Forest, 299
Scales
    distance, Fig. X–3
    time
        air-sea systems, 79, 82, 83
        atmospheric circulation, 91
        models of the atmosphere, 90
Scandinavia, 86, 314
Schaefer, Vincent J., 154, 183
Schistosomiasis, 217, 323, 367–369
Scholander pressure chamber: soil profile,
    202
Schove, D. J., 51
Sculpin in Great Lakes, 263
Sea farming, see Aquaculture
Sea floor
    oil, 361–363
    spreading, 22, 26–27, 29, 32
Sea lamprey in Great Lakes 262, 263,
    264, 266
Sea levels, Interglacial, 54
Sea-lion, 241
Seals in sub-antarctic, 232, 240, 241,
    242, 246, 247
Seas, see Oceans
Seattle, Wash., 53, Fig. VI–7, 270, 271
Seaweeds
    as food source, 236
    sub-antarctic, 232
Secchi disc, Fig. VIII–16
Sediment particles
    effect of land use, Fig. VII–7
    flow rate, Fairfax County, Fig. VII–6
    microfossils in lakes, 344
    ocean floor, 358, Fig. X–17
    pollen proples, 61, 72, 73
    water quality and, 206, 209
Seeding techniques for fog, 188–183
    see also Cloud seeding
Seedlings, Hurricane: surveillance of, 123,
    Fig. V–1, 125, 126
Seiches, 254, 255
Seismic measuring and monitoring, 28, 31
    seismographs, 22
    waves, 22, 28, 29
Seismicity of the earth, 35, Fig. II–5, 37
    U.S., Fig. II–7
Selenium, 215

Sellers, William D., 67
Semi-arid regions
    water supply, 198
    water conserving, 220
Semi-deciduous forests, 295
Severe local storms: prediction, 94, 98
Sewage
    as fertilizer, 251
    effect on aquatic life, 230, 231, 233–234,
        235
    effect on estuaries and coastal zones, 248
    effect on lakes, 254, 265
        Lake Washington, 270, 271, 272, 273
    in aquaculture, Fig. VIII–11
    in humid tropics, 300
    pollution, 230, 323, Fig. X–16
        oceans, 357, Fig. X–17
Shales, 203
Shallow-water communities
    predictions of change, 230–231
    seaweeds, 236
Sheepshead, 261, 263, 266
Shipping
    hazards to, 33–34, 41, 82, 180
    water use to maintain stream depth, 200
    weather forecasting for, 81
Ships: used for sea-air studies, 78, 79, 84,
    87, 100
Shock waves
    solar wind, 5
    seismic, 22, 35, 36, 38, 39
Shore zones
    lakes, 254, 255
    Great Lakes, 268
    see also Coastal areas
Shorebirds: tundra ecosystem, Fig. IX–16
Showa Shin-Zan, Japan, 43
Shrimp
    sergestid, 238
    Japan, 251
    aquaculture, 253
    see also Krill
Shrimp-seals, 241
Shull, George, 218
Siberia, 189, 314
Sicily, 35
Sickle cell anemia
    in Liberia, Fig. XI–3
    malaria and, 365, 377
    race and, 373, 374
Sierra Nevada Range (U.S.), 29
Signal Hill, Cal., 203
Silicic rock, 29
Silver bromide (AgBr): cloud seeding,
    Fig. VI–3
Silver iodide (AgI)
    cloud seeding, 128, 129, 141, 175, 192
        hailstorms, 151, 152, 153, 154
        lightning reduction, 161
        precipitation modification, 170, 172,
        Fig. VI–3, Fig. VI–4
        fog seeding, 180
Singapore, Fig. IV–5, 185, 238
SIRS (Satellite Infrared Spectrometer),
    90, 98
Skillet Fork River, Ill., Fig. VIII–15
Skin color in human populations, 374–375

Slash-and-burn technique in tropical
    agriculture, 296, Fig. XI–3
Smagorinsky, Joseph, 88
Smelt, 261, 263, 264
Smith, J. E., 232
Smithsonian Institution, 47, 52
Smog, 12, 65, 67, 68, 113
    adaptation to, 385–390
    chambers, 334
    photochemical, 335, 336, 385, 387, 390
        ecology of, 337–338
Smokes, 65, 67, 68
    air pollution, Fig. X–6
    forest fires, 33
    urban-induced, 113
Smut (plant diseases), 341 Fig. X–8, 343
Snails, see Schistosomiasis
Snake River Plain, 29
Snow
    cloud seeding and, 170, 171, 177
    cover
        climate and, 64, 68, 97
        satellite monitoring, 59
    tundra, 313
    urban areas, 114, 117
Social implications
    air pollution control, Fig. X–4, 334
    climatic changes, 57
    man-induced weather changes, 172,
        173, 175
    parasitic diseases, 367, 369
    pollution, 327
Social sciences: role in agricultural
    adaptations, 220, 221
Sodium arsenate (herbicide), 213
Soils
    fertility, 40, 45, 295, 296, 297
    fire and microorganisms, 311, 312
    in forest ecosystems, 292, 293
        southern pine areas, 311, 312
        tropical areas, 295, Fig. IX–10
    leaching
        irrigation, 216
        water storage and, 202
    pollution, 291, 323
    reserves of plant nutrients, 215
    studies for ecosystems, 291
    water storage, 200, 202, 211, 212
Solar constant, 52, 55
Solar flares, Fig. I–1, 5, 6, 13, 14
Solar radiation, 3, 52, 254, 287
    absorption by animals, 289
    atmosphere-ocean system, 66, 67, 70
    atmospheric circulation and, 89
    climatic changes and, 55, 64
    ecosystems, 285, 287, 288, Fig. IX–9, 301
        food chain, Fig. IX–6
    effect of dust, 57–58, 68, 191, 194
    effect of pollution, Fig. X–2, 332
    effect of snow, 89
    effect of volcanic activity, 45
    effect on climate, 52, 65–69, Fig. III–7
        tropical areas, 186
    extreme ultraviolet, 4, 9, 10
    modified by CO_2, 337
    plant energy, 287
    precipitation, 167, 173
    re-radiation, 70

scattering, 58, 89
    trophic dynamics, 225, 226
    urban effects on, 113, 114, 116, 119
    water movement and, 200, 206
Solar-terrestrial system, 3–13
Solar wind, 3, 5, 6, 8, 15
Sole, English, 249
Solfatara Volcano, Italy, 43
Solvents, Dry-cleaning: air pollution, 357
Sonar: fisheries management, 244
Sonoran Desert, Ariz., 282
Sound waves, 112
South America
    agriculture, 167, Fig. VII–8, 242
    air-sea system, 77, 86
    earth processes, 27, 28, 32, 35, 44, 59
    ecosystems, 286, 291, 297, 300
    environmental contamination, 364, 365,
        370
    human adaptation, 378
South Carolina, 309, 310
South Georgia Island, Antarctica, 239, 241
Southern hemisphere
    chronology of tree rings, 61
    dust measurements, 194
    monsoons, 184
    weather forecasting, 90, Fig. IV–7, 98, 103
Soybeans, 216, 217
Space Environment Laboratory
    (NOAA), 16
Spain, 252
Spinel, 29
Spiny lobsters, 250
Sponges, 232
Spores: air pollution, 339, 340, 342,
    343, 345
Sputum and cough, 386, 390
Squirrel, Gray, 302
Stabia (historic), 40
Stakman, E. C., 339
Standard of living, 330
Stanford Research Institute, Cal., 330
State, U.S., Department of, Fig. VI–11
Steam, Industrial: as pollutant, 329
Steering methods: weather prediction, 93,
    94, 95, 148
Stokes, G. G., 192
Stokinger, H. E., 389
Stommel, Henry Nelson, 79
Stone Age, 74
Stone-crabs, 241
Storm systems
    climatic records, 51
    droughts and, 165
    tropical, 189
        influence of dust, 191–194
        modification, 187
    turbulence in, 108
    urbanization and, 113
    see also Hurricanes; Severe local storms;
        Tornadoes
STORMFURY, Project, 126, 127–132
Strait of Magellan, 241
Stratopause, 3, 11
Stratosphere, 3, 69, 287
    drift of pollutants, 190
    dust in, Fig. III–10
    turbulence in, 105

Streamflows
    as part of water supply, 197, 198
    stability of channels, Fig. VII–7
Stress measurement: earthquake prediction
    and, 37, 38
Strontium, in isotopic studies, 30
Sturgeon, Great Lakes, 263
Sub-Antarctica
    islands, 313–314
    waters, 240, 241
Subsidence, in water and oil bearing
    formations, 203–204, Fig. VII–3
Subtropical belt of dryness, 165, 166, 167,
    191
Succession principle of natural communities
    aquatic, 230
    forests, 299, 304, 308
Suckers (fish), 261
Sukurajima (volcano), Japan, 45
Sulakvelidze, G. K., 152
Sulfur
    agriculture, 215
    sulfur oxides
        air pollution, 319, 337, 360, 385, 387,
            388, 390
        modeling, 335, 336
        natural causes, 330
        smog, 337
        urban areas, Fig. X–2, 319, 342
        volcanoes, 21, 41, 43
    sulphates
        contaminants, 322
        increase in Great Lakes, 268
Sumatra (island), Indonesia, 41, 44
Summer
    anomalies, 56
    droughts (U.S.), 166
    dust transport, 191, 192
        content, 193
    forest fires, 309, 310
    monsoons, 184
    stratification of lake water, 258
    urban effects on weather, 114, 116
Sun, 3–17
    climate and, 51
    damage to human beings, 325
    heat input on Great Lakes, 257
    radiation, 4, 14, 25
    sunspots, 3, 4, 13, Fig III–1, 52, 58
    see also Solar radiation
Sunflowers, 216
Sunnyvale, Cal., 204
Superior Province, Great Lakes, 31
Surtsey (volcano), Iceland, 47
Sverdrup, H. U., 79
Switzerland, 154, Fig. V–14
Systematic biology, 231
Systems analysis
    environmental design, 289, 340
        forest ecosystem, 294, 295, 300
    Great Lakes water management, 267, 269–
        270
    maintenance of the biosphere, 281
    meteorology, 339
    oceans and marine productivity, 233–235
    pest control, 352, 353
    plants, 289

T

Taiwan, 35
Talc, 359, 360
Tall Timber Research Station, Tallahassee, Fla., 307
Tanganyika, 220
Tanzania, Fig. VII–10
Tarawa (island), 87
Taxonomic identification of plankton, 228, 230
Tay-Sachs disease, 374
Teal, John M., 361, 363
Teleconnections, 85, 88, 100
Telemetry
    animal ecology, 302
    energy relations of animals in the ecosystem, 289
    field studies of animals, 289
Temperate zone
    agricultural practices, 295
    drought, 165
    forests, 292, 298–301
    hurricanes, 123, 124, 135
Temperature
    bacterial oxydation, 362
    climatic records, 51, 52,
    cloud-seeding, 176
    cloud-top, 175
    CO_2 content of atmosphere and, 64, 67, Fig. III–9, Fig. III–10, 72, 332
    deep earth processes, 22
    derived from sea-core dating, Fig. III–3
    earth and above it, 89
    historic records on, 58
    human beings, 374, 376
    northern hemisphere, Fig. III–4, 57, Fig. III–8, Fig. III–9, Fig. III–10
    nucleating agent effectiveness, 174
    sounding by satellites, Fig. IV–6
    worldwide effect of dust, 194
Temperature, Atmospheric, 11, 12
    distribution, Fig. I–5
    effect of CO_2, 119
    effect on clouds, 141, 174
    effect on mosquitoes, Fig. IX–3
    fluctuations, tropical vs. temperate species, 298, Fig. IX–11
    forecasting, 94, 100, 102
    forest fires, 306, 307, 311, 312
    formation of hailstones, Fig. V–11
    global variations, 55
    in ecosystems, 285, Fig. IX–5, 300, 301
    patterns, 102
    plants, 287, 288, 289
    Project STORMFURY, 129
    records, 51, 52
    smog, 337
    tropical areas, 188
    urban areas, 113, 114, 116, 119
Temperature, Water
    Antarctica, 83, 231–232
    Great Lakes, 261
    lakes, 254
        thermal influence, Fig. VIII–13
    sea-surface, Fig. III–2, Fig. IV–1
        drought causes, 165
        north Pacific, 78
        tropical regions, 85, Fig. IV–5

water cycle, 200, 201, 202
    forest areas, 206
Terrestrial ecosystems, 277–315
Tertiary era, 63, 358
Texas
    earth processes, Fig. II–7
    ecosystems, 306, 308
    groundwater, 203, 204
    range management, 74
    severe storms, 123, 124, 140, 147, 154
Texas Agricultural Experiment Station, 204
Texas Tech University, Lubbock, Tex., 306
Thailand, 184, 185
    aquaculture, 238
Thalassemia, 373
Thera (volcano), Crete, 44
Thermal bar
    Great Lakes, 268, 270
    lakes, 255, 258, 259
Thermal engine, 65–66, 67, 77, 123
Thermal plume in lake water, 259
Thermal pollution, *see* Pollution, Thermal
Thermocline, 84, 87
Thermohaline alterations, 83
Thermonuclear energy, 5, 8, 25
Thermosphere, 3, 11
Thomas, Heriberto V., 388
Thomson, J. J., 10
Thorium, 30, 53
Thorpe, Steven A., 106, 109
Thunderstorms
    hailstorm type, 154, Fig. V–13
    lightning and, 157, 160
    prediction, 93, 94, 95, Fig. V–10
    tornadoes and, 137, 138, 139, 144
    tropical areas, 186, 187
Tibet, 184, 186
Tidal waves, 35
    earthquakes and, 81
    volcanic eruptions and, 44
Tides, 81, 123
    atmospheric, 58
    gauges, 87
    sea-air system and, 78, 81
Time
    factor in water cycle, 202
    landscape stability, 211
Tin deposits, 32
TNT, 153
Tonga, Friendly Isls., Pac. Ocean, 35
Tornadoes, 137-148
    effect on water quality, 212
    hurricanes and, 123
    occurrence, 132
    predictions, 94, 98
Torrey Canyon, S.S. (ship), 361
Toxic substances
    agriculture and, 278
    changes in ecosystems, 280
    Lake Washington, 272
    see also Pollution, Chemical
Toyama, T., 388
Trace elements, 34, 296
Trade winds
    dust from Africa, 191, 192, 193, 358
    equatorial belt of wetness, 165
    hurricanes and, 123

pesticides spread by, 360
precipitation, 167
Transparency
    decrease in Great Lakes, 268
    measurements in Lake Washington, Fig. VIII–16, 272
Transpiration in plants, 287
Transportation
    hazards due to fog, Fig. VI–8
    impact of climatic change, 58, 59
Transportation, U.S. Department of, Fig. VI–11
Transverse Ranges, Cal., 29
Tree rings: climatic change shown by, 58, 59–61, Fig. III–5
Trees, *see* Forests; Vegetation
Triggering agents
    climatic events, 55, 69
    convection, 119
    earthquakes, 37, 39
    gravity waves and turbulence, 106
    precipitation, lead-contaminated, 118
    waves, 111
    waves and wind speed, 110
Trophic dynamics
    aquaculture and, 252
    estuaries, 248-253
    Great Lakes, 225–229, 230, 261
    world ocean, 236–247
Trophic levels
    aquatic, Fig. VIII–1, 226, 227, 228
    estuaries, 248
Tropic of Cancer: atmospheric dust, 191
Tropical medicine, 364–370
Tropical regions
    air-sea rhythms, 84–88
    animal diseases, 217
    atmospheric composition, 330
    climatic changes, 57, 133
    drought, 220
    effects of dust, 191–194
    human adaptation in, 378–379
    natural air contaminants, 330, 344
    radiative balance, 68
    soil studies, 291, 295–297
    storms
        see Hurricanes; Typhoons
    weather forecasting, 90, 91, 95, 98, 184–190
Tropopause, 105
Troposphere, 3, 11, 69
    atmospheric circulation studies in, 90, 105
    drift of pollutants, 190, 357
    dust in, Fig. III–10, 193
    tropical weather, 186
Trout
    freshwater, 225, 251, 261, 262, 263, 266, 271
    sea, 253
Trout, Dennis, 105
Trypanosomiasis, American, *see* Chagas' disease
Tsetse fly, 344
Tsunamis, *see* Tidal waves
Tundra biomes, Fig. IX–15, 314, 315
Tungsten, 31, 90
Turbidity
    atmosphere, 339

measurement, 194, 331
monitoring, 56, 58
role of aerosols, 68, 71
urban-induced weather change, 119
forested watersheds, 206, 209, 210
Turbulence
earth's magnetic field, 6
forest canopy, 201
in atmosphere, 91, 335
urban-induced, 113
wave-induced, 105–112
in mesosphere, 12
lake waters, 254, 256, 260
tornadoes, 138
Turkey (country), 35
Turkey, Wild, 302, 306
Turner, J. S., 140
Typhoons
study of effects, 185
weather forecasting, 102
models, 91

U

Uccle, Belgium, 68
Udall, Kans., 139
Ukraine, 216
Ultraviolet radiation, 55, 287
ionosphere, 9, 11
urban areas, 116
United Nations: environmental research, 344
United States
agriculture, 199, 215, 218, 219, 291,
Fig. X–8
air-sea interaction, 56, 73, 81, 89, 97, 106,
109
climatic change, 57, 68, 73, 74, 220
data networks, Fig. IV–7, 141, 147
drought, 165, 166, 219
earth processes, 28, 29, 32, 45, 48
ecosystems, 205, 232, 233, 241, 246, 251–
253, 261, 293, 295, 300, 302, 306, 308
environmental contamination, 69, 192,
194, 329–332, 334, 343, 345, Fig. X–9,
Fig. X–12, 367, 369, 390
human adaptation, 373, 374, 378, 379,
Fig. XI–6
pollution, 265–268, 270
regional weather, 185, 188
severe storms, 123, 126–128, 130, 133, 135,
137–139, 146, 149, 151, 153–155, 157,
158
urbanization, 113, 114, 118, 119, 283
volcanoes, Fig. II–8
water resources, 210, 361
weather forecasting, 35–40, 42, 44, 94, 100,
103, 104, 181
weather modification, 170, 172, 181–183
Updrafts, 149, 150
Upper Colorado Pilot Project, 172
Upwelling
coastal, 80, 86
lake water, 255, Fig. VIII–12, 259, 269
Uranium, 30, 32, 325
Urban areas
aircraft pollution, 65
atmospheric chemistry, 336
biological pollution, 342, 343
ecology of smog, 337

hurricane damage, 135
ice nuclei, Fig. VI–7
solar radiation in, 55
Urbanization
air pollution-smog, 385
effects on large lakes, 226
effects on water supply, 198
effects on weather, 114, 115, 118
environmental design requirements, 278
humid tropics, effect on ecology, 300
sea farming and, 251
spread of parasitic disease, 369
water quality and, 261
weather changes and, 113–120, Fig. IV–11
Urea
cloud-seeding nucleant, 174
fog-seeding nucleant, 180
Ury, Hans K., 388
USGS, see Geological Survey, U.S.
Utah
groundwater, 204
seismic refraction profile, 29, 31

V

Valley of Ten Thousand Smokes, Alaska,
42, 44
Vegetation
affected by smog, 337
carbon dioxide removed from air, 358
effect on aeroallergens, 349
effect on water movement, 200, 201, 202
effect on water quality, 212, 265
fire and, 306
forested areas, 302
fossil studies, 73
pollen profiles and, 61
restoration upon lava flows, 41
sulfur dioxide removal from air, 330
urban areas, 118
western America, 74
see also Plants
VELA program, 23
Venezuela, 33, 203
environmental disease, 369
genetic differences, 374, Fig. XI–1,
Fig. XI–2
Ventilation: water movement and storage,
200, 202
Ventura-Winnemucca earthquake zone
(Cal. and Nev.), 31
Verification systems: weather forecasts, 102,
103
Veronis, George, 82
Vesuvius (volcano), Italy, 40, 43, 45
Vigo, Bay of, Spain, 251
Virginia
effects of hurricanes, 133
Fairfax County, Fig. VII–6
urban-induced weather change, 118
Viruses, Fig. X–6, 341, Fig. X–8
Visibility: urbanization and, 113, 117
Vital statistics: high altitude populations,
385
Volcanoes, 21, 40–48
carbon gases, 43
effects on water quality, 212
forest soil, 295

records on, 58
sea floor topography, 27–28
see also, Ash, Volcanic
Von Neumann, John, 97
Vonnegut, B., 139, 183

W

Waite, P. J., 139
Walker's "southern oscillation", Fig. IV–5
Waller, H. J., 388
Walleye, 261, 263
Wallihan, Ellis F., 201
Wallops Island, Va., 109
Walter Reed Army Institute for Research,
365
Ward, N. B., 140
Warm fog, 181, 183
Warning systems
ecological changes, 344
ecological damage, 340
hurricanes, 136
tornadoes, 138, 144, 148
Wasatch Range, U.S., 31
Washington
crustal velocity, 29
fishery technology, 252
urban-related precipitation, 113, 119
volcanoes, 31, 40, 44
weather modification, 101
see also Seattle
Washington, D. C., 68, 98, 185
Washington, University of, 330
Forest Service, 306
Waste management
conservation and, 338
definition of wastes, 330
forestry and, 213, 301
human ecosystem, 278
land pollution, 248, 323
rivers and, Fig. X–2
Water
contamination, 329
hurricane clouds, 129
volcanic action and, 42, 43
Water budget
cloud systems, 171
Great Lakes, 269
Lake Washington, 273
precipitation augmentation, 177
urban areas, 116
Water conservation devices, 296
Water management
development schemes and parasitic
diseases, 369
Great Lakes, 266, 267
Water quality
arid regions, 291
diverted use, 198
environmental design and, 278
forest areas, 205–214
Great Lakes, 261–270
lakes, 226, 227, 230, 257
standards, 214
Water resources, 197–204
Water shortages, 178
priorities, Great Lakes, 270
Water supply
agriculture, 215–216

contaminants, 322
data bases, 197
desert areas, Fig. IX–3, 291
for tundra vegetation, 313, Fig. IX–16
forest land, 205, 292, 300, 307
tropics, Fig. IX–10
storage in rocks, 203
tropical areas, 187, 188
Water use, 198, 199–200
Water vapor
as pollutant, 337
disease carrier, Fig. X–21
atmosphere-ocean system, 66, 67, 71
hail clouds, 152
heat balance of the earth and, 287, 288
hurricanes, 131
in clouds, 331, 337
in pure air, 329
precipitation, Fig. VI–2
storm forecasting, 138
tornado models, 139
urban area weather, 119
Watersheds
forest areas, 206, 209, 211, 212
lakes, 273
northern hardwood, 293–295
Waterspouts, 144, 147
Waves
data, 78, 80
hurricanes, 127, 128
induced turbulence, 108–112, Fig. IV–10
kinds
gravity, 106, 111
Kelvin-Helmholtz, 109, 110, 111
Kelvin type, 255
lakes, 254, 255, 256, 259
models, 81
ocean-surface, Fig. IV–2
Weasels
in food chain, Fig. IX–6
tundra ecosystem, Fig. IX–16
Weather, 62
prescribed fire and, 311
urban-induced change, 119
see also Radar
Weather forecasting, Fig. IV–9
anomalies, 87, 88
climatology, 103
data base, 90-92, 93, Fig. IV–7, Fig. IV–8,
98, 103
extrapolation method, 93, 94, 95, 97
for fishing industry, Fig. VIII–7
models, 93, 94, 95, 96, 97, 102
extended periods, 99, 105
role of oceanography, 82, 100
short-range, 94–96, 101–104
tropical areas, 184, 189
storms and hurricanes, 187
urban-induced changes, 114, 115
Weather modification
at airfields, 101
environmental management, 283

hail, 151
hurricanes, 126
lightning, 158, 160–161
tornado windspeed, 145, 146
urban-induced, 113-120, Fig. IV–11
see also Climate: control; Precipitation:
modification
Weather stations, 137, 138, 146
Weatherald, Richard T., 67, 69
Weddell Sea, Antarctica, 84, 232
Weddell Seal, 232
Wegener, Alfred E., Fig. II–4
Well drilling, 203
Welland Canal, 261, 262
Weller, N., 139
Wells, Philip V., 73
West Germany, 181
West Indies, Lesser Antilles, 42, 134
West Virginia, 133
Western hemisphere
dust from Africa and, 191
model of sea-level pressure, Fig. III–6
Whales, 232, 241
in food chain, Fig. VIII–6
management of stocks, 245–246
source of food, 240, 242
Wheat, 216, 217, 220, 289
White Mountains, Cal., 61
White Mountains, N.H., 293
Whitefish
food fish, 227
Great Lakes, 261, 262, 263, 264
Lake Washington, 271
WHITETOP, Project, 170, 171, 172
WHO, see World Health Organization
Wilderness reserves
see Isle Royale ecosystem
Williams, Roger J., 376
Wilmington, Cal., 203
Wind
distribution
in tornado vortices, 138
tornado models, 139
flow patterns
atmospheric pollutants and, 335, 336,
344, 360
climatic change and, 56, 100
drought, 165
fog dispersal operations, 180
forecasting, 102, 104
hailstorms, 149
models, 89, 95
monsoons, 184
sea-surfaces and, 78, 86
severe storms, 125, 129, 130, 135, 138
tropical areas, 188
urbanization and, 113, 114, 116
water circulation, 254, Fig. VIII–12
weather modification systems, 174
shear, turbulence and, 108
speed
atmospheric pollution, 347, Fig. X–10

climatic records, 51
cloud seeding, 176
factor in plant growth, 287, 288
forest fires, 306, 310
hailstorms, 149, 150, Fig. V–13
hurricanes, 123, 127–128
tornadoes, 137, 144–145, 146
tunnels
air pollution research, 334
hail, 150
Wind River Basin, Wyo., 31
Winter
dust transport, 191, 192, 193
forest fires, 310
monsoon winds, 184
temperatures, 56, 57, 114
Wisconsin, 257, 263, 269
Wisconsin, University of, 269
WIT (wave induced turbulence), 108, 109,
110, 111, 112
WMO, see World Meteorological
Organization
Wolf, Timber, 302, 304–305
Woods, J. D., 106, 109
Woods Hole Oceanographic Institution,
Mass., 361
Work capacity, at high altitudes, Fig. XI–4,
Fig XI–5, 382
World Data Centers (Wash., D. C.; Moscow,
U.S.S.R., etc.): space data
clearinghouse, 15
World Health Organization (WHO), 379,
380, 385, 388
World Meteorological Organization
(WMO), 91, 100, 185, 188, 340
see also Commission for Climatology
World Weather Program (WWP), 91
World Weather Watch (WWW), 59, 91,
Fig. IV–7, 100, 101, 190
Wright, Sewall, 374
WWP, see World Weather Program
WWW, see World Weather Watch
Wyoming, 29, 31

X

XBT, see Expendable Bathy-Thermographs
X-rays, 4, 9, 10, 11, 15
effects on humans, 325
fluctuations, 55

Y

Yanomama Indians, Brazil, 374, Fig. XI–1,
Fig. XI–2, 378, 379
Young's modulus, 203
Young, Thomas, 203

Z

Zinc, 193
Zooplankton, Fig. VIII–5
in food chain, 234, 237, 240
in lakes, 227, 228, Fig. VIII–2, 262

CONTRIBUTORS

The following list is composed of (1) the names of people who responded in writing to a request for information in an area of their special interest and (2) the names of those people who contributed illustrative material for use in the report. In some cases, individuals contributed both text material and illustrations.

WILLIAM C. ACKERMANN, Illinois State Water Survey

CLIFFORD AHLGREN, Quetico-Superior Wilderness Research Station

DURWARD L. ALLEN, Purdue University

DAYTON L. ALVERSON, National Oceanic and Atmospheric Administration

DAVID ATLAS, National Center for Atmospheric Research

PAUL T. BAKER, The Pennsylvania State University

ROGER G. BARRY, University of Colorado

PAUL C. BEAVER, Tulane Medical Center

W. BOYNTON BECKWITH, United Air Lines

WILLIAM S. BENNINGHOFF, University of Michigan

JACOB BJERKNES, University of California at Los Angeles

F. HERBERT BORMANN, Yale University

DUNCAN C. BLANCHARD, State University of New York at Albany

ROSCOE R. BRAHAM, JR., The University of Chicago

WALLACE S. BROECKER, Lamont-Doherty Geological Observatory

JOHN L. BROOKS, National Science Foundation

LINCOLN P. BROWER, Amherst College

KIRK BRYAN, National Oceanic and Atmospheric Administration

REID A. BRYSON, The University of Wisconsin at Madison

SIR EDWARD C. BULLARD, University of Cambridge

T. C. BYERLY, U.S. Department of Agriculture

TOBY N. CARLSON, National Oceanic and Atmospheric Administration

DAVID C. CHANDLER, University of Michigan

STANLEY A. CHANGNON, JR., Illinois State Water Survey

GABRIEL CSANADY, University of Waterloo

ALLAN C. DeLACY, University of Washington

ROBERT E. DILS, Colorado State University

HANS DOLEZALEK, Office of Naval Research

WILBUR G. DOWNS, The Rockefeller Foundation

RICHARD C. DUGDALE, University of Washington

JOHN A. DUTTON, The Pennsylvania State University

W. THOMAS EDMONDSON, University of Washington

KENNETH O. EMERY, Woods Hole Oceanographic Institution

CESARE EMILIANI, University of Miami

ROBERT D. FLETCHER, Department of the Air Force (Retired)

THEODORE T. FUJITA, The University of Chicago

NORIHIKO FUKUTA, University of Denver

DONALD FUQUAY, Forest Service, Missoula

DAVID M. GATES, University of Michigan

R. CECIL GENTRY, National Oceanic and Atmospheric Administration

STANLEY P. GESSEL, University of Washington

JAMES GILLULY, Geological Survey (Retired)

RAYMOND M. GILMORE, Natural History Museum at San Diego

EDWARD D. GOLDBERG, Scripps Institution of Oceanography

JOHN R. GOLDSMITH, Department of Public Health, State of California

FRANK B. GOLLEY, University of Georgia

DAVID R. GOODALL, Utah State University

ARNOLD L. GORDON, Lamont-Doherty Geological Observatory

LEWIS O. GRANT, Colorado State University

WILLIAM E. GORDON, Rice University

ROBERT F. GROVER, University of Colorado Medical Center

JOEL W. HEDGPETH, Oregon State University at Newport

CHARLES L. HOSLER, The Pennsylvania State University

HENRY G. HOUGHTON, Massachusetts Institute of Technology (Retired)

CARL B. HUFFAKER, University of California at Berkeley

ROBERT R. HUMPHREY, The University of Arizona

PATRICK M. HURLEY, Massachusetts Institute of Technology

EDWIN S. IVERSON, University of Miami

CLAYTON E. JENSEN, National Oceanic and Atmospheric Administration

PHILIP L. JOHNSON, National Science Foundation

RALPH G. JOHNSON, The University of Chicago

ARCHIE M. KAHAN, Bureau of Reclamation

HIROSHI KASAHARA, Food and Agriculture Organization

ROBERT W. KATES, Clark University

WILLIAM W. KELLOGG, National Center for Atmospheric Research

GEORGE C. KENNEDY, University of California at Los Angeles

EDWIN KESSLER, National Oceanic and Atmospheric Administration

J. E. KIRBY, JR., Esso Eastern, Inc.

JOHN A. KNAUSS, University of Rhode Island

LEON KNOPOFF, University of California at Los Angeles

EDWIN V. KOMAREK, Tall Timbers Research Station

HELMUT E. LANDSBERG, University of Maryland

NOEL E. LaSEUR, The Florida State University

EDWARD R. LEMON, Agricultural Research Service and Cornell University

HELMUT H. LEITH, The University of North Carolina at Chapel Hill

GENE E. LIKENS, Cornell University

RAY K. LINSLEY, Stanford University

C. GORDON LITTLE, National Oceanic and Atmospheric Administration

FRANK B. LIVINGSTONE, The University of Michigan

JAMES P. LODGE, National Center for Atmospheric Research

EDWARD N. LORENZ, Massachusetts Institute of Technology

JOHN LYMAN, The University of North Carolina at Chapel Hill

GORDON A. MACDONALD, University of Hawaii

BASSETT MAGUIRE, JR., The University of Texas at Austin

PAUL S. MARTIN, The University of Arizona

THOMAS R. McGETCHIN, Massachusetts Institute of Technology

CARL E. McILWAIN, University of California at San Diego

WILLIAM G. MELSON, Smithsonian Institution

HENRY W. MENARD, Scripps Institution of Oceanography

RICHARD S. MILLER, Yale University

J. MURRAY MITCHELL, JR., National Oceanic and Atmospheric Administration

CLIFFORD H. MORTIMER, The University of Wisconsin at Milwaukee

WALTER H. MUNK, University of California at San Diego

GARTH I. MURPHY, University of Hawaii

JEROME NAMIAS, Scripps Institution of Oceanography

JAMES V. NEEL, The University of Michigan

MORRIS NEIBURGER, University of California at Los Angeles

JACK E. OLIVER, Cornell University

LOUIS J. OLIVIER, World Health Organization

HARRY ORVILLE, South Dakota School of Mines and Technology

RICHARD E. ORVILLE, State University of New York at Albany

LOUIS C. PAKISER, JR., Geological Survey

EUGENE N. PARKER, The University of Chicago

WILLIAM G. PEARCY, Oregon State University

ALLEN D. PEARSON, National Oceanic and Atmospheric Administration

SVERRE PETTERSSEN, London, England

GEORGE W. PLATZMAN, The University of Chicago

JOSEPH F. POLAND, Geological Survey

ROBIN D. POWELL, Veterans Administration

JOSEPH M. PROSPERO, University of Miami

COLIN S. RAMAGE, University of Hawaii

GILBERT S. RAYNOR, Brookhaven National Laboratory

RICHARD J. REED, University of Washington

GEORGE C. REID, National Oceanic and Atmospheric Administration

JOSEPH L. REID, Scripps Institution of Oceanography

ELMAR R. REITER, Colorado State University

HERBERT RIEHL, Colorado State University

WALTER O. ROBERTS, University Corporation for Atmospheric Research

GEORGE D. ROBINSON, The Center for the Environment and Man, Inc.

EMANUEL D. RUDOLF, The Ohio State University

RICHARD J. RUSSELL, Louisiana State University (Deceased)

JOHN R. RYTHER, Woods Hole Oceanographic Institution

ELVIO H. SADUN, Walter Reed Army Medical Center

LYLE S. ST. AMANT, Louisiana Wild Life and Fisheries Commission

FREDERICK SANDERS, Massachusetts Institute of Technology

☆ U. S. GOVERNMENT PRINTING OFFICE : 1973 O - 508- 993